Preface

This text is written for use in a sophomore- or junior-level course in discrete mathematics with emphasis on applied modern algebra. The choice of subjects covered and the outline follow in general the recommendations for an applied algebra course enumerated by the Committee on the Undergraduate Program in Mathematics. This course, usually taught by mathematics faculty, is designed to present the traditional subject matter of modern algebra and related topics with specific attention to their applications to computer science and combinatorics.

Traditional modern algebra courses spend considerable time on the study of infinite groups, rings and fields. *Discrete Mathematics and Applied Modern Algebra* devotes more coverage to finite topics and broadens its scope to include such subjects as Boolean algebras and finite-state machines. There is enough material for more than one semester to allow the instructor some choice in emphasis and topic coverage.

This text is written at the level of mathematical maturity attained by students after exposure to two semesters of calculus and perhaps to one semester of linear algebra. However, very little of this material is used explicitly. Proofs are included and are done carefully. But most of the text is devoted to examples and to computations. In fact, most theorems are followed first by an example and then by a proof. The example helps the student to understand the theorem's statement and then to follow the general argument of the proof.

The order of topics was decided upon during the course of class testing several drafts of the manuscript. Many students in the course were computer-science majors and were not going on in higher mathematics. To spark their interest, error-correcting codes was chosen as the first topic discussed. This relatively easy topic, readily appreciated by computer-science students, also introduces the student to new algebraic structures and provides motivation for the rather abstract chapter on groups.

There is considerable room for choice and emphasis by the instructor. For example, after groups are covered, a course focusing on finite-state machines as electronic networks, abstract mathematical models of digital computers, and language recognizers may be formed by continuing with Chapters Six, Seven, and Eight, or, finite-state machines may be presented from the viewpoint of graph theory and Boolean algebra via Chapters Four, Five, and Seven. Chapters Three, Five, and Nine yield a course emphasizing the algebraic structures exhibited by relations, additional group theory, Boolean algebra, rings, and fields.

Except for some material on ordered sets, all of the main topics in the CUPM recommendations are covered fully in the text. Additional topics, reflecting the preferences of the author, are also included. The order of presentation differs somewhat from that listed in the CUPM recommendations: Equivalence relations are postponed until meaningful applications, such as Lagrange's Theorem and Burnside's Theorem, are available. Mathematical induction is discussed in the appendix and is used formally only in Chapter 4 on graph theory. Students usually do not appreciate mathematical induction. Using the appendix, the instructor may introduce induction when it is really useful, rather than in an apparently artificial context.

As previously mentioned, the manuscript has been thoroughly class tested at the State University of New York at Stony Brook by six instructors and more than four hundred students. I am most grateful for the various suggestions resulting from these trial runs. Also, useful comments and criticisms have come from my colleagues, Alan Tucker, William Lister, and Anthony Phillips. I also want to acknowledge the very helpful reviewers enlisted by the publisher: Ezra Brown, Virginia Polytechnic Institute and State University; John J. Buoni, Youngstown State University; Adrienne Critcher, University of Iowa; Rosalyn Lee, Duquesne University; Diane Meuser, Boston University; James Simpson, University of Kentucky; William Smoke, University of California, Irvine. Susanne Brenner carefully proofread. My editor, Jerry Lyons, was constantly encouraging. I most gratefully thank them all.

Henry B. Laufer
Stony Brook, New York

Contents

1 Group Codes

Many applications of mathematics were developed long after the original mathematics was created. In this chapter, the nineteenth century mathematics of groups and matrices is used to solve the twentieth century problem of how to send a message accurately in the presence of occasional transmission noise. The basic solution, developed by R.W. Hamming in 1950, is to encode the message with enough redundancy so that any single transmission error caused by the noise may be detected and corrected. The most widely used error-correcting codes in today's computers are Hamming's original codes.

The first section of this chapter is a description of the general nature of the codes under consideration. It also contains a discussion of the nature of the expected transmission errors. The discussion in the second section develops a measure d that describes the error-detecting and error-correcting capabilities of a code. A type of addition for n-tuples of bits is introduced in the third section, leading to a definition of group codes. It is particularly easy to compute d for group codes. The remaining sections involve the use of matrices to give an efficient implementation of these ideas. Eventually, the original codes invented by Hamming are described.

1.1 Examples of Codes

Suppose that we wish to communicate with a computer. Humans are happier dealing with words and decimal numbers. Computers are usually constructed internally to handle only 0's and 1's. Typically, the user's terminal follows a code to translate each typed letter, digit, or special symbol such as "period" into some fixed number of **bits** (**bi**nary dig**its**), which are then transmitted to the computer. Two such common codes are **BCD** (**B**inary **C**oded **D**ecimal) and **ASCII** (**A**merican **S**tandard **C**ode for **I**nformation **I**nterchange). Table 1.1 gives the BCD and ASCII codes for capital letters, digits, and some special symbols. There are variations from Table 1.1 for some pieces of equipment. The apparently strange letter coding in BCD makes BCD more compatible with historical usage in punched cards. ASCII was designed much later than BCD, with terminals in mind. Table 1.1 gives the complete BCD code, but only part of the ASCII code. Other unlisted symbols available in ASCII include lower case letters and special control characters such as "carriage return" and "ring a bell."

Observe that BCD is like a dictionary. The "words" in BCD are the 48 characters in Table 1.1. The BCD "definition" of a character is the six corresponding bits. A sequence of six bits is called a **binary 6-tuple**, or simply a **6-tuple**. The correspondence from characters to 6-tuples is called an **encoding of messages into code words**. BCD thus has 48 code words. Since each bit place has two possible values, with six bits, a total of $2^6 = 64$ different 6-tuples are available. So in BCD some 6-tuples, such as 111 111, are not code words.

ASCII uses binary 8-tuples, yielding $2^8 = 256$ possible different 8-tuples. The full ASCII code, however, has only 128 characters. Since $128 = 2^7$, why are not just seven bits used for ASCII code? Some implementations of ASCII do use just seven bits. However, using the full eight bits gives, as illustrated in Example 1.1 on p. 4, the capability of detecting transmission errors between the user's terminal and the computer. Observe that in Table 1.1 each listed ASCII code word has an even number of 1's. The unlisted ASCII code words also all have an even number of 1's. Error detection for ASCII will be achieved using this property of ASCII code words. Observe that the number of 1's in a BCD code word may be either even or odd.

Table 1.1 BCD and ASCII codes

Character	BCD code word	ASCII code word
0	000 000	0011 0000
1	000 001	0111 0001
2	000 010	0111 0010
3	000 011	0011 0011
4	000 100	0111 0100
5	000 101	0011 0101
6	000 110	0011 0110
7	000 111	0111 0111
8	001 000	0111 1000
9	001 001	0011 1001
A	010 001	1000 0001
B	010 010	1000 0010
C	010 011	1100 0011
D	010 100	1000 0100

Table 1.1 *Continued*

Character	BCD code word	ASCII code word
E	010 101	1100 0101
F	010 110	1100 0110
G	010 111	1000 0111
H	011 000	1000 1000
I	011 001	1100 1001
J	100 001	1100 1010
K	100 010	1000 1011
L	100 011	1100 1100
M	100 100	1000 1101
N	100 101	1000 1110
O	100 110	1100 1111
P	100 111	1001 0000
Q	101 000	1101 0001
R	101 001	1101 0010
S	110 010	1001 0011
T	110 011	1101 0100
U	110 100	1001 0101
V	110 101	1001 0110
W	110 110	1101 0111
X	110 111	1101 1000
Y	111 000	1001 1001
Z	111 001	1001 1010
space	110 000	0110 0000
$	101 011	0010 0100
'	001 100	0010 0111
(	111 100	0010 1000
)	011 100	0110 1001
*	101 100	0110 1010
+	010 000	0010 1011
/	110 001	0110 1111
–	100 000	0010 1101
.	011 011	0010 1110
,	111 011	0110 1100
=	001 011	0111 1101

Example 1.1

We wish to send the letter G to a computer, perhaps as part of a longer text. Using BCD, G would be encoded as 010 111. It is possible that some bit would be incorrectly received by the computer. Suppose that a transmission error occurs in the last bit; the 1 is changed to a 0. The received binary 6-tuple is 010 110, which is interpreted as F, rather than as G. In summary, the following sequence of events occurs:

Original letter:	G
Corresponding code word:	010 111
Transmission error:	1 ↓ 0 (last bit)
Received word:	010 110
Corresponding letter:	F

On the other hand, see what happens using ASCII. G is encoded as 1000 0111. Suppose, as before, that a transmission error occurs in the last bit. Here is the summary of events:

Original letter:	G	
Corresponding code word:	1000 0111	
Transmission error:	1 ↓ 0 (last bit)	
Received word:	1000 0110	number of 1's is odd
Corresponding character:	none	

By arrangement, no ASCII word has an odd number of 1's. So the received 8-tuple must differ from the transmitted 8-tuple. So the computer "knows" that a transmission error has occurred. △

The general environment for codes is drawn schematically in Figure 1.1. Here, the (uncoded) messages may be in the form of letters or characters but more typically consist of arbitrary **binary *m*-tuples**, that is, sequences of m bits. The messages are encoded into binary n-tuples, which yields code words. The encoding may be done via tables, as in Table 1.1, or

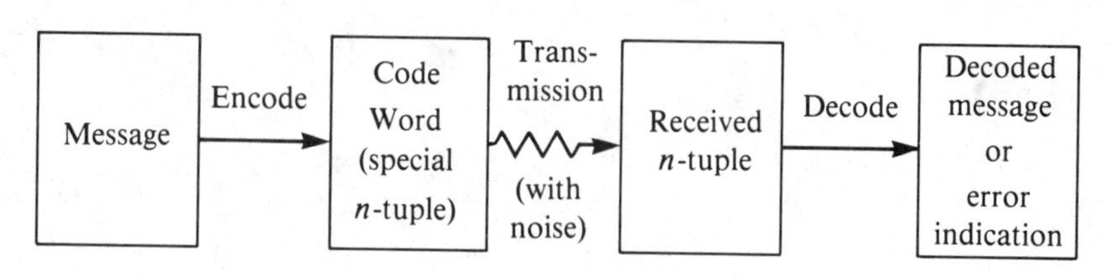

Figure 1.1 General scheme for codes

via the appending of additional bits to the original information, as done in Example 1.2, which follows later. More elaborate encoding schemes may also be useful, as will be seen in Chapter 9. However, any encoding scheme must have different code words for different messages. The code word is transmitted to the receiver. Only during transmission is the possibility of the occurrence of errors considered. Mathematically, an **error** is a change in some of the bits of the code word. A **single** error is a change in just one bit of a code word. A **decoding scheme** is some method that takes an (arbitrary) received n-tuple and gives either a decoded message or an error indication. If the received n-tuple is a code word, that is, one of the special n-tuples that are allowed to be transmitted, then the decoded message must be that unique message which encodes into the received code word. For received noncode words, the decoder must give an error indication or else, as discussed later, try to reconstruct the original message. A good code will give correct decoded messages or error indications as often as possible. Figure 1.1 applies not only to communication between a user and a computer, but also to internal computer communication and to general data transmission between stations.

By far the most common code used in computers is the addition of a parity check bit. Typically, a computer stores information as binary m-tuples, called **words**. Common word lengths, that is, lengths for the m-tuples, are 6, 8, 16, 32, 36, and 64 bits. An additional bit, called the **parity check bit**, is appended to each word, forming a binary $(m+1)$-tuple. Recall that the **parity** of a binary $(m+1)$-tuple is even or odd depending on whether the number of 1's in the $(m+1)$-tuple is even or odd. In a computer that uses an even parity check, the value of the parity check bit is chosen, depending on the contents of the m-tuple, so that the parity of the $(m+1)$-tuple is always even. An odd parity check requires, of course, odd parity for each $(m+1)$-tuple. Thus a computer that uses a parity check bit and has a word length of, say, 32 bits will actually store information as code words that are 33-tuples. Suppose that a (code) word is fetched from memory, that is, transmitted. Decoding is very easy: Consider, say, an even parity check. If the received $(m+1)$-tuple has even parity, just delete the parity check bit. If the received $(m+1)$-tuple has odd parity, give a parity error indication.

Example 1.2

Here are some encodings of 6-bit words to 7-bit code words:

	Word + check bit = code word	
Word	Even parity check	Odd parity check
000 000	000 000 0	000 000 1
110 000	110 000 0	110 000 1
110 111	110 111 1	110 111 0

△

Example 1.3

Here are some decodings of received 7-tuples that use an even parity check bit:

Received 7-tuple	Decoded word
001 000 1	001 000
101 010 0	Parity error
111 111 0	111 111
111 111 1	Parity error

△

Example 1.4

Seven-bit implementations of ASCII delete the second leftmost bit from the ASCII entries in Table 1.1. A partial encoding table for 7-bit ASCII thus looks like

Character	Code word
0	011 0000
1	011 0001
2	011 0010
A	100 0001
B	100 0010

Think of the second bit in the ASCII part of Table 1.1 as the (even) parity check bit. △

Recall from the BCD part of Example 1.1 that a single transmission error may result in an incorrect decoding. However, here is why the parity check code is useful.

Theorem 1.1

Adding a parity check bit allows the detection of all single errors, that is, all single errors result in an error indication.

Example 1.5

The proof of Theorem 1.1, which follows this example, is illustrated. Consider an even parity check bit that is appended to information in the form of 6-tuples. Transmit 110 011 0 and consider an error in the second bit. The received 7-tuple is 100 011 0, which has odd parity and so is not a code word. An error indication results. △

Proof of Theorem 1.1

Take the parity of the code words to be even since the proof for odd parity is entirely similar. Changing a code word, **c**, in a single bit either increases or decreases the number of 1's in **c** by one. In both cases, the parity of the number of 1's is changed from even to odd. Since all code words are constructed to have even parity, the changed **c** is not a code word. So an error indication results from the decoding. ◇

The parity check bit code is simple and very efficient. Just one parity check bit is needed, regardless of the computer's word length. Single parity check bits *are* sufficient for most computer purposes. However, this system has two limitations: it cannot detect some multiple errors or correct errors in case they do occur. For example, using an even parity check, we encode the word 110 010 as 110 010 1, a code word. Suppose that transmission errors occur in the third and fifth bits:

$$\begin{array}{ll} 110\ 010\ 1 & \text{code word} \\ \ \ \downarrow\ \ \downarrow & \\ 111\ 000\ 1 & \text{code word} \end{array}$$

The received 7-tuple is 111 000 1, which has even parity. So the receiver thinks that no error has occurred. Now suppose that we again encode 110 010 as 110 010 1, and that a single transmission error occurs in, say, the fourth bit as follows:

$$\begin{array}{ll} 110\ 010\ 1 & \text{code word} \\ \quad \downarrow & \\ 110\ 110\ 1 & \text{noncode word} \end{array} \tag{1.1}$$

The received 7-tuple is 110 110 1, which has odd parity. So the receiver knows that some error occurred in transmission but has no idea which bit is in error. As shown in (1.1), the error occurred in the fourth bit. However, if the first bit were in error, (1.2) could have happened as follows:

$$\begin{array}{ll} 010\ 110\ 1 & \text{code word} \\ \downarrow & \\ 110\ 110\ 1 & \text{noncode word} \end{array} \tag{1.2}$$

The same 7-tuple is received in both (1.1) and (1.2), so the receiver cannot distinguish between them. Possible errors in the other bits, including the parity check bit, work similarly.

In analyzing error-correcting codes, it is important to make explicit the assumptions about the likelihood and distribution of transmission errors. Then, in a particular application, it would be known if the error correction would actually work. We shall assume that transmission errors are rare and that when they do occur, transmission errors occur independently in each bit. This is true, for example, for fetching words from computer memory when each bit is transmitted over its own circuit. Our assumption about bit independence does not hold, for example, for numbers sent through computer adders. It follows from our assumptions that two errors occur much less frequently than one error, that three errors occur even less frequently than two errors, etc.

We shall use **maximum likelihood decoding** for any attempt to reconstruct an original message from a received noncode word. The original information is contained in the transmitted code word. So for decoding, we look for that code word which was most likely to have been transmitted. Our assumptions about the nature of transmission errors essentially say that *the* most likely transmitted code word, if any, is that code word which needs *fewest* errors to be changed into the received noncode word. Observe from (1.1) and (1.2) that there may be no *single* code word that is a candidate for the transmitted code word. In such cases, we shall restrict the decoder to giving an error indication. However, we could reasonably allow the decoder to choose one of the candidates.

Example 1.6

We now give the simplest error-correcting code. The message to be transmitted is just one bit, that is, 0 or 1. The message is encoded as three copies of itself as follows:

Message:	0	1
Code word:	000	111

Observe that 000 and 111 are the only 3-tuples that are code words. The decoding scheme must, of course, reverse the above encoding scheme for the decoding of a code word. Noncode words are decoded by taking the majority of the three received bits. The transmitted code word may also be recovered:

Received 3-tuple:	000	001	010	011	100	101	110	111
Decoded message:	0	0	0	1	0	1	1	1
Transmitted code word:	000	000	000	111	000	111	111	111

(1.3)

Now suppose that 000 is transmitted and that a single error occurs. Some 0 is changed to a 1, yielding either 001, 010, or 100 as the received 3-tuple. In all cases (1.3) correctly decodes the 3-tuple as 0. Similarly, this code corrects single errors in the transmission of 111.

We now analyze (1.3) in terms of maximum likelihood decoding. For each 3-tuple, we list the number of bits by which the 3-tuple differs from each of the two code words as follows:

		3-tuple								
		000	001	010	011	100	101	110	111	
Code	000	0	1	1	2	1	2	2	3	**(1.4)**
word	111	3	2	2	1	2	1	1	0	

In every instance in (1.4), (1.3) chooses the most likely transmitted code word, that is, the code word that differs least from the 3-tuple. △

Example 1.7

We now give a simple code that detects all single and double transmission errors, that is, all transmission errors in one or two bits. Use the encoding scheme of Example 1.6. Received code words are decoded, as in Example 1.6, as their corresponding messages. However, instead of decoding received noncode words by (1.3), we "decode" them by saying that a transmission error occurred. Since any one or two transmission errors change a code word such as 000 into a noncode word such as 011, up to two errors are detected.

While this code does detect up to two transmission errors, it does not allow the correction of such errors. For instance, suppose we transmit 000 with an error in the first bit:

$$\begin{array}{c} 000 \\ \downarrow\;\; \\ 100 \end{array}$$

The received 3-tuple 100 is decoded as "transmission error." Now suppose we transmit 111 with errors in the second two bits:

$$\begin{array}{c} 111 \\ \;\;\downarrow\downarrow \\ 100 \end{array}$$

Again the received 3-tuple 100 is decoded as "transmission error." Observe that receiving 100 and allowing up to two transmission errors, we cannot decide whether 000 or 111 was transmitted. △

Example 1.8

Every code will give an incorrect message, that is, there will be an undetected hardware error, if a sufficient number of (undoubtedly rare) transmission errors occur. For instance, let us use the encoding scheme of Example 1.6. Suppose we transmit 000 and that transmission errors occur in all three bits. The received 3-tuple is 111, a code word. So any decoding scheme incorrectly decodes the 3-tuple as 1 and assumes a transmitted code word of 111. △

A summary of the ideas of this section follows.

Definition 1.1

A **code** consists of **encoding** and **decoding** schemes.

(i) Messages are encoded into binary n-tuples, yielding **code words.** Different messages are encoded into different code words. So each code word corresponds to a unique message.

(ii) The decoding scheme must apply to all n-tuples. A code word is decoded as its corresponding message. A noncode word may be decoded either as a transmission error indication or into that message whose code word differs in the least number of bits from the noncode word, provided that there is only one such message. ○

The remaining sections of this chapter are devoted to the development of single-error-correcting codes for much longer messages than the single bits of Example 1.6. Some computers and data communication systems, however, use still more subtle codes. The Cray-1 and CYBER 205 computers, for example, have 64-bit words. Each computer appends eight suitable check bits to its words, giving it the ability to correct single errors and to detect double errors simultaneously.

Exercises 1.1

1. What is the parity (even or odd) of each of the following tuples of bits?

   a. 1010 b. 00101 c. 1111010 d. 1010001101

2. For each of the following tuples of bits, append a parity check bit so that the number of 1's is even.

   a. 00101 b. 01101 c. 011101 d. 0101000

3. Using the even parity check bit code, decode each of the following received 7-tuples. The last bit is the check bit.

   a. 110 011 0 b. 001 011 1

   c. 000 110 1 d. 101 011 1

4. 0 is encoded as 000. 1 is encoded as 111. Assuming only at most one transmission error, what was the transmitted code word for each of the following received 3-tuples?

   a. 000 b. 010 c. 100 d. 011

5. Prove Theorem 1.1 in the odd parity check bit case.

6. Suppose that we are using an even parity check bit code, with the last bit the check bit. Suppose that 001 011 0 is the received 7-tuple.

   a. List two code words that differ from 001 011 0 in just one bit.

   b. Explain why there is no *unique* code word that is a preferred candidate for the transmitted code word.

7. Why is the following encoding not acceptable?

Information:	0	1	2	3	4	5	6	7	8	9
Code word:	000	001	010	011	100	101	110	111	000	001

8. Explain why encoding 0 as 0000 and 1 as 1111 will detect up to triple errors.
9. Consider the following encoding. Messages are given as nine bits, arranged in a square array as shown. Append six even parity check bits, one for each row and column of the array. The check bits are indicated below with x's.

```
·  ·  ·  x
·  ·  ·  x
·  ·  ·  x
x  x  x
```

   a. What happens to the parity of the rows and columns, including the check bits, when there is a single transmission error in one of the original nine bits?
   b. Assuming a single transmission error, what does it mean for there to be just one row or column with an odd parity?
   c. Give the decoding scheme that corrects single errors for this encoding.
10. (For those readers who know probability)
A binary n-tuple is transmitted. Assume that the probability of an error in a single given bit is p. Assume that errors in different bits are independent of each other. Show that
   a. The probability of no errors is $(1-p)^n$.
   b. The probability of exactly one error is $np(1-p)^{n-1}$.
   c. The probability of exactly two errors is

$$\frac{n(n-1)}{2}p^2(1-p)^{n-2}.$$

   d. What is the probability of more than one error occurring?
11. Explain why our assumption that errors occur independently in the various bits and that multiple errors are much less frequent than single errors is an invalid assumption for errors in addition.

Hint: Give a suitable example of an "addition" for two binary numbers where an error occurs in the computation of just one of the carries. See what happens to the bits of the sum.

12. Anglish estences usualty convey sheir messagy destipe tygopraphicbl orrors. Explain this phenomenon in terms of a coding problem.

1.2 Error-Correcting Codes

In the previous section definitions and examples of codes were given. This section contains a description of those properties that are required of a code in order for it to correct single transmission errors. More generally, the minimum distance d is defined, which measures the error-detecting and error-correcting capability of a code.

For error detection, a decoder looks for noncode words. For error correction, a decoder is given a binary n-tuple and chooses a message. Since messages and code words correspond exactly, an equivalent problem for the decoder is to choose the transmitted code word. So, later questions of efficiency aside, it can be seen that *the ability of a code to detect or to correct errors depends solely on its set of code words.*

Example 1.9

Suppose that 1100 and 0100 are code words in some code. Suppose we transmit 1100 and that an error occurs in the first bit; 0100 is received. Since 0100 is a code word, the decoder incorrectly decodes 0100 as its corresponding message rather than as the message corresponding to 1100. So, regardless of the encoding method for the code, having both 1100 and 0100 as code words is bad for error detection. The trouble is that 1100 and 0100 differ in just one bit; an error in the transmission of this (first) bit is undetected. △

Example 1.10

Suppose that 1100 and 0101 are code words in some code. 1100 and 0101 differ in two bits, the first and the fourth. Suppose we transmit 1100 and assume that some single error occurs. Then the code word 0101 can never be received, because changing 1100 in, say, the first bit still leaves the received 4-tuple, 0100, differing from 0101 in the fourth bit. So 1100 and 0101 may be code words in a single-error-detecting code. △

Example 1.11

Consider the even-parity check bit code that encodes 3-tuples into 4-tuples. In at least how many bits do distinct code words differ? 0110 and 1010 are code words that differ in two (the first and second) bits. 0110 and 1001 differ in four bits. Table 1.2 considers all pairs of distinct code words and gives the number of bits in which they differ. The minimum entry in Table 1.2 is 2. △

Examples 1.9–1.11 suggest correctly that it is the number of bits by which code words differ that determines the error-detecting capability of a code. A formal definition follows.

Table 1.2 Number of different bits

	0000	0011	0101	0110	1001	1010	1100	1111
0000	–	2	2	2	2	2	2	4
0011	2	–	2	2	2	2	4	2
0101	2	2	–	2	2	4	2	2
0110	2	2	2	–	4	2	2	2
1001	2	2	2	4	–	2	2	2
1010	2	2	4	2	2	–	2	2
1100	2	4	2	2	2	2	–	2
1111	4	2	2	2	2	2	2	–

Definition 1.2

Let **a** and **b** be binary n-tuples. The number of bit places in which **a** and **b** differ is the **Hamming distance** between them. The Hamming distance is denoted by $H(\mathbf{a},\mathbf{b})$.

The Hamming distance is not defined between tuples of different length. ○

Example 1.12

Let $\mathbf{a}=00110$, $\mathbf{b}=11101$, $\mathbf{c}=11011$. Then $H(\mathbf{a},\mathbf{b})=4$, $H(\mathbf{c},\mathbf{a})=4$, $H(\mathbf{b},\mathbf{c})=2$, $H(\mathbf{a},\mathbf{a})=0$. △

Observe that $H(\mathbf{a},\mathbf{a})=0$ for any n-tuple **a**. That is, a binary n-tuple **a** agrees with itself in every bit place. Conversely, if $H(\mathbf{a},\mathbf{b})=0$, then **a** and **b** are the same binary n-tuple because they agree in all bit places.

$H(\mathbf{a},\mathbf{b})$ should also be interpreted, of course, as the number of transmission errors that are needed to change the transmitted n-tuple **a** to the received n-tuple **b**.

Definition 1.3

Consider a code whose code words are binary n-tuples. Then the **minimum distance**, d, for the code is the minimum of all of the Hamming distances $H(\mathbf{a},\mathbf{b})$, where **a** and **b** are distinct code words. ○

The entries in Table 1.2 are, of course, just the Hamming distances between distinct code words. Taking the minimum of the entries in Table 1.2 gives $d=2$ for the parity check bit code of Example 1.11. The diagonal entries in Table 1.2 were deliberately omitted since they do not contribute to the computation of d.

Theorem 1.2

Let d be the minimum distance for a code. If $d=1$, then the code cannot detect all transmission errors. If $d=2$, then the code can detect, but not correct, single transmission errors.

Proof of Theorem 1.2

Consider the case of $d = 1$. Then there are two code words, call them **a** and **b**, such that $H(\mathbf{a},\mathbf{b}) = 1$; that is, **a** and **b** differ in some single bit. Suppose we transmit **a** and an error occurs in that single bit where **a** and **b** differ. The error changes the bit and thus changes **a** to **b**. So the code word **b** is received, and no error message is given.

Now consider the case of $d = 2$. Suppose we transmit a code word, call it **a**, and that a single error occurs. Since **a** differs from the other code words in at least two bits, this single error cannot change **a** into another code word. So the received n-tuple is a noncode word, yielding an error indication.

Finally we must show that there is an uncorrectable single error. Since $d = 2$, there are two code words, call them **b** and **c**, such that $H(\mathbf{b},\mathbf{c}) = 2$. Then **b** and **c** differ in exactly two bit places. Suppose we transmit **b** and an error occurs in one of these two bit places. Then the received n-tuple, call it **r**, differs from each of **b** and **c** in exactly one place. Namely, **r** differs from **b** in the error bit; **r** differs from **c** in the other place where **b** and **c** differ. Receiving **r**, the decoder cannot decide between **b** and **c** for the correct transmitted code word. ◇

Example 1.13

Using the code words of Table 1.2, we exhibit an uncorrectable error. The binary n-tuples $\mathbf{b} = 1001$ and $\mathbf{c} = 1111$ are code words such that $H(\mathbf{b},\mathbf{c}) = 2$. We transmit **b** and consider an error in the second bit. The received 4-tuple is $\mathbf{r} = 1101$. $H(\mathbf{r},\mathbf{b}) = 1$ and $H(\mathbf{r},\mathbf{c}) = 1$, so this error cannot be corrected. △

The code of Example 1.6 is single-error-correcting. There are just two code words, 000 and 111, with a Hamming distance of 3. This suggests the following theorem.

Theorem 1.3

Let d be the minimum distance for a code. Suppose that $d \geq 3$. Then the maximum-likelihood decoding scheme corrects all single errors.

Example 1.14

We illustrate the proof below of Theorem 1.3. Let us consider the following set of code words, all 5-tuples:

$$\mathbf{c}_1 = 00000 \qquad \mathbf{c}_2 = 01110 \qquad \mathbf{c}_3 = 10111 \qquad \mathbf{c}_4 = 11001$$

It is easy to verify that d equals 3. Suppose that we transmit $\mathbf{c}_3$ and an error occurs in the second bit. How do we correct the error? The received 5-tuple is $\mathbf{r} = 11111$. Compute the Hamming distance from **r** to each code word:

$\mathbf{r} = 11111$

Code word $\mathbf{c}_i$	$H(\mathbf{r},\mathbf{c}_i)$
$\mathbf{c}_1 = 00000$	5
$\mathbf{c}_2 = 01110$	2
$\mathbf{c}_3 = 10111$	1
$\mathbf{c}_4 = 11001$	2

We see that the code word $\mathbf{c}_3$ is the *unique* code word with minimum Hamming distance to $\mathbf{r}$. So, receiving $\mathbf{r} = 11111$, the decoder correctly gives the transmitted code word $\mathbf{c}_3 = 10111$. △

Proof of Theorem 1.3

Start with a transmitted code word; call it $\mathbf{c}$. An error changes $\mathbf{c}$ in one bit to give the received n-tuple $\mathbf{r}$. Recover $\mathbf{c}$ from $\mathbf{r}$ as in the above example: Consider the Hamming distances from $\mathbf{r}$ to the various code words. $H(\mathbf{r},\mathbf{c}) = 1$ because $\mathbf{r}$ came from $\mathbf{c}$ via a change in exactly one bit. Let $\mathbf{c}'$ be another code word besides $\mathbf{c}$. $H(\mathbf{c},\mathbf{c}')$ is given to be at least 3. So at least three bits must be changed to change $\mathbf{c}$ to $\mathbf{c}'$. Changing one bit changed $\mathbf{c}$ to $\mathbf{r}$. So at least two more changes are needed to change $\mathbf{r}$ to $\mathbf{c}'$. (That is, we can change $\mathbf{c}$ to $\mathbf{c}'$ via the intermediate n-tuple $\mathbf{r}$.) Hence $H(\mathbf{r},\mathbf{c}') \geq 2$. So in terms of $\mathbf{r}$, the code word $\mathbf{c}$ may be reconstructed as the *unique* code word such that $H(\mathbf{r},\mathbf{c}) = 1$. So we can correct single errors. ◇

Example 1.15

Here is another illustration of maximum-likelihood decoding, as described in Theorem 1.3 and its proof. A code has the following code words:

11111 10001 01000 00110

Table 1.3 shows that $d = 3$. Theorem 1.3 guarantees that maximum-likelihood decoding will be successful in correcting single errors.

Table 1.3 $H(\mathbf{a},\mathbf{b})$, $\mathbf{a} \neq \mathbf{b}$, for Example 1.15

	11111	10001	01000	00110
11111	–	3	4	3
10001	3	–	3	4
01000	4	3	–	3
00110	3	4	3	–

For each of the received 5-tuples 10101, 01010, 10001, we find the transmitted code words. We must first compute the Hamming distances to the code words:

Code word	5-tuple 10101	01010	10001
11111	2	3	3
10001	①	4	⓪
01000	4	①	3
00110	3	2	4

In each column we have circled the minimum Hamming distance. Hence the transmitted 5-tuples were 10001, 01000, 10001. Observe that no error occurred in the transmission of the last 5-tuple. △

Example 1.16

Here is an example of double-error detection. A code has the following code words:

00110 01011 10001 11100

It is easy to verify that $d=3$. We transmit the code word 01011 with errors in the third and fourth bits. We can see that no code word is received as follows:

01011 code word
↓↓
01101 noncode word

The reception of the noncode word 01101 indicates a transmission error. △

In Example 1.16, $d=3$ and the code is double-error-detecting. The proof of the following general theorem is left as an exercise. Observe that Theorem 1.3 and Theorem 1.4 use different decoding schemes.

Theorem 1.4

Let d be the minimum distance for a code. Suppose that $d \geq 3$. Then decoding a received noncode word by "transmission error" detects all single and double errors. ◇

Exercises 1.2

1. Compute the Hamming distance between the following pairs of n-tuples.
   a. 0101 and 1011 b. 00000 and 10010
   c. 11110 and 10001 d. 111000 and 100101
2. For each of the following sets of code words, form a table, such as

Table 1.2, that will give the Hamming distance between distinct code words. Also compute d.

a. 101 100 000 b. 101 011 000

c. 010 100 111 d. 01000 00110 11111 10001

3. The following set of code words is given to have $d=3$:

00110 01011 10001 11100

For each of the following received 5-tuples, compute the Hamming distance to each code word and tell which code word was most likely to have been transmitted.

a. 10000 b. 01100 c. 00111 d. 01011

4. The following set of code words is given to have $d=3$:

000000 001110 010101 011011
100011 101101 110110 111000

The following 6-tuples are given to have been received via the transmission of a code word with at most one error. By inspection of the list of code words, tell which code word was transmitted in each case.

a. 110011 b. 110110 c. 111011
d. 001111 e. 011111 f. 100011

5. Explain why changing the values of any bit place in *all* of the code words will not change the minimum distance d.
6. Explain why choosing a subset of the code words can never decrease the minimum distance d.
7. Suppose that an encoding scheme has a minimum Hamming distance of d between distinct code words.
   a. Explain why the usual error-detection scheme will detect up to $d-1$ errors.
   b. Explain why no decoding scheme can detect all possible errors involving d bits.
8. Suppose that an encoding scheme has $d=3$. Show that no decoding scheme can both correct all single errors and detect all double errors; that is, show that there must be code words **a** and **b** and received n-tuple **r** such that **r** comes from **a** via one error and from **b** via two errors.

   Hint: How do you decode **r**? See also Example 1.16.
9. Suppose that an encoding scheme has $d=4$.
   a. Give a decoding scheme that both corrects all single errors and detects all double errors. Justify your scheme.

b. What is the difficulty in trying to correct double errors?

10. Does there exist a single-error-correcting code that uses 3-tuples and has three code words? Why?
11. The Hamming distance on the set of binary n-tuples is called a **distance** (or a **metric**) because it satisfies the following four conditions:

    i. $H(\mathbf{a},\mathbf{b}) \geq 0$ for all $\mathbf{a}$ and $\mathbf{b}$.
    ii. $H(\mathbf{a},\mathbf{b}) = 0$ if and only if $\mathbf{a} = \mathbf{b}$.
    iii. $H(\mathbf{a},\mathbf{b}) = H(\mathbf{b},\mathbf{a})$
    iv. $H(\mathbf{a},\mathbf{b}) \leq H(\mathbf{a},\mathbf{c}) + H(\mathbf{c},\mathbf{b})$

    Verify these properties.
12. Using Exercise 11, rewrite that part of the proof of Theorem 1.3 which shows that $H(\mathbf{r},\mathbf{c}') \geq 2$.

1.3 Group Codes

To construct single-error-correcting codes, Theorems 1.2 and 1.3 say that the minimum distance d should be at least 3. In a code with many code words, it could be very time consuming to check the Hamming distance between *all* code words. More importantly, without some plan, it would be very difficult to construct such a code. In this section, a special type of code is introduced, called a **group code**, where the computation of d is especially easy.

Consider the set $\{0,1\}$, which is just the set of possible values for a bit place. We shall call this set $\mathbb{Z}_2$, its usual name in Table 1.5. We now give a form of composition, called **addition modulo 2** or simply **addition**, for the elements of $\mathbb{Z}_2$. Think of 0 as standing for EVEN (numbers) and 1 as standing for ODD (numbers). As summarized in Table 1.4, the sum of two EVEN numbers is EVEN, the sum of two ODD numbers is EVEN, and the sum of an EVEN and an ODD number is ODD. So, using the usual + sign, addition in $\mathbb{Z}_2$ is given by

Table 1.4 Addition Table for {EVEN, ODD}

+	EVEN	ODD
EVEN	EVEN	ODD
ODD	ODD	EVEN

$$0+0=0 \qquad 1+1=0 \qquad 1+0=1 \qquad 0+1=1$$

These sums are given again in Table 1.5. Observe that addition in $\mathbb{Z}_2$ differs from the usual addition for whole numbers in that $1+1=0$ (rather than 2).

Table 1.5 Addition Table for $\mathbb{Z}_2 = \{0,1\}$

+	0	1
0	0	1
1	1	0

To follow standard notation in the later context of matrices, and also to minimize possible confusion with the addition of numbers written in binary notation, we shall now write binary n-tuples within parentheses. The bits will be separated by spaces. That is, instead of 00110, we now write (0 0 1 1 0). Table 1.5 tells how to add single bits. To add two binary n-tuples, we add corresponding bits, using the addition table Table 1.5. Addition is defined only between n-tuples with the same n.

Example 1.17

$$(1\ 1\ 0\ 1)+(0\ 1\ 1\ 1)=(1+0\quad 1+1\quad 0+1\quad 1+1)$$
$$=(1\ 0\ 1\ 0)$$
$$(0\ 0\ 1\ 1)+(0\ 1\ 0\ 1)=(0+0\quad 0+1\quad 1+0\quad 1+1)$$
$$=(0\ 1\ 1\ 0)$$
$$(1\ 1\ 1\ 0\ 1\ 0)+(0\ 0\ 1\ 1\ 1\ 0)=(1\ 1\ 0\ 1\ 0\ 0)$$
$$(0\ 0\ 0\ 1\ 1\ 0)+(0\ 1\ 1\ 0\ 0\ 1)=(0\ 1\ 1\ 1\ 1\ 1)$$

$(0\ 0\ 1)+(1\ 0\ 1\ 0)$ is not defined since we are trying to add a $\underline{3}$-tuple and a $\underline{4}$-tuple. △

We let $\mathbb{Z}_2^n$ denote the set of all binary n-tuples, with addition as previously defined. Then $\mathbb{Z}_2^2$ is all 2-tuples:

$$\mathbb{Z}_2^2=\{(0\ 0), (0\ 1), (1\ 0), (1\ 1)\}$$

while

$$\mathbb{Z}_2^3=\{(0\ 0\ 0), (0\ 0\ 1), (0\ 1\ 0), (0\ 1\ 1), (1\ 0\ 0), (1\ 0\ 1), (1\ 1\ 0), (1\ 1\ 1)\}$$

In general, since there are two choices for each bit place, $\mathbb{Z}_2^n$ has 2^n elements. Just as we formed Table 1.5, an addition table for $\mathbb{Z}_2$, we may form an addition table for $\mathbb{Z}_2^n$, for any n. Table 1.6 is the addition table for $\mathbb{Z}_2^2$.

Table 1.6 Addition table for $\mathbb{Z}_2^2$

+	(0 0)	(0 1)	(1 0)	(1 1)
(0 0)	(0 0)	(0 1)	(1 0)	(1 1)
(0 1)	(0 1)	(0 0)	(1 1)	(1 0)
(1 0)	(1 0)	(1 1)	(0 0)	(0 1)
(1 1)	(1 1)	(1 0)	(0 1)	(0 0)

Observe that in $\mathbb{Z}_2$, the addition of 1 interchanges 0 and 1; that is, the 1-column (or the 1-row) of Table 1.5 lists 0 and 1 in the reverse order 1 0. In terms of addition, the changed bit is underlined in the following:

$$\underline{0}+1=\underline{1}\qquad \underline{1}+1=\underline{0}$$

The addition on 0, on the other hand, preserves 0 and 1. Here the unchanged bits are underlined:

$$\underline{0}+0=\underline{0}\qquad \underline{1}+0=\underline{1}$$

This observation is useful in describing transmission errors, as follows. Suppose that the code word (1 0 0 1 1) of some code is transmitted. Suppose that a transmission error occurs in the fourth bit; that is, the fourth bit is changed. This transmission error corresponds to adding to the code word the 5-tuple that has a 1 in its fourth bit (to change the fourth bit) and a 0 in its other bits (to preserve them); that is, the 5-tuple (0 0 0 1 0). Indeed,

$$(1\ \ 0\ \ 0\ \ 1\ \ 1)+(0\ \ 0\ \ 0\ \ 1\ \ 0)=(1\ \ 0\ \ 0\ \ 0\ \ 1)$$

The fourth bit changed.

Example 1.18

Here are some transmission errors in the first bits of transmitted 6-tuples:

$$\begin{aligned}(1\ \ 1\ \ 0\ \ 0\ \ 0\ \ 1)+(1\ \ 0\ \ 0\ \ 0\ \ 0\ \ 0)&=(0\ \ 1\ \ 0\ \ 0\ \ 0\ \ 1)\\(0\ \ 0\ \ 1\ \ 1\ \ 0\ \ 0)+(1\ \ 0\ \ 0\ \ 0\ \ 0\ \ 0)&=(1\ \ 0\ \ 1\ \ 1\ \ 0\ \ 0)\\(1\ \ 0\ \ 1\ \ 1\ \ 1\ \ 1)+(1\ \ 0\ \ 0\ \ 0\ \ 0\ \ 0)&=(0\ \ 0\ \ 1\ \ 1\ \ 1\ \ 1)\end{aligned}$$

Transmission errors in the second *and* third bits correspond to the addition of (0 1 1 0 0 0):

$$\begin{aligned}(1\ \ 1\ \ 0\ \ 0\ \ 0\ \ 1)+(0\ \ 1\ \ 1\ \ 0\ \ 0\ \ 0)&=(1\ \ 0\ \ 1\ \ 0\ \ 0\ \ 1)\\(0\ \ 0\ \ 1\ \ 1\ \ 0\ \ 0)+(0\ \ 1\ \ 1\ \ 0\ \ 0\ \ 0)&=(0\ \ 1\ \ 0\ \ 1\ \ 0\ \ 0)\\(1\ \ 0\ \ 1\ \ 1\ \ 1\ \ 1)+(0\ \ 1\ \ 1\ \ 0\ \ 0\ \ 0)&=(1\ \ 1\ \ 0\ \ 1\ \ 1\ \ 1)\end{aligned}$$

△

Definition 1.4

A code whose code words are binary n-tuples is a **group** code if the sum in $\mathbb{Z}_2{}^n$ of any two code words is again a code word. ○

Example 1.19

Suppose that the messages for a code consist of all of the binary 2-tuples and that each message also serves as its own code word. Then this is a group code. Table 1.6 gives the sum of any two code words. △

Example 1.20

Let us see if the even parity check bit code that has 3-tuples as code words is a group code. We form a table for the sum in $\mathbb{Z}_2{}^3$ of pairs of code words:

+	(0 0 0)	(0 1 1)	(1 0 1)	(1 1 0)
(0 0 0)	(0 0 0)	(0 1 1)	(1 0 1)	(1 1 0)
(0 1 1)	(0 1 0)	(0 0 0)	(1 1 0)	(1 0 1)
(1 0 1)	(1 0 1)	(1 1 0)	(0 0 0)	(0 1 1)
(1 1 0)	(1 1 0)	(1 0 1)	(0 1 1)	(0 0 0)

A case by case check shows that each entry is again a code word. So we have a group code. △

Example 1.21

Is a code with the code words

$$(0\ \ 0\ \ 0\ \ 0) \qquad (0\ \ 1\ \ 0\ \ 1) \qquad (1\ \ 0\ \ 1\ \ 0)$$

a group code? We again form an addition table, this time, for the 4-tuples:

+	(0 0 0 0)	(0 1 0 1)	(1 0 1 0)
(0 0 0 0)	(0 0 0 0)	(0 1 0 1)	(1 0 1 0)
(0 1 0 1)	(0 1 0 1)	(0 0 0 0)	(1 1 1 1)
(1 0 1 0)	(1 0 1 0)	(1 1 1 1)	(0 0 0 0)

Most of the sums, such as $(0\ \ 0\ \ 0\ \ 0)+(0\ \ 1\ \ 0\ \ 1)=(0\ \ 1\ \ 0\ \ 1)$, are code words, but some, such as $(0\ \ 1\ \ 0\ \ 1)+(1\ \ 0\ \ 1\ \ 0)=(1\ \ 1\ \ 1\ \ 1)$, are not. The failure of even *one* sum to be a code word means that this is not a group code. △

Example 1.22

A code with code words

$$(0\ \ 0\ \ 0) \qquad (1\ \ 1\ \ 1)$$

has the addition table

+	(0 0 0)	(1 1 1)
(0 0 0)	(0 0 0)	(1 1 1)
(1 1 1)	(1 1 1)	(0 0 0)

and so is a group code. △

Notice in Examples 1.19, 1.20, and 1.22, which are examples of group codes, that $(0\ \ 0\ \ 0)$ is a code word. Moreover, $(0\ \ 0\ \ 0)$ appears along the diagonal in the addition tables, where diagonal entries come from adding code words to themselves. Theorem 1.5 below says that this is true in general.

Rather than writing $(0\ \ 0\ \ 0)$, we shall write $\mathbf{0}$ to denote a binary n-tuple of all 0's. $\mathbf{0}$ then varies according to the n in question: For $n=4$, $\mathbf{0}=(0\ \ 0\ \ 0\ \ 0)$. For $n=6$, $\mathbf{0}=(0\ \ 0\ \ 0\ \ 0\ \ 0\ \ 0)$.

Theorem 1.5 Let $\mathbf{c}$ be a code word in a group code. Then

$$\mathbf{c}+\mathbf{c}=\mathbf{0}$$

In particular, $\mathbf{0}$ is always a code word in a group code.

Proof of Theorem 1.5 Addition of code words is just addition for each bit place using Table 1.5. So

$$0+0=0 \quad \text{and} \quad 1+1=0$$

That is, adding any bit to itself gives 0. So $\mathbf{c}+\mathbf{c}=\mathbf{0}$. Since we are given a group code, $\mathbf{c}+\mathbf{c}$, as the sum of two code words, is also a code word. But $\mathbf{c}+\mathbf{c}=\mathbf{0}$. Then $\mathbf{0}$ is a code word. ◇

One important advantage of group codes is that the minimum distance d of Definition 1.3 may be computed without comparing *all* pairs of distinct code words. It suffices, in fact, to compute Hamming distances to $\mathbf{0}$ (which is known to be a code word by Theorem 1.5). We formalize and prove this as Theorem 1.8, which follows later.

Definition 1.5 The **weight** of a binary n-tuple, $\mathbf{a}$, is the number of 1's appearing in the n-tuple. The weight of $\mathbf{a}$ is denoted by $W(\mathbf{a})$. ○

Example 1.23 $W[(1\ \ 1\ \ 0\ \ 1)]=3$; $W[(1\ \ 0\ \ 0\ \ 0\ \ 1)]=2$; $W[(1\ \ 1\ \ 1)]=3$; $W[(0\ \ 0\ \ 0\ \ 0)]=0$. For all n, $W(\mathbf{0})=0$. △

Proposition 1.6 Let $\mathbf{a}$ be a binary n-tuple. Then

$$W(\mathbf{a})=H(\mathbf{a},\mathbf{0})$$

Proof of Proposition 1.6 Since a bit differs from 0 precisely when the bit equals 1, the computation for the weight of $\mathbf{a}$ is precisely the same as the computation for its Hamming distance to $\mathbf{0}$. □

Proposition 1.7 Let $\mathbf{a}$ and $\mathbf{b}$ be binary n-tuples. Then

$$H(\mathbf{a},\mathbf{b})=W(\mathbf{a}+\mathbf{b})$$

Example 1.24 This example illustrates the proof of Proposition 1.7, which follows. Let $\mathbf{a}=(1\ \ 0\ \ 0\ \ 1)$ and $\mathbf{b}=(0\ \ 0\ \ 1\ \ 1)$. $H(\mathbf{a},\mathbf{b})=2$, since $\mathbf{a}$ and $\mathbf{b}$ differ in the *first* and *third* bit places.

$$(1\ \ 0\ \ 0\ \ 1)+(0\ \ 0\ \ 1\ \ 1)=(1\ \ 0\ \ 1\ \ 0)=\mathbf{a}+\mathbf{b}$$

$W(\mathbf{a}+\mathbf{b})=2$, since $\mathbf{a}+\mathbf{b}$ has 1's in the *first* and *third* bit places. Observe that the computations for $H(\mathbf{a},\mathbf{b})$ and $W(\mathbf{a}+\mathbf{b})$ both consist of counting the first and third bit places. △

Proof of Proposition 1.7

Recall from Table 1.5 that addition in $\mathbb{Z}_2$ results in the sum of equal bits being 0 and the sum of unequal bits being 1:

$$0+0=0 \qquad 1+1=0$$
$$1+0=1 \qquad 0+1=1$$

Add the two given n-tuples $\mathbf{a}$ and $\mathbf{b}$. The bits of the sum $\mathbf{a}+\mathbf{b}$ are 1 in the bit places where $\mathbf{a}$ and $\mathbf{b}$ differ and are 0 in the bit places where $\mathbf{a}$ and $\mathbf{b}$ agree. That is, $W(\mathbf{a}+\mathbf{b})=H(\mathbf{a},\mathbf{b})$. □

Example 1.25

We apply Proposition 1.7 and prepare for Theorem 1.8. Suppose that a code has

$$(0\ 0\ 0\ 0\ 0)\quad(0\ 1\ 1\ 1\ 0)$$
$$(1\ 0\ 0\ 0\ 1)\quad(1\ 1\ 1\ 1\ 1)$$

as its set of code words. Table 1.7 is the addition table for these code words. Observe that all of the entries in Table 1.7 are again code words. So we have a group code. Proposition 1.7 says that the table of Hamming distances between distinct code words, Table 1.8, can be computed by taking the weights of the entries in Table 1.7. △

Table 1.7 Addition table for code words

+	(0 0 0 0 0)	(0 1 1 1 0)	(1 0 0 0 1)	(1 1 1 1 1)
(0 0 0 0 0)	(0 0 0 0 0)	(0 1 1 1 0)	(1 0 0 0 1)	(1 1 1 1 1)
(0 1 1 1 0)	(0 1 1 1 0)	(0 0 0 0 0)	(1 1 1 1 1)	(1 0 0 0 1)
(1 0 0 0 1)	(1 0 0 0 1)	(1 1 1 1 1)	(0 0 0 0 0)	(0 1 1 1 0)
(1 1 1 1 1)	(1 1 1 1 1)	(1 0 0 0 1)	(0 1 1 1 0)	(0 0 0 0 0)

Table 1.8 Hamming distances for Table 1.7

	(0 0 0 0 0)	(0 1 1 1 0)	(1 0 0 0 1)	(1 1 1 1 1)
(0 0 0 0 0)	–	3	2	5
(0 1 1 1 0)	3	–	5	2
(1 0 0 0 1)	2	5	–	3
(1 1 1 1 1)	5	2	3	–

Theorem 1.8 Let d be the minimum distance for a group code. Then d also equals the minimum of the weights of all of the code words except $\mathbf{0}$.

Example 1.26 We illustrate the statement and part of the proof of Theorem 1.8. We continue to use the code words of Example 1.25. Taking the minimum of the entries in Table 1.8 gives $d=2$. Here are the code words with their weights, except for $W(\mathbf{0})$:

Code word	Weight
(0 0 0 0 0)	–
(0 1 1 1 0)	3
(1 0 0 0 1)	2
(1 1 1 1 1)	5

The minimum weight is 2, in agreement with $d=2$.

Observe that Proposition 1.6 ensures that the table of weights agrees with the (0 0 0 0 0)-column in Table 1.8. Recall also, by Proposition 1.7, that every entry in Table 1.8 is the weight of a code word. △

Proof of Theorem 1.8 Let d' denote the minimum of the weights of all of the non-$\mathbf{0}$ code words. We shall prove the theorem by showing first that $d \leq d'$ and then that $d' \leq d$.

By Proposition 1.6, the weight of each non-$\mathbf{0}$ code word $\mathbf{a}$ is also the Hamming distance between $\mathbf{a}$ and $\mathbf{0}$. Thus, taking the minimum, d', of the weights is the same as taking the minimum of *some* of the Hamming distances between distinct code words. The minimum of *all* of these Hamming distances is d. Increasing the set over which a minimum is taken can only retain or lower the minimum. Hence $d \leq d'$.

Let $\mathbf{a}$ and $\mathbf{b}$ be distinct code words. Then $H(\mathbf{a},\mathbf{b}) \neq 0$, since $\mathbf{a}$ and $\mathbf{b}$ differ in some bit. By Proposition 1.7, $H(\mathbf{a},\mathbf{b}) = W(\mathbf{a}+\mathbf{b})$. Moreover, since $H(\mathbf{a},\mathbf{b}) \neq 0$, also $W(\mathbf{a}+\mathbf{b}) \neq 0$ and so $\mathbf{a}+\mathbf{b} \neq \mathbf{0}$. Since we have a group code, $\mathbf{a}+\mathbf{b}$ is also a code word. So, computing d may also be done by taking the minimum of the weights of the non-$\mathbf{0}$ code words $\mathbf{a}+\mathbf{b}$. Computing d' involves taking the minimum over the possibly larger set of all non-$\mathbf{0}$ code words. So $d' \leq d$. ◇

Example 1.27 Let us compute d for the following set of code words, given to be from a group code:

(0 0 0 0 0 0) (0 0 1 1 1 1) (0 1 0 1 1 0) (0 1 1 0 0 1)
(1 0 0 1 0 1) (1 0 1 0 1 0) (1 1 0 0 1 1) (1 1 1 1 0 0)

The weights of the non-**0** code words, given in the same order, are the following:

–	4	3	3
3	3	4	4

Taking the minimum gives $d=3$. △

Example 1.28

We compute d for the following set of code words, given to be from a group code:

(0 0 0 0 0 0 0) (0 0 0 1 1 1 1) (0 0 1 0 1 0 1) (0 0 1 1 0 1 0)
(0 1 0 0 1 1 0) (0 1 0 1 0 0 1) (0 1 1 0 0 1 1) (0 1 1 1 1 0 0)
(1 0 0 0 0 1 1) (1 0 0 1 1 0 0) (1 0 1 0 1 1 0) (1 0 1 1 0 0 1)
(1 1 0 0 1 0 1) (1 1 0 1 0 1 0) (1 1 1 0 0 0 0) (1 1 1 1 1 1 1)

The corresponding weights are

–	4	3	3
3	3	4	4
3	3	4	4
4	4	3	7

Taking the minimum gives $d=3$. △

Exercises 1.3

1. Compute the following in $\mathbb{Z}_2{}^n$.
   a. $(1\ \ 1\ \ 0\ \ 0)+(0\ \ 1\ \ 1\ \ 0)$, $n=4$
   b. $(1\ \ 1\ \ 1\ \ 0\ \ 1\ \ 0)+(1\ \ 0\ \ 1\ \ 1\ \ 1\ \ 0)$, $n=6$
   c. $(0\ \ 0\ \ 0\ \ 1\ \ 0)+(1\ \ 0\ \ 1\ \ 1\ \ 0)+(1\ \ 1\ \ 0\ \ 1\ \ 1)$, $n=5$
2. To which transmission error does the addition of $(0\ \ 0\ \ 0\ \ 1)$ correspond?

3. To transmission errors in which two bit places does the addition of (0 0 0 1 1 0) correspond?

4. Form addition tables for each of the following sets of n-tuples. Tell whether or not each set may be the set of code words for a group code.
   a. (0 0 0) (1 1 0) (1 0 0)
   b. (0 0 0) (1 0 0) (0 1 1) (1 1 1)
   c. (0 0 0 0 0) (0 1 1 1 0)
      (1 0 1 1 1) (1 1 0 0 1)

5. Without doing any additions in $\mathbb{Z}_2^4$, tell why the following may not be the set of code words for a group code.

   (0 0 1 1) (1 0 0 1)
   (0 1 0 0) (1 1 0 1)

6. Compute the weights of the following n-tuples.
   a. (1 1 0) b. (0 0 0)
   c. (1 1 1 0) d. (1 0 0 0 1 1)

7. Can the code words of Example 1.28 be used for a single-error-correcting code? Why?

8. Each of the following is given to be the set of code words for a group code. Compute d for each code.
   a. (0 0 0 0 0 0 0 0) (1 0 1 0 1 0 1 0)
      (0 1 0 1 0 1 0 1) (1 1 1 1 1 1 1 1)
   b. (0 0 0 0 0) (0 0 1 1 1)
      (0 1 0 1 1) (0 1 1 0 0)
      (1 0 0 1 1) (1 0 1 0 0)
      (1 1 0 0 0) (1 1 1 1 1)

9. A code word **c** is transmitted. A transmission error **e** gives $\mathbf{r}=\mathbf{c}+\mathbf{e}$ as the received n-tuple. Show that the error may be corrected by adding **e** to **r**; that is, show that $\mathbf{c}=\mathbf{r}+\mathbf{e}$.

10. Give an example of a set of code words such that d is *not* equal to d', the minimum of the weights of the non-**0** code words. Include **0** as a code word.

11. Suppose that we have a group code with $d \geq 2$. Suppose that we change all of the bit values in some bit place of all of the code words. (This will not change d; Section 1.2, Exercise 5.) Show that we no longer have a group code.

    Hint: What about **0** as a code word?

12. Suppose that instead of Table 1.5, we used the following table for addition in $\mathbb{Z}_2$. Show by example that Proposition 1.7 would no longer hold for all **a** and **b**.

+	0	1
0	0	1
1	0	1

13. Given a set of code words, explain why forming an addition table to check for a group code involves, roughly speaking, the same amount of calculation as computing d.

1.4 Construction of Group Codes

Section 1.3 introduced group codes, for which d was particularly easy to compute. This section covers an efficient general method for constructing group codes. This method uses binary matrices, which are added and multiplied very much like real matrices.

Recall that in $\mathbb{Z}_2$, we may interpret 0 as EVEN and 1 as ODD. This gave Tables 1.4 and 1.5 as addition tables for $\mathbb{Z}_2$. We can also give rules for multiplying EVEN and ODD numbers, as illustrated in Table 1.9. We use $\cdot$ to denote multiplication. Using 0 and 1, instead of EVEN and ODD, changes Table 1.9 into Table 1.10, the usual table for **multiplication modulo 2**, or just **multiplication**.

Table 1.9 Multiplication table for $\{\text{EVEN}, \text{ODD}\}$

	EVEN	ODD
EVEN	EVEN	EVEN
ODD	EVEN	ODD

For adding and multiplying real numbers or integers, there are various algebraic techniques such as clearing parentheses. The same techniques are also valid in $\mathbb{Z}_2$ since they are valid under the EVEN, ODD interpretation of Table 1.4 and Table 1.9.

Example 1.29

The distributive law requires that

$$a \cdot (b+c) = a \cdot b + a \cdot c$$

With $a = \text{ODD}$, $b = \text{EVEN}$, $c = \text{ODD}$, this becomes

$$\text{ODD} \cdot (\text{EVEN} + \text{ODD}) = \text{ODD} \cdot \text{EVEN} + \text{ODD} \cdot \text{ODD} \tag{1.5}$$

The left side of (1.5) evaluates as

$$\text{ODD} \cdot (\text{EVEN} + \text{ODD}) = \text{ODD} \cdot \text{ODD} = \text{ODD}$$

The right side of (1.5) evaluates as

$$\text{ODD} \cdot \text{EVEN} + \text{ODD} \cdot \text{ODD} = \text{EVEN} + \text{ODD} = \text{ODD}$$

Table 1.10 Multiplication table for $\mathbb{Z}_2 = \{0,1\}$

$\cdot$	0	1
0	0	0
1	0	1

So, as expected, the two sides of (1.5) are equal. Now take $a = 1$, $b = 0$, $c = 1$, the translation from EVEN, ODD to 0, 1. Equation (1.5) becomes

$$1 \cdot (0+1) = 1 \cdot 0 + 1 \cdot 1 \tag{1.6}$$

Evaluate the left side of (1.6):

$$1 \cdot (0+1) = 1 \cdot 1 = 1$$

The right side of (1.6) gives

$$1 \cdot 0 + 1 \cdot 1 = 0 + 1 = 1$$

So, as they must be, the two sides of (1.6) are equal. △

Example 1.30 The associative law says that

$$a + (b + c) = (a + b) + c$$

With $a = 1$, $b = 0$, and $c = 0$, we claim that

$$1 + (0 + 0) = (1 + 0) + 0$$

Computing both sides gives: $1 + (0 + 0) = 1 + 0 = 1$ versus $(1 + 0) + 0 = 1 + 0 = 1$. △

Recall the **inner product** (also called the **dot product**) for real vectors:

$$(2, 4, -3) \cdot (3, 1, -1) = 2 \cdot 3 + 4 \cdot 1 + (-3) \cdot (-1) = 6 + 4 + 3 = 13$$

$$\begin{aligned}(0, 5, -2, 1) \cdot (8, 0, 3, -2) &= 0 \cdot 8 + 5 \cdot 0 + (-2) \cdot 3 + 1 \cdot (-2) \\ &= 0 + 0 - 6 - 2 = -8\end{aligned}$$

We can define a similar inner product on binary n-tuples. Think of an n-tuple as a vector with n coordinates.

Definition 1.6 Let $\mathbf{a} = (a_1 \quad a_2 \ldots a_n)$ and $\mathbf{b} = (b_1 \quad b_2 \ldots b_n)$ be binary n-tuples. Then, with addition and multiplication following the rules of $\mathbb{Z}_2$, the **inner product** is defined as

$$\mathbf{a} \cdot \mathbf{b} = a_1 \cdot b_1 + a_2 \cdot b_2 + \ldots + a_n \cdot b_n$$ ○

Example 1.31 We compute some inner products.

$$(1 \quad 0 \quad 1) \cdot (0 \quad 1 \quad 1) = 1 \cdot 0 + 0 \cdot 1 + 1 \cdot 1 = 0 + 0 + 1 = 1$$

$$\begin{aligned}(1 \quad 0 \quad 1 \quad 1) \cdot (1 \quad 1 \quad 1 \quad 1) &= 1 \cdot 1 + 0 \cdot 1 + 1 \cdot 1 + 1 \cdot 1 \\ &= 1 + 0 + 1 + 1 = 1\end{aligned}$$

$(1\quad 0\quad 1\quad 1)\cdot(0\quad 0\quad 0\quad 0\quad 1)$ is not defined since we are using a $\underline{4}$-tuple and a $\underline{5}$-tuple. △

Example 1.32

Consider the even parity check bit code that encodes 3-tuples into 4-tuples. Let us see that the code words then consist of all binary 4-tuples $(a_1\quad a_2\quad a_3\quad a_4)$ such that

$$(1\quad 1\quad 1\quad 1)\cdot(a_1\quad a_2\quad a_3\quad a_4)=0$$

For example, the code word $(1\quad 0\quad 1\quad 0)$ satisfies

$$(1\quad 1\quad 1\quad 1)\cdot(1\quad 0\quad 1\quad 0)=1+0+1+0=0$$

The noncode word $(0\quad 1\quad 1\quad 1)$ satisfies

$$(1\quad 1\quad 1\quad 1)\cdot(0\quad 1\quad 1\quad 1)=0+1+1+1=1\neq 0$$

In general, a_4 is adjusted so that $(a_1\quad a_2\quad a_3\quad a_4)$ has an even number of 1's. On the other hand,

$$(1\quad 1\quad 1\quad 1)\cdot(a_1\quad a_2\quad a_3\quad a_4)=a_1+a_2+a_3+a_4 \tag{1.7}$$

Adding 0 has no effect on a sum in $\mathbb{Z}_2$, while adding 1 changes a value in $\mathbb{Z}_2$. Compute $a_1+a_2+a_3+a_4$ successively as

$$0, a_1, a_1+a_2, (a_1+a_2)+a_3, (a_1+a_2+a_3)+a_4 \tag{1.8}$$

Equation (1.7) is 0 precisely when the initial value of 0 in (1.8) is ultimately changed back to 0, rather than to 1; that is, when there is an even number of 1's among the a_1, a_2, a_3, and a_4. △

We now turn to binary matrices. Just as a real matrix is defined as a rectangular array of real numbers, a **binary matrix**, or simply a **matrix**, is a rectangular array of bits. A matrix with m rows and n columns is called an $\boldsymbol{m\times n}$ matrix. Here are some binary matrices:

$(1\quad 0\quad 0\quad 1\quad 0)$ a 1×5 matrix, also called a 5-tuple or a row 5-tuple

$\begin{pmatrix}1\\1\\0\\1\end{pmatrix}$ a 4×1 matrix, also called a column 4-tuple

$$\begin{pmatrix} 0 & 1 \\ 1 & 0 \\ 1 & 1 \\ 1 & 1 \end{pmatrix} \qquad \text{a } 4 \times 2 \text{ matrix}$$

$$\begin{pmatrix} 1 & 0 & 0 & 0 & 0 \\ 1 & 1 & 1 & 0 & 0 \\ 0 & 1 & 0 & 1 & 0 \end{pmatrix} \qquad \text{a } 3 \times 5 \text{ matrix}$$

$$(0) \qquad \text{a } 1 \times 1 \text{ matrix}$$

Example 1.33

Just as binary n-tuples are added by adding in $\mathbb{Z}_2$ the corresponding bit places, binary matrices of the same size are added by adding in $\mathbb{Z}_2$ the corresponding bit entries.

$$\begin{pmatrix} 1 \\ 0 \\ 1 \end{pmatrix} + \begin{pmatrix} 1 \\ 1 \\ 0 \end{pmatrix} = \begin{pmatrix} 1+1 \\ 0+1 \\ 1+0 \end{pmatrix} = \begin{pmatrix} 0 \\ 1 \\ 1 \end{pmatrix}$$

$$\begin{pmatrix} 1 & 0 \\ 1 & 1 \\ 0 & 0 \\ 1 & 0 \end{pmatrix} + \begin{pmatrix} 0 & 1 \\ 0 & 1 \\ 1 & 1 \\ 0 & 0 \end{pmatrix} = \begin{pmatrix} 1 & 1 \\ 1 & 0 \\ 1 & 1 \\ 1 & 0 \end{pmatrix}$$

△

Recall that inner products for real vectors are essentially just special cases of matrix multiplication. Just as Definition 1.6 gives inner products for binary n-tuples, addition and multiplication for $\mathbb{Z}_2$ can be used to define matrix products for matrices with binary entries. Thus the row binary n-tuple $(0 \quad 1 \quad 1 \quad 1)$ and the column binary n-tuple

$$\begin{pmatrix} 1 \\ 1 \\ 1 \\ 0 \end{pmatrix}$$

may be thought of as matrices. As in Definition 1.8, which follows later, the matrix product

$$(0 \quad 1 \quad 1 \quad 1) \cdot \begin{pmatrix} 1 \\ 1 \\ 1 \\ 0 \end{pmatrix}$$

equals the inner product

$$(0 \quad 1 \quad 1 \quad 1)\cdot(1 \quad 1 \quad 1 \quad 0) = 0\cdot 1 + 1\cdot 1 + 1\cdot 1 + 1\cdot 0 = 0.$$

Similarly,

$$(1 \quad 0 \quad 1 \quad 0 \quad 1)\cdot\begin{pmatrix}0\\1\\1\\0\\0\end{pmatrix} = (1 \quad 0 \quad 1 \quad 0 \quad 1)\cdot(0 \quad 1 \quad 1 \quad 0 \quad 0)$$

$$= 1\cdot 0 + 0\cdot 1 + 1\cdot 1 + 0\cdot 0 + 1\cdot 0 = 1$$

In order to have a more compact notation, we shall occasionally transpose an n-tuple, as in Definition 1.7, which follows immediately. For occasional use in later parts of this text, we shall also give a formal definition for the transpose of a matrix.

Definition 1.7

Let $\mathbf{a} = (a_1 \quad a_2 \ldots a_n)$ be a row binary n-tuple. The **transpose** of $\mathbf{a}$, $\mathbf{a}^t$, is the column binary n-tuple

$$\mathbf{a}^t = \begin{pmatrix}a_1\\a_2\\ \cdot\\ \cdot\\ \cdot\\ a_n\end{pmatrix}$$

Let $\mathbf{b} = \begin{pmatrix}b_1\\b_2\\ \cdot\\ \cdot\\ \cdot\\ b_n\end{pmatrix}$ be a column binary n-tuple. The **transpose** of $\mathbf{b}$, $\mathbf{b}^t$, is the row binary n-tuple

$$\mathbf{b}^t = (b_1 \quad b_2 \ldots b_n)$$

More generally, let A be an $m \times n$ matrix. Let A_{ij} denote the entry in the ith row and jth column of A. Then A^t, the **transpose** of A, is the $n \times m$

matrix such that

$$A_{ji}{}^{t} = A_{ij}$$

○

Example 1.34 We illustrate the transpose operation here.

$$(0 \quad 0 \quad 1)^t = \begin{pmatrix} 0 \\ 0 \\ 1 \end{pmatrix} \qquad (1 \quad 0 \quad 1 \quad 1)^t = \begin{pmatrix} 1 \\ 0 \\ 1 \\ 1 \end{pmatrix}$$

$$(1 \quad 1 \quad 1 \quad 1)^t = \begin{pmatrix} 1 \\ 1 \\ 1 \\ 1 \end{pmatrix}$$

$$\begin{pmatrix} 1 \\ 0 \\ 1 \\ 0 \end{pmatrix}^t = (1 \quad 0 \quad 1 \quad 0) \qquad \begin{pmatrix} 0 \\ 0 \\ 1 \\ 1 \end{pmatrix}^t = (0 \quad 0 \quad 1 \quad 1)$$

$$\begin{pmatrix} 1 \\ 1 \\ 0 \\ 0 \\ 1 \end{pmatrix}^t = (1 \quad 1 \quad 0 \quad 0 \quad 1)$$

△

Example 1.35 Let

$$A = \begin{pmatrix} 0 & 1 & 0 & 1 \\ 1 & 1 & 1 & 1 \end{pmatrix}. \qquad \text{Then } A^t = \begin{pmatrix} 0 & 1 \\ 1 & 1 \\ 0 & 1 \\ 1 & 1 \end{pmatrix}.$$

$$\begin{pmatrix} 0 & 1 & 1 \\ 1 & 1 & 1 \\ 1 & 0 & 0 \\ 0 & 0 & 0 \end{pmatrix}^t = \begin{pmatrix} 0 & 1 & 1 & 0 \\ 1 & 1 & 0 & 0 \\ 1 & 1 & 0 & 0 \end{pmatrix}$$

△

Definition 1.8 Let **a** be a row binary n-tuple and **b** be a column binary n-tuple. Then the **matrix product a · b** is the 1×1 matrix whose sole entry equals the inner product $\mathbf{a} \cdot \mathbf{b}^t$. ○

Example 1.36

$$(1 \quad 0 \quad 1) \cdot \begin{pmatrix} 1 \\ 1 \\ 0 \end{pmatrix} = (1 \cdot 1 + 0 \cdot 1 + 1 \cdot 0) = (1)$$

$$(1 \quad 1 \quad 1 \quad 1) \cdot \begin{pmatrix} 0 \\ 0 \\ 1 \\ 1 \end{pmatrix} = (1 \cdot 0 + 1 \cdot 0 + 1 \cdot 1 + 1 \cdot 1) = (0)$$

△

The products of arbitrary matrices (as will be illustrated in Example 1.37) are defined in the usual manner:

Definition 1.9 Let A be a binary $m \times n$ matrix and let B be a binary $n \times p$ matrix. Then $A \cdot B$, the **matrix product** of A and B, is the binary $m \times p$ matrix whose entry in the ith row and jth column equals the matrix product of the ith row of A and the jth column of B. ○

Example 1.37

$$\begin{pmatrix} 1 & 0 & 1 & 1 \\ 1 & 1 & 0 & 0 \end{pmatrix} \cdot \begin{pmatrix} 1 \\ 0 \\ 1 \\ 0 \end{pmatrix} = \begin{pmatrix} 0 \\ 1 \end{pmatrix}, \text{ via the computations}$$

$$(1 \quad 0 \quad 1 \quad 1) \cdot \begin{pmatrix} 1 \\ 0 \\ 1 \\ 0 \end{pmatrix} = 1 \cdot 1 + 0 \cdot 0 + 1 \cdot 1 + 1 \cdot 0 = 0 \quad \text{and}$$

$$(1 \quad 1 \quad 0 \quad 0) \cdot \begin{pmatrix} 1 \\ 0 \\ 1 \\ 0 \end{pmatrix} = 1 \cdot 1 + 1 \cdot 0 + 0 \cdot 1 + 0 \cdot 0 = 1$$

$$\begin{pmatrix} 1 & 0 & 1 & 0 & 1 \\ 1 & 0 & 1 & 1 & 0 \\ 0 & 1 & 0 & 1 & 0 \end{pmatrix} \cdot \begin{pmatrix} 1 \\ 1 \\ 1 \\ 0 \\ 1 \end{pmatrix} = \begin{pmatrix} 1 \\ 0 \\ 1 \end{pmatrix}, \text{ via the computations}$$

$$(1\ \ 0\ \ 1\ \ 0\ \ 1)\cdot\begin{pmatrix}1\\1\\1\\0\\1\end{pmatrix}=1\cdot1+0\cdot1+1\cdot1+0\cdot0+1\cdot1=1$$

$$(1\ \ 0\ \ 1\ \ 1\ \ 0)\cdot\begin{pmatrix}1\\1\\1\\0\\1\end{pmatrix}=1\cdot1+0\cdot1+1\cdot1+1\cdot0+0\cdot1=0$$

$$(0\ \ 1\ \ 0\ \ 1\ \ 0)\cdot\begin{pmatrix}1\\1\\1\\0\\1\end{pmatrix}=0\cdot1+1\cdot1+0\cdot1+1\cdot0+0\cdot1=1$$

$\begin{pmatrix}1 & 0 & 1\\0 & 1 & 1\end{pmatrix}\cdot\begin{pmatrix}1 & 1 & 1\\0 & 0 & 1\end{pmatrix}$ is not defined, since the number of columns in the first matrix differs from the number of rows in the second. △

Just as it holds for real matrices, the distributive law holds for binary matrices. The law is stated formally as Theorem 1.9, following. A complete proof of Theorem 1.9 is rather long, but not particularly difficult; it has been omitted.

Theorem 1.9 (Distributive Law) Let A, B, and C be binary matrices. Then, provided that the matrix additions and multiplications are defined,

$$A\cdot(B+C)=A\cdot B+A\cdot C$$
$$(B+C)\cdot A=B\cdot A+C\cdot A$$

◇

Example 1.38 We shall illustrate the first part of Theorem 1.9.

$$A=\begin{pmatrix}0 & 1 & 1 & 0\\1 & 1 & 0 & 0\end{pmatrix}\qquad B=\begin{pmatrix}0\\1\\1\\0\end{pmatrix}\qquad C=\begin{pmatrix}1\\1\\1\\1\end{pmatrix}$$

$$B+C=\begin{pmatrix}1\\0\\0\\1\end{pmatrix} \qquad A\cdot(B+C)=\begin{pmatrix}0&1&1&0\\1&1&0&0\end{pmatrix}\cdot\begin{pmatrix}1\\0\\0\\1\end{pmatrix}=\begin{pmatrix}0\\1\end{pmatrix}$$

$$A\cdot B=\begin{pmatrix}0&1&1&0\\1&1&0&0\end{pmatrix}\cdot\begin{pmatrix}0\\1\\1\\0\end{pmatrix}=\begin{pmatrix}0\\1\end{pmatrix}$$

$$A\cdot C=\begin{pmatrix}0&1&1&0\\1&1&0&0\end{pmatrix}\cdot\begin{pmatrix}1\\1\\1\\1\end{pmatrix}=\begin{pmatrix}0\\0\end{pmatrix}$$

$$A\cdot B+A\cdot C=\begin{pmatrix}0\\1\end{pmatrix}=A\cdot(B+C)$$

△

Proposition 1.10 Let **a** and **b** be binary n-tuples. Then

$$(\mathbf{a}+\mathbf{b})^t=\mathbf{a}^t+\mathbf{b}^t$$

□

The complete proof of Proposition 1.10 is left as an exercise. The next example, however, does verify Proposition 1.10 in a particular case.

Example 1.39

$$\mathbf{a}=(1\quad 0\quad 1\quad 1) \qquad \mathbf{b}=(1\quad 0\quad 1\quad 0) \qquad \mathbf{a}+\mathbf{b}=(0\quad 0\quad 0\quad 1)$$

$$(\mathbf{a}+\mathbf{b})^t=\begin{pmatrix}0\\0\\0\\1\end{pmatrix}$$

$$\mathbf{a}^t=\begin{pmatrix}1\\0\\1\\1\end{pmatrix} \qquad \mathbf{b}^t=\begin{pmatrix}1\\0\\1\\0\end{pmatrix} \qquad \mathbf{a}^t+\mathbf{b}^t=\begin{pmatrix}0\\0\\0\\1\end{pmatrix}=(\mathbf{a}+\mathbf{b})^t$$

△

There is now enough machinery to generalize Example 1.32 (for the even parity check bit code) to other group codes. Code words are being written as row n-tuples. In later definitions, it will be customary to use column n-tuples. This causes no difficulties; just use transposes, as in Definition 1.7 and Proposition 1.10.

Theorem 1.11 Let H be an $r \times n$ binary matrix. Suppose that the code words for a code consist of all binary n-tuples $\mathbf{c}$ such that $H \cdot \mathbf{c}^t = \mathbf{0}^t$. Then the code is a group code.

Example 1.40 Before proving Theorem 1.11, we check it for one case. Let

$$H = \begin{pmatrix} 0 & 1 & 0 & 1 & 0 \\ 1 & 1 & 1 & 1 & 0 \\ 0 & 0 & 1 & 1 & 1 \end{pmatrix}$$

Let

$$\mathbf{b} = (1 \quad 1 \quad 1 \quad 1 \quad 0) \quad \text{and} \quad \mathbf{c} = (1 \quad 0 \quad 1 \quad 0 \quad 1)$$

Checking that $H \cdot \mathbf{b}^t = \mathbf{0}^t$ and $H \cdot \mathbf{c}^t = \mathbf{0}^t$ shows that $\mathbf{b}$ and $\mathbf{c}$ are code words. The group code property requires that $\mathbf{b} + \mathbf{c}$ also be a code word.

$$\mathbf{b} + \mathbf{c} = (0 \quad 1 \quad 0 \quad 1 \quad 1)$$

$H \cdot (\mathbf{b} + \mathbf{c})^t = \mathbf{0}^t$, as shown by calculation. Then $\mathbf{b} + \mathbf{c}$ is also a code word. △

Proof of Theorem 1.11 It must be shown that the sum of two code words is again a code word. So let $\mathbf{b}$ and $\mathbf{c}$ be code words. The defining property for code words in this theorem is that

$$H \cdot \mathbf{b}^t = \mathbf{0}^t \quad \text{and} \quad H \cdot \mathbf{c}^t = \mathbf{0}^t \tag{1.9}$$

It must be shown that $H \cdot (\mathbf{b} + \mathbf{c})^t = \mathbf{0}^t$.

$$\begin{aligned} H \cdot (\mathbf{b} + \mathbf{c})^t &= H \cdot (\mathbf{b}^t + \mathbf{c}^t) && \text{by Proposition 1.10} \\ &= H \cdot \mathbf{b}^t + H \cdot \mathbf{c}^t && \text{by the Distributive Law} \\ &= \mathbf{0}^t + \mathbf{0}^t && \text{by (1.9)} \\ &= \mathbf{0}^t && \text{since all of the bits in } \mathbf{0} \text{ are 0.} \end{aligned}$$

◇

Example 1.41 Let us illustrate Theorem 1.11 using the 2×3 matrix $H = \begin{pmatrix} 1 & 0 & 1 \\ 1 & 1 & 0 \end{pmatrix}$. We shall not yet worry about encoding and decoding methods for the code; we will just determine the code words. The code words must be 3-tuples. There are eight binary 3-tuples. In Table 1.11 we list them all, compute $H \cdot \mathbf{c}^t$, and see which are code words by checking if $H \cdot \mathbf{c}^t = \mathbf{0}^t$. Table 1.11 then shows that the code words are $(0 \quad 0 \quad 0)$ and $(1 \quad 1 \quad 1)$. These are, of course, the code words for the single-error-correcting code of Example 1.6 and for the double-error-detecting code of Example 1.7. △

Table 1.11 Code words for $H=\begin{pmatrix}1 & 0 & 1\\ 1 & 1 & 0\end{pmatrix}$

3-tuple **c**	$H\cdot\mathbf{c}^t$	Code word?
(0 0 0)	$\begin{pmatrix}0\\0\end{pmatrix}$	Yes
(0 0 1)	$\begin{pmatrix}1\\0\end{pmatrix}$	No
(0 1 0)	$\begin{pmatrix}0\\1\end{pmatrix}$	No
(0 1 1)	$\begin{pmatrix}1\\1\end{pmatrix}$	No
(1 0 0)	$\begin{pmatrix}1\\1\end{pmatrix}$	No
(1 0 1)	$\begin{pmatrix}0\\1\end{pmatrix}$	No
(1 1 0)	$\begin{pmatrix}1\\0\end{pmatrix}$	No
(1 1 1)	$\begin{pmatrix}0\\0\end{pmatrix}$	Yes

Example 1.42

As shown in Table 1.12, we compute the code words for the matrix $H=(1\ \ 0\ \ 1)$, which has one row and three columns. The code words are (0 0 0), (0 1 0), (1 0 1), and (1 1 1). For these code words $d=1$. So any code that uses these code words is not even single-error-detecting. △

Table 1.12 Code words for $H=(1\ \ 0\ \ 1)$

3-tuple **c**	$H\cdot\mathbf{c}^t$	Code word?
(0 0 0)	(0)	Yes
(0 0 1)	(1)	No
(0 1 0)	(0)	Yes
(0 1 1)	(1)	No
(1 0 0)	(1)	No
(1 0 1)	(0)	Yes
(1 1 0)	(1)	No
(1 1 1)	(0)	Yes

It turns out that all group codes may have their code words given by the construction of Theorem 1.11. This theorem will not be proved. However, this theorem gives a good intuitive description of group codes, as follows. Look at Table 1.12. The computation for a 3-tuple $\mathbf{c}=(c_1 \quad c_2 \quad c_3)$ to satisfy $H\cdot\mathbf{c}^t=\mathbf{0}^t$ is

$$(1 \quad 0 \quad 1)\cdot\begin{pmatrix} c_1 \\ c_2 \\ c_3 \end{pmatrix}=(1\cdot c_1+0\cdot c_2+1\cdot c_3)=(c_1+c_3)=(0) \qquad \textbf{(1.10)}$$

$c_1+c_3=0$ may be interpreted to mean that the number of 1's appearing in the first and third bit places is even. So the code words given by Table 1.12 consist of those 3-tuples that satisfy an even parity check on the first and third bits.

Now look at the H of Table 1.11: $H=\begin{pmatrix} 1 & 0 & 1 \\ 1 & 1 & 0 \end{pmatrix}$. In order for $H\cdot\mathbf{c}^t$ to equal $\mathbf{0}^t=\begin{pmatrix} 0 \\ 0 \end{pmatrix}$, the matrix product of each row with $\mathbf{c}^t$ must be (0). That is, $(1 \quad 0 \quad 1)\cdot\mathbf{c}^t=(0)$ and $(1 \quad 1 \quad 0)\cdot\mathbf{c}^t=(0)$. The first multiplication, which coincides with (1.10), is an even parity check on the first and third bits. The second multiplication, $(1 \quad 1 \quad 0)\cdot\mathbf{c}^t=(0)$, is an even parity check on the first and second bits.

In general, the code words of a group code consist of all n-tuples that satisfy some multiple even parity checks on various bit places. To focus on the code words for group codes, a standard definition follows. To denote a row n-tuple $\mathbf{c}$ is used. So $\mathbf{c}^t$ denotes a column n-tuple.

Definition 1.10 Let H be an $m\times n$ binary matrix. The set of all column n-tuples $\mathbf{c}^t$ such that $H\cdot\mathbf{c}^t=\mathbf{0}^t$ is the **null space** (or **kernel**) of H. ○

To apply Theorem 1.11 fully, a systematic way to find the null space of a given matrix H is needed. This can be done in general using the techniques of linear algebra. For the purposes of this text, however, it will suffice to consider only some special types of H from Definition 1.11 below, where the computation of the null space is especially easy. These H will also suggest efficient encoding and decoding methods.

Recall that the **identity matrix** has entries of 1 along the main diagonal and entries of 0 elsewhere. There is one identity matrix for each size square. Here are various identity matrices:

$$\begin{pmatrix} 1 & 0 \\ 0 & 1 \end{pmatrix} \qquad 2\times 2 \text{ identity matrix}$$

$$\begin{pmatrix} 1 & 0 & 0 \\ 0 & 1 & 0 \\ 0 & 0 & 1 \end{pmatrix} \qquad 3\times 3 \text{ identity matrix}$$

$$\begin{pmatrix} 1 & 0 & 0 & 0 & 0 \\ 0 & 1 & 0 & 0 & 0 \\ 0 & 0 & 1 & 0 & 0 \\ 0 & 0 & 0 & 1 & 0 \\ 0 & 0 & 0 & 0 & 1 \end{pmatrix} \quad 5 \times 5 \text{ identity matrix}$$

Definition 1.11

Let H be a binary matrix with r rows and n columns. Suppose that n is at least as large as r. Suppose that the last r columns of H form the $r \times r$ identity matrix. Then H is a **canonical parity check matrix**. ○

Example 1.43

Here are some canonical parity check matrices. Extra vertical, dashed lines have been inserted to emphasize the identity matrices.

$$\left(\begin{array}{c:cc} 1 & 1 & 0 \\ 1 & 0 & 1 \end{array}\right) \quad \left(\begin{array}{cc:ccc} 1 & 1 & 1 & 0 & 0 \\ 1 & 0 & 0 & 1 & 0 \\ 1 & 1 & 0 & 0 & 1 \end{array}\right) \quad \left(\begin{array}{ccc:c} 1 & 0 & 1 & 1 \end{array}\right)$$

$$\left(\begin{array}{ccc:cccc} 1 & 1 & 0 & 1 & 0 & 0 & 0 \\ 0 & 1 & 1 & 0 & 1 & 0 & 0 \\ 1 & 0 & 0 & 0 & 0 & 1 & 0 \\ 0 & 1 & 1 & 0 & 0 & 0 & 1 \end{array}\right)$$

△

Recall that, in constructing code words using Theorem 1.11, the rows of H represent parity checks on some of the bit positions of the n-tuple. *For canonical parity check matrices, the 1's in the identity matrix represent parity check bits for the 1's in the same row.* This is best illustrated by example.

Example 1.44

Let $H = \begin{pmatrix} 1 & 1 & 1 & 0 & 0 \\ 1 & 0 & 0 & 1 & 0 \\ 1 & 1 & 0 & 0 & 1 \end{pmatrix}$. Let $\mathbf{c} = (c_1 \quad c_2 \quad c_3 \quad c_4 \quad c_5)$ be an arbitrary 5-tuple.

$$H \cdot \mathbf{c}^t = \begin{pmatrix} 1 & 1 & 1 & 0 & 0 \\ 1 & 0 & 0 & 1 & 0 \\ 1 & 1 & 0 & 0 & 1 \end{pmatrix} \cdot \begin{pmatrix} c_1 \\ c_2 \\ c_3 \\ c_4 \\ c_5 \end{pmatrix} = \begin{pmatrix} c_1 + c_2 + c_3 \\ c_1 + c_4 \\ c_1 + c_2 + c_5 \end{pmatrix}$$

The condition $H \cdot \mathbf{c}^t = \mathbf{0}^t$ is thus equivalent to the three equations in $\mathbb{Z}_2$:

$$\begin{aligned} c_1 + c_2 + c_3 &= 0 \\ c_1 + c_4 &= 0 \\ c_1 + c_2 + c_5 &= 0 \end{aligned} \tag{1.11}$$

From (1.11), it can be seen that c_3 functions as a parity check bit for c_1 and c_2, that c_4 is a parity check bit for c_1, and that c_5 is (like c_3) a parity check bit for c_1 and c_2. The identity matrix condition described in Definition 1.11 keeps the check bits c_3, c_4, and c_5 from having to check on each other. Given that (1.11) is used to compute the null space, it can be seen that c_1 and c_2 may be arbitrary bits. Then c_3, c_4, and c_5 must be chosen to verify the parity checks. So

$$\text{Null space for } H = \left\{ \begin{pmatrix} 0 \\ 0 \\ 0 \\ 0 \\ 0 \end{pmatrix}, \begin{pmatrix} 0 \\ 1 \\ 1 \\ 0 \\ 1 \end{pmatrix}, \begin{pmatrix} 1 \\ 0 \\ 1 \\ 1 \\ 1 \end{pmatrix}, \begin{pmatrix} 1 \\ 1 \\ 0 \\ 1 \\ 0 \end{pmatrix} \right\}$$

Taking transposes gives

$$\begin{aligned} \{\text{Code words}\} = \{&(0\ \ 0\ \ 0\ \ 0\ \ 0), \quad (0\ \ 1\ \ 1\ \ 0\ \ 1), \\ &(1\ \ 0\ \ 1\ \ 1\ \ 1), \quad (1\ \ 1\ \ 0\ \ 1\ \ 0)\} \end{aligned}$$

Since c_3, c_4, and c_5 are considered check bits, the following convenient encoding method can be employed. Let the messages of the code consist of all 2-tuples $(c_1 c_2)$. The encoding method consists of appending the three check bits c_3, c_4, and c_5 so as to satisfy (1.11). Decoding a received code word consists merely of deleting the check bits. △

The calculations of Example 1.44 work in general to give Theorem 1.12, following. The proof of Theorem 1.12, which is omitted, consists of writing out the calculations of Example 1.44 using letters instead of numbers.

Theorem 1.12 Let H be an $r \times n$ canonical parity check matrix. Let $\mathbf{c}$ denote a row n-tuple. The null space of H consists of all column n-tuples $\mathbf{c}^t$ whose first $(n-r)$ bits are arbitrary but whose last r bits are determined by the $H \cdot \mathbf{c}^t = \mathbf{0}^t$ condition. Each of the last r bits serves as an even parity check bit for some of the first $(n-r)$ bits. In $\mathbf{c}$, call the first $(n-r)$ bits **information** bits. The last r bits are called **check** bits. ◇

Example 1.45

We illustrate Theorem 1.12. Let $H=\begin{pmatrix} 0 & 1 & 1 & 1 & 1 & 0 & 0 \\ 1 & 0 & 1 & 1 & 0 & 1 & 0 \\ 1 & 1 & 0 & 1 & 0 & 0 & 1 \end{pmatrix}$. We look at an arbitrary 7-tuple $\mathbf{c}=(c_1 \quad c_2 \quad c_3 \quad c_4 \quad c_5 \quad c_6 \quad c_7)$.

$$H\cdot\mathbf{c}^t=\begin{pmatrix} c_2+c_3+c_4+c_5 \\ c_1+c_3+c_4+c_6 \\ c_1+c_2+c_4+c_7 \end{pmatrix}$$

So c_5 is an even parity check bit for c_2, c_3, and c_4. The bit c_6 checks c_1, c_3, and c_4. The bit c_7 checks c_1, c_2, and c_4. The first four bits are the information bits. We have the following sixteen code words that satisfy the condition $H\cdot\mathbf{c}^t=\mathbf{0}^t$.

$(0\ 0\ 0\ 0\ 0\ 0\ 0)$ $(0\ 0\ 0\ 1\ 1\ 1\ 1)$ $(0\ 0\ 1\ 0\ 1\ 1\ 0)$ $(0\ 0\ 1\ 1\ 0\ 0\ 1)$
$(0\ 1\ 0\ 0\ 1\ 0\ 1)$ $(0\ 1\ 0\ 1\ 0\ 1\ 0)$ $(0\ 1\ 1\ 0\ 0\ 1\ 1)$ $(0\ 1\ 1\ 1\ 1\ 0\ 0)$
$(1\ 0\ 0\ 0\ 0\ 1\ 1)$ $(1\ 0\ 0\ 1\ 1\ 0\ 0)$ $(1\ 0\ 1\ 0\ 1\ 0\ 1)$ $(1\ 0\ 1\ 1\ 0\ 1\ 0)$
$(1\ 1\ 0\ 0\ 1\ 1\ 0)$ $(1\ 1\ 0\ 1\ 0\ 0\ 1)$ $(1\ 1\ 1\ 0\ 0\ 0\ 0)$ $(1\ 1\ 1\ 1\ 1\ 1\ 1)$

By construction, Theorem 1.11 applies, showing that we have a group code. A very easy calculation using Theorem 1.8 gives $d=3$. So we have a single-error-correcting code by Theorem 1.3. △

Exercises 1.4

1. Verify the distributive law for the following computations in $\mathbb{Z}_2$.
   a. $1\cdot(1+1)$ b. $(1+0)\cdot 1$ c. $(1+0)\cdot 0$
2. Compute the following inner products of real vectors.
   a. $(2,3,1)\cdot(1,5,1)$ b. $(1,-2,4,0)\cdot(0,-3,-2,1)$
3. Compute the following inner products of binary n-tuples.
   a. $(0\ 1\ 1\ 0)\cdot(1\ 1\ 0\ 1)$
   b. $(1\ 0\ 0\ 0\ 1)\cdot(1\ 1\ 1\ 0\ 0)$
   c. $(1\ 1\ 1\ 1\ 1)\cdot(1\ 0\ 1\ 1\ 1)$
   d. $(1\ 1\ 0\ 0\ 0\ 0)\cdot(0\ 0\ 0\ 0\ 1\ 1)$
4. Compute the following matrix products. All of the matrices have binary entries.

a. $(1\ \ 1\ \ 0)\cdot\begin{pmatrix}1\\0\\1\end{pmatrix}$ b. $\begin{pmatrix}1&0&1&0\\1&1&1&0\end{pmatrix}\cdot\begin{pmatrix}1\\0\\0\\1\end{pmatrix}$

c. $\begin{pmatrix}0&1&1&0&1\\0&1&1&0&1\end{pmatrix}\cdot\begin{pmatrix}1\\1\\0\\0\\1\end{pmatrix}$ d. $\begin{pmatrix}0&0&1&1&1\\0&0&1&0&1\\0&1&1&1&1\end{pmatrix}\cdot\begin{pmatrix}0\\0\\1\\1\\1\end{pmatrix}$

5. $A=(1\ \ 1\ \ 0)$, $B=\begin{pmatrix}1&1\\0&0\\1&0\end{pmatrix}$, $C=\begin{pmatrix}1&0\\1&1\\0&1\end{pmatrix}$. Verify that $A\cdot(B+C)=A\cdot B+A\cdot C$.

6. $B=(1\ \ 1\ \ 0)$, $C=(0\ \ 1\ \ 0)$, $A=\begin{pmatrix}1&1\\0&1\\1&0\end{pmatrix}$. Verify that $(B+C)\cdot A = B\cdot A+C\cdot A$.

7. Let $H=\begin{pmatrix}0&0\\1&1\end{pmatrix}$. As in Tables 1.11 and 1.12, list all four 2-tuples **c**. Compute each $H\cdot\mathbf{c}^t$. Tell whether or not each **c** is a code word.

8. Tell whether or not each of the following matrices is a canonical parity check matrix.

a. $\begin{pmatrix}1&1\\0&0\end{pmatrix}$ b. $\begin{pmatrix}1&1&0\\0&0&1\end{pmatrix}$

c. $\begin{pmatrix}1&1&1&0&0\\1&0&0&1&0\\1&1&0&0&1\end{pmatrix}$ d. $(1\ \ 0\ \ 1\ \ 0)$

e. $\begin{pmatrix}1&1&0&0&0\\1&0&1&0&0\\1&0&0&1&0\\1&0&0&0&1\end{pmatrix}$ f. $\begin{pmatrix}1&0&1&1&0&0&0\\0&0&1&0&1&0&0\\1&0&1&0&0&1&0\\0&0&1&0&0&0&1\end{pmatrix}$

9. Compute d for Example 1.45 by finding the weights of the code words.

10. Compute the null space for each of the following canonical parity check matrices. Compute d as well.

a. $\begin{pmatrix}0&1&0\\1&0&1\end{pmatrix}$ b. $\begin{pmatrix}0&1&1&0&0\\1&0&0&1&0\\1&1&0&0&1\end{pmatrix}$

c. $\begin{pmatrix} 1 & 1 & 0 & 0 & 0 \\ 1 & 0 & 1 & 0 & 0 \\ 1 & 0 & 0 & 1 & 0 \\ 1 & 0 & 0 & 0 & 1 \end{pmatrix}$ d. $\begin{pmatrix} 1 & 0 & 0 & 1 & 0 & 0 & 0 \\ 0 & 0 & 1 & 0 & 1 & 0 & 0 \\ 1 & 0 & 1 & 0 & 0 & 1 & 0 \\ 0 & 0 & 1 & 0 & 0 & 0 & 1 \end{pmatrix}$

11. A group code from Theorem 1.12 has $(n-r)$ information positions. How many code words are there?

12. Prove Proposition 1.10.

13. Let $\mathbf{a}=(a_1 \quad a_2 \ldots a_n)$ be a row n-tuple. Simplify the expression $(\mathbf{a}^t)^t$.

14. Explain why using multiple *odd* parity checks can never give a group code.

    Hint: What about $\mathbf{0}$?

15. What effect does adding a row of 0's have on the null space of a matrix?

16. Why cannot the code words $(0 \quad 0 \quad 0)$, $(0 \quad 0 \quad 1)$, $(0 \quad 1 \quad 0)$, and $(0 \quad 1 \quad 1)$ be the complete set of code words given by a canonical parity check matrix?

17. The matrix H of Theorem 1.11 for a group code is not unique; that is, different H may have the same null space.

    a. By computing the null spaces, show that they coincide for the following two matrices.

    $$\begin{pmatrix} 1 & 1 & 1 & 0 \\ 0 & 1 & 0 & 1 \end{pmatrix} \quad \begin{pmatrix} 0 & 1 & 0 & 1 \\ 1 & 0 & 1 & 1 \end{pmatrix}$$

    b. Explain why interchanging two rows of a matrix preserves its null space.

18. Suppose that a group code is known to come from a canonical parity check matrix H. Show that H is uniquely determined by the code words.

    Hint: Determine n and r. Give a procedure to determine if an information bit is checked by a check bit.

19. Some matrices, such as the identity matrices, have only the column n-tuple $\mathbf{0}^t$ in their null space. Why do such matrices lead to uninteresting codes?

20. Let I_p be the $p \times p$ identity matrix. Let E (for encoding) and D (for decoding) be $n \times p$ and $p \times n$ matrices, respectively, such that $D \cdot E = I_p$. Let the messages of a code consist of all row p-tuples. If $\mathbf{m}$ is a message, let the corresponding code word be the transpose of $E \cdot \mathbf{m}^t$.

    a. Given that $D \cdot E = I_p$, show that different messages are encoded as different code words.

b. Let $\mathbf{c}$ be a received n-tuple that is a code word. Show that the transpose of $D \cdot \mathbf{c}^t$ is the corresponding message.
c. Show that we have constructed a *group* code.

1.5 Construction of Error-Correcting Codes

Section 1.4 gives an efficient construction for group codes. Given a group code, Sections 1.2 and 1.3 enable an easy computation of its error-detection and error-correction capabilities. But given a matrix H, it would be good to know, without a complete listing of its null space, whether or not its null space is suitable for error detection or error correction. Such knowledge would allow the construction of many error-correcting codes. This section will deal with estimating d directly from H.

Example 1.46

Let $H = \begin{pmatrix} 0 & 1 & 1 & 1 & 0 \\ 1 & 1 & 0 & 1 & 1 \end{pmatrix}$. Let the null space of H be the code words for some group code. Theorem 1.8 says that d may be computed as the minimum of the weights of all of the non-$\mathbf{0}$ code words. We are going to see that d is at least 2. The sole 5-tuple of weight 0 is $\mathbf{0}$; but $\mathbf{0}$ is excluded from the computation of d. For d to be at least 2, it is thus only necessary that 5-tuples of weight 1 be excluded as code words. Weight 1 means just one 1 in the 5-tuple. Here then are the 5-tuples of weight 1:

$$\begin{matrix} (1 \quad 0 \quad 0 \quad 0 \quad 0) & (0 \quad 1 \quad 0 \quad 0 \quad 0) & (0 \quad 0 \quad 1 \quad 0 \quad 0) \\ (0 \quad 0 \quad 0 \quad 1 \quad 0) & (0 \quad 0 \quad 0 \quad 0 \quad 1) & \end{matrix} \tag{1.12}$$

Does a 5-tuple $\mathbf{e}$ from (1.12) satisfy $H \cdot \mathbf{e}^t = \mathbf{0}^t$? Take $\mathbf{e}_1 = (1 \quad 0 \quad 0 \quad 0 \quad 0)$ and compute as follows:

$$\begin{pmatrix} \underline{0} & 1 & 1 & 1 & 0 \\ \underline{1} & 1 & 0 & 1 & 1 \end{pmatrix} \cdot \begin{pmatrix} 1 \\ 0 \\ 0 \\ 0 \\ 0 \end{pmatrix} = \begin{pmatrix} 0 \\ 1 \end{pmatrix} \tag{1.13}$$

which is not $\mathbf{0}^t = \begin{pmatrix} 0 \\ 0 \end{pmatrix}$. The key observation in (1.13) for the general case is that multiplying H by $\mathbf{e}_1{}^t$ yields the *first* column of H, which is underlined for clarity in (1.13); $\mathbf{e}_1$, of course, has the bit 1 solely in its *first* position.

Now multiply H by $\mathbf{e}_2{}^t$, with $\mathbf{e}_2 = (0 \quad 1 \quad 0 \quad 0 \quad 0)$.

$$\begin{pmatrix} 0 & \underline{1} & 1 & 1 & 0 \\ 1 & \underline{1} & 0 & 1 & 1 \end{pmatrix} \cdot \begin{pmatrix} 0 \\ 1 \\ 0 \\ 0 \\ 0 \end{pmatrix} = \begin{pmatrix} 1 \\ 1 \end{pmatrix}$$

which is not $\mathbf{0}^t = \begin{pmatrix} 0 \\ 0 \end{pmatrix}$. $H \cdot \mathbf{e}_2{}^t$ equals the *second* column of H. Continuing with all of the $\mathbf{e}_i$ from (1.12) gives $H \cdot \mathbf{e}_i{}^t$ successively equal to all of the columns of H. Since all of these columns differ from $\mathbf{0}^t$, no $\mathbf{e}_i$ from (1.12) is a code word. Therefore, $d \geq 2$. △

The key observation for (1.13) is restated as a separate proposition with no formal proof.

Proposition 1.13 Let $\mathbf{e}$ be an n-tuple of weight 1 with a 1 in its ith bit place. Let H be an $r \times n$ matrix. Then $H \cdot \mathbf{e}^t$ equals the ith column of H. □

Example 1.46 illustrates the proof of the following general theorem. Note that, as in Example 1.46, it is not required that H be a canonical parity check matrix.

Theorem 1.14 Let H be a binary matrix. Then the null space of H comes from a single-error-detecting code if and only if no column of H is $\mathbf{0}^t$.

Proof of Theorem 1.14 Look at d. Theorem 1.2 says that if $d = 1$, then the code is not single-error-detecting. If $d \geq 2$, Theorems 1.2 and 1.4 say that the code can detect all single errors. By Theorem 1.8, d may be computed by taking the minimum weight of the non-$\mathbf{0}$ code words.

$d = 1$ precisely when there is some n-tuple $\mathbf{e}$ such that $W(\mathbf{e}) = 1$ and $\mathbf{e}$ is a code word; that is, $H \cdot \mathbf{e}^t = \mathbf{0}^t$. An $\mathbf{e}$ such that $W(\mathbf{e}) = 1$ has just one 1, say in the ith bit place. Then, by Proposition 1.13, $H \cdot \mathbf{e}^t$ equals the ith column of H. So $d = 1$ precisely when some column of H equals $\mathbf{0}^t$. Thus $d \neq 1$, or $d \geq 2$, precisely when no column of H equals $\mathbf{0}^t$. ◇

Example 1.47 Let $H = \begin{pmatrix} 0 & 1 & 0 \\ 0 & 0 & 1 \end{pmatrix}$, a canonical parity check matrix. The first column of H is all 0's. So Theorem 1.14 says that we should expect the code not to be single-error-detecting. An easy computation shows that the code words are

$$(0 \quad 0 \quad 0) \quad \text{and} \quad (1 \quad 0 \quad 0)$$

(1 0 0) is the expected code word of weight 1. An error in the first bit in the transmission of (1 0 0) leads to the code word (0 0 0). This error cannot be detected. △

Example 1.48 Let $H=\begin{pmatrix}1 & 1 & 0\\ 0 & 0 & 1\end{pmatrix}$. Theorem 1.14 says the code will be single-error-detecting. Indeed, the code words are

$$(0\quad 0\quad 0)\quad\text{and}\quad(1\quad 1\quad 0)$$

These code words differ in two bits, as is necessary for the detection of single transmission errors. △

Theorem 1.15 Let H be a binary matrix. Then the null space of H may be used for the code words of a single-error-correcting code if and only if no column of H is $\mathbf{0}^t$ and no two columns of H are equal.

Example 1.49 As an illustration of part of the proof of Theorem 1.15, which will follow, we continue with Example 1.46, where $d \geq 2$. In this example, we decide whether $d=2$ or $d \geq 3$. If $d=2$, then some n-tuple $\mathbf{e}$ of weight 2 satisfies $H \cdot \mathbf{e}^t = \mathbf{0}^t$. One such n-tuple might have 1's in the first and second bits; call it $\mathbf{e}_{12}=(1\quad 1\quad 0\quad 0\quad 0)$.

$$H \cdot \mathbf{e}_{12}{}^t = \begin{pmatrix}\underline{0} & \underline{1} & 1 & 1 & 0\\ \underline{1} & \underline{1} & 0 & 1 & 1\end{pmatrix} \cdot \begin{pmatrix}1\\1\\0\\0\\0\end{pmatrix} \tag{1.14}$$

$$= \begin{pmatrix}\underline{0}\cdot 1+\underline{1}\cdot 1+1\cdot 0+1\cdot 0+0\cdot 0\\ \underline{1}\cdot 1+\underline{1}\cdot 1+0\cdot 0+1\cdot 0+1\cdot 0\end{pmatrix} = \begin{pmatrix}1\\0\end{pmatrix}$$

The answer in (1.14), $\begin{pmatrix}1\\0\end{pmatrix}$, is, in fact, the sum of the first and second columns of H.

Now we look at $\mathbf{e}_{24}=(0\quad 1\quad 0\quad 1\quad 0)$, of weight 2, with 1's in the second and fourth bit places. $H \cdot \mathbf{e}_{24}{}^t$ will equal the sum of the second and fourth columns, as follows:

$$H \cdot \mathbf{e}_{24}{}^t = \begin{pmatrix}0 & \underline{1} & 1 & \underline{1} & 0\\ 1 & \underline{1} & 0 & \underline{1} & 1\end{pmatrix} \cdot \begin{pmatrix}0\\1\\0\\1\\0\end{pmatrix}$$

$$= \begin{pmatrix} 0\cdot 0+\underline{1}\cdot 1+1\cdot 0+\underline{1}\cdot 1+0\cdot 0 \\ 1\cdot 0+\underline{1}\cdot 1+0\cdot 0+\underline{1}\cdot 1+1\cdot 0 \end{pmatrix} = \begin{pmatrix} 0 \\ 0 \end{pmatrix}$$

Since $H\cdot \mathbf{e}_{24}{}^t = \mathbf{0}^t$, $\mathbf{e}_{24}$ is a code word. Thus $d=2$.

Let $\mathbf{e}_1 = (1\ \ 0\ \ 0\ \ 0\ \ 0)$ and $\mathbf{e}_2 = (0\ \ 1\ \ 0\ \ 0\ \ 0)$. Then $\mathbf{e}_{12} = \mathbf{e}_1 + \mathbf{e}_2$. Similarly, $\mathbf{e}_{24} = \mathbf{e}_2 + \mathbf{e}_4$. △

Proof of Theorem 1.15

Consider the various possible values for d.

For $d=1$, some column of H equals $\mathbf{0}^t$, as shown in the proof of Theorem 1.14. The code cannot even detect all single errors, by Theorem 1.2.

$d=2$ precisely when $d \neq 1$ and some n-tuple $\mathbf{e}$ satisfies $W(\mathbf{e})=2$, and $\mathbf{e}$ is a code word; that is, $H\cdot\mathbf{e}^t = \mathbf{0}^t$. Suppose that $\mathbf{e}$ has 1's in the i and j bit places, $i \neq j$; rename $\mathbf{e}$ to $\mathbf{e}_{ij}$. Let $\mathbf{e}_i$ and $\mathbf{e}_j$ have 1's in the ith and jth bit places respectively, with 0's elsewhere. Proposition 1.13 says that $H\cdot\mathbf{e}_i{}^t$ equals the ith column of H.

$$\begin{aligned} H\cdot\mathbf{e}_{ij}{}^t &= H\cdot(\mathbf{e}_i+\mathbf{e}_j)^t \\ &= H\cdot\mathbf{e}_i{}^t + H\cdot\mathbf{e}_j{}^t \end{aligned}$$

which is the sum of the ith and jth columns of H. When is this sum equal to $\mathbf{0}^t$? From Table 1.5 for addition in $\mathbb{Z}_2$, it can be seen that the sum of two bits is 0 precisely when the two bits are equal. So adding the ith and jth columns gives all 0's precisely when the two columns are equal. That is, $\mathbf{e}_{ij}$ is a code word if and only if the ith column of H equals the jth column of H. So $d=2$ precisely when no column of H equals $\mathbf{0}^t$ (corresponding to $d\neq 1$) and some two columns of H are equal. Theorem 1.2 says that $d=2$ does not allow single-error-correction.

$d\geq 3$ corresponds to $d\neq 1$ and $d\neq 2$; that is, no column of H is $\mathbf{0}^t$, and no two columns of H are equal. By Theorem 1.3, $d\geq 3$ also corresponds to the ability to correct single errors. ◇

Example 1.50

$H = \begin{pmatrix} 0 & 0 & 1 & 0 & 1 \\ 1 & 0 & 0 & 1 & 1 \\ 1 & 1 & 0 & 0 & 0 \end{pmatrix}$ gives a single-error-correcting set of code words, since no column is $\begin{pmatrix} 0 \\ 0 \\ 0 \end{pmatrix}$ and all of the columns are different.

$H = \begin{pmatrix} 0 & 1 & 1 & 1 & 1 \\ 1 & 0 & 0 & 1 & 0 \\ 1 & 1 & 0 & 0 & 1 \end{pmatrix}$ does not give a single-error-correcting set of code words, since the second and fifth columns are both $\begin{pmatrix}1\\0\\1\end{pmatrix}$.

$H=\begin{pmatrix}0&1&1&1\\0&0&1&1\\0&0&0&1\end{pmatrix}$ does not give a single-error-correcting code because the first column equals $\begin{pmatrix}0\\0\\0\end{pmatrix}$. In fact, by Theorem 1.14, H does not give even a single-error-detecting code. △

Example 1.51

Let $H=\begin{pmatrix}1&0&0&1&1&1\\0&1&0&0&1&1\\1&0&1&1&0&1\end{pmatrix}$. Then H does not give a single-error-correcting code since its first and fourth columns are equal. Let us find an explicit uncorrectable error. $\mathbf{e}_{14}=(1\quad 0\quad 0\quad 1\quad 0)$ has weight 2 since it has two 1's. Since its 1's are in the equal columns of H, $\mathbf{e}_{14}$ is a code word. Transmit $\mathbf{e}_{14}$ with a transmission error in the first bit. The received 5-tuple is $\mathbf{r}=(0\quad 0\quad 0\quad 1\quad 0)$. But $\mathbf{r}$ also differs from the code word $\mathbf{0}=(0\quad 0\quad 0\quad 0\quad 0)$ in just one bit, the fourth. So receiving $\mathbf{r}$, the decoder cannot choose between the transmitted code words $\mathbf{e}_{14}$ and $\mathbf{0}$. This error cannot be successfully corrected. △

Example 1.52

Let us see which single-error-correcting codes we can get using canonical parity check matrices with two check bits. $r=2$; H has two rows. H must look something like the following:

$$H=\begin{pmatrix}?&?&1&0\\?&?&0&1\end{pmatrix} \tag{1.15}$$

By Theorem 1.14, the unknown columns may not be $\begin{pmatrix}0\\0\end{pmatrix}$, nor may they coincide with $\begin{pmatrix}1\\0\end{pmatrix}$, with $\begin{pmatrix}0\\1\end{pmatrix}$, or with each other. So the only candidates for H in (1.15) are (i) no additional columns or (ii) one additional column of $\begin{pmatrix}1\\1\end{pmatrix}$.

(i) $H=\begin{pmatrix}1&0\\0&1\end{pmatrix}$ gives the uninteresting set $\{(0\quad 0)\}$ of code words. Only one message may be sent.

(ii) $H = \begin{pmatrix} 1 & 1 & 0 \\ 1 & 0 & 1 \end{pmatrix}$ gives the familiar set of code words: $(0 \quad 0 \quad 0)$ and $(1 \quad 1 \quad 1)$. △

Example 1.53

Let us look at canonical parity check matrices with $r = 3$. H must look like

$$H = \begin{pmatrix} ? & ? & ? & 1 & 0 & 0 \\ ? & ? & ? & 0 & 1 & 0 \\ ? & ? & ? & 0 & 0 & 1 \end{pmatrix} \quad \textbf{(1.16)}$$

The unknown columns in (1.16) have 3 bits; there are $2^3 = 8$ distinct possibilities for columns. Theorem 1.13 excludes $\begin{pmatrix} 0 \\ 0 \\ 0 \end{pmatrix}, \begin{pmatrix} 1 \\ 0 \\ 0 \end{pmatrix}, \begin{pmatrix} 0 \\ 1 \\ 0 \end{pmatrix}$, and $\begin{pmatrix} 0 \\ 0 \\ 1 \end{pmatrix}$. So in (1.16), we may add as many as four columns to the identity matrix and still have single-error-correcting capability. Let n denote the total number of columns. Recall that the first $(n - r)$ positions in the code words are information positions; their values may be arbitrary. So there are 2^{n-r} code words. The more columns that we add in (1.16), the more messages that can be transmitted. Adding all four possible columns gives the H and the code words of Example 1.45. Adding fewer columns allows less information to be sent, but fewer bits are used. △

Example 1.54

Suppose that we have a canonical parity check matrix with r rows and n columns. There will be $(n - r)$ information positions. How big may $(n - r)$ be with respect to r while still giving a single-error-correcting code? Each column has r bits. There are 2^r possible distinct columns. For error-correction, we must exclude the $\mathbf{0}^t$ column. Also, we may not duplicate the r columns of the identity matrix. So, in all, $2^r - 1 - r$ additional columns are available for information positions. In other words, r check positions may provide single-error-correction capability for up to $2^r - 1 - r$ information positions. (Exercise 11 in Exercises 1.5 shows that even for nongroup codes, r check positions can provide single-error-correction for at most $2^r - 1 - r$ information positions.) For instance, five check positions allow $2^5 - 1 - 5 = 26$ information positions. Six check positions allow $2^6 - 1 - 6 = 57$ information positions. Single-error-correcting codes with r check positions and $2^r - 1 - r$ information positions are called **perfect**.

Our initial single-error-correcting code, Example 1.6, with 000 and 111 as code words, was misleading. It suggested that in order to permit error-correction, many additional check bits are needed. However, $2^r - 1 - r$ increases very rapidly as a function of r. So for messages with a large number of bits, only a small percentage of additional check bits are needed for single-error-correction. Of course, for very long messages, there is the very real possibility of multiple errors ... △

Exercises 1.5

1. List all binary 4-tuples of weight 1.
2. Do the following binary matrix multiplications. Some of the matrix entries have been deliberately omitted.

a. $\begin{pmatrix} 1 & 1 & 0 & - \\ 1 & 0 & - & 1 \end{pmatrix} \cdot \begin{pmatrix} 0 \\ 1 \\ 0 \\ 0 \end{pmatrix}$ b. $\begin{pmatrix} 1 & 1 & - & 0 \\ - & - & 1 & 1 \\ - & - & 0 & 1 \end{pmatrix} \cdot \begin{pmatrix} 0 \\ 0 \\ 0 \\ 1 \end{pmatrix}$

c. $\begin{pmatrix} - & - & 0 & - & - \\ - & - & 1 & - & - \end{pmatrix} \cdot \begin{pmatrix} 0 \\ 0 \\ 1 \\ 0 \\ 0 \end{pmatrix}$

d. $\begin{pmatrix} - & - & - & 1 & - \\ - & - & - & 0 & - \\ - & - & - & 1 & - \end{pmatrix} \cdot \begin{pmatrix} 0 \\ 0 \\ 0 \\ 1 \\ 0 \end{pmatrix}$

3. Do the following matrix multiplications. Some of the matrix entries have been deliberately omitted.

a. $\begin{pmatrix} 1 & 1 & 0 & - \\ - & 1 & 0 & 0 \\ - & 1 & 1 & 1 \end{pmatrix} \cdot \begin{pmatrix} 0 \\ 1 \\ 1 \\ 0 \end{pmatrix}$ b. $\begin{pmatrix} - & 1 & 0 & - \\ - & 1 & 1 & - \\ - & 1 & 0 & - \end{pmatrix} \cdot \begin{pmatrix} 0 \\ 1 \\ 1 \\ 0 \end{pmatrix}$

c. $\begin{pmatrix} 1 & 1 \\ 0 & 0 \\ 0 & 1 \\ 1 & 1 \end{pmatrix} \begin{matrix} - & - & - \\ - & - & - \\ - & - & - \\ - & - & - \end{matrix} \cdot \begin{pmatrix} 1 \\ 1 \\ 0 \\ 0 \\ 0 \end{pmatrix}$

d. $\begin{pmatrix} - & - & - & 1 & 1 \\ - & - & - & 1 & 0 \\ - & - & - & 1 & 0 \end{pmatrix} \cdot \begin{pmatrix} 0 \\ 0 \\ 0 \\ 1 \\ 1 \end{pmatrix}$

4. let $H = \begin{pmatrix} 1 & 0 & 1 & 0 & 0 \\ 1 & 0 & 0 & 1 & 0 \\ 1 & 0 & 0 & 0 & 1 \end{pmatrix}$. Show directly that the null space of H cannot be used for an error-detecting code by exhibiting two code words that have a Hamming distance of 1.

5. Let $H = \begin{pmatrix} 1 & 0 & 1 & 0 & 0 \\ 1 & 1 & 0 & 1 & 0 \\ 1 & 0 & 0 & 0 & 1 \end{pmatrix}$. Show directly that the null space of H cannot be used for an error-correcting code by exhibiting two code words that have a Hamming distance of 2.

6. For each of the following binary matrices, say whether the null spaces may be used for single-error-correcting codes, only for single-error-detecting codes, or neither.

   a. $\begin{pmatrix} 0 & 0 & 1 & 0 \\ 0 & 0 & 0 & 0 \\ 1 & 0 & 1 & 1 \end{pmatrix}$

   b. $\begin{pmatrix} 1 & 1 & 1 & 0 & 0 \\ 1 & 0 & 1 & 1 & 1 \\ 1 & 1 & 1 & 0 & 1 \end{pmatrix}$

   c. $\begin{pmatrix} 1 & 0 & 0 & 0 & 0 \\ 1 & 1 & 0 & 0 & 0 \\ 0 & 0 & 0 & 1 & 1 \\ 0 & 0 & 1 & 0 & 1 \end{pmatrix}$

   d. $\begin{pmatrix} 1 & 0 & 0 & 0 & 1 & 1 \\ 1 & 0 & 0 & 1 & 0 & 0 \\ 1 & 0 & 1 & 0 & 1 & 0 \end{pmatrix}$

   e. $\begin{pmatrix} 1 & 0 & 1 & 0 & 0 & 1 & 1 \\ 0 & 1 & 0 & 0 & 1 & 1 & 1 \\ 0 & 0 & 1 & 0 & 0 & 0 & 1 \\ 0 & 1 & 0 & 0 & 1 & 0 & 1 \\ 0 & 0 & 1 & 0 & 0 & 0 & 1 \\ 1 & 1 & 1 & 1 & 1 & 0 & 0 \end{pmatrix}$

7. Find the canonical parity check matrix that gives the even parity check bit code with three information positions.

8. List the code words of a single-error-correcting code with three information positions and three check positions.

9. Using a canonical parity check matrix, list the code words for a single-error-correcting code with two information positions. Use as few check positions as possible.

10. For the codes of this section, how many check positions are needed for a single-error-correcting code with 20 information positions; with 32 information positions?

11. Let the messages for a code consist of all binary m-tuples. With $n = m + r$, let the encoding into n-tuples be given by appending r check bits. Do not assume that the code is a group code. Suppose that $d \geq 3$, which is equivalent to single-error-correcting capability by

Theorems 1.2 and 1.3. As follows, estimate m in terms of r. For simplicity, assume that $\mathbf{0}$ is a code word. (See Exercises 1.2, Exercise 5.)

a. Look at those code words with just one 1 in the first m positions. Explain why the check positions for these code words must have at least two 1's.

b. Why must the code words of part (a) have different values in their check positions?

c. Show that there are $2^r - r - 1$ possible sets of values for the check positions that have at least two 1's.

d. Explain why, with r check positions, m can be at most $2^r - r - 1$ for a single-error-correcting code.

12. Let H be a binary matrix. Let d be computed for the code words corresponding to the null space of H. Show that d is at least 4 if and only if (i), (ii), and (iii) hold.

    (i) No column of H equals $\mathbf{0}^t$.
    (ii) No two columns of H are equal.
    (iii) No three columns of H have a sum of $\mathbf{0}^t$.

13. Show that conditions (i) and (iii) of Exercise 12 may be achieved by requiring that one row of H be all 1's.

14. Suppose that a code with $d=3$ is obtained from a canonical parity check matrix. Show that a code with $d=4$ may be formed by the appending of just one even parity check bit.

1.6 Efficient Error Correction

In the previous section, a suitable canonical parity check matrix H was used to construct a single-error-correcting code with a known number of information and check positions. In this section, H is used to give an efficient decoding method for such a code. Also included is a discussion of the special group codes called Hamming codes.

The previous decoding method, as in Example 1.15, involved checking a received n-tuple $\mathbf{r}$ against each possible code word. But these comparisons can take a very long time. Suppose, however, that the code words correspond to the null space of some matrix H. Then it is easy to check if $\mathbf{r}$ is a code word, and thus has been transmitted without error. Namely, compute $H \cdot \mathbf{r}^t$; $\mathbf{r}$ is a code word if and only if $H \cdot \mathbf{r}^t = \mathbf{0}^t$.

Example 1.55

Let $H = \begin{pmatrix} 0 & 1 & 1 & 0 & 0 \\ 1 & 1 & 0 & 1 & 0 \\ 1 & 1 & 0 & 0 & 1 \end{pmatrix}$. Then

$$H \cdot \mathbf{0}^t = \mathbf{0}^t, \quad \mathbf{0} \text{ is a code word.}$$

$$\begin{pmatrix} 0 & 1 & 1 & 0 & 0 \\ 1 & 1 & 0 & 1 & 0 \\ 1 & 1 & 0 & 0 & 1 \end{pmatrix} \cdot \begin{pmatrix} 1 \\ 1 \\ 0 \\ 1 \\ 1 \end{pmatrix} = \begin{pmatrix} 1 \\ 1 \\ 1 \end{pmatrix}, \quad (1\ \ 1\ \ 0\ \ 1\ \ 1) \text{ is not a code word.}$$

$$\begin{pmatrix} 0 & 1 & 1 & 0 & 0 \\ 1 & 1 & 0 & 1 & 0 \\ 1 & 1 & 0 & 0 & 1 \end{pmatrix} \cdot \begin{pmatrix} 1 \\ 0 \\ 0 \\ 1 \\ 1 \end{pmatrix} = \begin{pmatrix} 0 \\ 0 \\ 0 \end{pmatrix}, \quad (1\ \ 0\ \ 0\ \ 1\ \ 1) \text{ is a code word.}$$

$$\begin{pmatrix} 0 & 1 & 1 & 0 & 0 \\ 1 & 1 & 0 & 1 & 0 \\ 1 & 1 & 0 & 0 & 1 \end{pmatrix} \cdot \begin{pmatrix} 0 \\ 1 \\ 0 \\ 0 \\ 0 \end{pmatrix} = \begin{pmatrix} 1 \\ 1 \\ 1 \end{pmatrix}, \quad (0\ \ 1\ \ 0\ \ 0\ \ 0) \text{ is not a code word.}$$

△

Definition 1.12 Let H be a given binary matrix with r rows and n columns. Let $\mathbf{r}$ be a row binary n-tuple. Then the **syndrome** of $\mathbf{r}$ is the column binary r-tuple $H \cdot \mathbf{r}^t$.

○

Recall from Example 1.18 that transmission errors may be interpreted as the addition of n-tuples to the transmitted code word. Let $\mathbf{e}$ denote the n-tuple that corresponds to the error. Then $\mathbf{e}$ has a 1 in each incorrectly transmitted bit place. The key observation is the following.

Proposition 1.16 Let the code words of a code correspond to the null space of the $r \times n$ matrix H. Let $\mathbf{r}$ be a received n-tuple. Write $\mathbf{r} = \mathbf{c} + \mathbf{e}$, where $\mathbf{c}$ is the transmitted code word and $\mathbf{e}$ is the transmission error. Then the syndrome $H \cdot \mathbf{r}^t$ of $\mathbf{r}$ equals the syndrome $H \cdot \mathbf{e}^t$ of $\mathbf{e}$. In particular, the syndrome of $\mathbf{r}$ depends solely on the transmission error, and not at all on the transmitted code word.

Example 1.56 Here is an illustration of the statement of Proposition 1.16. A proof of Proposition 1.16 will follow. Let H be as in Example 1.55. Let $\mathbf{r} = (1\ \ 1\ \ 0\ \ 1\ \ 1)$, $\mathbf{c} = (1\ \ 0\ \ 0\ \ 1\ \ 1)$, and $\mathbf{e} = (0\ \ 1\ \ 0\ \ 0\ \ 0)$. Indeed, $\mathbf{r} = \mathbf{c} + \mathbf{e}$. We know $\mathbf{c}$ is a code word since, as computed in Example 1.55, $H \cdot \mathbf{c}^t = \mathbf{0}^t$. Also as computed in Example 1.55, both $\mathbf{r}$ and $\mathbf{e}$ have $\begin{pmatrix} 1 \\ 1 \\ 1 \end{pmatrix}$ as their syndromes.

△

Proof of Proposition 1.16

Compare $H \cdot \mathbf{r}^t$ and $H \cdot \mathbf{e}^t$.

$$\begin{aligned} H \cdot \mathbf{r}^t &= H \cdot (\mathbf{c}+\mathbf{e})^t, && \mathbf{r}=\mathbf{c}+\mathbf{e} \\ &= H \cdot \mathbf{c}^t + H \cdot \mathbf{e}^t, && \text{the Distributive Law} \\ &= \mathbf{0}^t + H \cdot \mathbf{e}^t, && \mathbf{c} \text{ is a code word} \\ &= H \cdot \mathbf{e}^t, && \mathbf{0} \text{ is all 0's} \end{aligned}$$

□

Example 1.57

Let $H = \begin{pmatrix} 0 & 1 & 1 & 0 & 0 \\ 1 & 1 & 0 & 1 & 0 \\ 1 & 1 & 0 & 0 & 1 \end{pmatrix}$.

$\mathbf{c} = (1 \quad 0 \quad 0 \quad 1 \quad 1)$ and $\mathbf{c}' = (0 \quad 1 \quad 1 \quad 1 \quad 1)$ are easily checked to satisfy $H \cdot \mathbf{c}^t = \mathbf{0}^t$ and $H \cdot \mathbf{c}'^t = \mathbf{0}^t$, and so are code words. Let $\mathbf{e} = (1 \quad 0 \quad 0 \quad 0 \quad 0)$ be a transmission error in the first bit. Then $\mathbf{r} = \mathbf{c} + \mathbf{e} = (0 \quad 0 \quad 0 \quad 1 \quad 1)$ and $\mathbf{r}' = \mathbf{c}' + \mathbf{e} = (1 \quad 1 \quad 1 \quad 1 \quad 1)$ should have the same syndromes. Indeed,

$$\begin{pmatrix} 0 & 1 & 1 & 0 & 0 \\ 1 & 1 & 0 & 1 & 0 \\ 1 & 1 & 0 & 0 & 1 \end{pmatrix} \cdot \begin{pmatrix} 0 \\ 0 \\ 0 \\ 1 \\ 1 \end{pmatrix} = \begin{pmatrix} 0 \\ 1 \\ 1 \end{pmatrix} \quad \text{and}$$

$$\begin{pmatrix} 0 & 1 & 1 & 0 & 0 \\ 1 & 1 & 0 & 1 & 0 \\ 1 & 1 & 0 & 0 & 1 \end{pmatrix} \cdot \begin{pmatrix} 1 \\ 1 \\ 1 \\ 1 \\ 1 \end{pmatrix} = \begin{pmatrix} 0 \\ 1 \\ 1 \end{pmatrix}$$

$\begin{pmatrix} 0 \\ 1 \\ 1 \end{pmatrix}$ also equals the syndrome of $\mathbf{e}$. Recall that, by Proposition 1.13, since $\mathbf{e}$ has a 1 in just the first bit place, the syndrome of $\mathbf{e}$ also equals the first column of H. △

Theorem 1.17

Let H be an $r \times n$ binary matrix whose null space corresponds to the code words of a single-error-correcting code. Let $\mathbf{r}$ be a received n-tuple that was transmitted with at most one error. If the syndrome of $\mathbf{r}$ is $\mathbf{0}^t$, then no error occurred. Otherwise, the syndrome of $\mathbf{r}$ equals some column of H, say the ith, and an error occurred in the transmission of the ith bit.

Proof of Theorem 1.17

$H \cdot \mathbf{r}^t = \mathbf{0}^t$ is, of course, the condition for $\mathbf{r}$ to be a code word, and for no transmission error to have occurred. Otherwise, we are given that

$$\mathbf{r} = \mathbf{c} + \mathbf{e}$$

with $\mathbf{c}$ a code word and the error $\mathbf{e}$ with exactly one 1 in, say, the ith bit.

By Proposition 1.16, $\mathbf{r}$ and $\mathbf{e}$ have the same syndrome. By Proposition 1.13, this syndrome equals the ith column of H. By Theorem 1.15, all of the columns of H are distinct. So the syndrome *uniquely* specifies the ith column and hence the bit that is in error. $\mathbf{c}$ is found by changing $\mathbf{r}$ in the ith bit. ◇

Example 1.58

Let $H = \begin{pmatrix} 0 & 1 & 1 & 0 & 0 \\ 1 & 1 & 0 & 1 & 0 \\ 1 & 1 & 0 & 0 & 1 \end{pmatrix}$. Let $\mathbf{c} = (1 \quad 1 \quad 1 \quad 0 \quad 0)$. Suppose that an error occurs in the transmission of the *third* bit. $\mathbf{r} = (1 \quad 1 \quad 0 \quad 0 \quad 0)$.

$$H \cdot \mathbf{r}^t = \begin{pmatrix} 0 & 1 & 1 & 0 & 0 \\ 1 & 1 & 0 & 1 & 0 \\ 1 & 1 & 0 & 0 & 1 \end{pmatrix} \cdot \begin{pmatrix} 1 \\ 1 \\ 0 \\ 0 \\ 0 \end{pmatrix} = \begin{pmatrix} 1 \\ 0 \\ 0 \end{pmatrix}$$

the *third* column of H. Theorem 1.17 says that we get $\mathbf{c}$ from $\mathbf{r}$ by changing $\mathbf{r}$ in the *third* bit, and this is correct.

Continue with H and $\mathbf{c}$ and suppose that there is an error in the *first* bit, making $\mathbf{r} = (0 \quad 1 \quad 1 \quad 0 \quad 0)$.

$$H \cdot \mathbf{r}^t = \begin{pmatrix} 0 & 1 & 1 & 0 & 0 \\ 1 & 1 & 0 & 1 & 0 \\ 1 & 1 & 0 & 0 & 1 \end{pmatrix} \cdot \begin{pmatrix} 0 \\ 1 \\ 1 \\ 0 \\ 0 \end{pmatrix} = \begin{pmatrix} 0 \\ 1 \\ 1 \end{pmatrix}$$

the *first* column of H. Changing $\mathbf{r}$ in the ***first*** bit gives $\mathbf{c}$. △

Examples 1.59

Let $H = \begin{pmatrix} 1 & 0 & 1 & 1 & 0 & 0 \\ 0 & 1 & 1 & 0 & 1 & 0 \\ 1 & 1 & 1 & 0 & 0 & 1 \end{pmatrix}$. Let us decode the following received 6-tuples:

$$(1 \quad 1 \quad 1 \quad 1 \quad 1 \quad 0) \qquad (0 \quad 1 \quad 0 \quad 1 \quad 1 \quad 1) \qquad (1 \quad 1 \quad 1 \quad 1 \quad 1 \quad 1)$$

$$\begin{pmatrix} 1 & 0 & 1 & 1 & 0 & 0 \\ 0 & 1 & 1 & 0 & 1 & 0 \\ 1 & 1 & 1 & 0 & 0 & 1 \end{pmatrix} \cdot \begin{pmatrix} 1 \\ 1 \\ 1 \\ 1 \\ 1 \\ 0 \end{pmatrix} = \begin{pmatrix} 1 \\ 1 \\ 1 \end{pmatrix}$$

the *third* column of H. The transmitted code word was $(1\ \ 1\ \ 0\ \ 1\ \ 1\ \ 0)$. Deleting the last three check bits gives the transmitted message $(1\ \ 1\ \ 0)$. △

$$\begin{pmatrix} 1 & 0 & 1 & 1 & 0 & 0 \\ 0 & 1 & 1 & 0 & 1 & 0 \\ 1 & 1 & 1 & 0 & 0 & 1 \end{pmatrix} \cdot \begin{pmatrix} 0 \\ 1 \\ 0 \\ 1 \\ 1 \\ 1 \end{pmatrix} = \begin{pmatrix} 1 \\ 0 \\ 0 \end{pmatrix}$$

the *fourth* column of H. The transmitted code word was $(0\ \ 1\ \ 0\ \ 0\ \ 1\ \ 1)$. Deleting the last three check bits gives the transmitted message $(0\ \ 1\ \ 0)$. In this case, the error occurred in the transmission of one of the check bits. △

$$\begin{pmatrix} 1 & 0 & 1 & 1 & 0 & 0 \\ 0 & 1 & 1 & 0 & 1 & 0 \\ 1 & 1 & 1 & 0 & 0 & 1 \end{pmatrix} \cdot \begin{pmatrix} 1 \\ 1 \\ 1 \\ 1 \\ 1 \\ 1 \end{pmatrix} = \begin{pmatrix} 1 \\ 1 \\ 0 \end{pmatrix}$$

which is *not* a column of H. What happened? More than one bit was changed in transmission. Some possible multiple errors with a syndrome of $\begin{pmatrix} 1 \\ 1 \\ 0 \end{pmatrix}$ are $(0\ \ 0\ \ 0\ \ 1\ \ 1\ \ 0)$, $(0\ \ 0\ \ 1\ \ 0\ \ 0\ \ 1)$, and $(0\ \ 1\ \ 1\ \ 0\ \ 1\ \ 0)$. The first two errors are double errors and the third is a triple error. By assumption, the double errors are more likely than the triple error. But we have no way of choosing the more likely of the double errors. So our decoder just gives a multiple error indication. △

Example 1.60

Look at what may happen if the hypotheses of Theorem 1.17 are not satisfied. let $H = \begin{pmatrix} 1 & 1 & 1 & 0 & 0 \\ 0 & 1 & 0 & 1 & 0 \\ 0 & 1 & 0 & 0 & 1 \end{pmatrix}$. Let $\mathbf{r} = (0 \quad 1 \quad 0 \quad 1 \quad 1)$ be the received 5-tuple.

$$\begin{pmatrix} 1 & 1 & 1 & 0 & 0 \\ 0 & 1 & 0 & 1 & 0 \\ 0 & 1 & 0 & 0 & 1 \end{pmatrix} \cdot \begin{pmatrix} 0 \\ 1 \\ 0 \\ 1 \\ 1 \end{pmatrix} = \begin{pmatrix} 1 \\ 0 \\ 0 \end{pmatrix}$$

So the syndrome of $\mathbf{r}$ is both the first and the third columns of H. Any single transmission error occurred in either the first or third bits, but we cannot say which. Of course, Theorem 1.15 says that the code for H is not single-error-correcting. △

Example 1.61

Here is a single-error-correcting code of the type that was first invented by Hamming. It uses a 3×6 binary matrix H that is almost a canonical parity check matrix. Count from one to six in binary, using column 3-tuples:

$$\begin{pmatrix} 0 \\ 0 \\ 1 \end{pmatrix} \quad \begin{pmatrix} 0 \\ 1 \\ 0 \end{pmatrix} \quad \begin{pmatrix} 0 \\ 1 \\ 1 \end{pmatrix} \quad \begin{pmatrix} 1 \\ 0 \\ 0 \end{pmatrix} \quad \begin{pmatrix} 1 \\ 0 \\ 1 \end{pmatrix} \quad \begin{pmatrix} 1 \\ 1 \\ 0 \end{pmatrix} \qquad \textbf{(1.17)}$$

$$H = \begin{pmatrix} 0 & 0 & 0 & 1 & 1 & 1 \\ 0 & 1 & 1 & 0 & 0 & 1 \\ 1 & 0 & 1 & 0 & 1 & 0 \end{pmatrix} \qquad \textbf{(1.18)}$$

is the 3×6 matrix whose columns come from (1.17).

By Theorem 1.15, H gives code words that are suitable for a single-error-correcting code. Theorem 1.17 says that the column giving the syndrome marks the bit place that is in error. But, by construction, the syndrome for the ith column is just the number i written in binary. So *the syndrome itself tells which bit is in error.*

For example, suppose that the 6-tuple $(1 \quad 0 \quad 1 \quad 1 \quad 1 \quad 0)$ is received.

$$\begin{pmatrix} 0 & 0 & 0 & 1 & 1 & 1 \\ 0 & 1 & 1 & 0 & 0 & 1 \\ 1 & 0 & 1 & 0 & 1 & 0 \end{pmatrix} \cdot \begin{pmatrix} 1 \\ 0 \\ 1 \\ 1 \\ 1 \\ 0 \end{pmatrix} = \begin{pmatrix} 0 \\ 1 \\ 1 \end{pmatrix}$$

$\begin{pmatrix} 0 \\ 1 \\ 1 \end{pmatrix}^t = (0 \quad 1 \quad 1)$, which is binary for three. The error occurred in the third bit. $(1 \quad 0 \quad 0 \quad 1 \quad 1 \quad 0)$ was transmitted.

For canonical parity check matrices, the check bits correspond to the columns of the identity matrix. For H in (1.18), use the columns with just one 1 to correspond to check bits. Thus, the check bits are in places 1, 2, and 4. The information bits are in places 3, 5, and 6. As for canonical parity check matrices, the values in the information bits may be chosen arbitrarily. These information values then determine the values of the check bits. △

Example 1.61 generalizes as follows: a **Hamming code** with m information bits and r check bits,

$$2^{r-1} - r < m \leq 2^r - r - 1$$

has code words corresponding to the null space of the $r \times (m+r)$ binary matrix H whose ith column is the number i written in binary with r bits. With $n = m + r$, a message m-tuple is encoded into an n-tuple by inserting check bits, as specified by H, in places

$$2^0 = 1, \quad 2^1 = 2, \quad 2^2 = 4, \quad 2^3 = 8, \ldots, \quad 2^{r-1} \tag{1.19}$$

Since all of the columns of H are different and non-$\mathbf{0}^t$, Theorem 1.15 ensures that single-error-correction is possible. As in Example 1.61, to decode a received n-tuple $\mathbf{r}$, first compute its syndrome $H \cdot \mathbf{r}^t$. If a single transmission error occurred, then $H \cdot \mathbf{r}^t$ is the binary representation of the bit place in error.

As in Example 1.54, Hamming codes with $m = 2^r - r - 1$, which have the maximum possible number of information bits with r check bits, are called **perfect**. For perfect Hamming codes, every syndrome except for $\mathbf{0}^t$ occurs as a column. Hamming codes with $m < 2^r - r - 1$ are called **shortened**. For shortened Hamming codes, some syndromes represent multiple errors.

Example 1.62

Here is the (perfect) Hamming code with four information bits and three check bits.

$$H = \begin{pmatrix} 0 & 0 & 0 & 1 & 1 & 1 & 1 \\ 0 & 1 & 1 & 0 & 0 & 1 & 1 \\ 1 & 0 & 1 & 0 & 1 & 0 & 1 \end{pmatrix}$$

Consider a 7-tuple $\mathbf{a} = (a_1 \quad a_2 \quad a_3 \quad a_4 \quad a_5 \quad a_6 \quad a_7)$ as a possible code word.

$$H \cdot \mathbf{a}^t = \begin{pmatrix} a_4 + a_5 + a_6 + a_7 \\ a_2 + a_3 + a_6 + a_7 \\ a_1 + a_3 + a_5 + a_7 \end{pmatrix} \tag{1.20}$$

The check bit places are given in (1.19). The condition for **a** to be a code word is $H \cdot \mathbf{a}^t = \mathbf{0}^t$. So from (1.20),

Place 1 is a parity check on places 3, 5, and 7.

Place 2 is a parity check on places 3, 6, and 7.

Place 4 is a parity check on places 5, 6, and 7.

Here is an example: the message $(\mathbf{0} \quad \mathbf{1} \quad \mathbf{1} \quad \mathbf{0})$ encodes as $(1 \quad 1 \quad \mathbf{0} \quad 0 \quad \mathbf{1} \quad \mathbf{1} \quad \mathbf{0})$; the information bits are boldface for clarity.

The received 7-tuple $(1 \quad 1 \quad 0 \quad 1 \quad 0 \quad 1 \quad 1)$ has syndrome $\begin{pmatrix} 1 \\ 1 \\ 0 \end{pmatrix}$, which indicates a transmission error in the sixth bit. So the most likely transmitted code word is $(1 \quad 1 \quad \mathbf{0} \quad 1 \quad \mathbf{0} \quad \mathbf{0} \quad \mathbf{1})$. Retaining the (boldface) information bits gives $(0 \quad 0 \quad 0 \quad 1)$ as the decoded message. △

Example 1.63

We use the H of Example 1.61, which corresponds to a shortened Hamming code. Suppose that the 6-tuple $(0 \quad 0 \quad 0 \quad 1 \quad 1 \quad 1)$ is received. The syndrome is $\begin{pmatrix} 1 \\ 1 \\ 1 \end{pmatrix}$, which is the binary representation of seven. This code has 6-tuples as code words. So the syndrome does not occur as a column of H; there was more than one transmission error. △

Exercises 1.6

1. Let $H = \begin{pmatrix} 1 & 1 & 0 & 0 \\ 1 & 0 & 1 & 0 \\ 1 & 1 & 0 & 1 \end{pmatrix}$. Compute the syndrome for each of the following 4-tuples.

   a. $(1 \quad 0 \quad 0 \quad 1)$ b. $(0 \quad 0 \quad 1 \quad 0)$

   c. $(1 \quad 1 \quad 1 \quad 0)$ d. $(0 \quad 1 \quad 1 \quad 0)$

2. Let $H = \begin{pmatrix} 1 & 0 & 1 & 0 & 0 \\ 1 & 1 & 0 & 1 & 0 \\ 0 & 1 & 0 & 0 & 1 \end{pmatrix}$. Suppose that a 5-tuple in the null

space of H is transmitted. Compute the syndrome caused by each of the following transmission errors.

a. An error in the third bit.

b. An error in the first bit.

c. An error in the fifth bit.

d. An error in the third and fourth bits.

3. Let $H = \begin{pmatrix} 0 & 1 & 1 & 1 & 1 & 0 & 0 & 0 \\ 1 & 1 & 0 & 0 & 0 & 1 & 0 & 0 \\ 1 & 1 & 1 & 0 & 0 & 0 & 1 & 0 \\ 0 & 1 & 0 & 1 & 0 & 0 & 0 & 1 \end{pmatrix}$. An 8-tuple in the null space of H is transmitted with at most one transmission error. For each of the following syndromes, tell which single bit, if any, had an error in transmission.

a. $\begin{pmatrix} 0 \\ 1 \\ 1 \\ 0 \end{pmatrix}$ b. $\begin{pmatrix} 0 \\ 0 \\ 0 \\ 0 \end{pmatrix}$ c. $\begin{pmatrix} 1 \\ 1 \\ 1 \\ 1 \end{pmatrix}$ d. $\begin{pmatrix} 0 \\ 1 \\ 0 \\ 0 \end{pmatrix}$

4. Let H be as in Exercise 2. Decode each of the following received 5-tuples. Take the first two bits as the information bits and the last three as the check bits. Give both the transmitted code word and the decoded message.

a. (1 1 1 1 0) b. (1 1 0 1 1) c. (1 1 1 0 1)
d. (0 0 0 1 0) e. (1 0 1 1 1) f. (0 0 1 1 0)

5. Let H be as in Exercise 3. For an 8-tuple, which are the information bits; the check bits? Decode each of the following received 8-tuples. Give both the transmitted code word and the decoded message.

a. (0 1 1 1 0 1 0 1) b. (1 1 1 1 1 0 1 0)
c. (0 0 0 1 1 1 0 1) d. (1 1 0 0 0 0 0 0)

6. a. Give the binary matrix H for the Hamming code with six information positions and four check positions.

b. For code words, which are the check positions; the information positions?

c. Encode the messages

(i) (1 0 1 1 0 1) (ii) (0 0 1 0 0 1)

d. Decode the following received 10-tuples. Give both the transmitted code word and the decoded message.

(i) (0 0 1 0 0 0 0 1 0 1)
(ii) (0 0 0 0 1 0 1 1 0 0)

7. Let H be an $r \times n$ canonical parity check matrix with $n = 2^r - 1$ that yields a single-error-correcting code. Explain why every possible

syndrome corresponds either to no error or to a transmission error in just one bit.

8. Let H be an $r \times n$ canonical parity check matrix that is suitable for a single-error-correcting code. How many possible syndromes correspond to transmission errors in two or more bits?
9. Reprove Theorems 1.14 and 1.15 using Propositions 1.13 and 1.16.
10. Recall Exercises 1.2, Exercise 9 and Exercises 1.5, Exercises 12–14, about codes that can simultaneously correct all single errors and detect all double errors. Verify that

$$H = \begin{pmatrix} 1 & 0 & 1 & 1 & 0 & 0 & 0 \\ 0 & 1 & 1 & 0 & 1 & 0 & 0 \\ 1 & 1 & 0 & 0 & 0 & 1 & 0 \\ 1 & 1 & 1 & 1 & 1 & 1 & 1 \end{pmatrix}$$

gives such a code, with the first three bits as information bits and the last four bits as check bits. For each of the following received 7-tuples, find the most likely transmitted code word or say that two bits had transmission errors.

a. $(0\ 1\ 0\ 1\ 0\ 1\ 0)$ b. $(1\ 0\ 0\ 1\ 0\ 0\ 0)$

c. $(1\ 1\ 1\ 0\ 0\ 0\ 1)$ d. $(1\ 0\ 0\ 0\ 1\ 1\ 1)$

11. In the definition of Hamming codes, why is it required that $2^{r-1} - r < m$?

Hints: $2^{r-1} - r = 2^{r-1} - (r-1) - 1$. For $m \le 2^{r-1} - r$, how many check bits suffice? For $n = m + r < 2^{r-1}$, do we actually count up to 2^{r-1} in (1.19)?

2 Groups

Group theory pervades modern mathematics and also has important scientific and technological applications. Chapter 1 included a discussion of how group codes, which are a special type of group, are useful in the design of error-correcting codes. Fixed point addition in computers is a finite group operation. Later in this text a few more of the many applications of group theory will be introduced.

This chapter gives an axiomatic development of elementary group theory, concentrating on finite groups. Section 2.1 starts with the computation of the symmetries of some common polygons. These symmetries, under map composition, serve as good examples of typical groups. Section 2.2 gives the axioms that define a group, along with many examples of groups and nongroups. Modular number systems, which include fixed point addition and multiplication, are discussed in the third section. In Section 2.4, the group axioms are used to derive the basic properties that are common to all groups. The important topic of subgroups is introduced in Section 2.5. Many groups are easily realized as subgroups of larger groups. Also, groups may often be analyzed via their subgroups. The last section is devoted to permutations and their compositions.

2.1 Groups of Symmetries

In the next section, axioms will be given for a general group. To provide some illustrations for these axioms, in this section we will compute the symmetry groups of some simple polygons. The concept of composition is central to the group axioms. Symmetries are composed by the composition of maps. For computational purposes, it is convenient to represent the symmetries as permutations.

In general, a symmetry of an object is a rearrangement of that object which preserves all of its "essential features." Exactly what is an essential feature depends very much on the context in which the object is considered. For symmetries of polygons, vertices must be rearranged to vertices and sides to sides. In Euclidean geometry, symmetries must also preserve distances and angles. Maps of the plane to itself that do preserve distances and angles are called **rigid motions**.

Example 2.1

We are going to compute the symmetries of the equilateral triangle $\triangle ABC$ of Figure 2.1. To find a symmetry of $\triangle ABC$, we start with a rearrangement, or **permutation**, of the vertices A, B, and C and then ask if this permutation extends to a symmetry of the full triangle. Suppose that A, B, and C are moved respectively to B, C, and A. We denote this permutation by

$$\begin{matrix} A & B & C \\ \downarrow & \downarrow & \downarrow \\ B & C & A \end{matrix}$$

This movement is drawn in Figure 2.2. Then, also as drawn in Figure 2.2, this permutation of the vertices may be realized by the **rotation** of the entire plane through 120° about O, the center of $\triangle ABC$.

Now we consider the permutation $\begin{matrix} A & B & C \\ \downarrow & \downarrow & \downarrow \\ A & C & B \end{matrix}$ of the vertices of $\triangle ABC$. This permutation is drawn in Figure 2.3. Also as drawn in Figure 2.3, this permutation may be realized by rotating $\triangle ABC$ 180° about a vertical axis through A. This rigid motion requires that $\triangle ABC$ be moved temporarily out of the plane of the paper. Such a motion is usually called a

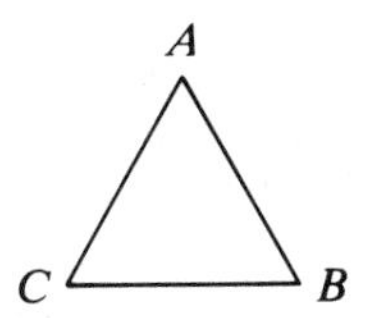

Figure 2.1 An equilateral triangle

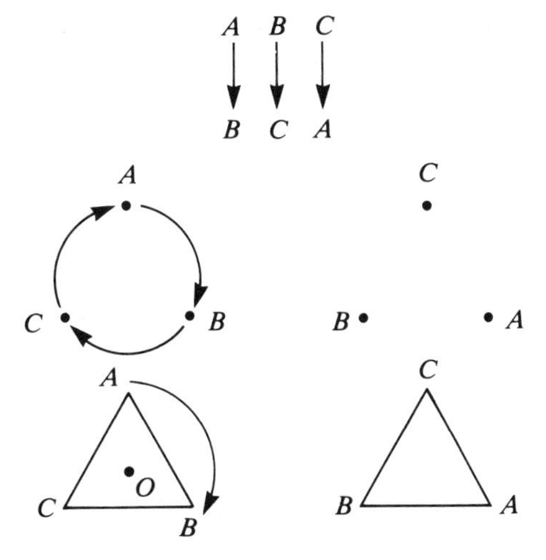

Figure 2.2 A rotation of Figure 2.1

Figure 2.3 A reflection for Figure 2.1

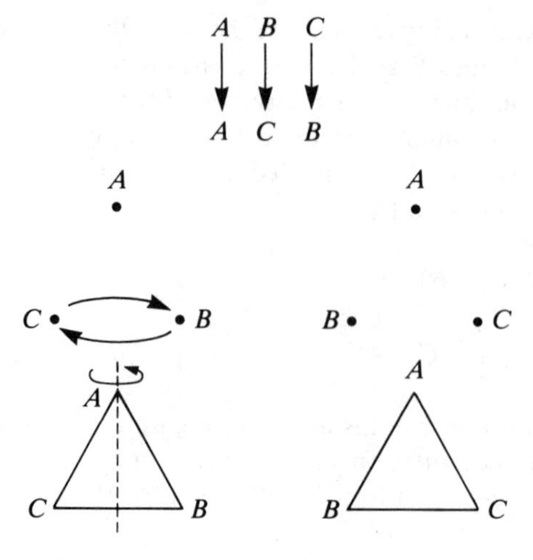

reflection, since it can also be achieved by thinking of the vertical axis as a mirror.

We also allow as a symmetry the rigid motion that keeps everything the same. This motion is called the **identity** map. For $\triangle ABC$ the corresponding permutation on the vertices is

$$\begin{matrix} A & B & C \\ \downarrow & \downarrow & \downarrow \\ A & B & C \end{matrix}$$

This symmetry is drawn in Figure 2.4.

There are in fact six symmetries of the equilateral triangle. They are listed in Figure 2.5. For use later, these symmetries are named f_1, f_2, f_3, f_4, f_5, and f_6. Certainly all of the maps in Figure 2.5 are symmetries. They are distinct because they come from different permutations of the vertices. But how do we know that we have found *all* of the symmetries? A triangle is determined by its vertices. So for any given permutation of the vertices of a triangle, there can be at most one symmetry that yields this permutation.

Figure 2.4 Identity map for Figure 2.1

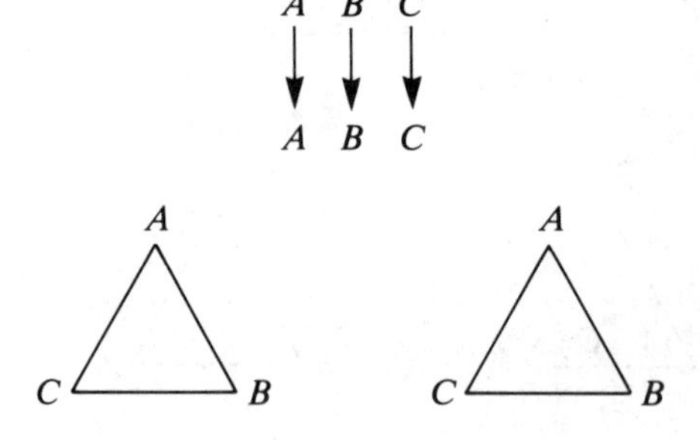

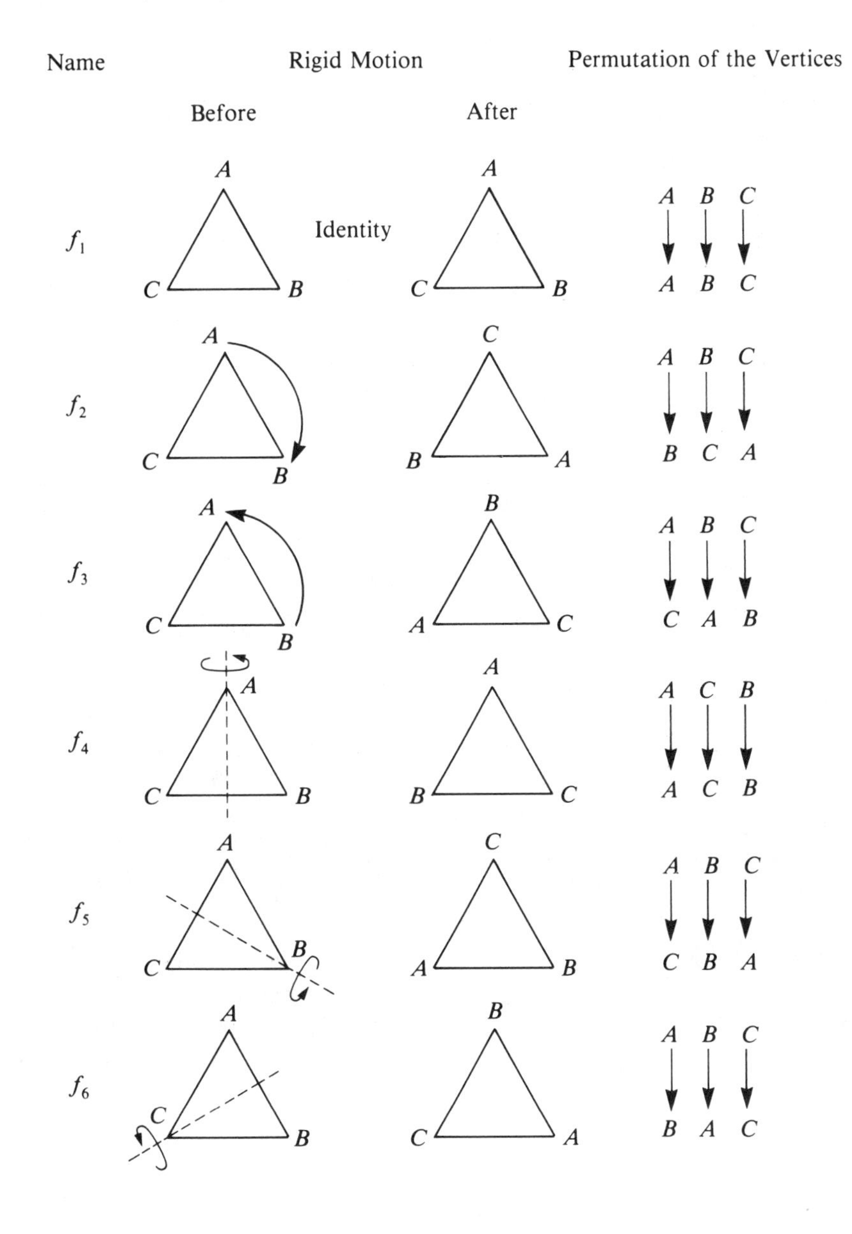

Figure 2.5 The symmetries of the equilateral triangle

Three vertices have $3! = 6$ permutations. So a triangle has at most six symmetries. △

Example 2.2

In Figure 2.6 we list the symmetries of the isosceles triangle $\triangle DEF$. As with any triangle, each permutation of the vertices yields at most one symmetry. So why do the other permutations not occur? In contrast to the equilateral triangle, in triangle $\triangle DEF$, the angle at vertex D is different

Figure 2.6 The symmetries of the isosceles triangle

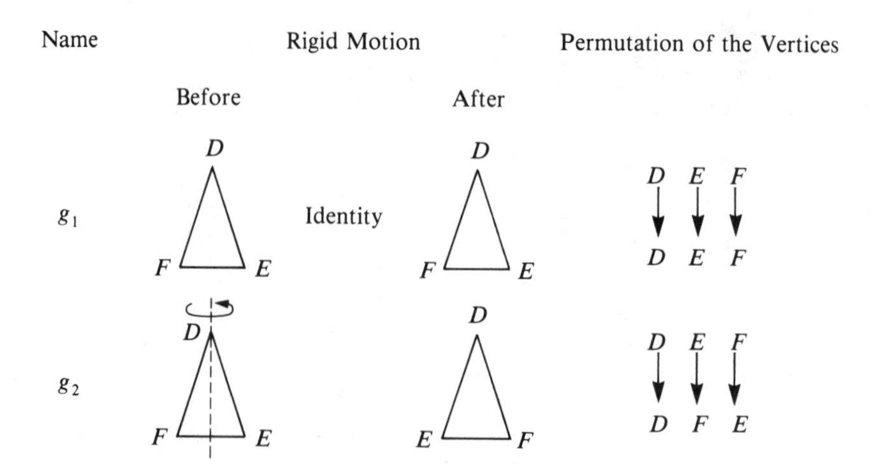

from the angles at the other two vertices. A symmetry preserves angles and so must **fix** D; that is, map vertex D to itself. The two possible permutations under this condition occur in Figure 2.6. △

Let us observe that *for any polygon, the effect of a symmetry on the vertices determines the symmetry.* Indeed, if two vertices are connected by a (unique) side of the polygon, then their images under the symmetry are also connected by a (unique) side of the polygon. So the connecting side is mapped to the connecting side. Hence the permutation of the vertices also determines the symmetry's permutation of the sides.

Example 2.3

Figure 2.7 gives the eight symmetries of the square $\square GHIJ$. By the observation of the previous paragraph, to verify that Figure 2.7 does indeed give all of the symmetries of $\square GHIJ$, we merely need to check that only the indicated permutations can occur. This is done in the exercises. △

We are now going to compose symmetries. Recall that a symmetry of an object X is, in particular, a map from X to itself. We compose symmetries as we compose maps or functions.

Definition 2.1

Let X be a set. Let $f: X \to X$ and $g: X \to X$ be maps of X to itself. The **composition** of f and g, also called "f composed with g," is denoted by $f \circ g$. $f \circ g: X \to X$ is the map from X to itself given by first performing g and then performing f. For x an element of X,

$$(f \circ g)(x) = f(g(x)).$$

○

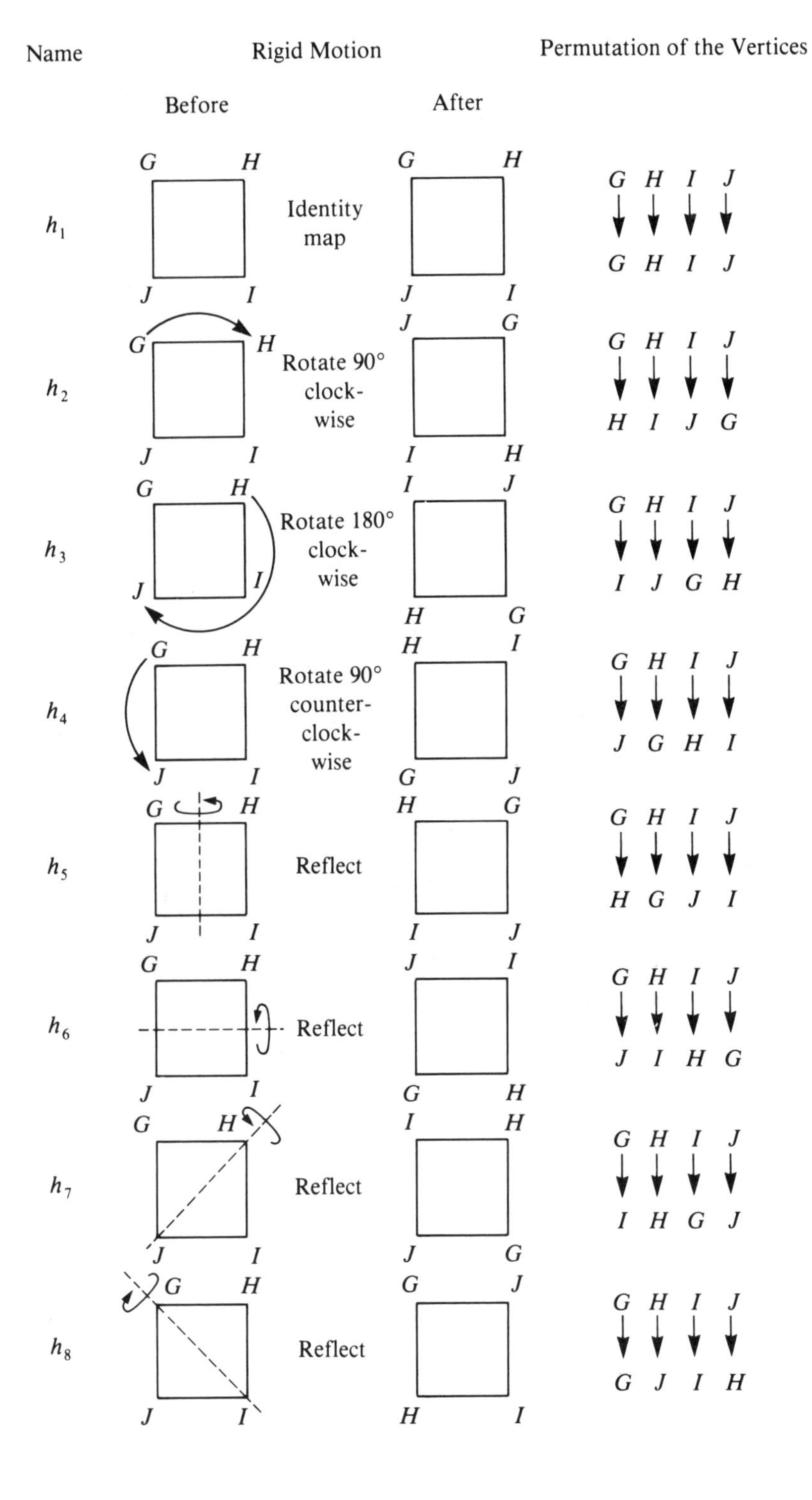

Figure 2.7 The symmetries of the square

Example 2.4

Let us look at the symmetries given in Figure 2.7 for the square $\square GHIJ$. Which symmetry is $h_5 \circ h_2$? By using a cut-out square, we may easily verify that h_2 followed by h_5 yields h_8. Without actually moving squares, we may also verify this by computing the effects of the symmetries on the vertices, as follows: h_2 maps G to H and h_5 maps H to G. So the composition of h_5 and h_2 maps G to itself. We write

$$(h_5 \circ h_2)(G) = h_5(h_2(G)) = h_5(H) = G \tag{2.1}$$

Similarly,

$$\begin{aligned}(h_5 \circ h_2)(H) &= h_5(h_2(H)) = h_5(I) = J \\ (h_5 \circ h_2)(I) &= h_5(h_2(I)) = h_5(J) = I \\ (h_5 \circ h_2)(J) &= h_5(h_2(J)) = h_5(G) = H\end{aligned} \tag{2.2}$$

Observe from (2.1) and (2.2) that

$$\begin{aligned}(h_5 \circ h_2)(G) &= G = h_8(G) \\ (h_5 \circ h_2)(H) &= J = h_8(H) \\ (h_5 \circ h_2)(I) &= I = h_8(I) \\ (h_5 \circ h_2)(J) &= H = h_8(J)\end{aligned}$$

So $h_5 \circ h_2 = h_8$.

We now do the corresponding calculation for $h_2 \circ h_5$; that is, for first the map h_5 and then the map h_2.

$$\begin{aligned}(h_2 \circ h_5)(G) &= h_2(h_5(G)) = h_2(H) = I \\ (h_2 \circ h_5)(H) &= h_2(h_5(H)) = h_2(G) = H \\ (h_2 \circ h_5)(I) &= h_2(h_5(I)) = h_2(J) = G \\ (h_2 \circ h_5)(J) &= h_2(h_5(J)) = h_2(I) = J\end{aligned} \tag{2.3}$$

In all, we see that $h_2 \circ h_5 = h_7$. In particular, $h_5 \circ h_2 \neq h_2 \circ h_5$. This non-equality implies that the order in which maps (or functions) are composed can make a difference.

With a moderate amount of work, we can compose as above all pairs of symmetries of the square. Of course, most of the notation in (2.1), (2.2), and (2.3) can be omitted in a calculation. We end up with a **composition table**, as shown in Table 2.1, for the symmetries of the square. △

Table 2.1 is read as follows: to find the composition of, say, h_2 and h_5, we look in the h_2-row and the h_5-column and we find h_7. More

Table 2.1 Composition table for the symmetries of the square

$\circ$	h_1	h_2	h_3	h_4	h_5	h_6	h_7	h_8
h_1	h_1	h_2	h_3	h_4	h_5	h_6	h_7	h_8
h_2	h_2	h_3	h_4	h_1	h_7	h_8	h_6	h_5
h_3	h_3	h_4	h_1	h_2	h_6	h_5	h_8	h_7
h_4	h_4	h_1	h_2	h_3	h_8	h_7	h_5	h_6
h_5	h_5	h_8	h_6	h_7	h_1	h_3	h_4	h_2
h_6	h_6	h_7	h_5	h_8	h_3	h_1	h_2	h_4
h_7	h_7	h_5	h_8	h_6	h_2	h_4	h_1	h_3
h_8	h_8	h_6	h_7	h_5	h_4	h_2	h_3	h_1

Table 2.2 Composition table for the symmetries of the isosceles triangle

$\circ$	g_1	g_2
g_1	g_1	g_2
g_2	g_2	g_1

precisely, in the computation of Table 2.1, we placed h_7 in the h_2-row and h_5-column since $h_2 \circ h_5 = h_7$. Similarly, since $h_5 \circ h_2 = h_8$, in the h_5-row and the h_2-column we find the entry h_8.

In an analogous manner, we may compute Table 2.2; this is the composition table for the symmetries of the isosceles triangle. The notation used in Table 2.2 for the symmetries has been taken from Figure 2.6. The computation of the composition table for the symmetries of the equilateral triangle is left for the exercises.

Exercises 2.1

1. For each of the following figures, give the analog for Figures 2.5, 2.6, and 2.7. That is, for each symmetry

   A) Draw a labeled "before" and "after" picture.

   B) Say if the symmetry is the identity map, a rotation, or a reflection.

   C) Give the corresponding permutation of the indicated vertices.

   For each figure, the total number of symmetries is given.

   a. an isosceles right triangle; two symmetries

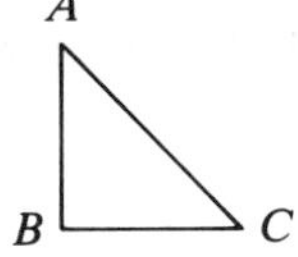

   b. a rectangle; four symmetries

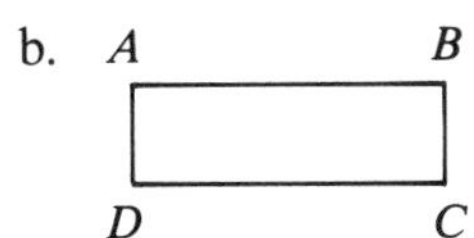

   c. a parallelogram; two symmetries

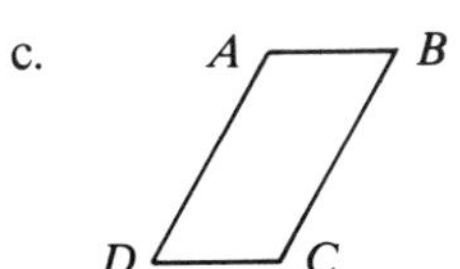

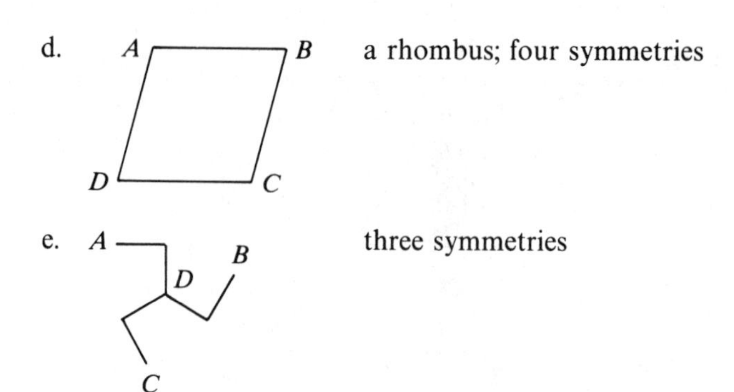

d. a rhombus; four symmetries

e. three symmetries

2. From Table 2.1, compute the following compositions.
   a. $h_2 \circ h_3$ b. $h_3 \circ h_7$ c. $h_8 \circ h_1$
   d. $(h_3 \circ h_4) \circ h_2$ e. $h_3 \circ (h_4 \circ h_2)$
3. Compute the composition table for the six symmetries of the equilateral triangle, as given in Figure 2.5.
4. Compute the composition table for the four symmetries of the rectangle.
5. Explain why the two parts of Figure 2.8 have essentially the same six symmetries.

Figure 2.8

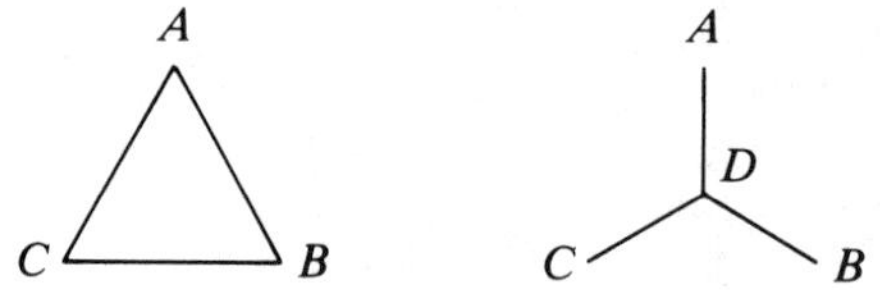

6. A scalene triangle is a triangle with sides all of different lengths. How many symmetries does a scalene triangle have? Why?
7. Describe the two symmetries of Figure 2.9. Observe that both symmetries fix A and B. Why does this not contradict the statement for polygons that a symmetry is determined by its effect on the vertices?

Figure 2.9

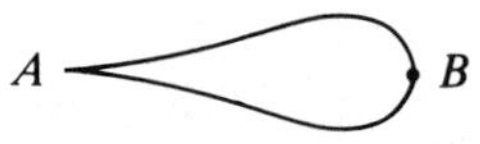

8. Complete the argument of Example 2.3 to show that Figure 2.7 lists *all* of the symmetries of the square.

   Hint: By considering the lengths of a side and of a diagonal, show that for a symmetry,

   a. If G is fixed, then also I is fixed.
   b. If G is mapped to I, then I is mapped to G.
   c. If G is mapped to H, then I is mapped to J.

9. Given the square $\square ABCD$, prove that it has at most eight different symmetries.
   a. First observe that a symmetry can take AB to any of four different sides.
   b. Next show that AB can be moved to another side in two different ways.
   c. Complete the argument for at most eight symmetries.
10. Explain why the circle has an infinite number of symmetries.
11. Show that a cube has 48 symmetries.
    a. Start with a face. How many choices are there for a corresponding face under a symmetry?
    b. How many ways can one face be mapped to another face? *Hint:* How many symmetries are there for a square?
    c. Why do all choices for parts (a) and (b) combine to give a symmetry of the cube?
12. Figure 2.10 is a picture of a regular tetrahedron. Explain why the regular tetrahedron has $4! = 24$ symmetries.

Figure 2.10

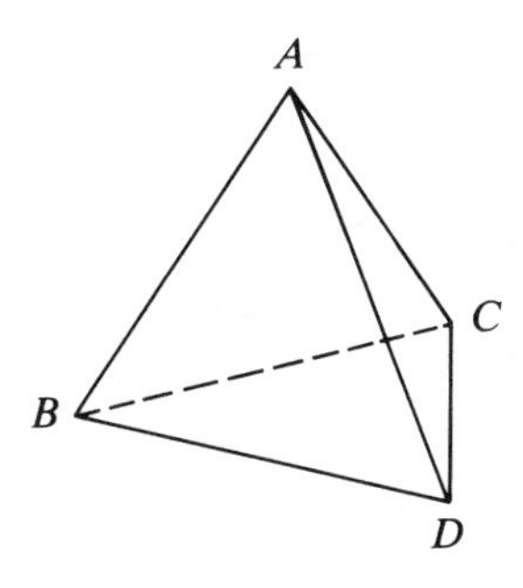

13. Consider the functions $f(x) = x + 1$ and $g(x) = x^2$. Show that $(f \circ g)(x) \neq (g \circ f)(x)$.
14. a. In Table 2.1, is any composition of two reflections also a reflection?
    b. Make a conjecture about what type of rigid motion occurs in the instance that two reflections with intersecting axes of reflection are composed.

2.2 The Definition of a Group

The symmetries of a square, or in fact of any mathematical object, form what is called a **group**. Groups also arise in many other important contexts. In this section the formal abstract definition of a group is given and illustrated.

Definition 2.2 A **law of composition** $\circ$ (also called a **binary operation**) on a set G is a rule (or function) that assigns to each pair a,b of elements of G, a third element $a \circ b$ of G, called the **composition** of a and b. ○

Example 2.5 Let G be the set of symmetries of some polygon. Then, as in Section 2.1, the composition of symmetries is a law of composition in the sense of Definition 2.2. As seen in Example 2.4,

$$a \circ b \quad \textit{need not equal} \quad b \circ a$$ △

Example 2.6 Let $\mathbb{Z}$ denote the set of all integers (whole numbers), including 0 and the negative integers.

$$\mathbb{Z} = \{\ldots, -2, -1, 0, 1, 2, \ldots\}$$

The following operations are well-known laws of composition on $\mathbb{Z}$.

Addition, denoted by $+$; for example, $2+7=9$

Subtraction, denoted by $-$; for example, $5-9=-4$

Multiplication, denoted by $\cdot$; for example, $(-2)\cdot 7=-14$ △

Since, as in Example 2.6, the same set may have several laws of composition, we shall often denote a set G with a law of composition $\circ$ by $(G,\circ)$. Thus, from Example 2.6, $(\mathbb{Z},+)$, $(\mathbb{Z},-)$, and $(\mathbb{Z},\cdot)$ are sets with a law of composition. Sometimes, if the meaning is clear in context, the explicit listing of the law of composition will be omitted and thus the set with the law of composition will also be denoted by G.

Example 2.7 Let $\mathbb{Z}$ be the set of integers, as in Example 2.6. Then division, denoted by $\div$, fails to be a law of composition on $\mathbb{Z}$ for two reasons. First, division by 0 is not defined. Second, in most cases where division is defined, as in $8 \div 5$, the answer is not an integer. That is, the third (rational) number obtained by composing 8 and 5 via division is not in the specified set $\mathbb{Z}$. △

Definition 2.3 A **group** $(G,\circ)$ is a set $G=\{a,b,c,d,\ldots\}$, with a law of composition $\circ$ that satisfies the following axioms:

(o) (Closure) For any two elements a,b of G, $a \circ b$ is also an element of G.
(i) (Associativity) For any three elements a,b,c of G,

$$(a \circ b) \circ c = a \circ (b \circ c)$$

(ii) (Identity) There is a special element e of G, called the **identity**, such that for any element a of G,

$$e \circ a = a \qquad a \circ e = a$$

(iii) (Inverses) For every element a of G, there is an inverse element in G, denoted by a^{-1}, such that

$$a \circ a^{-1} = e \qquad a^{-1} \circ a = e$$

○

The closure axiom of Definition 2.3 is numbered by (o) because it is redundant with the definition for a law of composition: The law of composition $\circ$ necessarily makes $a \circ b$ an element of G. Nonetheless, it is convenient to list the closure axiom because often, as in Example 2.7 above for division, the "law of composition" $\circ$ may come from some other context and not actually be a law of composition *for* G. Also, the explicit mention of closure will be convenient in the later section in which subgroups are discussed.

In Example 2.8, following, we shall illustrate axioms (i)–(iii) from Definition 2.3 as we see which of $(\mathbb{Z}, +)$, $(\mathbb{Z}, -)$ and $(\mathbb{Z}, \cdot)$ are groups.

Example 2.8

Is $(\mathbb{Z}, +)$ a group? Associativity requires that the result of two compositions be independent of the order in which we perform the compositions. For example, let $a = 3$, $b = 7$, and $c = 2$.

$$(a + b) + c = (3 + 7) + 2 = 10 + 2 = 12$$
$$a + (b + c) = 3 + (7 + 2) = 3 + 9 = 12$$

We get the same answer both ways. We may look at associativity in another way. What is $3 + 7 + 2$? In order to compute $3 + 7 + 2$, either we can first compute $3 + 7$ and then add 2, or we can first compute $7 + 2$ and then add to 3 the sum. The answer is 12 in both cases. For associativity to hold, this must happen regardless of which three numbers are added. This is indeed a property of the integers, which we shall accept without proof. For a composition, such as $+$, which is associative, it is convenient to omit parentheses and just to write $3 + 7 + 2$, rather than $(3 + 7) + 2$ or $3 + (7 + 2)$.

Does $(\mathbb{Z}, +)$ have an identity? Yes, 0 serves as an identity. For example, let us take $a = 17$.

$$0 + 17 = 17 \qquad 17 + 0 = 17$$

Now let us take $a = -4$.

$$0 + (-4) = -4 \qquad (-4) + 0 = -4$$

We observe that Axiom (ii) of Definition 2.3 requires both that $e \circ a = a$ and that $a \circ e = a$. This requirement may be redundant for addition, but is necessary for compositions for which we do not automatically know that $a \circ e = e \circ a$.

Does every element of $\mathbb{Z}$ have an inverse under the composition $+$? Yes. We consider, for example, $a = 23$. To verify Axiom (iii), we must find an integer, temporarily denoted by x, such that

$$23 + x = 0 \quad \text{and} \quad x + 23 = 0$$

Clearly $x = -23$ is the inverse for 23. What is the inverse in $(\mathbb{Z}, +)$ for -4?

$$(-4) + 4 = 0 \quad \text{and} \quad 4 + (-4) = 0$$

So 4 is the inverse for -4. In general, the inverse of an element in $(\mathbb{Z}, +)$ is its negative. Of course, the notation a^{-1} is not used for inverses in $(\mathbb{Z}, +)$. Instead, $-a$ denotes the inverse of a in $(\mathbb{Z}, +)$.

In all, we have seen that $(\mathbb{Z}, +)$ *is* a group. △

Example 2.9

Is $(\mathbb{Z}, -)$ a group? Let us look at the associativity axiom for, say, $a = 3$, $b = 2$, $c = 7$.

$$(3 - 2) - 7 = 1 - 7 = -6$$

$$3 - (2 - 7) = 3 - (-5) = 8$$

So $(3-2)-7 \neq 3-(2-7)$. Thus Axiom (i) does not hold in all cases. Therefore $(\mathbb{Z}, -)$ is *not* a group.

Observe how much more quickly we were able to decide that $(\mathbb{Z}, -)$ is not a group than to decide in Example 2.8 that $(\mathbb{Z}, +)$ is a group. For an object such as $(\mathbb{Z}, +)$ to be a group, the axioms must hold in *all* cases. For an object such as $(\mathbb{Z}, -)$ not to be a group, just *one* axiom has to fail in just *one* case.

Conceding that $(\mathbb{Z}, -)$ is not a group, we may still ask if Axioms (ii) and/or (iii) are true. There is in fact no identity in $(\mathbb{Z}, -)$. For if

$$\begin{aligned} e - a &= a \quad \text{and} \\ a - e &= a \end{aligned} \tag{2.4}$$

are regarded as a pair of simultaneous equations in the unknowns a and e, an easy solving of (2.4) gives $e = 0$ and $a = 0$. But for e to be an identity, (2.4) must be true for all a, and not just for $a = 0$. Since $(\mathbb{Z}, -)$ does not have an identity, Axiom (iii) about the existence of inverses does not make sense.

△

Example 2.10

Is $(\mathbb{Z}, \cdot)$ a group? Multiplication is associative; for example,

$$(5 \cdot 7) \cdot 2 = 35 \cdot 2 = 70$$
$$5 \cdot (7 \cdot 2) = 5 \cdot 14 = 70$$

So, $(5 \cdot 7) \cdot 2 = 5 \cdot (7 \cdot 2)$. As with addition, we shall not verify associativity in all cases.

The number 1 serves as an identity under the composition multiplication. Namely, for any integer a,

$$1 \cdot a = a \quad \text{and} \quad a \cdot 1 = a$$

What about inverses? Does -1 have an inverse in $(\mathbb{Z}, \cdot)$? Let x denote a possible inverse to -1. The integer x must satisfy the equations

$$(-1) \cdot x = 1 \quad \text{and} \quad x \cdot (-1) = 1 \tag{2.5}$$

Since $(-1) \cdot x = x \cdot (-1)$, the two equations in (2.5) are, of course, equivalent. Solving either one gives $x = -1$, the inverse for -1 in $(\mathbb{Z}, \cdot)$.

Does 2 have an inverse in $(\mathbb{Z}, \cdot)$? Let x denote a possible inverse. The integer x must satisfy

$$2 \cdot x = 1 \quad \text{and} \quad x \cdot 2 = 1 \tag{2.6}$$

Solving either of the equivalent equations in (2.6) gives $x = \frac{1}{2}$. But $\frac{1}{2}$ is *not* an integer; that is, it is not an element of $\mathbb{Z}$. So 2 has no inverse in $(\mathbb{Z}, \cdot)$. So $(\mathbb{Z}, \cdot)$ is not a group. △

Example 2.11

The code words of any group code from Chapter 1 form a group, as proved later in Example 2.48. Here we will just check some of the group axioms for the even parity check code of Example 1.20. The code words are all 3-tuples with even parity.

The closure axiom, which requires that the sum of two code words be again a code word, was verified in Example 1.20. Here is one case for the associativity axiom:

$$\begin{aligned}[(0\ \ 1\ \ 1) + (1\ \ 1\ \ 0)] + (1\ \ 0\ \ 1) &= (1\ \ 0\ \ 1) + (1\ \ 0\ \ 1) \\ &= (0\ \ 0\ \ 0)\end{aligned}$$

$$\begin{aligned}(0\ \ 1\ \ 1) + [(1\ \ 1\ \ 0) + (1\ \ 0\ \ 1)] &= (0\ \ 1\ \ 1) + (0\ \ 1\ \ 1) \\ &= (0\ \ 0\ \ 0)\end{aligned}$$

$\mathbf{0} = (0\ \ 0\ \ 0)$ serves as the identity, since adding 0 to a bit preserves the value of the bit.

Theorem 1.5 implies that every code word is its own inverse. △

Example 2.12

Composing the symmetries G of a square, as in Definition 2.1, gives a law of composition $\circ$. Moreover, as will be shown in Theorem 2.1 below, $(G,\circ)$ is a group. In this example, we will content ourselves with checking some special cases of the groups axioms for $(G,\circ)$. For the sake of convenience, Table 2.1, the composition table for $(G,\circ)$, is reproduced as Table 2.3.

Table 2.3 Composition table for the symmetries of the square

$\circ$	h_1	h_2	h_3	h_4	h_5	h_6	h_7	h_8
h_1	h_1	h_2	h_3	h_4	h_5	h_6	h_7	h_8
h_2	h_2	h_3	h_4	h_1	h_7	h_8	h_6	h_5
h_3	h_3	h_4	h_1	h_2	h_6	h_5	h_8	h_7
h_4	h_4	h_1	h_2	h_3	h_8	h_7	h_5	h_6
h_5	h_5	h_8	h_6	h_7	h_1	h_3	h_4	h_2
h_6	h_6	h_7	h_5	h_8	h_3	h_1	h_2	h_4
h_7	h_7	h_5	h_8	h_6	h_2	h_4	h_1	h_3
h_8	h_8	h_6	h_7	h_5	h_4	h_2	h_3	h_1

The set G for the group in Table 2.3 is given by $G=\{h_1,h_2,h_3,h_4,h_5,h_6,h_7,h_8\}$. Axiom (o), Definition 2.3, for closure requires that each entry in Table 2.3 actually be an element of G. This is, of course, true; $\circ$ is indeed a law of composition for G.

Axiom (i) for associativity requires in particular that

$$(h_5\circ h_3)\circ h_7 = h_5\circ(h_3\circ h_7) \tag{2.7}$$

We compute both sides of (2.7) using Table 2.3.

$$h_5\circ h_3 = h_6$$

$$(h_5\circ h_3)\circ h_7 = h_6\circ h_7 = h_2$$

$$h_3\circ h_7 = h_8$$

$$h_5\circ(h_3\circ h_7) = h_5\circ h_8 = h_2$$

So (2.7) is correct.

h_1 serves as the identity element e for G. Indeed, we see that $h_1\circ a = a$ for all a in G because the h_1-row in Table 2.3 coincides with the outer labeling row for the columns. Similarly, $a\circ h_1 = a$ for all a in G since the h_1-column coincides with the outer labeling column for the rows.

Let us find h_4^{-1}. Let $x = h_4^{-1}$. It is first necessary that $h_4\circ x = h_1$. The various compositions that start with h_4 are given in the h_4-row of

Table 2.3. In the h_4-row, h_1 appears only in the h_2-column. So

$$h_4 \circ h_2 = h_1 \tag{2.8}$$

and h_2 is our only candidate for h_4^{-1}. For h_2 to actually be h_4^{-1}, it is necessary, in addition to (2.8), that

$$h_2 \circ h_4 = h_1.$$

This is in fact true. So $h_4^{-1} = h_2$.

Similarly, since $h_5 \circ h_5 = h_1$, $h_5^{-1} = h_5$. △

Example 2.13

Let $G = \{a,b,c,d,e,f\}$. Let G have the law of composition given in Table 2.4. We see that $\circ$ is indeed a law of composition since each entry in Table 2.4 is an element of G.

Table 2.4 A composition table

$\circ$	a	b	c	d	e	f
a	a	e	e	d	a	f
b	e	e	f	a	b	c
c	e	c	d	d	c	e
d	a	e	f	b	d	a
e	a	b	c	d	e	f
f	b	b	a	c	f	b

Let us see that $\circ$ is not an associative law of composition. Consider $c \circ d \circ f$.

$$(c \circ d) \circ f = d \circ f = a$$

$$c \circ (d \circ f) = c \circ a = e$$

So $(c \circ d) \circ f \neq c \circ (d \circ f)$.

Even though the associative law fails for $(G, \circ)$, we may still ask about an identity and about inverses. The identity for $(G, \circ)$ is e. Namely, as in Example 2.12, we look to see that the e-row coincides with the outer row and that the e-column coincides with the outer column.

Does a^{-1} exist? We need an element x such that

$$a \circ x = e \quad \text{and} \quad x \circ a = e$$

From the a-row in Table 2.4, we see that

$$a \circ b = e \quad \text{and} \quad a \circ c = e$$

So both b and c are candidates for a^{-1}. From Table 2.4, also

$$b \circ a = e \quad \text{and} \quad c \circ a = e$$

So *both* b and c are inverses for a in Table 2.4. We shall see in a later section that multiple inverses never occur for associative laws of composition.

Does d^{-1} exist? From the d-row in Table 2.4, we see that

$$d \circ b = e$$

So b is the only candidate for d^{-1}. But $b \circ d = a$, which is not e. So d has no inverse in Table 2.4.

The f-row in Table 2.4 has no entry equal to e. So f^{-1} does not exist. △

For the square, the rectangle, the equilateral triangle, etc., in which cases do the symmetries form a group? The answer is that the symmetries of *any* mathematical object form a group. The partial proof of Theorem 2.1, which follows, indicates how the proof for polygons may be reduced to a corresponding statement about permutations of the vertices. Permutations will be treated more carefully in the last section of this chapter.

Theorem 2.1

Let X be a polygon. Let $(G, \circ)$ be the symmetries of X with $\circ$ given by the composition of maps. Then $(G, \circ)$ is a group.

Partial Proof of Theorem 2.1

We first examine the closure axiom. Let $f: X \to X$ and $g: X \to X$ be symmetries of X. Then $f \circ g: X \to X$. The symmetries f and g each preserve distances and angles, so $f \circ g$ also preserves distances and angles. Since both f and g "rearrange" X, this is also true for $f \circ g$. Thus $f \circ g$ is again a symmetry of X.

As was observed before in Example 2.3, each symmetry of a polygon is completely determined by its corresponding permutation of the vertices of the polygon. So checking Axioms (i)–(iii) of Definition 2.3 for symmetries is the same as checking these axioms for the corresponding permutations. This will be done in Theorems 2.16 and 2.13. ◇

Example 2.14

The identity in Table 2.1 is h_1, the identity map for the square. The identity in Table 2.2 is g_1, the identity map for the isosceles triangle. Let *id* denote the identity map for any polygon. Then, in fact, *id* is the identity element in the group of symmetries. We can prove this as follows: let $f: X \to X$ be a symmetry of the polygon X. We must establish that $id \circ f = f$ and $f \circ id = f$. The identity map *id* has the defining property that $id(x) = x$ for any point x in X. So

$$(id \circ f)(x) = id(f(x)), \qquad \text{by Definition 2.1}$$

$$= f(x), \qquad id(y) = y. \quad \text{Let } y = f(x)$$

So, indeed, $id \circ f = f$. The argument that $f \circ id = f$ is left for the exercises. △

Example 2.15

What do inverses look like in the symmetry group of a polygon X? A symmetry $f: X \to X$ comes from a rigid motion of the plane. For polygons, it turns out that f is always either the identity map, a rotation, or a reflection. The inverse to f in the group of symmetries is f^{-1}, the inverse map; f^{-1} is the map that reverses whatever f does. The identity map is its own inverse. The inverse to a rotation is the rotation in the opposite direction but through the same number of degrees. The inverse to a reflection is the reflection itself. △

Definition 2.4

A law of composition $\circ$ on a set G is **commutative** (also called **abelian**) if for any two elements a,b of G,

$$a\circ b=b\circ a$$

A group $(G,\circ)$ is commutative if $\circ$ is a commutative law of composition. ○

Examples 2.16

Let $\mathbb{Z}$ denote the set of integers, as in Example 2.6. Then $+$ and $\cdot$ are commutative compositions, for example,

$$5+3=3+5=8$$

$$8\cdot(-2)=(-2)\cdot 8=-16$$

$(\mathbb{Z},+)$ is a commutative group. Subtraction is not commutative; this fact can be illustrated by the following:

$$4-3=1 \quad \text{while} \quad 3-4=-1$$ △

As we have already seen, Table 2.3 does not have a commutative law of composition. For example, $h_7\circ h_2\neq h_2\circ h_7$. So $(G,\circ)$ of Example 2.12 is a noncommutative group. △

Table 2.5 A commutative law of composition?

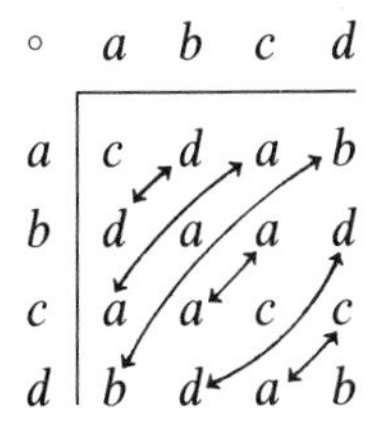

$\circ$	a	b	c	d
a	c	d	a	b
b	d	a	a	d
c	a	a	c	c
d	b	d	a	b

Example 2.17

Is the composition given in Table 2.5 commutative? That $a\circ b=b\circ a$ means that the entry in the a-row, b-column must equal the entry in the b-row, a-column. We check all such pairs of entries in Table 2.5 for commutativity and find that $c\circ d\neq d\circ c$. Therefore, $\circ$ of Table 2.5 is not commutative. △

Exercises 2.2

1. Why does the following table *not* give a law of composition on the set $G=\{a,b,c,d\}$?
   Hint: Is the composition always defined in G?

$\circ$	a	b	c	d
a	a	b	c	d
b	b	d	c	f
c	c	d	d	d
d	d	a	f	a

2. Show that each of the following laws of composition are not associative.

a.

$\circ$	a	b	c
a	b	a	c
b	c	b	a
c	a	b	c

b.

$\circ$	a	b	c	d
a	a	b	c	d
b	b	a	d	c
c	c	a	b	d
d	d	d	a	b

3. Tell whether or not each of the following composition tables has an identity. Tell which element is the identity in case it exists.

a.

$\circ$	a	b	c
a	b	a	b
b	a	b	c
c	c	c	c

b.

$\circ$	a	b	c	d
a	a	b	c	d
b	b	b	d	c
c	d	c	b	a
d	a	b	c	d

c.

$\circ$	a	b	c	d	e
a	b	a	c	a	e
b	d	d	e	b	a
c	a	b	c	c	c
d	a	b	c	d	e
e	c	a	b	e	d

d.

$\circ$	a	b	c	d	e
a	b	a	b	e	d
b	e	b	d	c	a
c	a	c	d	e	e
d	b	d	e	d	a
e	e	e	b	b	a

4. The identity element in the following composition table is e. For each element x in $G = \{a,b,c,d,e,f,g\}$, find all elements of G, if any, that may serve as x^{-1}. There may be several such elements.

$\circ$	a	b	c	d	e	f	g
a	c	b	f	e	a	f	d
b	d	a	e	f	b	e	b
c	b	e	d	f	c	a	e
d	e	d	e	c	d	c	g
e	a	b	c	d	e	f	g
f	f	f	c	b	f	d	b
g	a	e	e	f	g	c	b

5. Decide whether or not each of the following laws of composition is commutative.

a.

$\circ$	a	b	c	d
a	b	c	d	a
b	c	c	a	b
c	d	a	d	a
d	a	b	a	b

b.

$\circ$	a	b	c	d	e
a	b	c	d	a	a
b	c	a	d	b	a
c	d	d	c	a	b
d	a	a	a	d	c
e	a	a	b	c	d

6. Let $(G,\circ)$ be such that $a\circ b=b$ for all a,b in G. Show that $\circ$ is associative.
7. Consider multiplication of one-place decimal numbers such as $2.6 \times 1.3 \times 3.7$ and consider approximate products that are also one-place decimal numbers.
   a. Show that a one-decimal-place computation via rounding off is not associative.
   b. Show that a one-decimal-place computation via truncation is not associative.
8. Show that only 1 and -1 have inverses in $(\mathbb{Z},\cdot)$.
9. Give the proof, left from Example 2.14, for the argument that $f\circ id=f$.
10. Let G be the set of positive real numbers. Let the law of composition be multiplication, denoted by $\cdot$. $(G,\cdot)$ is in fact a group.
    a. What is the identity? b. For r in G, what is r^{-1}?
11. Consider the square, the rectangle, the equilateral triangle, and the isosceles triangle. In which cases is the group of symmetries commutative?
12. Let G be the set of positive real numbers. Is division a commutative law of composition? Why?
13. Let $\circ$ be a law of composition on a set G. Suppose that G has n elements. How many double compositions $a\circ b\circ c$ must be checked to verify that $\circ$ is associative?

2.3 Modular Number Systems; Products

In the previous sections, groups were defined and illustrated. In this section, the focus is on the special class of groups coming from addition in modular systems. Products of such groups are also considered. This section concludes with an informal discussion of isomorphism for groups.

Think of how the minute counter of a digital clock counts; it starts at 0 and counts up to 59. One minute after reaching 59, it starts again at 0.

Suppose that the counter is at 0 minutes, and that we want to compute what the minute counter will show after, say, 162 minutes. To do this, we divide by 60 and keep the remainder, 42. Again suppose that the counter is at 0 minutes. To compute what the minute counter will show after successive intervals of say, 45 and 28 minutes, we add 45 and 28, divide by 60, and keep the remainder, 13. This last operation, $45 \circ 28 = 13$, is an example of an important group composition.

In order to be able to give conveniently a complete composition table, let us replace 60, the number of minutes in an hour, by the smaller number 6. Let

$$\mathbb{Z}_6 = \{0,1,2,3,4,5\}$$

Let the law of composition on $\mathbb{Z}_6$, denoted temporarily by $\circ$, be defined as the addition of two elements of $\mathbb{Z}_6$, division by 6, and keeping the remainder. Thus

$3+4=7$ 7 divided by 6 leaves a remainder of 1.

$3 \circ 4 = 1$

$2+3=5$ 6 divides 0 times into 5 with a remainder of 5.

$2 \circ 3 = 5$

$4+2=6$ 6 divides into 6 exactly; the remainder is 0.

$4 \circ 2 = 0$

Table 2.6 Composition table for $(\mathbb{Z}_6, +)$

+	0	1	2	3	4	5
0	0	1	2	3	4	5
1	1	2	3	4	5	0
2	2	3	4	5	0	1
3	3	4	5	0	1	2
4	4	5	0	1	2	3
5	5	0	1	2	3	4

As is customary, we now replace the composition symbol $\circ$ for $\mathbb{Z}_6$ by the ordinary plus sign, $+$. This will cause no confusion in context. The complete composition table for $(\mathbb{Z}_6, +)$ is given in Table 2.6.

$(\mathbb{Z}_6, +)$ is a group. In $\mathbb{Z}_6$, $+$ is associative because $+$ is associative in $\mathbb{Z}$, the set of all integers. The identity element in $(\mathbb{Z}_6, +)$ is 0; $0^{-1} = 0$. Otherwise, for a in $\mathbb{Z}_6$, $a^{-1} = 6 - a$, where $-$ is the usual subtraction in $\mathbb{Z}$. Observe that $(\mathbb{Z}_6, +)$ is commutative.

More generally, we may replace 6 by any positive whole number n. $\mathbb{Z}_n$ then consists of all integers from 0 through $n-1$.

Definition 2.5

Let $\mathbb{Z}_n = \{0,1,2,\ldots,n-2,n-1\}$. The **sum** $a+b$ in $\mathbb{Z}_n$ of two elements a,b in $\mathbb{Z}_n$ is the remainder when $a+b$, computed in $\mathbb{Z}$ as the sum of ordinary integers, is divided by n. ○

Theorem 2.2

$(\mathbb{Z}_n, +)$ is a commutative group. ◇

The proof of Theorem 2.2 is left as an exercise. Note that 0 is the identity in $(\mathbb{Z}_n, +)$ and that 0 is its own inverse. For $a \neq 0$, $n-a$ is a^{-1} in $(\mathbb{Z}_n, +)$. $(\mathbb{Z}_n, +)$ is called the **additive group of integers modulo n.**

Example 2.18

Table 2.7 gives the composition table for $(\mathbb{Z}_2, +)$. Observe that Table 2.7 is exactly the same as Table 1.5, in which we used $\mathbb{Z}_2$ for group codes. △

Table 2.7 Composition table for $(\mathbb{Z}_2, +)$

+	0	1
0	0	1
1	1	0

We recall from Example 2.8 that in $(\mathbb{Z}, +)$, the inverse of an integer is its negative. Since the notation for composition in $(\mathbb{Z}_n, +)$ is also additive, it is customary to write the inverse in related notation. Thus for a in $\mathbb{Z}_n$, we write $-a$ for the inverse, rather than a^{-1}. In $(\mathbb{Z}_4, +)$, whose composition table is given in Table 2.8, the inverses are as follows:

$$-0=0 \qquad -1=3 \qquad -2=2 \qquad -3=1$$

Table 2.8 Composition table for $(\mathbb{Z}_4, +)$

+	0	1	2	3
0	0	1	2	3
1	1	2	3	0
2	2	3	0	1
3	3	0	1	2

In $\mathbb{Z}_6$, both addition and multiplication are possible. Multiplication is defined in analogy to addition. Namely, to multiply in $\mathbb{Z}_6$, first multiply in the usual way in $\mathbb{Z}$, divide the product by 6, and keep the remainder. This multiplication in $\mathbb{Z}_6$ is denoted by $\cdot$. For example,

In $\mathbb{Z}$, $4 \cdot 5 = 20$. Dividing 20 by 6 leaves a remainder of 2.

In $\mathbb{Z}_6$, $4 \cdot 5 = 2$.

In $\mathbb{Z}$, $2 \cdot 3 = 6$. Dividing 6 by 6 leaves a remainder of 0.

In $\mathbb{Z}_6$, $2 \cdot 3 = 0$.

Table 2.9 is the complete composition table for $(\mathbb{Z}_6, \cdot)$.

Example 2.19

Is $(\mathbb{Z}_6, \cdot)$ a group? Closure is satisfied since all of the entries in Table 2.9 are in $\mathbb{Z}_6$. That is, of course, why we take the remainder after we divide by 6. The operation $\cdot$ is an associative composition on $\mathbb{Z}_6$ since multiplication is associative for $\mathbb{Z}$, the usual integers. The identity is 1. But $(\mathbb{Z}_6, \cdot)$ is not a group since not all the elements have inverses. For example, $0 \cdot a = 0$ for all a in $\mathbb{Z}_6$. So 0 certainly has no inverse. Neither does 2 have an inverse in $(\mathbb{Z}_6, \cdot)$ since the identity 1 does not appear in the 2-row of Table 2.9; that is, $2 \cdot x$ is never 1. It is true that the elements 1 and 5 have inverses in $(\mathbb{Z}_6, \cdot)$. △

Table 2.9 Composition table for $(\mathbb{Z}_6, \cdot)$

·	0	1	2	3	4	5
0	0	0	0	0	0	0
1	0	1	2	3	4	5
2	0	2	4	0	2	4
3	0	3	0	3	0	3
4	0	4	2	0	4	2
5	0	5	4	3	2	1

Multiplication can be defined similarly to $\cdot$ in $\mathbb{Z}_6$ for any $\mathbb{Z}_n$. The set $\mathbb{Z}_n$ with the two laws of composition $+$ and $\cdot$ is called the **modular number system with base n.** Fixed point addition and multiplication in a digital computer are essentially $+$ and $\cdot$ in some $\mathbb{Z}_n$, with n very large.

We will consider the formation of new groups from old groups next.

Definition 2.6

Let $(G,\circ)$ and $(H,\cdot)$ be given groups. The **product** of G and H, denoted by $G \times H$, consists of all ordered pairs (g,h) with g an element of G, and h an element of H. $G \times H$ has a law of composition $*$ given by

$$(g_1,h_1)*(g_2,h_2)=(g_1 \circ g_2, h_1 \cdot h_2).$$ ○

Example 2.20

Let us illustrate the construction of $G \times H$ as a set. Suppose that $G=\{a,b,c\}$ and that $H=\{x,y\}$. In choosing an element for $G \times H$, we have three choices, a, b, and c, for the first component g of the pair (g,h) and two choices, x and y, for the second component h. So $G \times H$ has $3 \cdot 2 = 6$ elements. They are

$$\begin{array}{ll} (a,x) & (a,y) \\ (b,x) & (b,y) \\ (c,x) & (c,y) \end{array}$$ △

Example 2.21

We construct the composition table, Table 2.10, for $(\mathbb{Z}_2 \times \mathbb{Z}_2, +)$. $\mathbb{Z}_2 = \{0,1\}$. So the set $\mathbb{Z}_2 \times \mathbb{Z}_2$ is given by

$$\mathbb{Z}_2 \times \mathbb{Z}_2 = \{(0,0), (0,1), (1,0), (1,1)\}$$

From Definition 2.6, composition (called addition) in $\mathbb{Z}_2 \times \mathbb{Z}_2$ is done by separately composing each component according to $+$ in $\mathbb{Z}_2$. For instance,

$$(0,1)+(1,1)=(0+1, 1+1)=(1,0)$$

Additional computations give all of Table 2.10. △

Table 2.10 Composition table for $(\mathbb{Z}_2 \times \mathbb{Z}_2, +)$

+	(0,0)	(0,1)	(1,0)	(1,1)
(0,0)	(0,0)	(0,1)	(1,0)	(1,1)
(0,1)	(0,1)	(0,0)	(1,1)	(1,0)
(1,0)	(1,0)	(1,1)	(0,0)	(0,1)
(1,1)	(1,1)	(1,0)	(0,1)	(0,0)

Observe that, except for the commas, Table 2.10 is exactly the same as Table 1.6. That is, $\mathbb{Z}_2{}^2$ as introduced in group codes is the same as $\mathbb{Z}_2 \times \mathbb{Z}_2$ from Definition 2.6. This similarity is clear from the definitions and without consulting the composition tables. We may extend

Definition 2.6 to allow more than two groups in the product; for example, with n factors, $\mathbb{Z}_2 \times \mathbb{Z}_2 \times \cdots \times \mathbb{Z}_2$ coincides with $\mathbb{Z}_2{}^n$ of Chapter 1.

Example 2.22

Let us consider Table 2.11, the composition table for $(\mathbb{Z}_3 \times \mathbb{Z}_2, +)$. Here are some typical calculations for $+$ in $\mathbb{Z}_3 \times \mathbb{Z}_2$.

$$(1,0)+(2,1)=(1+2, 0+1)$$

$1+2=0$ in $\mathbb{Z}_3$. $0+1=1$ in $\mathbb{Z}_2$. So

$$(1,0)+(2,1)=(0,1) \qquad \text{in } \mathbb{Z}_3 \times \mathbb{Z}_2$$

$$(1,1)+(1,1)=(1+1, 1+1)=(2,0)$$

△

Table 2.11 Composition table for $(\mathbb{Z}_3 \times \mathbb{Z}_2, +)$

+	(0,0)	(0,1)	(1,0)	(1,1)	(2,0)	(2,1)
(0,0)	(0,0)	(0,1)	(1,0)	(1,1)	(2,0)	(2,1)
(0,1)	(0,1)	(0,0)	(1,1)	(1,0)	(2,1)	(2,0)
(1,0)	(1,0)	(1,1)	(2,0)	(2,1)	(0,0)	(0,1)
(1,1)	(1,1)	(1,0)	(2,1)	(2,0)	(0,1)	(0,0)
(2,0)	(2,0)	(2,1)	(0,0)	(0,1)	(1,0)	(1,1)
(2,1)	(2,1)	(2,0)	(0,1)	(0,0)	(1,1)	(1,0)

Theorem 2.3

Let $(G,\circ)$ and $(H,\cdot)$ be groups. Then the product $(G \times H, *)$ is a group when $*$ is defined by $(g_1,h_1)*(g_2,h_2)=(g_1 \circ g_2, h_1 \cdot h_2)$.

Example 2.23

Before proving Theorem 2.3, we shall illustrate its statement. We consider the composition table for $(\mathbb{Z}_3 \times \mathbb{Z}_2, +)$, Table 2.11. Each entry in Table 2.11 is in $\mathbb{Z}_3 \times \mathbb{Z}_2$, so the closure axiom is verified. We shall not verify associativity. The identity in Table 2.11 is (0,0). Inverses are as follows:

$$-(0,0)=(0,0) \qquad -(0,1)=(0,1) \qquad -(1,0)=(2,0)$$

$$-(1,1)=(2,1) \qquad -(2,0)=(1,0) \qquad -(2,1)=(1,1)$$

Therefore, $(\mathbb{Z}_3 \times \mathbb{Z}_2, +)$ is a group. △

Proof of Theorem 2.3

First we look at the closure axiom. We consider $(g_1,h_1)*(g_2,h_2)$. By the closure axiom for G and H, $g_1 \circ g_2$ and $h_1 \cdot h_2$ are in G and H respectively. So

$$(g_1,h_1)*(g_2,h_2)=(g_1 \circ g_2, h_1 \cdot h_2)$$

is an element of $G \times H$.

The associativity axiom for $(G \times H, *)$ follows from the associativity axiom for G and H. Details are left to the exercises.

Let e_G and e_H be the identities in G and H respectively. Then (e_G, e_H) is the identity in $G \times H$. Indeed, for (g,h) in $G \times H$,

$$(e_G,e_H)*(g,h) = (e_G \circ g, e_H \cdot h), \quad \text{by the definition of } *$$
$$= (g,h), \quad e_G \circ g = g \quad \text{and} \quad e_H \cdot h = h$$

Similarly, $(g,h)*(e_G,e_H) = (g,h)$.

Finally, we show that inverses exist. Let (g,h) be an element of $G \times H$. Then g^{-1} exists in G, since G is a group. Similarly, h^{-1} exists in H. That $(g,h)^{-1} = (g^{-1},h^{-1})$ is shown as follows:

$$(g,h)*(g^{-1},h^{-1}) = (g \circ g^{-1}, h \cdot h^{-1}), \quad \text{by the definition of } *$$
$$= (e_G, e_H), \quad \text{by the definition of } g^{-1} \text{ and } h^{-1}$$

Similarly, $(g^{-1},h^{-1})*(g,h) = (e_G,e_H)$. ◇

Observe that Definition 2.6 does not require that G and H be additive groups of integers modulo n, or even commutative groups. It is shown in the exercises that if G and H are commutative, then $G \times H$ is also commutative.

Only sometimes does forming a product create a new type of group, as we shall see. Informally, we can say that two groups $(G, \circ)$ and $(H, *)$ are the same, or **isomorphic**, if there is a renaming, or **isomorphism**, from (all) the elements of G to (all) the elements of H. This renaming must respect the laws of composition $\circ$ and $*$. A formal definition of isomorphism will be given in Chapter 6, Section 6.5.

Example 2.24

Recall the groups $(\mathbb{Z}_6, +)$ and $(\mathbb{Z}_3 \times \mathbb{Z}_2, +)$. Their composition tables are given in Table 2.6 and Table 2.11, respectively. Instead of writing the elements of $\mathbb{Z}_3 \times \mathbb{Z}_2$ in the order: (0,0), (1,0), (2,0), (0,1), (1,1), (2,1), we write them in the order

$$(0,0), (1,1), (2,0), (0,1), (1,0), (2,1) \tag{2.9}$$

This new order for the elements of $\mathbb{Z}_3 \times \mathbb{Z}_2$ gives Table 2.12 as a new addition table for $\mathbb{Z}_3 \times \mathbb{Z}_2$. Obviously, Tables 2.11 and 2.12 describe the same group; only the order of the elements has been changed.

But Tables 2.6 and 2.12 are really the same; only the names have been changed! Indeed, and the reader should check this, the following renaming changes Table 2.6 into Table 2.12:

$$\begin{array}{lll} 0\to(0,0) & 1\to(1,1) & 2\to(2,0) \\ 3\to(0,1) & 4\to(1,0) & 5\to(2,1) \end{array} \qquad \textbf{(2.10)}$$

Table 2.13 represents a partial renaming of Table 2.6, using (2.10). In summary, $(\mathbb{Z}_6, +)$ and $(\mathbb{Z}_3 \times \mathbb{Z}_2, +)$ have essentially the same composition table and so are isomorphic. △

Table 2.12 Another addition table for $(\mathbb{Z}_3 \times \mathbb{Z}_2, +)$

+	(0,0)	(1,1)	(2,0)	(0,1)	(1,0)	(2,1)
(0,0)	(0,0)	(1,1)	(2,0)	(0,1)	(1,0)	(2,1)
(1,1)	(1,1)	(2,0)	(0,1)	(1,0)	(2,1)	(0,0)
(2,0)	(2,0)	(0,1)	(1,0)	(2,1)	(0,0)	(1,1)
(0,1)	(0,1)	(1,0)	(2,1)	(0,0)	(1,1)	(2,0)
(1,0)	(1,0)	(2,1)	(0,0)	(1,1)	(2,0)	(0,1)
(2,1)	(2,1)	(0,0)	(1,1)	(2,0)	(0,1)	(1,0)

Table 2.13 $(\mathbb{Z}_6, +)$ and $(\mathbb{Z}_3 \times \mathbb{Z}_2, +)$

+	(0,0)	(1,1)	(2,0)	3	4	5
(0,0)	(0,0)	(1,1)	(2,0)	3	4	5
(1,1)	(1,1)	(2,0)	(0,1)	4	5	0
(2,0)	(2,0)	(0,1)	(1,0)	5	0	1
3	3	4	5	0	1	2
4	4	5	0	1	2	3
5	5	0	1	2	3	4

Example 2.25

The groups $(\mathbb{Z}_4, +)$ and $(\mathbb{Z}_2 \times \mathbb{Z}_2, +)$ both have four elements. Their composition tables are given in Tables 2.8 and 2.10, respectively. Are the two groups isomorphic? Let us try the renaming (2.11) below and see if it is an isomorphism; that is, whether (2.11) respects the laws of addition in $\mathbb{Z}_4$ and in $\mathbb{Z}_2 \times \mathbb{Z}_2$.

$$0\to(0,0) \qquad 1\to(0,1) \qquad 2\to(1,0) \qquad 3\to(1,1) \qquad \textbf{(2.11)}$$

(2.11) changes Table 2.8 into Table 2.14 on p. 88.

Table 2.14 differs from Table 2.10 in the underlined entries, so (2.11) is not an isomorphism. But would perhaps some other renaming besides (2.11) demonstrate that $(\mathbb{Z}_4, +)$ and $(\mathbb{Z}_2 \times \mathbb{Z}_2, +)$ are in fact isomorphic? No, $(\mathbb{Z}_4, +)$ and $(\mathbb{Z}_2 \times \mathbb{Z}_2, +)$ are not isomorphic: all of the diagonal entries

Table 2.14 A renaming of $(\mathbb{Z}_4, +)$

$+$	(0,0)	(0,1)	(1,0)	(1,1)
(0,0)	(0,0)	(0,1)	(1,0)	(1,1)
(0,1)	(0,1)	$\underline{(1,0)}$	(1,1)	$\underline{(0,0)}$
(1,0)	(1,0)	(1,1)	(0,0)	(0,1)
(1,1)	(1,1)	$\underline{(0,0)}$	(0,1)	$\underline{(1,0)}$

in Table 2.10 are the same, namely (0,0). There are two different diagonal entries, 0 and 2, in Table 2.8. No renaming of the elements in Table 2.8 can change the nonequality of the diagonal entries. △

Example 2.26

Let G and H be given groups. Then the group $G \times H$ is isomorphic to the group $H \times G$. Namely, if we rename the element (g,h) in $G \times H$ as the element (h,g) in $H \times G$, then this renaming respects the laws of composition for $G \times H$ and for $H \times G$ from Definition 2.6. △

Determining whether or not two groups are isomorphic can be a very difficult problem. Certainly, if the two groups have a different number of elements, or if one is commutative while the other is not, then the two groups are not isomorphic. More refined criteria are available, using the ideas of the following sections. It is true, however, that every finite commutative group is isomorphic to a product of suitable $(\mathbb{Z}_n, +)$.

Exercises 2.3

1. It is now 10:26. What will the minute counter show 52 minutes from now?
2. Compute the following expressions in $(\mathbb{Z}_6, +)$.
   a. $3+5$ b. $0+4$ c. $(2+3)+2$ d. -4
3. Verify associativity for the following sum in $\mathbb{Z}_6$.

$$(3+5)+2 \quad \text{and} \quad 3+(5+2)$$

4. Give the composition table for $(\mathbb{Z}_3, +)$.
5. Give the composition table for $(\mathbb{Z}_5, +)$.
6. a. Write down the composition table for $(\mathbb{Z}_4, \cdot)$.
   b. Why is $(\mathbb{Z}_4, \cdot)$ not a group?
7. Let $G = \{1,5\}$ with composition $\cdot$ given by multiplication in $\mathbb{Z}_6$. Show that $(G, \cdot)$ is a group.
8. Explain why $\cdot$ is not a law of composition on the set $S = \{1,2,3,4,5\}$ in $(\mathbb{Z}_6, \cdot)$.

9. Compute the following expressions in $(\mathbb{Z}_3 \times \mathbb{Z}_4, +)$.
   a. $(1,2)+(2,1)$ b. $(0,2)+(2,3)$
   c. $-(1,3)$ d. $(1,1)+(2,1)+(2,2)$
10. How many elements are there in $\mathbb{Z}_m \times \mathbb{Z}_n$, in $\mathbb{Z}_m \times \mathbb{Z}_n \times \mathbb{Z}_p$?
11. Compute the following expressions in $(\mathbb{Z}_3 \times \mathbb{Z}_4 \times \mathbb{Z}_5, +)$.
    a. $(1,1,2)+(2,3,4)$ b. $-(2,2,2)$
12. Let $(G,\circ)$ and $(H,\cdot)$ be groups. Show that $(G \times H,*)$ has an associative law of composition.
13. Suppose that $(G,\circ)$ and $(H,\cdot)$ are commutative groups. Show that $(G \times H,*)$ is also commutative.
14. Suppose that $(G,\circ)$ is a commutative group and $(H,\cdot)$ is not a commutative group. Is $(G \times H,*)$ commutative? Why?
15. Explain why the group of symmetries for the square, as given in Table 2.1, is not isomorphic to $(\mathbb{Z}_8, +)$.
16. a. Write out the composition table for $(\mathbb{Z}_2 \times \mathbb{Z}_3, +)$.
    b. As in Example 2.26, explain why $(\mathbb{Z}_2 \times \mathbb{Z}_3, +)$ is isomorphic to $(\mathbb{Z}_3 \times \mathbb{Z}_2, +)$.
17. Explain why $(\mathbb{Z}_2 \times \mathbb{Z}_2 \times \mathbb{Z}_2, +)$ is not isomorphic to $(\mathbb{Z}_8, +)$.
18. Let $G=\{1,2,3,4\}$. Let $\cdot$ be a law of composition on G given by multiplication in $\mathbb{Z}_5$.
    a. Compute the composition table for $(G,\cdot)$.
    b. Assuming associativity, verify the group axioms for $(G,\cdot)$.
    c. Find an isomorphism between $(G,\cdot)$ and $(\mathbb{Z}_4, +)$.

2.4 Elementary Properties of Groups

Section 2.3 gave many examples of groups and of their composition tables. We may form additional groups through products. In this section we use the group axioms to show that some properties are common to all groups.

Consider an identity element e from Definition 2.3(ii). Then $e \circ a = a$ and $a \circ e = a$ for all group elements a. In Table 2.1, h_1 is the identity. In Table 2.2, g_1 is the identity. In $(\mathbb{Z}, +)$ of Example 2.8, 0 is the identity. Observe that all of the groups have *just one* identity; we say that the identity element is *unique*. We can see intuitively why a group can have only one identity element by trying, as in Table 2.15, to write down a composition table with both e and e' as identity elements. Recall, as in Examples 2.12 and 2.13, that in a composition table, the rows and columns for an identity match the outside rows and columns.

Table 2.15 Two identity elements?

$\circ$	e	e'	a	b	c
e	e	e'? e?	a	b	c
e'	e'? e?	e'	a	b	c
a	a	a			
b	b	b			
c	c	c			

We run into trouble at the e-row, e'-column entry and at the e'-row, e-column entry. With e an identity, the e-row coincides with the outside row. With e' an identity, the e'-column coincides with the outside column. These two conditions are not compatible at the intersection of the e-row and the e'-column. Theorem 2.4 states the preceding formally.

Theorem 2.4 A group $(G,\circ)$ has a unique identity.

Proof of Theorem 2.4 Let e and e' be identities. That is, for all group elements a,

$$e\circ a=a \qquad a\circ e=a \qquad \text{and} \qquad e'\circ a=a \qquad a\circ e'=a \tag{2.12}$$

We must show that $e=e'$.

Consider the expression $e\circ e'$. Since e is an identity, letting a be e' in (2.12), we see that

$$e\circ e'=e' \tag{2.13}$$

Since e' is an identity, letting a be e in (2.12),

$$e\circ e'=e \tag{2.14}$$

The left sides of (2.13) and (2.14) agree. So $e=e'$. ◇

Theorem 2.5 Let a be an element in the group $(G,\circ)$. Then there is a unique inverse element a^{-1} in G such that

$$a\circ a^{-1}=e \quad \text{and} \quad a^{-1}\circ a=e$$

Let x be an element of G that satisfies $a\circ x=e$. Then necessarily also $x\circ a=e$ and so $x=a^{-1}$. Similarly, if $x\circ a=e$, then also $a\circ x=e$ and $x=a^{-1}$.

Example 2.27 Before proving Theorem 2.5, we shall illustrate its statement. Consider the group with Table 2.1 as its composition table. h_1 is the identity. Take $a=h_4$. Then h_2 is the sole group element such that $h_4\circ h_2=h_1$ and $h_2\circ h_4=h_1$. So $h_2=h_4{}^{-1}$.

How do we find $h_4{}^{-1}$ from Table 2.1? We look in the h_4-row for an entry of h_1. That is, we solve the equation

$$h_4\circ x=h_1 \tag{2.15}$$

Theorem 2.5 says that any solution to (2.15) automatically solves the column condition $x\circ h_4=h_1$ and gives the inverse. △

Proof of Theorem 2.5 Suppose that a' is a group element such that

$$a\circ a'=e \quad \text{and} \quad a'\circ a=e \tag{2.16}$$

We must show that $a'=a^{-1}$. We look at the expression $a'\circ a\circ a^{-1}$; we may associate the double composition in two ways:

$$\begin{aligned}(a' \circ a) \circ a^{-1} &= e \circ a^{-1}, && \text{from (2.16), which is given} \\ &= a^{-1}, && \text{by the definition of } e\end{aligned} \tag{2.17}$$

$$\begin{aligned}a' \circ (a \circ a^{-1}) &= a' \circ e, && \text{by the definition of } a^{-1} \\ &= a' && \text{by the definition of } e\end{aligned} \tag{2.18}$$

Associativity guarantees that $(a' \circ a) \circ a^{-1} = a' \circ (a \circ a^{-1})$. So $a^{-1} = a'$, as required.

Now suppose that $a \circ x = e$. We look at $a^{-1} \circ a \circ x$.

$$\begin{aligned}(a^{-1} \circ a) \circ x &= e \circ x, && \text{by the definition of } a^{-1} \\ &= x, && \text{by the definition of } e\end{aligned}$$

$$\begin{aligned}a^{-1} \circ (a \circ x) &= a^{-1} \circ e, && a \circ x = e \text{ is given} \\ &= a^{-1}, && \text{by the definition of } e\end{aligned}$$

Again by associativity, $x = a^{-1}$. Then also $x \circ a = e$.

The case that $x \circ a = e$ is left as an exercise. ◇

Example 2.28

Recall Table 2.4, as discussed in Example 2.13. There, the element a has *two* inverses, b and c. Also,

$$d \circ x = e$$

has $x = b$ as a solution. But $b \circ d \neq e$ in Table 2.4. Example 2.13 does not contradict Theorem 2.5; Table 2.4 is simply not a *group* composition table since associativity fails. Where must associativity fail? The elements b and c are inverses for a. Looking at (2.17) and (2.18), we will try $b \circ a \circ c$.

$$(b \circ a) \circ c = e \circ c = c$$

$$b \circ (a \circ c) = b \circ e = b$$

△

Let a and b be typical elements of the group $(G, \circ)$. The expression $a \circ b$ is also an element of G, so $(a \circ b)^{-1}$ exists. What does $(a \circ b)^{-1}$ equal? One guess might be

$$(a \circ b)^{-1} = a^{-1} \circ b^{-1} \tag{?}$$

Let us try this guess for Table 2.3. Let $a = h_2$ and $b = h_7$. Then $h_2 \circ h_7 = h_6$. So

$$(h_2 \circ h_7)^{-1} = h_6{}^{-1} = h_6 \tag{2.19}$$

The guess for $(h_2 \circ h_7)^{-1}$ is

$$h_2^{-1} \circ h_7^{-1} = h_4 \circ h_7 = h_5 \quad \textbf{(2.20)}$$

(2.19) and (2.20) are different, so (?) cannot hold in general. The correct result is as in the following theorem.

Theorem 2.6 Let a and b be elements of the group $(G, \circ)$. Then

$$(a \circ b)^{-1} = b^{-1} \circ a^{-1}$$

Examples 2.29 Before proving Theorem 2.6, we will illustrate its statement. Look at Table 2.3 with $a = h_2$ and $b = h_7$.

$$(h_2 \circ h_7)^{-1} = h_6^{-1} = h_6$$
$$h_7^{-1} \circ h_2^{-1} = h_7 \circ h_4 = h_6 \quad \triangle$$

Intuitively, the reason that Theorem 2.6 is true is as follows: suppose that the elements of G are maps. The expression $a \circ b$ says first to do the map b and then to do the map a. In order to find the inverse map, we must undo the effects of the maps a and b. Since a was done last, we undo it first via a^{-1}. Then we undo b via b^{-1}. That is, $(a \circ b)^{-1} = b^{-1} \circ a^{-1}$. △

Proof of Theorem 2.6 By Theorem 2.5 (with a replaced by $a \circ b$, and x replaced by $b^{-1} \circ a^{-1}$), it suffices to show that

$$(a \circ b) \circ (b^{-1} \circ a^{-1}) = e$$

$(a \circ b) \circ (b^{-1} \circ a^{-1}) = a \circ (b \circ b^{-1}) \circ a^{-1}$,	by several applications of associativity
$= a \circ e \circ a^{-1}$,	by the definition of b^{-1}
$= (a \circ e) \circ a^{-1}$,	by associativity
$= a \circ a^{-1}$,	by the definition of e
$= e$,	by the definition of a^{-1} ◇

Example 2.30 Let $(G, +)$ be a commutative group. Let $-a$ denote a^{-1} in $(G, +)$.

$-(a+b) = (-b) + (-a)$,	by Theorem 2.6
$= (-a) + (-b)$,	by commutativity

That is, Equation (?) is true for a commutative group. △

Theorem 2.7, which follows, says that taking inverses two times in a group brings you back to the original element. The proof of Theorem 2.7 will be very easy. Check the definitions carefully in order to understand that it is a proof.

Theorem 2.7 Let a be an element of the group $(G,\circ)$. Then $(a^{-1})^{-1}=a$.

Example 2.31 Let G have Table 2.3 as its composition table. Let $a=h_2$. Then $a^{-1}=h_2{}^{-1}=h_4$.

$$(a^{-1})^{-1}=h_4{}^{-1}=h_2=a \qquad \triangle$$

Proof of Theorem 2.7 Let x denote the inverse of a^{-1}. Then $x=(a^{-1})^{-1}$; x satisfies

$$a^{-1}\circ x=e \quad \text{and} \quad x\circ a^{-1}=e \tag{2.21}$$

By Theorem 2.5, x is *uniquely* specified if it satisfies (2.21).

Since a^{-1} is the inverse to a,

$$a\circ a^{-1}=e \quad \text{and} \quad a^{-1}\circ a=e \tag{2.22}$$

When the equations of (2.22) are interchanged, we see that $x=a$ is a solution to (2.21). ◇

Examples 2.32 We shall use Theorems 2.6 and 2.7 to simplify some complicated expressions involving group compositions. Let a, b, and c be elements of the group $(G,\circ)$. Recall that, because of associativity, we can write $a\circ b\circ c$ and mean either $(a\circ b)\circ c$ or $a\circ(b\circ c)$.

$$\begin{aligned}(a\circ b\circ c)^{-1} &= ((a\circ b)\circ c)^{-1}, && \text{by the definition of } a\circ b\circ c\\ &= c^{-1}\circ(a\circ b)^{-1}, && \text{by Theorem 2.6}\\ &= c^{-1}\circ b^{-1}\circ a^{-1}, && \text{by Theorem 2.6}\end{aligned} \tag{2.23}$$

△

$$\begin{aligned}(a\circ b^{-1}\circ c)^{-1} &= c^{-1}\circ(b^{-1})^{-1}\circ a^{-1}, && \text{by Equation (2.23)}\\ &= c^{-1}\circ b\circ a^{-1}, && \text{by Theorem 2.7}\end{aligned}$$

△

$$\begin{aligned}&(a\circ b)\circ(c^{-1}\circ b)^{-1}\circ c^{-1}\\ &\quad = (a\circ b)\circ(b^{-1}\circ(c^{-1})^{-1})\circ c^{-1}, && \text{by Theorem 2.6}\\ &\quad = a\circ b\circ b^{-1}\circ c\circ c^{-1}, && \text{by Theorem 2.7 and associativity}\\ &\quad = a\circ(b\circ b^{-1})\circ(c\circ c^{-1}), && \text{by associativity}\\ &\quad = a\circ e\circ e, && \text{by the definition of inverse}\\ &\quad = a, && \text{by the definition of } e\end{aligned}$$

△

Now we look at a row or column of a group composition table, say the 4-row of Table 2.6 for $(\mathbb{Z}_6, +)$. We observe that the row,

$$4 \quad 5 \quad 0 \quad 1 \quad 2 \quad 3$$

has no duplications and is in fact a reordering, or permutation of the outside row,

$$0 \quad 1 \quad 2 \quad 3 \quad 4 \quad 5$$

It is always true that the rows and columns are permutations of the outside rows and columns. What does this mean in terms of the group structure? The outside rows and columns, of course, just list all of the group elements.

Let a be an element of the group G. To get the a-row, we let x vary over the elements of G and look at all of the compositions $a \circ x$. To say that the a-row is a permutation of G is to say that $a \circ x$ takes on all values in G exactly once. That is, for b an element of G, the equation

$$a \circ x = b$$

has a unique solution. The statement that the columns are also permutations of G corresponds to saying that the equation

$$x \circ a = b$$

has a unique solution in G.

Theorem 2.8 Let a and b be elements of the group G. Then the equation

$$a \circ x = b$$

has a unique solution in G. In particular, each row of the composition table is a permutation of the outside row. Similarly, the equation

$$x \circ a = b$$

has a unique solution in G. Each column of the composition table is a permutation of the outside column.

Proof of Theorem 2.8 We look at the equation

$$a \circ x = b \tag{2.24}$$

As in high-school algebra, we can retain equality by doing the same thing to both sides of the equation. The idea is to move a from the left side to the right side in (2.24). Using the axioms for a group, we proceed as follows:

$a \circ x = b,$	equation given
$a^{-1} \circ (a \circ x) = a^{-1} \circ b,$	compose both sides on the left with a^{-1}
$(a^{-1} \circ a) \circ x = a^{-1} \circ b,$	by associativity
$e \circ x = a^{-1} \circ b,$	by the definition of a^{-1}
$x = a^{-1} \circ b,$	by the definition of e

So x, if it exists, must equal $a^{-1} \circ b$. By Theorem 2.5, a^{-1} is unique. So x is unique.

We verify that $x = a^{-1} \circ b$ satisfies (2.24) by substitution as follows:

$a \circ (a^{-1} \circ b) = (a \circ a^{-1}) \circ b,$	by associativity
$= e \circ b,$	by the definition of a^{-1}
$= b,$	by the definition of e

The case of the equation $x \circ a = b$ is left as an exercise. ◇

Example 2.33

Theorem 2.8 strongly depends on the group properties. Let us look at Table 2.9, the composition table for $(\mathbb{Z}_6, \cdot)$. The set with composition $(\mathbb{Z}_6, \cdot)$ satisfies all of the axioms for a group except for the existence of inverses. We observe that the 0-row, 2-row, 3-row, and 4-row of Table 2.9 are not permutations of the outside row; 0, 2, 3, and 4 lack inverses in $(\mathbb{Z}_6, \cdot)$. The 1-row and the 5-row are permutations of the outside row; 1 and 5 have inverses in $(\mathbb{Z}_6, \cdot)$. △

Example 2.34

We shall use Theorem 2.8 to show that all groups with three elements are isomorphic. We need to see that, except for the choice of names, a 3×3 group composition table is unique. We call the group elements e, a, b with e the identity. Table 2.16 gives a partial composition table using the properties of e.

Table 2.16 Partial composition table for a group with three elements

$\circ$	e	a	b
e	e	a	b
a	a		
b	b		

The complete a-row in Table 2.16 must be a permutation of e, a, b, by Theorem 2.8. So there are two possibilities for the a-row: (i) a, e, b and (ii) a, b, e. These possibilities are tried in Table 2.17 on p. 96.

Table 2.17(i) cannot be part of a group composition table since the b-column has duplicate entries of b. This contradicts the requirement of Theorem 2.8 that every column be a permutation of the outside column. Now we continue with Table 2.17(ii). Since the a-column must be a permutation of the outside column, the last entry in the a-column must be e. Similarly, the last entry in the b-column of Table 2.17(ii) must be a. This

Table 2.17 Possible partial composition tables

(i)

$\circ$	e	a	b
e	e	a	b
a	a	e	b
b	b		

(ii)

$\circ$	e	a	b
e	e	a	b
a	a	b	e
b	b		

gives Table 2.18 as the *only* possible composition table for a group with three elements. Since $(\mathbb{Z}_3, +)$ is a group with three elements, Table 2.18 must have a renaming of its elements as the elements of the composition table for $(\mathbb{Z}_3, +)$.

Table 2.18 The group with three elements

$\circ$	e	a	b
e	e	a	b
a	a	b	e
b	b	e	a

$$e \to 0 \qquad a \to 1 \qquad b \to 2$$

is such a renaming. △

Exercises 2.4

1. Using Table 2.3, solve the following equations for x.
   a. $h_2 \circ x = h_4$ b. $h_4 \circ x = h_5$
   c. $x \circ h_3 = h_4$ d. $x \circ h_8 = h_2$
2. In each of the following cases, compute $a \circ b$, $(a \circ b)^{-1}$, a^{-1}, b^{-1}, and $b^{-1} \circ a^{-1}$.
   a. Table 2.3: $a = h_3$, $b = h_8$ b. Table 2.3: $a = h_4$, $b = h_5$
   c. Table 2.6: $a = 2$, $b = 3$ d. Table 2.11: $a = (1,0)$, $b = (2,1)$
3. Let a, b, and c be elements of the group $(G, \circ)$. Simplify the following expressions.
   a. $(a \circ b^{-1})^{-1}$ b. $(a^{-1} \circ b)^{-1} \circ (c \circ a)^{-1}$
   c. $(a \circ b \circ c \circ a)^{-1}$ d. $(a^{-1} \circ b^{-1}) \circ (c^{-1} \circ a)^{-1} \circ c^{-1}$
4. It is given that $x \circ a = e$ in a group. Show that $x = a^{-1}$.
   Hint: Consider $x \circ a \circ a^{-1}$.
5. Give reasons for the correctness of each of the following manipulations, which solve $x \circ a = b$ for x, in some group.

$$\begin{aligned} x \circ a &= b \\ (x \circ a) \circ a^{-1} &= b \circ a^{-1} \\ x \circ (a \circ a^{-1}) &= b \circ a^{-1} \\ x \circ e &= b \circ a^{-1} \\ x &= b \circ a^{-1} \end{aligned}$$

6. The proof of Theorem 2.8 verified directly that $x = a^{-1} \circ b$ satisfied the equation $a \circ x = b$. This verification was needed because not all "solutions" to an equation that are found by algebraic manipulation

are necessarily true solutions. Consider the equation for real numbers given by $x^2 = x$. Which of the "roots" found by the following process are true roots? Which step should have been avoided? Why?

$x^2 = x,$	equation given
$x^4 = x^2,$	by squaring both sides
$x^4 - x^2 = 0,$	by subtracting x^2 from both sides
$x^2(x^2 - 1) = 0,$	by factoring
$x^2(x+1)(x-1) = 0,$	by factoring
$x = 0, \quad x+1 = 0,$ or	
$x - 1 = 0,$	by setting each factor to 0
$x = 0, -1, 1,$	by solving simple equations

7. Find a group axiom that fails in the following composition table. Is the conclusion of Theorem 2.8 true for this composition table?

	a	b	c	d	e	f
a	c	e	a	b	f	d
b	f	c	b	a	d	e
c	a	b	c	d	e	f
d	e	a	d	f	c	b
e	d	f	e	c	b	a
f	b	d	f	e	a	c

8. Explain why Theorem 2.4 follows from just axioms (o) and (ii) of Definition 2.3.

9. (Right Cancellation Law) Let $(G, \circ)$ be a group. Let x, y, and a be group elements such that $x \circ a = y \circ a$. Show that $x = y$.

10. Formulate and prove a Left Cancellation Law.

11. Let $(G, \circ)$ be a group. Show that G is commutative if and only if, for all elements a, b in G,

$$(a \circ b) \circ (a \circ b) = (a \circ a) \circ (b \circ b)$$

12. Show that all groups with two elements are isomorphic.

13. Show that the renaming $e \to 0$, $a \to 2$, $b \to 1$ also is an isomorphism between the group of Table 2.18 and $(\mathbb{Z}_3, +)$.

14. The following table is given to be part of the composition table for a commutative group. (In fact, all groups with four elements are commutative.) Fill in the missing entries.

$\circ$	a	b	c	d
a	b			
b				
c				
d			a	

2.5 Subgroups

In the previous section we saw that the group axioms have important consequences. However, the complete verification of the axioms is lengthy in many cases. In this section we shall see that the verification of the group axioms is particularly easy in the case of subgroups, which thus provide many additional computable examples.

Let us look once again at the symmetries of the square. Table 2.1 is the composition table. Let us consider the identity map h_1 and the three rotations h_2, h_3, and h_4. Is $S=\{h_1,h_2,h_3,h_4\}$ a group under the usual composition of maps? Table 2.19 is the composition table for $(S,\circ)$. Table 2.19 is, of course, just that part of Table 2.1 which comes from the rows and columns for elements of S.

Table 2.19 Composition table for $\{h_1,h_2,h_3,h_4\}$

$\circ$	h_1	h_2	h_3	h_4
h_1	h_1	h_2	h_3	h_4
h_2	h_2	h_3	h_4	h_1
h_3	h_3	h_4	h_1	h_2
h_4	h_4	h_1	h_2	h_3

All of the entries in Table 2.19 are in the set S. So the closure axiom holds. Associativity follows from later results in this section, but could be checked with much calculation directly from Table 2.19. The identity is h_1. Inverses are as follows:

$$h_1^{-1}=h_1 \qquad h_2^{-1}=h_4 \qquad h_3^{-1}=h_3 \qquad h_4^{-1}=h_2$$

So, as claimed, Table 2.19 is the composition table for a group.

Definition 2.7 Let $(G,\circ)$ be a given group. Let S be a subset of G. Then $(S,\circ)$ is a **subgroup** of $(G,\circ)$ if $\circ$ is a law of composition on S that makes $(S,\circ)$ into a group. ○

Table 2.20 "Composition" table for $S=\{h_1,h_2\}$

$\circ$	h_1	h_2
h_1	h_1	h_2
h_2	h_2	h_3

Example 2.35 Let $(G,\circ)$ be given again by Table 2.1. Let $S=\{h_1,h_2\}$. Is $(S,\circ)$ a subgroup of $(G,\circ)$? Table 2.20 is the "composition" table for $(S,\circ)$. Observe that the closure axiom is not satisfied since $h_2\circ h_2=h_3$ and h_3 is not an element of S. So $(S,\circ)$ is not a subgroup (and $\circ$ is not a law of composition on S). △

Example 2.36

Let $(G,\circ)$ be as in Table 2.1. Let $S=\{h_1,h_5\}$. It is easily checked that $(S,\circ)$ is a subgroup. △

Examples 2.37

Let $(\mathbb{Z},+)$ be the usual group of all integers under the composition given by addition. Let $E=\{\ldots,-4,-2,0,2,4,\ldots\}$ be the set of all even integers, including 0 and negative numbers. Then $(E,+)$ is easily seen to be a subgroup of $(\mathbb{Z},+)$. △

Let $S=\{0,1,2,3,\ldots\}$ be the set of all nonnegative integers. Is $(S,+)$ a subgroup of $(\mathbb{Z},+)$? We must check the group axioms. If $a\geq 0$ and $b\geq 0$, then $a+b\geq 0$. So closure holds in $(S,+)$. Addition is associative in $\mathbb{Z}$ and so also in S. The identity for $(S,+)$ is 0. But inverses generally fail to exist in $(S,+)$; the only candidate for the inverse under addition to 2, for example, is the negative integer -2. But -2 is not in S. So 2 has no inverse in $(S,+)$. Hence $(S,+)$ is not a group and so is not a subgroup of $(\mathbb{Z},+)$. △

In Definition 2.7, we assume that S and G have essentially the same law of composition. But we do not assume that $(S,\circ)$ and $(G,\circ)$ have the same identity elements and the same inverses. These assumptions are not necessary because they in fact follow from the group axioms. Theorem 2.9 states this formally.

Theorem 2.9

Let $(S,\circ)$ be a subgroup of $(G,\circ)$. Then the identity in $(S,\circ)$ is the same as the identity in $(G,\circ)$. Let s be an element of S. Then the inverse of s in $(S,\circ)$ is the same as the inverse for s in $(G,\circ)$.

Example 2.38

Before proving Theorem 2.9, we shall illustrate its statement. Let $(G,\circ)$ be given from Table 2.1. Let $(S,\circ)$ be from Table 2.19. The identity in Table 2.1 is h_1. The identity in Table 2.19 is also h_1. Let $s=h_4$. From Table 2.1, $h_4{}^{-1}=h_2$. From Table 2.19, also $h_4{}^{-1}=h_2$. △

Proof of Theorem 2.9

Let e_S denote the identity in S. Then $e_S\circ s=s$ and $s\circ e_S=s$ for all elements s in $\underline{S}$. Let e_G denote the identity for G. Then $e_G\circ g=g$ and $g\circ e_G=g$ for all elements g in $\underline{G}$ (and also for g in S). To show that $e_S=e_G$, we let $e_S{}^{-1}$ denote the inverse of e_S as an element of G; that is, $e_S\circ e_S{}^{-1}=e_G$ and $e_S{}^{-1}\circ e_S=e_G$.

$e_S\circ e_S=e_S,$	$e_S\circ s=s$ for all s in S and in particular for $s=e_S$
$e_S{}^{-1}\circ e_S\circ e_S=e_S{}^{-1}\circ e_S,$	by composing both sides on the left by $e_S{}^{-1}$
$e_G\circ e_S=e_G,$	by the definition of $e_S{}^{-1}$ in G
$e_S=e_G,$	$e_G\circ g=g$ for all g in G. Let $g=e_S$.

Now we consider an element s in S. Let s^{-1} be the inverse of s <u>in S</u>. That is, $s \circ s^{-1} = e_S$ and $s^{-1} \circ s = e_S$. But $e_S = e_G$, as we just illustrated. Then s^{-1} is also an inverse for s <u>in G</u>. By Theorem 2.5, inverses in G are unique. So s^{-1} is also *the* inverse for s in G. ◇

Example 2.39

We shall give an example of a set G, a subset S and a law of composition $\circ$ on G and S such that the conclusions of Theorem 2.9 fail. Of course, $(G,\circ)$ and $(S,\circ)$ cannot be a group and a subgroup. Let $G = \{e,a,b\}$ have the law of composition as given in Table 2.21. The law of composition $\circ$ is, in fact, an associative law of composition. Let $S = \{a,b\}$. Then $\circ$ is also a law of composition on S. The identity element in $(G,\circ)$ is e. This is different from a, the identity element in $(S,\circ)$. In $(S,\circ)$, $a^{-1} = a$. But a has no inverse in $(G,\circ)$. △

Theorem 2.10

Let $(G,\circ)$ be a group. Let S be a subset of G that contains at least one element. Then $(S,\circ)$ is a subgroup of $(G,\circ)$ if and only if

(i) if a and b are elements of S, then also $a \circ b$ is an element of S and
(ii) if s is an element of S, then also s^{-1}, the inverse of s in G, is an element of S.

Proof of Theorem 2.10

It is easy to verify that $(S,\circ)$ a subgroup of $(G,\circ)$ implies (i) and (ii); indeed, (i) is just the closure axiom for $(S,\circ)$. As for (ii), Theorem 2.9 says that s^{-1} is also the inverse for s in <u>S</u>. But the inverse axiom for the group $(S,\circ)$ says, in particular, that s has an inverse <u>in S</u>. So s^{-1} is in S.

We now show that a subset S satisfying (i) and (ii) is a subgroup of $(G,\circ)$. We show that $(S,\circ)$ is a group by verifying the group axioms. The closure axiom is just (i).

Associativity. Let a, b, and c be elements of S.

$$(a \circ b) \circ c = a \circ (b \circ c)$$

since $\circ$ is associative as a law of composition on G. S has the same law of composition as has G. So associativity holds for S.

Identity. An identity element in S must be shown to exist. Let e denote the identity element G. Theorem 2.9 says that e is the only candidate for an identity element of S.

$$e \circ g = g \quad \text{and} \quad g \circ e = g$$

for all elements of G and in particular for all elements of S. So it suffices to show that e is an element of S. It is assumed that S has at least one element; we shall call it s. Then by (ii), s^{-1} is also in S. By (i), $s \circ s^{-1}$ is in S; furthermore, $s \circ s^{-1} = e$. So e is in S.

Inverses. This axiom is just (ii). ◇

Table 2.21 Composition table for $G = \{e,a,b\}$

$\circ$	e	a	b
e	e	a	b
a	a	a	b
b	b	b	a

We shall now start to see that condition (ii) of Theorem 2.10 may often be omitted. Our goal is Theorem 2.13, which follows later.

Example 2.40

Look at h_2 of Table 2.1 on p. 69. Let us see what happens if we keep composing h_2 with itself.

$$\begin{aligned} h_2 &= h_2 \\ h_2 \circ h_2 &= h_3 \\ h_2 \circ h_2 \circ h_2 &= h_4 \\ h_2 \circ h_2 \circ h_2 \circ h_2 &= h_1 \\ h_2 \circ h_2 \circ h_2 \circ h_2 \circ h_2 &= h_2 \\ h_2 \circ h_2 \circ h_2 \circ h_2 \circ h_2 \circ h_2 &= h_3 \\ &\cdots \end{aligned} \tag{2.25}$$

We observe that the right sides in (2.25) reach h_1, the identity in Table 2.1, and then start repeating. △

Example 2.41

In $(\mathbb{Z}_3, +)$ let us keep composing 2 with itself:

$$\begin{aligned} 2 &= 2 \\ 2+2 &= 1 \\ 2+2+2 &= 0 \\ 2+2+2+2 &= 2 \\ 2+2+2+2+2 &= 1 \\ &\cdots \end{aligned} \tag{2.26}$$

As in (2.25), the right sides of (2.26) reach 0, the identity in $(\mathbb{Z}_3, +)$, and then start repeating. △

Notice that the right sides in (2.25) give the subgroup of Table 2.19. The right sides in (2.26) give all of $\mathbb{Z}_3$. $\mathbb{Z}_3$ is, of course, a subgroup of itself. This phenomenon is described in Theorems 2.11 and 2.12, which will follow. We simplify the notation for (2.25) and (2.26) as follows: Let g be an element of the group $(G, \circ)$. We define

$$\begin{aligned} g^1 &= g \\ g^2 &= g \circ g \\ g^3 &= g \circ g \circ g \\ g^4 &= g \circ g \circ g \circ g \\ g^n &= g \circ g \circ \cdots \circ g, \qquad \text{with } n \text{ factors of } g \end{aligned}$$

We observe that the usual law of exponents holds. That is, with i and j positive integers,

$$g^i \circ g^j = g^{i+j} \tag{2.27}$$

With g an element of the group $(G, +)$, where we are using additive notation, it is customary to write

$$\begin{aligned} 1 \cdot g &= g \\ 2 \cdot g &= g + g \\ 3 \cdot g &= g + g + g \\ 4 \cdot g &= g + g + g + g \\ n \cdot g &= g + g + \cdots + g, \qquad \text{with } n \text{ summands of } g \end{aligned} \tag{2.28}$$

A group $(G, \circ)$ is **finite** if the set G has a finite number of elements. A group that is not finite is **infinite**. For example, $(\mathbb{Z}_n, +)$ is a finite group with n elements. $(\mathbb{Z}, +)$ is an infinite group.

Theorem 2.11 Let g be an element of the finite group $(G, \circ)$. Then there is a least positive integer n, called the **order** of g, such that $g^n = e$. Also, the group elements $g = g^1, g^2, g^3, \ldots, g^{n-1}, g^n = e$ are all distinct.

Proof of Theorem 2.11 We look at the sequence of elements $g, g^2, g^3, g^4, \ldots$ in G. Since G is a finite set, this infinite sequence must have duplications. We choose such a duplication:

$$g^p = g^q, \qquad \text{with } p \text{ greater than } q \tag{2.29}$$

$$\begin{aligned} g^q \circ g^{p-q} &= g^q, \qquad \text{by (2.27) and (2.29)} \\ (g^q)^{-1} \circ g^q \circ g^{p-q} &= (g^q)^{-1} \circ g^q \\ e \circ g^{p-q} &= e \\ g^{p-q} &= e \end{aligned}$$

Thus $g^m = e$ for the positive integer $m = p - q$. So we can let n be the smallest such positive integer.

We must still show that $g, g^2, g^3, \ldots, g^{n-1}, g^n$ has no duplications. Suppose that

$$g^i = g^j \tag{2.30}$$

with $i \neq j$ and i and j between 1 and n, inclusive. We shall show that (2.30) contradicts the assumption that n is minimal. In (2.30) we may take $i > j$.

Then (2.30) is exactly the same as (2.29) with $p=i$ and $q=j$. Then the previous argument shows that

$$g^{i-j}=e$$

But $1 \leq i-j < n$. This is the desired contradiction. ◇

Example 2.42

What is the order of (1,1) in $(\mathbb{Z}_2 \times \mathbb{Z}_4, +)$? $e=(0,0)$. In $\mathbb{Z}_2 \times \mathbb{Z}_4$, we use additive notation.

$$\begin{aligned} (1,1) &= (1,1) \\ 2\cdot(1,1) &= (0,2) \\ 3\cdot(1,1) &= (1,3) \\ 4\cdot(1,1) &= (0,0) \end{aligned}$$

(1,1) has order 4 in $(\mathbb{Z}_2 \times \mathbb{Z}_4, +)$. △

Example 2.43

Let G be a finite set with $\circ$ a law of composition on G. In forming the sequence $g, g^2, g^3, \ldots$, we necessarily have duplications. It is the axiom for inverses, however, that forces e to be the last nonduplicated value.

Let us consider $G=\{e,a,b\}$ with $\circ$ given by the composition table Table 2.22. Then $(G,\circ)$ satisfies closure, associativity, and has an identity. We consider successive compositions of b with itself as follows:

Table 2.22 Composition table

$\circ$	e	a	b
e	e	a	b
a	a	a	a
b	b	a	a

$$\begin{aligned} b &= b \\ b^2 &= a \\ b^3 &= a \\ b^4 &= a \\ &\cdots \end{aligned}$$

Then e never appears. △

Theorem 2.12

Let g be an element of order n in the finite group $(G,\circ)$. Let $\langle g \rangle = \{g=g^1, g^2, \ldots, g^{n-1}, g^n=e\}$. Then $(\langle g \rangle, \circ)$ is a subgroup of $(G,\circ)$. $(\langle g \rangle, \circ)$ is called the **cyclic subgroup** of $(G,\circ)$ **generated** by g. ◇

Example 2.44

We shall illustrate the proof of Theorem 2.12, which follows. As in Example 2.42, let $g=(1,1)$ in $(\mathbb{Z}_2 \times \mathbb{Z}_4, +)$. We apply Theorem 2.10 to check if $(\langle g \rangle, +)$ is a subgroup. Table 2.23 is the composition table for $\langle g \rangle$, and so checks Theorem 2.10(i). Inverses for the verification of

Table 2.23 Composition table

	(1,1)	(0,2)	(1,3)	(0,0)
(1,1)	(0,2)	(1,3)	(0,0)	(1,1)
(0,2)	(1,3)	(0,0)	(1,1)	(0,2)
(1,3)	(0,0)	(1,1)	(0,2)	(1,3)
(0,0)	(1,1)	(0,2)	(1,3)	(0,0)

Theorem 2.10(ii) are:

$$-(1,1)=(1,3) \qquad -(0,2)=(0,2) \qquad -(1,3)=(1,1) \qquad -(0,0)=(0,0)$$

△

Proof of Theorem 2.12

We shall apply Theorem 2.10 to verify that $(\langle g\rangle,\circ)$ is a subgroup. We look at $g^i \circ g^j$, with $1 \leq i, j \leq n$.

$$g^i \circ g^j = g^{i+j}$$

If $i+j \leq n$, then Theorem 2.10(i) is automatically satisfied. Otherwise, $n+1 \leq i+j \leq 2n$. Then $1 \leq i+j-n \leq n$. Let $m=i+j-n$. Then g^m is in $\langle g\rangle$. Also,

$$\begin{aligned} g^{i+j} &= g^{m+n}, && i+j=m+n \\ &= g^m \circ g^n, && \text{by (2.27)} \\ &= g^m \circ e, && g^n = e, \text{ by the definition of } n \\ &= g^m, && \text{by the definition of } e \end{aligned}$$

So (i) of Theorem 2.10 is true in all cases.

$g^n = e$ is in $\langle g\rangle$. Also, $g^i \circ g^{n-i} = g^n = g^{n-i} \circ g^i$. So $g^{n-i} = (g^i)^{-1}$ is in $\langle g\rangle$. So (ii) of Theorem 2.10 is true. ◇

Suppose that g is an element of order n in $(G,\circ)$ and that h is an element of the same order n in $(H,*)$. Then the renaming $g^i \rightarrow h^i$, $i=1,2,\ldots,n$, shows that $(\langle g\rangle,\circ)$ is isomorphic to $(\langle h\rangle,*)$. Observe that in $(\mathbb{Z}_n,+)$, $\langle 1\rangle = \mathbb{Z}_n$. So necessarily $(\langle g\rangle,\circ)$ and $(\langle h\rangle,*)$ are also isomorphic to $(\mathbb{Z}_n,+)$. A group $(S,\circ)$ is said to be a **cyclic group** if $S=\langle s\rangle$ for some element s in S. Then all cyclic groups with n elements are isomorphic to $(\mathbb{Z}_n,+)$.

Example 2.45

In Example 2.44, the renaming

$$(1,1)\rightarrow 1 \qquad (0,2)\rightarrow 2 \qquad (1,3)\rightarrow 3 \qquad (0,0)\rightarrow 0$$

changes Table 2.23 into the composition table for $(\mathbb{Z}_4,+)$. △

For finite groups we can prove the following very simple criterion for a subgroup; the *only* condition that must be checked is closure.

Theorem 2.13 Let $(G,\circ)$ be a finite group. Let S be a subset of G with at least one element. Suppose that if a and b are elements of S, then also $a\circ b$ is an element of S. Then $(S,\circ)$ is a subgroup of $(G,\circ)$.

Proof of Theorem 2.13 We are going to apply Theorem 2.10. The hypothesis of Theorem 2.13 is just (i) of Theorem 2.10. So we must show Theorem 2.10(ii). Let s be an element of S. By Theorem 2.12, $(\langle s\rangle,\circ)$ is a subgroup of $(G,\circ)$. So s^{-1} is an element of $\langle s\rangle$. Since $\langle s\rangle$ consists only of compositions of s with itself, the hypothesis of Theorem 2.13 ensures that $\langle s\rangle$ is a subset of S. Then s^{-1} is in S. ◇

Example 2.46 Is $S=\{0,2,3\}$ a subgroup of $(\mathbb{Z}_6,+)$? We form Table 2.24, a tentative composition table for $S=\{0,2,3\}$ under the composition of $+$ in $\mathbb{Z}_6$. We see that some of the sums are not in S. So S is not a subgroup of $(\mathbb{Z}_6,+)$. △

Table 2.24 Composition table for $S=\{0,2,3\}$ in $(\mathbb{Z}_6,+)$

+	0	2	3
0	0	2	3
2	2	4	5
3	3	5	0

Example 2.47 Is $S=\{h_1,h_3,h_5,h_6\}$ a subgroup of the group of Table 2.1? As in Table 2.25, we form a tentative composition table for S. Observe that in Table 2.25, all of the compositions lie in the given set S. So $(S,\circ)$ is, in fact, a subgroup. △

Table 2.25 Composition table

$\circ$	h_1	h_3	h_5	h_6
h_1	h_1	h_3	h_5	h_6
h_3	h_3	h_1	h_6	h_5
h_5	h_5	h_6	h_1	h_3
h_6	h_6	h_5	h_3	h_1

Example 2.48 Recall that Definition 1.4 only requires that the sum of code words be a code word in order to call a code a *group* code. We know that $(\mathbb{Z}_2,+)$ is a group. Theorem 2.3 guarantees that $(\mathbb{Z}_2{}^n,+)$ is a group. Then Theorem 2.13 says that a group code in the sense of Definition 1.4 has code words that form a group also in the sense of Definition 2.3. △

Exercises 2.5

1. Tell whether or not each of the following subsets satisfies the closure axiom.
   a. $\{1,2,3\}$ in $(\mathbb{Z}_6, +)$ b. $\{0,2\}$ in $(\mathbb{Z}_4, \cdot)$
   c. $\{h_1,h_2,h_3\}$ in Table 2.1 d. $\{0,-1,-2,-3,\ldots\}$ in $(\mathbb{Z},+)$
2. Tell whether or not each of the following subsets are subgroups.
   a. $\{(0,0), (1,1), (1,2)\}$ in $(\mathbb{Z}_2 \times \mathbb{Z}_3, +)$
   b. $\{h_1,h_3,h_7,h_8\}$ in Table 2.1
   c. $\{0,2,4,6,8\}$ in $(\mathbb{Z}_{10}, +)$
   d. $\{\ldots,-9,-6,-3,0,3,6,9,\ldots\}$ in $(\mathbb{Z},+)$
3. For each of the following elements g, give the order of g and compute $\langle g \rangle$.
   a. 1 in $(\mathbb{Z}_6,+)$ b. 2 in $(\mathbb{Z}_6,+)$
   c. 3 in $(\mathbb{Z}_6,+)$ d. 5 in $(\mathbb{Z}_6,+)$
   e. 0 in $(\mathbb{Z}_4,+)$ f. h_4 in Table 2.1
   g. h_5 in Table 2.1 h. $(1,1)$ in $(\mathbb{Z}_2 \times \mathbb{Z}_3, +)$
4. Let $P=\{1,2,3,\ldots\}$ be the set of positive integers. Let $+$ be usual addition. Which of the group axioms are satisfied by $(P,+)$? Is $(P,+)$ a subgroup of $(\mathbb{Z},+)$? Why does this example not contradict Theorem 2.13?
5. A given element g in the group $(G,\circ)$ has order 1. Which group element is g?
6. What is the analog of (2.27) in additive notation?
7. Explain why $(\mathbb{Z}_2 \times \mathbb{Z}_2, +)$ is not a cyclic group.
8. Let g be an element of the finite group $(G,\circ)$. Why may $(\langle g \rangle,\circ)$ be called the *smallest* subgroup of $(G,\circ)$ that contains g?
9. Let $\circ$ be a law of composition on a set G such that $(G,\circ)$ satisfies axioms (o), (i), and (ii) of Definition 2.3. Let S be the subset of G that consists of all elements s such that s^{-1} exists. Show that $(S,\circ)$ is a group.
10. Let $(G,\circ)$ be a group. Let $(H,\circ)$ be a subgroup of $(G,\circ)$. Let $(K,\circ)$ be a subgroup of $(H,\circ)$. Explain why $(K,\circ)$ is also a subgroup of $(G,\circ)$.
11. Let $(H,\circ)$ and $(K,\circ)$ be subgroups of $(G,\circ)$. Show that $(H\cap K,\circ)$ is also a subgroup of $(G,\circ)$.
12. a. Show that $(\langle 2\rangle \cup \langle 3 \rangle, +)$ is not a subgroup of $(\mathbb{Z}_6,+)$.
    b. Does the union of subgroups have to be a subgroup?
13. a. Let $(G,\circ)$ be a possibly infinite group. Define what it means for an element g in G to be of finite order. If g is not of finite order, say that g is of infinite order.
    b. Let $(\mathbb{Z}_2{}^\infty,+)$ denote the group of all infinite sequences of 0's and 1's with $+$ being componentwise addition in $\mathbb{Z}_2$. Show that $(\mathbb{Z}_2{}^\infty,+)$ is an infinite group, all of whose elements have finite order.

14. Explain why every element in $(\mathbb{Z}, +)$ except for 0 has infinite order.
15. Let g be an element of the group $(G,\circ)$. Justify the notation $g^0 = e$, $g^{-n} = (g^{-1})^n$.
16. Let g be an element of infinite order in the group $(G,\circ)$.
    a. With p and q any two distinct integers, show that $g^p \neq g^q$.
    b. Let $\langle g\rangle = \{\ldots,g^{-2},g^{-1},g^0,g^1,g^2,\ldots\}$. Show that $(\langle g\rangle,\circ)$ is a subgroup of $(G,\circ)$.

2.6 Permutation Groups

So far in this chapter, the beginnings of a general theory for groups have been given. In this section the apparently special class of groups called permutation groups is introduced. The symmetries of polygons discussed in Section 2.1 were represented by permutation groups. Moreover, as we shall see in the exercises, essentially *all* groups may be given as permutation groups. Permutations will also be important later when we count the symmetries of more complicated objects than polygons.

Recall that, informally, a permutation of a set X is simply a reordering of the set. Initially we shall use the following notation for permutations: Suppose that $X = \{A,B,C,D\}$. Suppose that the permutation f reorders A to B, B to D, C to itself and D to A. We write

$$f = \begin{pmatrix} A & B & C & D \\ B & D & C & A \end{pmatrix} \tag{2.31}$$

In (2.31), the top row lists the elements of X. Below each element of X is the element of X to which it is mapped via f (or reordered). In (2.31), $f(A) = B$, $f(B) = D$, etc.

$$f = \begin{pmatrix} A & B & C & D & E \\ E & D & B & A & C \end{pmatrix}$$

is the permutation on $X = \{A,B,C,D,E\}$ given by $f(A) = (E)$, $f(B) = D$, $f(C) = B$, $f(D) = A$, $f(E) = C$.

$\begin{pmatrix} A & B & C & D & E & F \\ A & B & C & D & E & F \end{pmatrix}$ is the permutation of $X = \{A,B,C,D,E,F\}$ that maps every element to itself. There is no need for the elements of X to be the first letters of the alphabet; $\begin{pmatrix} 0 & 1 & 2 & 3 & 4 & 5 \\ 1 & 4 & 3 & 2 & 5 & 0 \end{pmatrix}$ is a permutation on the set $X = \{0,1,2,3,4,5\}$.

The following is the formal definition of a permutation.

Definition 2.8

Let $f: X \to Y$ be a map (or function) from the set X to the set Y. The map f is **one-to-one** if, for every pair of distinct elements $x_1 \neq x_2$ in X, also

$f(x_1) \neq f(x_2)$. The map f is **onto** if, for every element y of Y, there is an element x of X such that $f(x)=y$. The map f is a **one-to-one correspondence** if f is one-to-one and onto. ○

Examples 2.49

Let $X=\{A,B,C\}$ and $Y=\{D,E,F,G\}$. Then the map $f:X\to Y$ given by $f(A)=G$, $f(B)=E$, $f(C)=F$ is drawn in (2.32). This f is one-to-one but not onto.

A B C

D E F G

(2.32)

△

Now we let $f:Y\to X$ be given by $f(D)=B$, $f(E)=B$, $f(F)=C$, $f(G)=A$. The map f is drawn below in (2.33). This time, f is onto but not one-to-one.

(2.33)

△

f of (2.31) is both one-to-one and onto and hence is a one-to-one correspondence. △

If $f:X\to Y$ is a one-to-one correspondence, then X and Y have the same number of elements. If X and Y are finite sets with the same number of elements and f is one-to-one, then f is automatically onto. Conversely, again with X and Y finite sets with the same number of elements, if f is onto, then f is automatically one-to-one.

Definition 2.9

Let X be a set. A **permutation** of X is a map $f:X\to X$ that is a one-to-one correspondence. ○

Example 2.50

Let $X=\{A,B,C,D,E\}$. Then $f=\begin{pmatrix} A & B & C & D & E \\ C & B & E & D & A \end{pmatrix}$ is a permutation (of X). On the other hand, with the usual notation, the map $g:X\to X$ given by $g=\begin{pmatrix} A & B & C & D & E \\ A & C & D & C & A \end{pmatrix}$ is not a permutation because it is neither one-to-one nor onto. Indeed, g is not one-to-one since $g(B)=g(D)$; g is not onto, since $g(x)=E$ is not satisfied for any x in X. △

Example 2.51

Let X be the infinite set of all integers. Then the function $f(x)=x+1$, x in X, is a permutation of X. The function $g(x)=x^3$, x in X, is one-to-one. But g is not a permutation since it is not onto. △

We compose permutations as we compose maps in Definition 2.1. We shall prove later that the composition of permutations is again a permutation, but first let us do some examples.

Example 2.52

Let $X=\{A,B,C,D\}$. Let

$$f=\begin{pmatrix} A & B & C & D \\ B & C & D & A \end{pmatrix}, \quad g=\begin{pmatrix} A & B & C & D \\ B & C & A & D \end{pmatrix}, \quad \text{and}$$
$$h=\begin{pmatrix} A & B & C & D \\ D & A & B & C \end{pmatrix}$$

be permutations of X.

$$f\circ g=\begin{pmatrix} A & B & C & D \\ B & C & D & A \end{pmatrix}\circ\begin{pmatrix} A & B & C & D \\ B & C & A & D \end{pmatrix}=\begin{pmatrix} A & B & C & D \\ C & D & B & A \end{pmatrix}$$

is computed as follows:

$$(f\circ g)(A)=f(g(A))=f(B)=C$$
$$(f\circ g)(B)=f(g(B))=f(C)=D$$
$$(f\circ g)(C)=f(g(C))=f(A)=B$$
$$(f\circ g)(D)=f(g(D))=f(D)=A$$

Similarly, $g\circ f=\begin{pmatrix} A & B & C & D \\ C & A & D & B \end{pmatrix}$. Note that $f\circ g\neq g\circ f$. That is, the order in which permutations are composed is important.

$f\circ h=\begin{pmatrix} A & B & C & D \\ A & B & C & D \end{pmatrix}$. Also, $h\circ f=\begin{pmatrix} A & B & C & D \\ A & B & C & D \end{pmatrix}$. In this case, $f\circ h=h\circ f$. △

Definition 2.10

Let X be a set. The **identity map** on X, $id_X:X\rightarrow X$, is that map given by $id_X(x)=x$ for all x in X. Let $f:X\rightarrow Y$ and $g:Y\rightarrow X$ be maps between sets. f and g are **inverse** maps, written $g=f^{-1}$ and $f=g^{-1}$, if $g\circ f=id_X$ and $f\circ g=id_Y$.

Example 2.53

Finding inverse functions (or maps) often amounts to solving for the independent variable in terms of the dependent variable. Let x and y denote real numbers. The assertion that $y=f(x)$ and $x=g(x)$ are inverse functions is equivalent to the assertion that (x,y) satisfies $y=f(x)$ if and only if (x,y) satisfies $x=g(y)$. For example, let $y=f(x)=2x+1$. Solving $y=2x+1$ for x gives $x=\frac{1}{2}y-\frac{1}{2}$. Let $x=g(y)=\frac{1}{2}y-\frac{1}{2}$. Then

$$(g\circ f)(x)=\frac{1}{2}(2x+1)-\frac{1}{2}=x$$

and

$$(f\circ g)(y)=2\left(\frac{1}{2}y-\frac{1}{2}\right)+1=y$$

So f and g are inverse functions. △

Example 2.54 Let $X=\{A,B,C,D\}$. Then id_X is the permutation $id_X=\begin{pmatrix} A & B & C & D \\ A & B & C & D \end{pmatrix}$. Since id_X will be a group identity, We shall often write e for id_X.

Here are some examples of inverse permutations:

Let $f=\begin{pmatrix} A & B & C & D & E \\ B & E & C & A & D \end{pmatrix}$. Then

$$f^{-1}=\begin{pmatrix} A & B & C & D & E \\ B & E & C & A & D \end{pmatrix}^{-1}=\begin{pmatrix} A & B & C & D & E \\ D & A & C & E & B \end{pmatrix}$$

because $f(A)=B$, so $f^{-1}(B)=A$; $f(B)=E$, so $f^{-1}(E)=B$; $f(C)=C$, so $f^{-1}(C)=C$; $f(D)=A$, so $f^{-1}(A)=D$; $f(E)=D$, so $f^{-1}(D)=E$; f^{-1} may also be computed with much less writing by interchanging the two rows, as follows:

$$\begin{pmatrix} A & B & C & D & E \\ B & E & C & A & D \end{pmatrix}^{-1}=\begin{pmatrix} B & E & C & A & D \\ A & B & C & D & E \end{pmatrix}$$

Now we rearrange the columns into their usual order:

$$\begin{pmatrix} A & B & C & D & E \\ B & E & C & A & D \end{pmatrix}^{-1}=\begin{pmatrix} B & E & C & A & D \\ A & B & C & D & E \end{pmatrix}$$
$$=\begin{pmatrix} A & B & C & D & E \\ D & A & C & E & B \end{pmatrix}$$

Here is another example:

$$\begin{pmatrix} A & B & C & D & E & F & G \\ G & F & D & E & A & B & C \end{pmatrix}^{-1}=\begin{pmatrix} G & F & D & E & A & B & C \\ A & B & C & D & E & F & G \end{pmatrix}$$
$$=\begin{pmatrix} A & B & C & D & E & F & G \\ E & F & G & C & D & B & A \end{pmatrix}$$ △

Theorem 2.14 Let $f: X \to Y$ be a map from the set X to the set Y. Then f has an inverse map g if and only if f is a one-to-one correspondence. The inverse map g is unique if it exists.

Example 2.55 Before proving Theorem 2.14 below, let us see what can happen if f is not one-to-one or onto. The map of (2.32) is one-to-one but not onto. We do not know what value to give to $g(D)$. The map of (2.33) is onto, but not one-to-one. Both D and E are possible values for $g(B)$. △

Proof of Theorem 2.14 Suppose that g exists, as in Definition 2.10. We must show that f is a one-to-one correspondence, as in Definition 2.8. We consider $x_1 \neq x_2$ in X and show that $f(x_1)=f(x_2)$ leads to a contradiction. If $f(x_1)=f(x_2)$, then $g(f(x_1))=g(f(x_2))$. However, $g \circ f = id_X$. So $g(f(x_1))=x_1$ and $g(f(x_2))=x_2$. So $x_1=x_2$, the desired contradiction. So f is one-to-one.

Now we consider y in Y. Let $x=g(y)$. Then $f(x)=f(g(y))$. However, $f \circ g = id_Y$. So $f(g(y))=y$. So f is both onto and one-to-one and so is a one-to-one correspondence.

Given that f is a one-to-one correspondence, we now show that the inverse function g exists. For y in Y, let $g(y)$ be that element of x of X such that $f(x)=y$. At least one such x exists because f is onto. At most one such element x exists since f is one-to-one. So an x such that $f(x)=y$ exists and is unique. The verifications that g is indeed the inverse function to f and that g is unique are left to the exercises. ◇

Theorem 2.15 Let X be a set. Let f, g, and h be maps of X to itself. Then

$$(f \circ g) \circ h = f \circ (g \circ h)$$

That is, the composition of self-maps is associative. ◇

The proof of Theorem 2.15 is left for the exercises. Observe that, in Theorem 2.15, we do not assume that f, g, and h are permutations.

Example 2.56 Let $X=\{A,B,C,D,E\}$. With notation analogous to that for permutations, we consider the following self-maps of X.

$$f=\begin{pmatrix} A & B & C & D & E \\ C & B & B & E & A \end{pmatrix} \qquad g=\begin{pmatrix} A & B & C & D & E \\ B & C & E & D & A \end{pmatrix}$$

$$h=\begin{pmatrix} A & B & C & D & E \\ A & A & C & D & E \end{pmatrix}$$

$$f\circ g=\begin{pmatrix}A & B & C & D & E\\ B & B & A & E & C\end{pmatrix} \qquad (f\circ g)\circ h=\begin{pmatrix}A & B & C & D & E\\ B & B & A & E & C\end{pmatrix}$$

$$g\circ h=\begin{pmatrix}A & B & C & D & E\\ B & B & E & D & A\end{pmatrix} \qquad f\circ(g\circ h)=\begin{pmatrix}A & B & C & D & E\\ B & B & A & E & C\end{pmatrix}$$

So $(f\circ g)\circ h=f\circ(g\circ h)$. △

Theorem 2.16

Let $X=\{A,B,C,D,\ldots\}$ be a finite set with n elements. Let S_n denote the set of all permutations of the set X. Then S_n has $n!$ elements. $(S_n,\circ)$ is a group with $\circ$ denoting the composition of permutations as maps. S_n is called the **symmetric group on n letters.**

Example 2.57

Before proving Theorem 2.16, we shall illustrate its statement for $n=3$. Let $X=\{A,B,C\}$. The six elements of S_3 are as follows:

$$f_1=\begin{pmatrix}A & B & C\\ A & B & C\end{pmatrix} \quad f_2=\begin{pmatrix}A & B & C\\ B & C & A\end{pmatrix} \quad f_3=\begin{pmatrix}A & B & C\\ C & A & B\end{pmatrix}$$
$$f_4=\begin{pmatrix}A & B & C\\ A & C & B\end{pmatrix} \quad f_5=\begin{pmatrix}A & B & C\\ C & B & A\end{pmatrix} \quad f_6=\begin{pmatrix}A & B & C\\ B & A & C\end{pmatrix} \qquad \textbf{(2.34)}$$

Table 2.26 is the composition table for S_3. The composition $\circ$ is associative. The identity is f_1. Inverses are easily found. △

Table 2.26 Composition table for $(S_3,\circ)$

	f_1	f_2	f_3	f_4	f_5	f_6
f_1	f_1	f_2	f_3	f_4	f_5	f_6
f_2	f_2	f_3	f_1	f_6	f_4	f_5
f_3	f_3	f_1	f_2	f_5	f_6	f_4
f_4	f_4	f_5	f_6	f_1	f_2	f_3
f_5	f_5	f_6	f_4	f_3	f_1	f_2
f_6	f_6	f_4	f_5	f_2	f_3	f_1

Proof of Theorem 2.16

We must check the group axioms of Definition 2.3. The closure axiom will be checked only later in the proof. So until its verification, it should be checked that all indicated compositions are in fact defined in $(S_n,\circ)$.

Identity. The identity map $id_X\colon X\to X$ of Definition 2.10 serves as the identity e in $(S_n,\circ)$. The identity map id_X is certainly a one-to-one correspondence and so a permutation. The verification that $e\circ f=f$ and $f\circ e=f$ for all permutations of X is left as an exercise.

Inverses. Let $f: X \to X$ be a permutation. By Theorem 2.14, f has an inverse map $f^{-1}: X \to X$. Then again by Theorem 2.14, f^{-1} is a one-to-one correspondence and so f^{-1} is also an element of S_n. Since id_X is the identity element e in $(S_n, \circ)$, f and f^{-1} are also inverse elements in the sense of groups.

Closure. Let f and g be permutations. The composition $f \circ g: X \to X$ is a map, but $f \circ g$ must also be shown to be a permutation, that is, a one-to-one correspondence. We shall apply Theorem 2.14 by showing that $f \circ g$ has an inverse map. We know from Theorem 2.14 that f and g have inverse maps f^{-1} and g^{-1}, respectively. Theorem 2.6 suggests that $f \circ g$ has $g^{-1} \circ f^{-1}$ as its inverse map. Theorem 2.15 says that the composition of maps is associative. The verification that

$$(g^{-1} \circ f^{-1}) \circ (f \circ g) = id_X \quad \text{and} \quad (f \circ g) \circ (g^{-1} \circ f^{-1}) = id_X$$

is now as in the proof of Theorem 2.6.

Associativity. This follows immediately from Theorem 2.15. ◇

Example 2.58

Compare (2.34) with Figure 2.5. The notation has been chosen so that it is the same in both places. Since symmetries of polygons are determined by their effect on vertices, Table 2.26, the composition table for (2.34), is also the composition table for the symmetries of the equilateral triangle. △

Example 2.59

Let $X = \{A, B\}$. S_2 has the two elements as follows:

$$e = \begin{pmatrix} A & B \\ A & B \end{pmatrix} \quad f = \begin{pmatrix} A & B \\ B & A \end{pmatrix}$$

Table 2.27 is the composition table for $(S_2, \circ)$. △

Table 2.27 Composition table for $(S_2, \circ)$

$\circ$	e	f
e	e	f
f	f	e

Let us look at the symmetries of the square, as given in Figure 2.7. Each symmetry is described by its permutation of the vertices G, H, I, and J. The composition of symmetries corresponds to the composition of permutations. So the group $(G, \circ)$ of symmetries of the square may also be regarded as a group of permutations of the set $X = \{G, H, I, J\}$. Observe that a square has eight symmetries, while there are $4! = 24$ permutations of X. So $(G, \circ)$ is a subgroup of $(S_4, \circ)$, but it is not the entire group $(S_4, \circ)$.

We see similarly that the symmetries of the isosceles triangle, as given in Figure 2.6, may be thought of as a subgroup of $(S_3, \circ)$. More generally, we make the following definition.

Definition 2.11

A subgroup of $(S_n, \circ)$ is called a **permutation group**. ○

Given a set S of permutations of the same finite set X, Theorem 2.13 says that $(S,\circ)$ is a permutation group if the closure axiom is satisfied.

Example 2.60

The following is a permutation group. The permutations have been named, so that the composition table may be given conveniently as Table 2.28.

$$e=\begin{pmatrix} A & B & C & D \\ A & B & C & D \end{pmatrix} \quad a=\begin{pmatrix} A & B & C & D \\ B & C & D & A \end{pmatrix}$$

$$b=\begin{pmatrix} A & B & C & D \\ C & D & A & B \end{pmatrix} \quad c=\begin{pmatrix} A & B & C & D \\ D & A & B & C \end{pmatrix}$$

△

Table 2.28 Composition table

$\circ$	e	a	b	c
e	e	a	b	c
a	a	b	c	e
b	b	c	e	a
c	c	e	a	b

Example 2.61

Let $a=\begin{pmatrix} A & B & C & D \\ B & A & C & D \end{pmatrix}$ and $b=\begin{pmatrix} A & B & C & D \\ A & B & D & C \end{pmatrix}$. Then $S=\{a,b\}$ is not a permutation group since $a\circ b=\begin{pmatrix} A & B & C & D \\ B & A & D & C \end{pmatrix}$ is not an element of S.

△

The representation of permutations by means of their **cycle decomposition** is explained next. This will give a compact notation for permutations that will also be convenient for the computation of compositions.

For example, let $X=\{A,B,C,D,E,F\}$. Let

$$f=\begin{pmatrix} A & B & C & D & E & F \\ F & C & B & D & A & E \end{pmatrix}$$

f maps X to itself. Let us see what happens to A under successive applications of f. In (2.35), the notation $A\xrightarrow{f}F$ is another way of writing $f(A)=F$.

$$A\xrightarrow{f}F\xrightarrow{f}E\xrightarrow{f}A\xrightarrow{f}F\xrightarrow{f}\cdots \tag{2.35}$$

The permutation f eventually takes A back to itself, with no repetitions until then. The sequence A,F,E, which appears in (2.35), is called a **cycle** for f and is denoted (AFE). Now we take an element of X, say B, that does not appear in the cycle (AFE). We repeat the calculation of (2.35) starting at B.

$$B\xrightarrow{f}C\xrightarrow{f}B\xrightarrow{f}C\xrightarrow{f}\cdots$$

This time we obtain the cycle (BC). D is the only element of X not yet listed in a cycle. Applying f successively to D yields

$$D\xrightarrow{f}D\xrightarrow{f}D\xrightarrow{f}\cdots$$

This cycle is denoted (D). Suppose the calculation starts at F, which has already appeared in the cycle (AFE) for (2.35):

$$F \xrightarrow{f} E \xrightarrow{f} A \xrightarrow{f} F \xrightarrow{f} E \xrightarrow{f} \cdots \tag{2.36}$$

This gives the cycle (FEA). Since (2.35) and (2.36) repeat in the same way, we regard (AFE) and (FEA) as two different notations for the *same* cycle. In all, and this happens for any permutation, the elements of X are divided by f into disjoint cycles. The cycles are uniquely determined by f, but may have more than one name.

Let us see how to reconstruct the permutation f from its cycles (AFE), (BC), and (D). Each cycle yields a permutation, as follows; we look at (AFE). The elements B, C, and D of X, which are not listed in (AFE), are left fixed by the permutation. Otherwise, $A \to F$, $F \to E$, and $E \to A$. That is, we map elements of the cycle to the next elements of the cycle; we map the last element of the cycle to the first.

$$(AFE) = \begin{pmatrix} A & B & C & D & E & F \\ F & B & C & D & A & E \end{pmatrix}$$

Similarly,

$$(BC) = \begin{pmatrix} A & B & C & D & E & F \\ A & C & B & D & E & F \end{pmatrix}$$

$$(D) = \begin{pmatrix} A & B & C & D & E & F \\ A & B & C & D & E & F \end{pmatrix} = e$$

Then, since the cycles are disjoint, f is the product of (AFE), (BC), and (D) as permutations:

$$\begin{aligned}(AFE)\circ(BC)\circ(D) \\ &= \begin{pmatrix} A & B & C & D & E & F \\ F & B & C & D & A & E \end{pmatrix} \circ \begin{pmatrix} A & B & C & D & E & F \\ A & C & B & D & E & F \end{pmatrix} \circ \begin{pmatrix} A & B & C & D & E & F \\ A & B & C & D & E & F \end{pmatrix} \\ &= \begin{pmatrix} A & B & C & D & E & F \\ F & C & B & D & A & E \end{pmatrix} = f\end{aligned}$$

We write more compactly: $f = (AFE)\circ(BC)\circ(D)$. Since $(D) = e$, when X is understood, we may simply write $f = (AFE)\circ(BC)$. Since the cycles are disjoint, the order in which they are composed does not matter: $f = (BC)\circ(AFE)$. We call the representation of f as the composition of disjoint cycles f's **cycle decomposition**. We shall usually omit the composition symbol $\circ$ and just write $f = (AFE)(BC)$.

Example 2.62

Let $X=\{A,B,C,D,E,F,G\}$. We give the cycle decomposition of some permutations.

$$f=\begin{pmatrix} A & B & C & D & E & F & G \\ G & A & D & C & B & E & F \end{pmatrix}$$

Via f, $A\to G\to F\to E\to B\to A$, stop. The first cycle is $(AGFEB)$. C is not in this cycle. Via f, $C\to D\to C$, stop. (CD) is the remaining cycle.

$$f=(AGFEB)(CD)$$

$$g=\begin{pmatrix} A & B & C & D & E & F & G \\ A & D & G & B & C & F & E \end{pmatrix}=(A)(BD)(CGE)(F)=(BD)(CGE)$$

$$h=\begin{pmatrix} A & B & C & D & E & F & G \\ G & B & C & F & A & D & E \end{pmatrix}=(AGE)(B)(C)(DF)=(AGE)(DF)$$

△

Example 2.63

$X=\{1,2,3,4,5,6,7,8\}$. We shall write out some permutations from their cycle decompositions. It is not necessary to write out explicitly the permutations corresponding to the cycles.

$$(2341)(68)=\begin{pmatrix} 1 & 2 & 3 & 4 & 5 & 6 & 7 & 8 \\ 2 & 3 & 4 & 1 & 5 & 8 & 7 & 6 \end{pmatrix}$$

$$(1253487)=\begin{pmatrix} 1 & 2 & 3 & 4 & 5 & 6 & 7 & 8 \\ 2 & 5 & 4 & 8 & 3 & 6 & 1 & 7 \end{pmatrix}$$

$$(15368)(274)=\begin{pmatrix} 1 & 2 & 3 & 4 & 5 & 6 & 7 & 8 \\ 5 & 7 & 6 & 2 & 3 & 8 & 4 & 1 \end{pmatrix}$$

△

Example 2.64

Let us compute the composition of the following cycles. When the cycles are disjoint, the order of composition is not important. But, as here, when the cycles are not disjoint, the law of composition requires that we start with the rightmost cycle (or permutation).

Let us consider $(ABC)(ABD)$. First we find the cycle containing A:

$$A\xrightarrow{(ABD)}B\xrightarrow{(ABC)}C$$

$$C\xrightarrow{(ABD)}C\xrightarrow{(ABC)}A$$

This completes the cycle. Now we find the cycle containing B:

$$B\xrightarrow{(ABD)}D\xrightarrow{(ABC)}D$$

$$D\xrightarrow{(ABD)}A\xrightarrow{(ABC)}B, \text{ stop}$$

$$(ABC)(ABD)=(AC)(BD)$$

$$(ABD)(BCE) = (ABCED)$$
$$(BCE)(ABD) = (ACEBD)$$
$$(AC)(BDA)(AEC) = (AE)(BDC)$$
$$(CE)(BD)(DAB) = (AD)(B)(CE) = (AD)(CE)$$

△

Example 2.65

Here is a permutation group. Table 2.29 gives its composition table. $X = \{1,2,3,4,5\}$.

$$G = \{e, (123), (132), (45), (123)(45), (132)(45)\}$$

△

Table 2.29 Composition table for permutations

$\circ$	e	(123)	(132)	(45)	(123)(45)	(132)(45)
e	e	(123)	(132)	(45)	(123)(45)	(132)(45)
(123)	(123)	(132)	e	(123)(45)	(132)(45)	(45)
(132)	(132)	e	(123)	(132)(45)	(45)	(123)(45)
(45)	(45)	(123)(45)	(132)(45)	e	(123)	(132)
(123)(45)	(123)(45)	(132)(45)	(45)	(123)	(132)	e
(132)(45)	(132)(45)	(45)	(123)(45)	(132)	e	(123)

Example 2.66

Consider the group $(\mathbb{Z}_3, +)$. Its addition table is given in Table 2.30. As guaranteed by Theorem 2.8, each row in Table 2.30 is a permutation of the outside row. (2.37) gives the cycle decomposition for each of the row permutations.

$$0 \to \begin{pmatrix} 0 & 1 & 2 \\ 0 & 1 & 2 \end{pmatrix} = e \qquad 1 \to \begin{pmatrix} 0 & 1 & 2 \\ 1 & 2 & 0 \end{pmatrix} = (012)$$
$$2 \to \begin{pmatrix} 0 & 1 & 2 \\ 2 & 0 & 1 \end{pmatrix} = (021) \tag{2.37}$$

Table 2.30 Composition table for $(\mathbb{Z}_3, +)$

+	0	1	2
0	0	1	2
1	1	2	0
2	2	0	1

To see that the permutations of (2.37) are a permutation group, we form their composition table, Table 2.31. Observe that (2.37) gives an isomorphism between $(\mathbb{Z}_3, +)$ of Table 2.30 and the group of Table 2.31. In the exercises, it is shown that the row permutations of any finite group are a permutation group isomorphic to the given group. △

Table 2.31 A permutation group

$\circ$	e	(012)	(021)
e	e	(012)	(021)
(012)	(012)	(021)	e
(021)	(021)	e	(012)

Exercises 2.6

1. Tell whether each of the following maps is a permutation.

a. $\begin{pmatrix} A & B & C & D \\ A & C & B & D \end{pmatrix}$

b. $\begin{pmatrix} A & B & C & D & E \\ E & D & C & A & C \end{pmatrix}$

c. $\begin{pmatrix} A & B & C & D & E & F \\ F & E & D & A & B & C \end{pmatrix}$

d. $\begin{pmatrix} A & B & C & D & E & F \\ A & C & D & E & F & A \end{pmatrix}$

2. Compute the following compositions of permutations.

a. $\begin{pmatrix} A & B & C & D \\ C & D & A & B \end{pmatrix} \circ \begin{pmatrix} A & B & C & D \\ A & B & D & C \end{pmatrix}$

b. $\begin{pmatrix} A & B & C & D & E \\ B & C & D & A & E \end{pmatrix} \circ \begin{pmatrix} A & B & C & D & E \\ A & B & D & E & C \end{pmatrix}$

c. $\begin{pmatrix} A & B & C & D & E \\ B & C & D & E & A \end{pmatrix} \circ \begin{pmatrix} A & B & C & D & E \\ E & D & C & B & A \end{pmatrix}$

d. $\begin{pmatrix} A & B & C & D & E & F \\ C & D & E & F & A & B \end{pmatrix} \circ \begin{pmatrix} A & B & C & D & E & F \\ B & D & E & F & C & A \end{pmatrix}$

3. Compute the inverses of the following permutations.

a. $\begin{pmatrix} A & B & C & D & E \\ B & C & E & A & D \end{pmatrix}$

b. $\begin{pmatrix} A & B & C & D & E & F \\ A & C & E & F & D & B \end{pmatrix}$

c. $\begin{pmatrix} A & B & C & D & E & F \\ F & E & A & B & C & D \end{pmatrix}$

d. $\begin{pmatrix} A & B & C & D & E & F & G \\ E & F & C & D & A & B & G \end{pmatrix}$

4. Decide whether or not each of the following sets of permutations is a permutation group.

a. $\begin{pmatrix} A & B & C \\ A & B & C \end{pmatrix}, \begin{pmatrix} A & B & C \\ C & A & B \end{pmatrix}, \begin{pmatrix} A & B & C \\ C & B & A \end{pmatrix}, \begin{pmatrix} A & B & C \\ A & C & B \end{pmatrix}$

b. $\begin{pmatrix} A & B & C \\ A & B & C \end{pmatrix}, \begin{pmatrix} A & B & C \\ A & C & B \end{pmatrix}$

c. $\begin{pmatrix} A & B & C \\ B & C & A \end{pmatrix}, \begin{pmatrix} A & B & C \\ C & A & B \end{pmatrix}, \begin{pmatrix} A & B & C \\ A & B & C \end{pmatrix}$

d. $\begin{pmatrix} A & B & C & D \\ B & C & A & D \end{pmatrix}, \begin{pmatrix} A & B & C & D \\ A & B & C & D \end{pmatrix}, \begin{pmatrix} A & B & C & D \\ B & A & C & D \end{pmatrix},$
$\begin{pmatrix} A & B & C & D \\ D & C & B & A \end{pmatrix}$

5. Find the cycle decomposition for each of the following permutations.

a. $\begin{pmatrix} A & B & C & D \\ C & B & D & A \end{pmatrix}$

b. $\begin{pmatrix} A & B & C & D & E \\ C & E & A & D & B \end{pmatrix}$

c. $\begin{pmatrix} A & B & C & D & E & F & G \\ A & D & F & G & C & E & B \end{pmatrix}$

d. $\begin{pmatrix} A & B & C & D & E & F & G & H \\ D & E & H & A & F & G & B & C \end{pmatrix}$

6. Write out the following compositions of disjoint cycles in the form $\begin{pmatrix} A & B & C & D & \ldots \\ ? & ? & ? & ? & \ldots \end{pmatrix}$.
   a. $(ACDB)$; $X = \{A,B,C,D\}$
   b. $(AC)(BDE)$; $X = \{A,B,C,D,E\}$
   c. $(AD)(BE)$; $X = \{A,B,C,D,E\}$
   d. $(BCD)(FE)$; $X = \{A,B,C,D,E,F\}$
7. Compute the following compositions of cycles. Write the answer as the composition of disjoint cycles.
   a. $(ACB)(DEA)(BC)$ b. $(FBA)(CDA)(AB)(BC)$
8. Give the cycle decomposition for each permutation in (2.34).
9. Explain why S_n has $n!$ elements.
10. Complete the proof of Theorem 2.14 as follows.
    a. Show that $(f \circ g)(y) = y$ and $(g \circ f)(x) = x$.
    b. Show that g is unique by showing that if $g \circ f = id_X$ and $y = f(x)$, then $x = g(y)$.

    Hint: $y = f(x)$. Apply g to both sides.
11. Show that the composition of self-maps is associative by explaining how Definition 2.1 justifies each of the following steps:

$$\begin{aligned}[(f \circ g) \circ h](x) &= (f \circ g)(h(x)) \\ &= f(g(h(x)))\end{aligned}$$

$$\begin{aligned}[f \circ (g \circ h)](x) &= f((g \circ h)(x)) \\ &= f(g(h(x)))\end{aligned}$$

12. Let X and Y each be sets with n elements. Let $(S_n, \circ)$ and $(T_n, \circ)$ denote the groups of all permutations of X and of Y respectively. Explain why $(S_n, \circ)$ and $(T_n, \circ)$ are isomorphic.
13. Let X be an infinite set. Explain briefly why the set of all permutations of X is a group under the composition of maps.

    Hint: Do any of the proofs use the fact that X is finite?
14. a. Show that $(123)^{-1} = (132)$. Show that also $(123)^{-1} = (321)$.
    b. Why does part (a) not contradict the uniqueness of inverses?
    c. Let f be a permutation given by its cycle decomposition. Show that writing f's cycle decomposition backwards gives f^{-1}.
15. a. Show that the order of a cycle equals the number of elements in the cycle.
    b. Show that the order of a permutation is the least common multiple of the orders of the cycles in its cycle decomposition.

16. Let f be a permutation on the finite set $X=\{A,B,C,D,...\}$.
    a. Use Theorem 2.11 to show that the sequence $A, f(A), f^2(A), f^3(A), \ldots$ eventually repeats.
    b. Let x be the element of X that first appears twice in the sequence $A, f(A), f^2(A), \ldots$. Why must x be A?
       Hint: If $x \neq A$, part (a), with x in place of A, implies that A never reappears.
    c. Explain why f has a decomposition into *disjoint* cycles.
17. Let $(G,\circ)$ be a finite group. For g an element of G, let p_g denote the permutation given by the g-row of the composition table for G; that is, for x in G, $p_g(x)=g\circ x$.
    a. Using the associativity axiom, show that $p_a \circ p_b = p_{a\circ b}$.
    b. Why does part (a) show that the row permutations form a permutation group?
    c. Show that the row permutations are all distinct.
       Hint: Look at $p_a(e)$ and $p_b(e)$.
    d. Explain why parts (a) and (c) verify that the renaming $g \rightarrow p_g$ is an isomorphism from $(G,\circ)$ to the row permutation group.

3 Relations

The notion of a relation on a set is very general. This chapter focuses on two important types of relations: equivalence relations, which abstract the idea of "is the same as," and partial orders, which abstract the idea of "less-than-or-equal-to."

We use an equivalence relation to prove Lagrange's Theorem, a basic theorem for the theory of finite groups. Many counting problems amount to counting equivalence classes. We develop Burnside's Theorem, a very important aid in counting problems.

Partial orders are introduced in Section 3.4. Partially ordered sets are described by their Hasse diagrams and their covering matrices. The abstract notion of a partial order will be useful in Chapter 5 on Boolean Algebras.

3.1 Relations; Equivalence Relations

This section introduces the notion of a relation. In one sense, relations may be thought of as multiple-valued "functions." However, here we focus instead on relations that are generalizations of the notion of equality. These are called **equivalence relations**. We show that an equivalence relation on a set X corresponds to a partition of X into nonempty disjoint subsets.

Example 3.1

As in the calculus, let $\mathbb{R}$ denote the set of all real numbers. Let $f: \mathbb{R} \to \mathbb{R}$ be the function $y = f(x) = x^2$. We denote the (x, y)-plane by $\mathbb{R}^2 = \mathbb{R} \times \mathbb{R}$. Recall that the *graph* G of f, as drawn in Figure 3.1 on p. 122, consists of all points (x, y) in $\mathbb{R} \times \mathbb{R}$ such that $y = f(x)$.

Recall that *not* every subset G of $\mathbb{R} \times \mathbb{R}$ is the graph of a *function* from $\mathbb{R}$ to $\mathbb{R}$. Indeed, the definition of function requires that for each x in $\mathbb{R}$, there is a unique y in $\mathbb{R}$ such that (x, y) is in G. △

Example 3.2

Take the function $y = f(x) = x^2$ from Example 3.1 and attempt to solve for x in terms of y.

$$x = g(y) = \pm\sqrt{y} \tag{3.1}$$

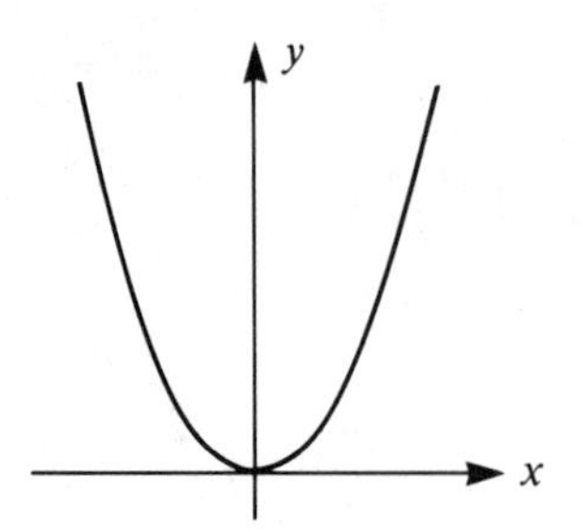

Figure 3.1 Graph G of the function $y=x^2$

(3.1) does not give x as a function of y for two reasons: $\pm\sqrt{y}$ is only defined for $y \geq 0$. Moreover, for $y > 0$, $\pm\sqrt{y}$ gives two values for x, and a function must assign a single value to the dependent variable for each value of the independent variable. Nonetheless, (3.1) does contain useful information. (3.1) is called a **relation** between y and x. The "graph" of (3.1), as drawn in Figure 3.2, consists of all (y,x) that satisfy (3.1). Figure 3.2 is not the graph of a function.

Squaring both sides of (3.1) gives the relation

$$x^2 = y \tag{3.2}$$

(3.1) and (3.2) are the same relation in the sense that (y,x) satisfies (3.1) if and only if (y,x) satisfies (3.2). So Figure 3.2 is also the "graph" of (3.2). (3.2) shows that Figure 3.2 may be obtained from Figure 3.1 by interchanging the positions of the x-axis and the y-axis. △

We make the following general definition. Recall that $X \times X$ denotes all (ordered) pairs (x,y) with x and y in X. Rather than the letter G used in Examples 3.1 and 3.2, we now use the usual notation R to denote a relation.

Definition 3.1 Let X be a set. A **relation** R on X is a subset of $X \times X$. If (x,y) is in R, we say that x **is related to** y and write xRy. ○

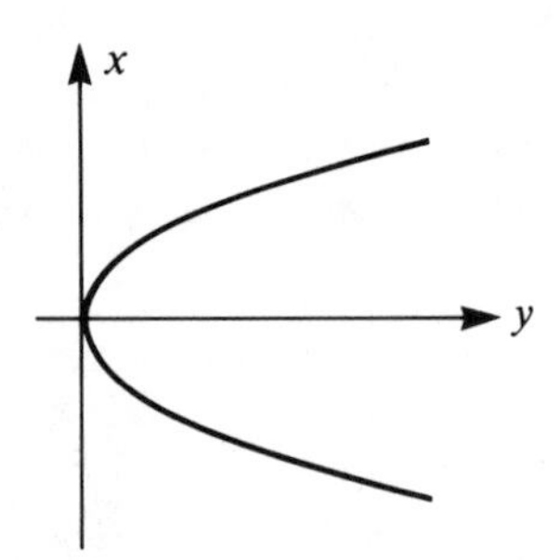

Figure 3.2 Graph G of the relations $x = \pm\sqrt{y}$ and $x^2 = y$

Example 3.3

The "graphs" of Figures 3.1 and 3.2 are relations on X, with X denoting the set of all real numbers. △

Definition 3.1 is exceedingly general. Additional conditions must be put on relations to make them interesting or useful. In this chapter, we focus on relations similar to the relations $=$, $\leq$, $<$, and $\neq$ for the real numbers. We classify relations by whether or not they satisfy the properties in Definition 3.2, which follows. These properties will be discussed as the above relations are classified. Table 3.1 will summarize the results of the classifications.

Definition 3.2

Let R be a relation on the set X.

R is **reflexive** if, for all x in X, xRx.

R is **symmetric** if, for all x,y in X, xRy implies that yRx.

R is **antisymmetric** if, for all x,y in X, xRy and yRx implies that $x=y$.

R is **transitive** if, for all x,y,z in X, xRy and yRz implies that xRz. ○

Table 3.1 Properties of some relations

	$=$	$\leq$	$<$	$\neq$	$\equiv$
Reflexive	x	x			x
Symmetric	x			x	x
Antisymmetric	x	x	x		
Transitive	x	x	x		x

Examples 3.4

First we consider $\leq$, less-than-or-equal-to. Since for all x, $x \leq x$ is true, $\leq$ is reflexive. Since $3 \leq 4$, while $4 \leq 3$ is false, $\leq$ is not symmetric. Since $x \leq y$ and $y \leq x$ does imply that $x=y$, $\leq$ is antisymmetric. If $x \leq y$ and $y \leq z$, then also $x \leq z$. So $\leq$ is transitive. △

We drop the "equal-to" part from $\leq$ and consider $<$, the "less-than" part. $3<3$ is now false, so $<$ is not reflexive. It is easily seen that $<$ is not symmetric, but is transitive. The relation $<$ is antisymmetric for the trivial reason that $x<y$ and $y<x$ cannot both be true at the same time. So the question of whether or not $x=y$ is not considered in the definition of antisymmetry. △

Since $x=x$, $=$ is reflexive. Since $x=y$ implies that $y=x$, $=$ is symmetric. The relation $=$ is antisymmetric for the trivial reason that if $x=y$ (and regardless that also $y=x$), then $x=y$. If $x=y$ and $y=z$, then

$x=z$. So $=$ is transitive. (This is the axiom "Quantities equal to the same quantity are equal" from Euclidean geometry.) △

Now we consider $\neq$, not-equal-to. Since $3 \neq 3$ is a false statement, $\neq$ is not reflexive. Since, for all real numbers x, y, $x \neq y$ implies that $y \neq x$, $\neq$ is symmetric. Since $5 \neq 7$ and $7 \neq 5$, $\neq$ is not antisymmetric. Although $4 \neq 6$ and $6 \neq 4$, $4 \neq 4$ is false. So $\neq$ is not transitive. △

Example 3.5

Let n be a positive integer. Let $\mathbb{Z}$ be the set of all integers, including 0 and the negative integers. For x and y in $\mathbb{Z}$, we say that

$$x \equiv y \pmod{n} \quad \text{(read } x \text{ is congruent to } y \text{, modulo } n\text{)}$$

if $\dfrac{x-y}{n}$ is an integer, that is, if n *divides* $(x-y)$ exactly.

Modulo $n=1$, all integers are congruent to each other; the relation $\equiv$ mod 1 is very uninteresting on $\mathbb{Z}$. Here are some other examples for $\equiv$:

$$\begin{array}{ll} 4 \equiv 13 \pmod{3} & -2 \equiv 10 \pmod{3} \\ 1 \equiv 7 \pmod{6} & 4 \not\equiv 11 \pmod{6} \end{array} \tag{3.3}$$

For $n \geq 2$, let us check the properties in Definition 3.2. Is $x \equiv x \pmod{n}$? $\dfrac{x-x}{n} = \dfrac{0}{n} = 0$ *is* an integer. So $\equiv$ is reflexive. Given that $x \equiv y \pmod{n}$, is necessarily $y \equiv x \pmod{n}$? $\dfrac{x-y}{n}$ is given to be an integer. Then also $-\dfrac{x-y}{n} = \dfrac{y-x}{n}$ is an integer. So $y \equiv x \pmod{n}$ and $\equiv$ is symmetric. Is $\equiv$ antisymmetric? If $x \equiv y$, then automatically $y \equiv x$ by symmetry. However, as in (3.3), it is not necessarily true that $x = y$. So $\equiv$ is not antisymmetric. Finally, we look at transitivity. Suppose that $x \equiv y \pmod{n}$ and $y \equiv z \pmod{n}$.

$$\frac{x-y}{n} = p \quad \text{and} \quad \frac{y-z}{n} = q \tag{3.4}$$

with p and q integers. Adding the two equations in (3.4) gives

$$\frac{x-z}{n} = p+q$$

$p+q$ is an integer. So $x \equiv z \pmod{n}$ and $\equiv$ is a transitive relation. △

Definition 3.3 Let R be a relation on the set X. R is an **equivalence relation** if R is reflexive, symmetric, and transitive. We shall often employ the conventional symbol $\sim$, rather than R, to denote an equivalence relation. ○

As we shall see, an equivalence relation $\sim$ abstracts some "sameness" property for the elements of X. Let, for example, X be the set of all people. Then, trivial objections aside, the following are equivalence relations on X:

x and y have the *same* colored eyes.

x and y are both male or both female; that is,
x and y have the *same* sex. **(3.5)**

x and y are natives of the *same* country.

x and y were born the *same* year.

In Table 3.1 only $=$ and $\equiv$ are equivalence relations. To which "sameness" properties do they correspond? The relation $x=y$ means, of course, that x and y are exactly the same. It is easy to see that $x \equiv y \pmod{n}$ means that x and y leave the *same* remainder after division by n.

Proposition 3.1 Let X be a set. Let $(G,\circ)$ be a group of permutations on X. Let x and y be elements of X. Say that $x \sim y$ if there is a permutation g in G such that $g(x)=y$. Then $\sim$ is an equivalence relation, called ***G*-equivalence**, on X.

Example 3.6 Before proving Proposition 3.1 we shall illustrate its statement. Let $X=\{D,E,F\}$ be the vertices of an isosceles triangle as in Figure 2.6. Let $G=\{g_1,g_2\}$, also as in Figure 2.6, be given by

$$g_1 = \begin{pmatrix} D & E & F \\ D & E & F \end{pmatrix} \qquad g_2 = \begin{pmatrix} D & E & F \\ D & F & E \end{pmatrix}$$

The condition $g_1(x)=y$ from Proposition 3.1 gives the following relations among elements of X:

$$D \sim D \qquad E \sim E \qquad F \sim F \tag{3.6}$$

The condition $g_2(x)=y$ yields

$$D \sim D \qquad E \sim F \qquad F \sim E \tag{3.7}$$

Observe that the relation $D \sim D$ appears in both (3.6) and (3.7).

A case-by-case check shows that (3.6) and (3.7) do indeed give an equivalence relation. More easily, however, $x \sim y$ in (3.6) and (3.7) may be thought of as requiring that x and y have equal angles in the isosceles triangle of Figure 2.6. △

Proof of Proposition 3.1

We must verify the conditions of Definitions 3.3 and 3.2.

Reflexivity. The identity element of $(G, \circ)$ is the identity map id_X on X. For x in X, $\mathrm{id}_X(x) = x$. So $x \sim x$.

Symmetry. $x \sim y$ means that there is an element g in G such that

$$
\begin{aligned}
g(x) &= y && \\
g^{-1}(g(x)) &= g^{-1}(y), && \text{by applying } g^{-1} \text{ to both sides} \\
(g^{-1} \circ g)(x) &= g^{-1}(y), && \text{by the definition of } \circ \\
\mathrm{id}_X(x) &= g^{-1}(y), && \text{by the definition of } g^{-1} \\
x &= g^{-1}(y), && \text{by the definition of } \mathrm{id}_X \\
y &\sim x, && \text{by the definition of } \sim
\end{aligned}
$$

Transitivity. Given that $x \sim y$ and $y \sim z$, there exist elements g and h of G such that

$$g(x) = y \quad \text{and} \quad h(y) = z$$

$h \circ g$ is in G by the closure axiom. Then

$$(h \circ g)(x) = h(g(x)) = h(y) = z$$

So $x \sim z$. □

Notice that all of the group axioms were needed for the proof of Proposition 3.1.

Definition 3.4

Let $\sim$ be an equivalence relation on the set X. Let x be in X. Then $[x]$, the **equivalence class** of X, is the set of all elements y in X such that $x \sim y$. ○

Example 3.7

Let $\sim$ be $\equiv$ mod 2, as in Example 3.5. Let us compute [3]: for $3 \equiv y \pmod 2$ to hold,

$$\frac{3-y}{2} = p, \qquad \text{with } p \text{ an integer} \tag{3.8}$$

Solving (3.8) for y gives $y = 3 - 2p$. That is, y differs from 3 by the even integer $2p$. So

$$[3] = \{\ldots, -1, 1, 3, 5, 7, 9, \ldots\}$$

[3] may thus also be thought of as the set of all odd integers.

A similar calculation shows that [6] consists of all integers that differ from 6 by an even integer.

$$[6] = \{\ldots, 0, 2, 4, 6, 8, 10, 12, \ldots\}$$

So [6] may also be thought of as the set of all even integers. △

Example 3.8

We shall compute the equivalence classes for Example 3.6.

$D \sim y$ only for $y = D$. So $[D] = \{D\}$.

$E \sim y$ for $y = E$, from (3.6), and for $y = F$, from (3.7).
So $[E] = \{E, F\}$.

$F \sim y$ for $y = F$ and for $y = E$. So $[F] = \{F, E\}$. The order in which the elements of a set are listed is unimportant. So $[F] = [E]$. △

Observe in Examples 3.7 and 3.8 that equivalence classes either coincided or did not intersect at all. This is true in general.

Proposition 3.2

Let $\sim$ be an equivalence relation on X. Let x be an element of X. Then x is in $[x]$. Let $[x]$ and $[y]$ be the equivalence classes of x and y respectively. Then $[x] = [y]$ if and only if $x \sim y$. Otherwise, $[x] \cap [y] = \varnothing$.

Proof of Proposition 3.2

$x \sim x$ since $\sim$ is reflexive. Hence x is in $[x]$.

Suppose that $[x] = [y]$; that is, suppose the two sets have the same elements. Since $y \in [y]$, also $y \in [x]$. That is, $x \sim y$, by Definition 3.4.

Now let us suppose that $x \sim y$ and show that $[x] = [y]$. Suppose that $z \in [x]$. Then $x \sim z$. Since $\sim$ is symmetric, $y \sim x$. Then also $y \sim z$, since $\sim$ is transitive. So $z \in [y]$. Similarly, if $z \in [y]$, then also $z \in [x]$. That is, $[x] = [y]$. We have shown that $[x] = [y]$ if and only if $x \sim y$.

Suppose that $[x] \cap [y] \neq \varnothing$. We complete the proof of Proposition 3.2 by showing that $[x] = [y]$. Given that there is some z in both $[x]$ and $[y]$, then $x \sim z$ and $y \sim z$. By the previous paragraph, $[x] = [z]$ and $[y] = [z]$. Hence $[x] = [y]$. □

Theorem 3.3

Let $\sim$ be an equivalence relation on the set X. Then X is the union of nonempty, disjoint equivalence classes. This union is called an **equivalence class decomposition** of X.

Proof of Theorem 3.3

By Proposition 3.2, each element x of X appears in its own equivalence class $[x]$. So X *is* the union of the equivalence classes. Proposition 3.2 also says that equivalence classes either coincide or are disjoint. So choosing just one copy of each equivalence class gives a union of sets without common elements. ◇

Example 3.9

Let $\mathbb{Z}$ be the set of all integers. Let the equivalence relation for Theorem 3.3 be $\equiv$ mod 2. We wish to compute the equivalence class decomposition. As in Example 3.5, $x \equiv y \pmod 2$ requires that $\frac{x-y}{2} = \frac{x}{2} - \frac{y}{2}$ be an integer. However, in order for 2 to divide $x - y$ (without a remainder), the remainders for x and y after division by 2 must be the same. So we may reinterpret the relation $x \equiv y \pmod 2$ as requiring that x and y leave the same remainder after division by 2. The possible remainders after division by 2 are 0 and 1. Even numbers leave a remainder of 0 after division by 2, while odd numbers leave a remainder of 1. So all even numbers are equivalent to each other and all odd numbers are equivalent to each other. Since 0 is even, $[0]$ is the set of all even integers. Similarly, $[1]$ is the set of all odd integers. We write the equivalence class decomposition of $\mathbb{Z}$ as

$$\mathbb{Z} = [0] \cup [1] \tag{3.9}$$

In (3.9), we may replace 0 and 1 by any even and any odd integer, respectively. Thus the equivalence class decomposition may also be written

$$\mathbb{Z} = [6] \cup [-3]$$ △

Example 3.10

Let $X = \{1,2,3,4,5\}$. Let G be the group of permutations of X in Example 2.65. Recall that $G = \{e, (123), (132), (45), (123)(45), (132)(45)\}$. We compute the equivalence class decomposition for G-equivalence in Proposition 3.1. From the listing of elements in G,

$$1 \sim 1, \quad 1 \sim 2, \quad 1 \sim 3, \quad 1 \sim 1, \quad 1 \sim 2, \quad 1 \sim 3 \tag{3.10}$$

Eliminating the redundancies in (3.10) gives

$$[1] = \{1,2,3\} \tag{3.11}$$

Proposition 3.2 gives from (3.11), *without additional calculation*, that

$$[2] = [3] = \{1,2,3\}$$

Similarly, $[4]=[5]=\{4,5\}$. In all, the equivalence class decomposition is

$$X=\{1,2,3\}\cup\{4,5\} \tag{3.12}$$

Observe that (3.12) and Proposition 3.2 automatically give the equivalence class for each element. △

Example 3.11

Let us look at Figure 2.7, the symmetries of the square. Each symmetry is given by a permutation of the vertices. So we have a permutation group to which Proposition 3.1 applies. What are the equivalence classes? We start by computing $[G]$.

$$\begin{array}{llll} h_1(G)=G, & G\sim G & h_2(G)=H, & G\sim H \\ h_3(G)=I, & G\sim I & h_4(G)=J, & G\sim J \\ h_5(G)=H, & G\sim H & h_6(G)=J, & G\sim J \\ h_7(G)=I, & G\sim I & h_8(G)=G, & G\sim H \end{array}$$

So, eliminating duplications, $[G]=\{G,H,I,J\}$. Thus all of the vertices of the square are equivalent. Intuitively, this means that the square has no distinguished vertices. △

We may also apply Theorem 3.3 to the nonmathematical equivalence relations of (3.5): Equivalence according to eye color divides people into those with brown eyes, with blue eyes, with green eyes, etc. Equivalence according to sex divides people into men and women. Equivalence according to nativity divides people into those born in the United States, those born in Canada, etc.

This section concludes with a brief discussion of equivalence and sameness: If $\sim$ is an equivalence relation on X, then Proposition 3.2 says that $x\sim y$ if and only if x and y belong to the *same* equivalence class. Theorem 3.3 says that $\sim$ induces an equivalence class decomposition of X. Any decomposition of a set X into a union of nonempty, nonintersecting subsets is called a **partition** of X. Given a partition of X, an equivalence relation $\sim$ on X can be defined by: $x\sim y$ if x and y are elements of the *same* subset of the partition. The partition may be reconstructed from $\sim$ as the equivalence class decomposition.

Exercises 3.1

1. Let X be the set of all people. Tell whether or not each of the following relations on X is (i) reflexive, (ii) symmetric, (iii) transitive.
   a. x is a sister of y. (Do not consider a woman to be her own sister.)

b. x is a first cousin of y.

c. x is a blood relative of y; that is, x and y have a common ancestor.

d. x is a descendant of y. (Do not consider a person to be a descendant of himself.)

2. For each of the following sets X and permutation groups $(G,\circ)$ on X, give the equivalence class decomposition for G-equivalence from Proposition 3.1.

   a. $X=\{1,2,3,4\}$. $G=\{e, (12), (34), (12)(34)\}$.

   b. $X=\{1,2,3,4,5\}$. $G=\{e, (234), (243)\}$.

   c. $X=\{1,2,3,4,5,6\}$.
   $G=\{e, (123), (132), (45), (123)(45), (132)(45)\}$.

3. Find the equivalence class decomposition for $\mathbb{Z}$, the set of integers, under the equivalence relation $\equiv$ mod 3.

4. Does a rectangle have any distinguished vertices? Why?

5. Let $X=\{A,B,C,D\}$ be the vertices of a rhombus, as in Exercise 1(d) of Chapter 2, Section 2.1. Let $(G,\circ)$ be the group of symmetries of the rhombus.

   a. Find the G-equivalence class decomposition of X.

   b. Interpret part (a) geometrically.

6. Let R be a relation on a set X such that R is reflexive, symmetric, and antisymmetric. Show that R and $=$ are the same relation on X.

7. Find the error in the following argument that symmetry and transitivity imply reflexivity. Take x and y such that xRy. By symmetry, yRx. By transitivity, xRx.

8. Let g be a permutation of the finite set X, which has n elements. Let $\langle g\rangle$ be the subgroup of S_n generated by g. Show that the $\langle g\rangle$-equivalence class decomposition of X coincides with the cycles in the cycle decomposition for g.

9. Let $(G,\circ)$ be a group. Let x and y be elements of G. Say that x and y are conjugate, written $x\sim y$, if there is an element g of G such that $g\circ x\circ g^{-1}=y$.

   a. Show that conjugacy is an equivalence relation on G.

   b. If $(G,\circ)$ is commutative, show that for every x in G, $[x]$ consists only of x.

   c. Determine the conjugacy classes of elements in $(S_3,\circ)$.

10. Let $\mathbb{R}$ be the set of all real numbers. For x,y in $\mathbb{R}$, define $x\equiv y \pmod 1$ as requiring that $x-y$ be an integer.

   a. Show that $\equiv$ mod 1 is an equivalence relation on $\mathbb{R}$.

   b. Interpret $x\equiv y \pmod 1$ in terms of the fractional parts of x and y.

3.2 Lagrange's Theorem

This section is devoted to Lagrange's Theorem, an important application of the notion of equivalence to the theory of subgroups. In turn, Lagrange's Theorem is applied to group codes and to abstract group theory. Burnside's Theorem, as discussed in the next section, makes essential use of Lagrange's Theorem in its proof.

Example 3.12

Let $X=\{1,2,3\}$. Let $(S_3,\circ)$ be the group of permutations of X. Let $H=\{e,(12)\}$, a subset of S_3. It is then easily checked that $(H,\circ)$ is a subgroup of $(S_3,\circ)$. As will be explained later, $(H,\circ)$ yields an equivalence class decomposition of S_3 into the three equivalence classes: $H=\{e,(12)\}$, $\{(23),(132)\}$, and $\{(13),(123)\}$. Table 3.2 shows what this decomposition looks like in terms of the group composition table. Table 3.2 is the composition table for $(S_3,\circ)$. The vertical lines in Table 3.2 divide the top row into the equivalence classes. Observe that each box in Table 3.2 contains precisely one equivalence class. △

Table 3.2 Composition table for $(S_3,\circ)$

$\circ$	e	(12)	(23)	(132)	(13)	(123)
e	e	(12)	(23)	(132)	(13)	(123)
(12)	(12)	e	(123)	(13)	(132)	(23)
(23)	(23)	(132)	e	(12)	(123)	(13)
(132)	(132)	(23)	(13)	(123)	(12)	e
(13)	(13)	(123)	(132)	(23)	e	(12)
(123)	(123)	(13)	(12)	e	(23)	(132)

Example 3.13

Now we consider the group $(\mathbb{Z}_6,+)$ and the subgroup $(H,+)$ with $H=\{0,2,4\}$. This time H yields two equivalence classes: $H=\{0,2,4\}$ and $\{1,3,5\}$. Observe that, as in Example 3.12, the subgroup H is one of the equivalence classes. Table 3.3 gives the composition table for $(\mathbb{Z}_6,+)$ with the elements partitioned into equivalence classes. As in Table 3.2, each box in Table 3.3 contains precisely one equivalence class. △

Table 3.3 Composition table for $(\mathbb{Z}_6,+)$

	0	2	4	1	3	5
0	0	2	4	1	3	5
2	2	4	0	3	5	1
4	4	0	2	5	1	3
1	1	3	5	2	4	0
3	3	5	1	4	0	2
5	5	1	3	0	2	4

Observe that the equivalence classes in Table 3.2 all have two elements. Similarly, the equivalence classes in Table 3.3 both have three elements. Next the definition of the equivalence relation coming from a subgroup $(H,\circ)$ of a group $(G,\circ)$ will be given. We shall then show that all of the equivalence classes are the same size. This is the essence of the proof of Lagrange's Theorem.

Proposition 3.4

Let $(H,\circ)$ be a subgroup of the group $(G,\circ)$. Let $\sim$ be the relation on G such that $x\sim y$ if there is an element h of H such that $y=x\circ h$. Then $\sim$ is an equivalence relation.

Example 3.14

Before proving Proposition 3.4, we shall illustrate the relation $\sim$. Let $(G,\circ)$ be $(S_3,\circ)$, as given in Table 3.2. Let $H=\{e,(12)\}$, as in Example 3.12, and let us find [(23)], the equivalence class of (23). [(23)] consists of all elements equivalent to (23), so we look for elements of S_3 of the form $(23)\circ h$, with h in H. That is, we look in the (23)-row in Table 3.2 in the columns given by the elements of H:

$$(23)\circ e=(23) \text{ and } (23)\circ(12)=(132).\ [(23)]=\{(23),(132)\}$$

We find [(123)] by looking in the (123)-row of Table 3.2 in the e- and (12)-columns. $[(123)]=\{(123),(13)\}$. △

Proof of Proposition 3.4

We use the group theory of Chapter 2 to verify the conditions of Definition 3.3 and Definition 3.2.

Reflexivity. $x=x\circ e$. By Theorem 2.9, e is in H. So $x\sim x$.

Symmetry. $x\sim y$ implies that

$$\begin{aligned} x\circ h&=y, && \text{for } h \text{ in } H. \text{ Then}\\ x\circ h\circ h^{-1}&=y\circ h^{-1}, && \text{by composing with } h^{-1}\\ x\circ e&=y\circ h^{-1}, && \text{by the definition of } h^{-1}\\ x&=y\circ h^{-1}, && \text{by the definition of } e \end{aligned}$$

By Theorem 2.9, since h is in H, also h^{-1} is in H. So $y\sim x$.

Transitivity. Given that $x\sim y$ and $y\sim z$, there are elements h_1 and h_2 in H such that

$$y=x\circ h_1 \quad \text{and} \quad z=y\circ h_2$$

Substitution for y above gives $z=(x\circ h_1)\circ h_2=x\circ(h_1\circ h_2)$. Furthermore, $h_1\circ h_2$ is in H by the closure axiom. So also $x\sim z$. □

The standard notation for the equivalence classes in Proposition 3.4 differs from the previous [ ] notation as will be seen in Definition 3.5.

Definition 3.5

Let $(H,\circ)$ be a subgroup of the group $(G,\circ)$. Let g be an element of G. Then gH, the **left coset** of g with respect to H, consists of all elements in G of the form $g\circ h$, with h in H. That is, gH denotes the equivalence class of g under the equivalence relation of Proposition 3.4. ○

Right cosets are written Hg and are defined analogously. In this text, it will suffice to consider only left cosets. Of course, if $(G,\circ)$ is commutative, then $g\circ h=h\circ g$ and left and right cosets coincide. If $(G,+)$ is commutative and written with additive notation, cosets will be written as $g+H$, rather than as gH.

The equivalence class decomposition for the equivalence relation of Proposition 3.4 is called the **left coset decomposition** of G with respect to H. Observe that $H = eH$ is necessarily a coset.

Example 3.15

Let $(H, +)$ be the subgroup of $(\mathbb{Z}_6\ +)$ given by $H = \{0,2,4\}$. Let us compute the coset decomposition, as stated in Example 3.13.

Let us look at Table 3.3. Then $0 + H = \{0,2,4\}$. As observed above, this coset is just H. To continue the coset decomposition, we look for an element of H that is not in a previously found coset. Take the element 1, for instance. From Table 3.3, $1 + H = \{1,3,5\}$. $0 + H$ and $1 + H$ exhaust $\mathbb{Z}_6$, so the computation of the coset decomposition is complete as follows:

$$G = (0 + H) \cup (1 + H) = \{0,2,4\} \cup \{1,3,5\} \qquad \triangle$$

Example 3.16

Let $(H, +)$ be the subgroup of $(\mathbb{Z}, +)$ given by $H = \{\ldots, -9, -6, -3, 0, 3, 6, 9, 12, \ldots\}$; that is, H is all multiples of 3. Let us determine the coset decomposition of $\mathbb{Z}$ with respect to H.

$0 + H = H$ is one coset.

Take 1, which is not in H.

$$1 + H = \{\ldots, -5, -2, 1, 4, 7, \ldots\}$$

that is, all integers that leave a remainder of 1 upon division by 3.

Take 2, which is not in H or in $1 + H$. Then

$$2 + H = \{-4, -1, 2, 5, 8, \ldots\}$$

that is, all integers that leave a remainder of 2 upon division by 3.

The coset decomposition is $\mathbb{Z} = H \cup (1 + H) \cup (2 + H)$.

Observe that $\equiv$ mod 3 gives the same equivalence class decomposition. So, as may easily be checked directly, Proposition 3.4 and $\equiv$ mod 3 give the same equivalence relation. $\triangle$

Example 3.17

Let $(G, \circ)$ be the symmetries of the square, as given in Table 2.1. Let $(H, \circ)$ be the subgroup given by $H = \{h_1, h_6\}$. Let us determine the left coset decomposition.

$eH = H = \{h_1, h_6\}$ is one coset.

h_2 is not previously listed, so we compute its coset.

$$h_2 H = \{h_2, h_8\}$$

h_3 does not appear in the two previous cosets. $h_3 H = \{h_3, h_5\}$.

h_4 does not appear above. $h_4 H = \{h_4, h_7\}$.

All elements of G have now appeared in some listed coset. So we have determined that the left coset decomposition is $G = H \cup h_2H \cup h_3H \cup h_4H$. △

Observe in the above examples that all of the cosets in a given example are the same size. This is always so as is expressed by Proposition 3.5.

Proposition 3.5 Let $(H, \circ)$ be a subgroup of the group $(G, \circ)$. Let g be an element of G. There is a map $f: H \to gH$ given by $f(h) = g \circ h$. f is a one-to-one correspondence.

Example 3.18 Before proving Proposition 3.5, we shall illustrate the map f in its statement. We consider Example 3.12. Take, for instance, $g = (13)$. Then $(13)H = \{(13), (123)\}$ is just the box in Table 3.2 that is the (13)-row and the e- and (12)-columns. The map f from H to $(13)H$ is given by going from e and (12) in the outside row to their entries below in the $(13)H$ box:

$$f(e) = (13) \circ e = (13), \qquad f((12)) = (13) \circ (12) = (123)$$

△

Proof of Proposition 3.5 For h in H, $f(h)$ is defined as $f(h) = g \circ h$. We must establish that $g \circ h$ is in gH; however, this follows immediately from Definition 3.5.

Let us prove that f is one-to-one. Suppose that $f(h_1) = f(h_2)$; we need to show that $h_1 = h_2$. The equation $f(h_1) = f(h_2)$ implies that

$$g \circ h_1 = g \circ h_2$$

$$g^{-1} \circ g \circ h_1 = g^{-1} \circ g \circ h_2, \quad \text{by composing both sides with } g^{-1}$$

$$e \circ h_1 = e \circ h_2, \quad \text{by the definition of } g^{-1}$$

$$h_1 = h_2, \quad \text{by the definition of } e$$

Finally, we must see that f is onto. Since every element in gH is of the form $g \circ h$, for h in H, f is onto. □

Definition 3.6 Let $(G, \circ)$ be a group. The **order** of $(G, \circ)$, denoted by $|G|$, is the number of elements in G. If $|G|$ is not finite, G is said to have infinite order. ○

Examples 3.19

$$|\mathbb{Z}_6| = 6 \qquad |\mathbb{Z}_n| = n \qquad |S_3| = 6 \qquad |S_n| = n! \qquad |\mathbb{Z}_2 \times \mathbb{Z}_4| = 8$$

△

For a and b integers, we say that a *divides* b if $\frac{b}{a}$ is an integer. Thus 8 divides 24, 7 divides 35, but 4 does not divide 9.

Theorem 3.6 (*Lagrange's Theorem*) Let $(G,\circ)$ be a finite group. Let $(H,\circ)$ be a subgroup of $(G,\circ)$. Then $|H|$ divides $|G|$. $|G|/|H|$ equals the number of distinct cosets for H.

Example 3.20 We shall illustrate the proof of Theorem 3.6. Consider Example 3.12 and Table 3.2. The top row of Table 3.2 is partitioned into the cosets; $|H|=2$ and also each other coset has two elements. The three cosets exhaust G. So $|H|=2$ divides exactly three times into $|G|=6$. △

Proof of Theorem 3.6 By Proposition 3.4 and Theorem 3.3, G is partitioned into disjoint left cosets (or distinct right cosets). By Proposition 3.5, all cosets have $|H|$ elements. So $|G|/|H|$ is the integer equal to the number of cosets. ◇

Examples for Theorem 3.6 abound; look at Examples 3.15 and 3.17 for instance.

Cosets and Lagrange's Theorem provide a good framework for a reexamination of the group codes of Chapter 1. Recall that the set of all binary n-tuples forms the commutative group $(\mathbb{Z}_2{}^n,+)$. $|\mathbb{Z}_2{}^n|=2^n$. The code words of a group code form a subgroup $(H,+)$ of $(\mathbb{Z}_2{}^n,+)$. In Chapter 1, we constructed group codes via canonical parity check matrices. This gave group codes with 2^m code words. But suppose there were only 48 messages to encode. Forty-eight is not a power of 2. Could we perhaps find a group code, anyway, that has exactly 48 code words? No, because of the following easy argument using Lagrange's Theorem: let H be the code words of a group code. Then, by Lagrange's Theorem, $|H|$ divides 2^n, the order of $\mathbb{Z}_2{}^n$. But since 2^n is a prime power, the only divisors of 2^n are of the form 2^m, with $0 \le m \le n$. So, indeed, all group codes have 2^m code words.

Recall that $\mathbf{0}$, rather than e, denotes the identity element in $\mathbb{Z}_2{}^n$. Let $\mathbf{e}$ be a transmission error; try to correct it. Let $\mathbf{c}$ be a transmitted code word. Then $\mathbf{c}+\mathbf{e}=\mathbf{e}+\mathbf{c}$ is the received n-tuple. As $\mathbf{c}$ varies, $\mathbf{e}+\mathbf{c}$ varies over $\mathbf{e}+H$, the coset of $\mathbf{e}$. That is, the transmission error $\mathbf{e}$ determines the coset of the received n-tuple. So a single-error-correcting code should have cosets that correspond to different single transmission errors. For canonical parity check matrices, it can be shown that cosets correspond to syndromes. So the analysis in Chapter 1 of group codes in terms of syndromes could be redone in terms of cosets.

This section concludes with two easy applications of Lagrange's Theorem to group theory.

Theorem 3.7 Let g be an element of the finite group $(G,\circ)$. Then the order of g, as defined in Theorem 2.11, divides $|G|$.

Examples 3.21 Before proving Theorem 3.7, we shall illustrate its statement. As in Example 2.42, $(1,1)$ has order 4 in $\mathbb{Z}_2 \times \mathbb{Z}_4$. $|\mathbb{Z}_2 \times \mathbb{Z}_4|=8$. Four divides 8. △

In S_3, (12) has order 2. $|S_3|=6$. Two divides 6. △

Proof of Theorem 3.7

As in Theorem 2.12, let $\langle g\rangle$ be the subgroup generated by g. By Theorems 2.11 and 2.12, $|\langle g\rangle|$ equals the order of g. By Theorem 3.6, $|\langle g\rangle|$ divides $|G|$. ◇

Theorem 3.8

Let $(G,\circ)$ be a group such that $|G|$ is a prime number. Let g be an element of G other than the identity. Then $(G,\circ)$ is a cyclic group with g as a generator. So all groups with the same prime order are isomorphic.

Example 3.22

We shall illustrate the statement of Theorem 3.8 before giving its proof. Let $(G,\circ)$ be $(\mathbb{Z}_7,+)$. Let $g=4$. We compute $\langle 4\rangle$: in $(\mathbb{Z}_7,+)$,

$$4=4 \qquad 2\cdot 4=1 \qquad 3\cdot 4=5 \qquad 4\cdot 4=2$$

$$5\cdot 4=6 \qquad 6\cdot 4=3 \qquad 7\cdot 4=0 \qquad \text{Stop}$$

So $\langle 4\rangle=\{4,1,5,2,6,3,0\}=\{0,1,2,3,4,5,6\}=\mathbb{Z}_7$. △

Proof of Theorem 3.8

By Theorem 3.6, $|\langle g\rangle|$ divides $|G|$. Since $|G|$ is given to be a prime number, its only divisors are 1 and $|G|$. So either (i) $|\langle g\rangle|=1$ or (ii) $|\langle g\rangle|=|G|$. Since g is not the identity, case (i) is excluded. So $|\langle g\rangle|=|G|$ and $\langle g\rangle=G$. ◇

Exercises 3.2

1. Let $(G,\circ)$ be the group given by the composition table below. Let $(H,\circ)$ be the subgroup given by $H=\{e,c\}$.

	e	a	b	c
e	e	a	b	c
a	a	e	c	b
b	b	c	e	a
c	c	b	a	e

   Let $\sim$ be the relation of Proposition 3.4. Determine which of the following are true.

   a. $a\sim b$ b. $a\sim c$ c. $b\sim e$ d. $b\sim c$
2. Verify the left coset decomposition of Example 3.12.
3. Let $(H,+)$ be the subgroup of $(\mathbb{Z}_2\times\mathbb{Z}_4,+)$ given by $H=\{(0,0),(1,2)\}$. Compute the coset decomposition of $\mathbb{Z}_2\times\mathbb{Z}_4$ with respect to H.

4. Let $(G,\circ)$ be the group of Table 2.1. Let $(H,\circ)$ be the subgroup given by $H=\{h_1,h_3\}$. Give the left coset decomposition of G with respect to H.

5. Let $G=(\mathbb{Z}_4,+)$. Let $H=\{0,1\}$. Observe that H is not a subgroup of $\mathbb{Z}_4$. Show that the relation of Proposition 3.4, which may still be defined, is not an equivalence relation in this case.

6. Let $(H,\circ)$ be a subgroup of the group $(G,\circ)$. Let x and y be elements of G. Let $\sim$ be the equivalence relation of Proposition 3.4. Show that $x\sim y$ if and only if $x^{-1}\circ y$ is an element of H.

7. Let $(H,\circ)$ be the subgroup of $(S_4,\circ)$ given by $H=\{e,(1234),(13)(24),(1432)\}$. Let $\sim$ be the relation of Proposition 3.4. Using Exercise 6, determine whether or not the following are true.

   a. $(14)\sim(1342)$ b. $(123)\sim(234)$

   c. $(12)(34)\sim(23)$ d. $(14)\sim(123)$

8. Let $(H,\circ)$ be a subgroup of the finite group $(G,\circ)$ such that $|H|=\frac{1}{2}|G|$. What must be the coset decomposition of G with respect to H?

9. a. Define right cosets.

   b. Give an equivalence relation, similar to that of Proposition 3.4, such that the equivalence classes equal the right cosets.

   c. Compute the right coset decomposition of S_3 with respect to $H=\{e,(12)\}$.

   d. Is the right coset decomposition of part (c) the same as the left coset decomposition of Example 3.12?

10. Let $(H,\circ)$ be a subgroup of $(G,\circ)$. Let g and a be elements of G.

    a. Show that the map $f:aH\rightarrow(g\circ a)H$ given by $f(a\circ h)=g\circ a\circ h$ is a one-to-one correspondence.

    b. Using part (a), explain why the boxes in Tables 3.2 and 3.3 each contain precisely one coset.

11. Let a group code have $(0\quad 0\quad 0)$ and $(1\quad 1\quad 1)$ as code words.

    a. Compute the coset decomposition of $\mathbb{Z}_2{}^3$ with respect to $H=\{(0\quad 0\quad 0),(1\quad 1\quad 1)\}$.

    b. Tell to which single transmission error, if any, each coset corresponds.

12. Let $(H,+)$ be the code words of a group code. Let $g+H$ be a coset in $\mathbb{Z}_2{}^n$. An element of $g+H$ of smallest weight is called a **coset leader**. There may be more than one coset leader. An n-tuple g is received. Explain why the coset leaders of $g+H$ are the most likely transmission errors.

13. Suppose that a finite group $(G,\circ)$ has an element g with order 5 and an element h with order 7. Show that $|G|\geq 35$.

3.3 Burnside's Theorem

A typical combinatorial problem is to count the number of ways of doing something such as painting the faces of a cube. This section introduces Burnside's Theorem, which is a first step towards sophisticated counting techniques.

Example 3.23

We count the number of G-equivalence classes for an example for Proposition 3.1. Let $X=\{1,2,3,4,5,6\}$. Let $(G,\circ)$ be the permutation group on X that consists of the following permutations:

$$e, (12)(3456), (35)(46), (12)(3654)$$

These permutations take 1 to 1, 2, 1, and 2 respectively. So the G-equivalence class of 1 is $[1]=\{1,2\}$. Similarly, $[3]=\{3,4,5,6\}$. This exhausts X, so we have two G-equivalence classes. △

A **switching function** of n variables is a function from all binary n-tuples to the set $\{0,1\}$ of binary 1-tuples. The set of all switching functions of n variables is denoted by $\mathscr{F}_n$. The reason for the name "switching function" is as follows: Suppose that, as in Figure 3.3, there is an electronic circuit that accepts n binary inputs and produces one binary output. The output should depend only on the input; that is, the circuit has no memory. Then the external workings of the circuit are described mathematically as a switching function of n variables. One way of describing the internal structure of the circuit will be given in the chapter on Boolean algebras. Sometimes a switching function is also called a **Boolean function**.

There are 2^n binary n-tuples. A switching function can take one of two values for each binary n-tuple. So there are 2^{2^n} switching functions of n variables. That is, there are essentially 2^{2^n} different black boxes for Figure 3.3. For $n=2$, there are $2^{2^2}=2^4=16$ switching functions. These are listed in Table 3.4. For $n=3$, there are $2^{2^3}=2^8=256$ switching functions. For $n=4$, there are $2^{2^4}=2^{16}=65{,}536$ switching functions.

Large electronic circuits are often constructed by combining smaller circuits, or modules. Each module implements a switching function of a small number of variables. Sometimes, one module can replace another module at little additional cost. For example, in Figure 3.4, the module that acts as $f(x,y)$ can also act as $f(y,x)$ by simply reversing the inputs. For general n, allowing permutations of the inputs greatly reduces the number

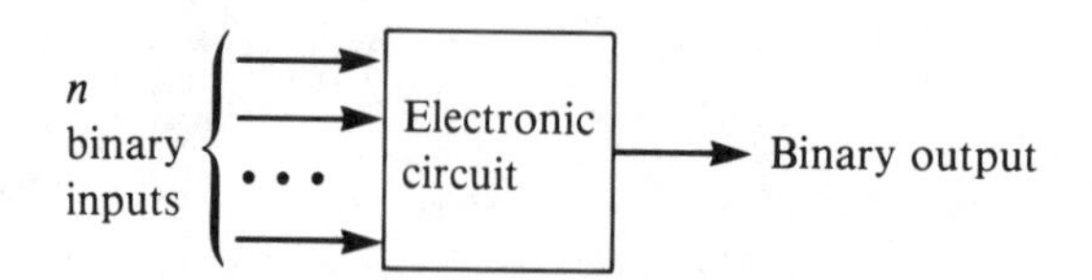

Figure 3.3 Black box switching circuit

Table 3.4 Switching functions of two variables, x and y

x	y	f_0	f_1	f_2	f_3	f_4	f_5	f_6	f_7	f_8	f_9	f_{10}	f_{11}	f_{12}	f_{13}	f_{14}	f_{15}
0	0	0	0	0	0	0	0	0	0	1	1	1	1	1	1	1	1
0	1	0	0	0	0	1	1	1	1	0	0	0	0	1	1	1	1
1	0	0	0	1	1	0	0	1	1	0	0	1	1	0	0	1	1
1	1	0	1	0	1	0	1	0	1	0	1	0	1	0	1	0	1

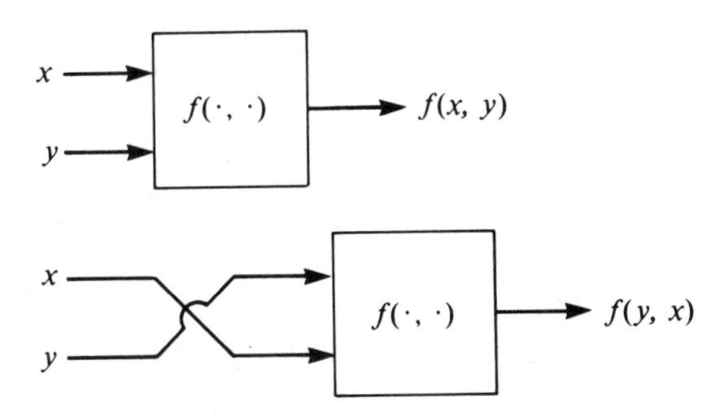

Figure 3.4 Permuting inputs

of *different* kinds of modules with n inputs that are needed to build a large circuit. Additional low-cost techniques for reducing the needed number of different modules are also available. The actual computation of which modules are needed is already very long for $n=4$. Only $n=2$ will be discussed in some detail, but the techniques are applicable for all n.

Example 3.24

Let $\mathscr{F}_2$ be the set of all switching functions of the two variables x and y. Say that two switching functions f and g are equivalent if g can be obtained from f via a permutation of the variables x and y. That is, if $g(x,y)=f(y,x)$, then $g \sim f$ via the permutation (xy). Observe that $f \sim f$ via the identity permutation. Let us determine all equivalence classes of switching functions. In terms of electronic circuits, equivalent switching functions may replace each other as in Figure 3.4.

Each permutation of the variables induces a permutation of $\mathscr{F}_2$. It is easy to see that these permutations form a group $(G,\circ)$ of permutations and so give a G-equivalence relation in the sense of Proposition 3.1. The elements of $\mathscr{F}_2$ are named in Table 3.4. The identity permutation on the variables gives the identity permutation on $\mathscr{F}_2$. The permutation (xy) on the variables gives the permutation

$$g=(f_0)(f_1)(f_2f_4)(f_3f_5)(f_6)(f_7)(f_8)(f_9)(f_{10}f_{12})(f_{11}f_{13})(f_{14})(f_{15})$$

of $\mathscr{F}_2$. Then the G-equivalence class decomposition of $\mathscr{F}_2$ is just the cycle decomposition of g, as above. There are 12 equivalence classes.

Of course, solving the problem of this example does not require as formal an argument as we used. However, we will need this type of argument in more complicated problems. △

$\mathscr{F}_3$ has 256 elements. So asking, as in Example 3.24, for equivalence classes via permutations of the variables is too long a problem for an easy hand-calculation with current techniques. Even the following example about $\mathscr{F}_2$, which we only start, requires a long calculation with current techniques. Burnside's Theorem, however, will later provide an easy method for the computation of the number of equivalence classes.

Example 3.25

Another way to reduce the number of different modules needed to realize all switching functions, is to apply *inverters*, or *NOT gates*, to the variables; an **inverter** exchanges the two possible values for a bit. Let x denote an input variable. Let x' denote the inverted input variable. So when $x=0$, $x'=1$; when $x=1$, $x'=0$. Using the notation of Table 3.4, if $g(x,y)=f_3(x',y)$, then g has the values

$$g(0,0)=f_3(1,0)=1$$
$$g(0,1)=f_3(1,1)=1$$
$$g(1,0)=f_3(0,0)=0$$
$$g(1,1)=f_3(0,1)=0$$

From Table 3.4, we see that $f_3(x',y)=g(x,y)=f_{12}(x,y)$. Figure 3.5 gives the standard circuit notation for an inverter.

How many different switching functions of two variables are needed to yield all of $\mathscr{F}_2$ if the input variables may be both permuted and inverted? We shall answer this question in Example 3.36 later in the chapter. △

Definition 3.7

Let $(G,\circ)$ be a group of permutations on the set X. Let g be an element of G. The **fixed-point-set** of g in X, denoted by X_g, consists of all elements x in X such that $g(x)=x$.

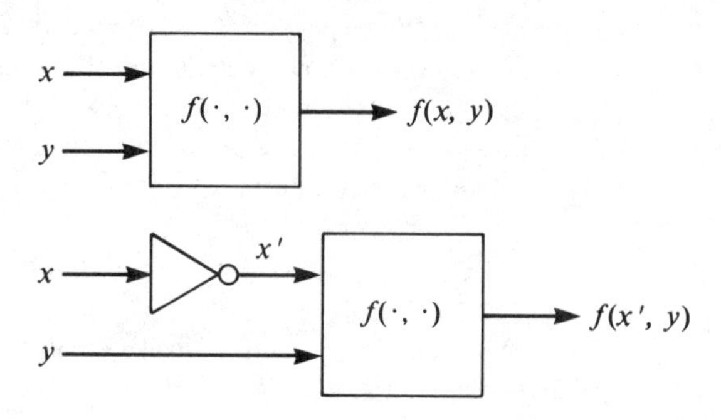

Figure 3.5 Inverting an input

Let x be an element of X. The **stabilizer** of x, denoted by G_x, is the set of all elements g in G such that $g(x) = x$. ○

Observe in Definition 3.7 that a group element g of G yields a subset X_g of X. Similarly, a set element x in X yields a subset G_x of G. We shall see in Proposition 3.9, which follows shortly, that G_x is in fact a sub*group* of G.

Example 3.26

Let X and $(G, \circ)$ be as in Example 3.23. We compute the fixed-point-sets and the stabilizers.

$$X_e = X, \quad X_{(12)(3456)} = \varnothing, \quad X_{(35)(46)} = \{1,2\}, \quad X_{(12)(3654)} = \varnothing$$

Observe that the fixed-point-set for a permutation is just its cycles with one element. For instance, from above, $(35)(46) = (1)(2)(35)(46)$ and $X_{(35)(46)} = \{1,2\}$.

Here are the stabilizers. Observe that they are indeed subgroups of G.

$$G_1 = G_2 = \{e, (35)(46)\}$$

$$G_3 = G_4 = G_5 = G_6 = \{e\}$$ △

Proposition 3.9

Let $(G, \circ)$ be a group of permutations on the set X. Let x be an element of X. Then G_x is a subgroup of G.

Proof of Proposition 3.9

We apply Theorem 2.10. The identity permutation, e, is always in G_x. To verify condition (i) of Theorem 2.10, we consider permutations g and h in G_x. Then $g(x) = x$ and $h(x) = x$. So

$$(g \circ h)(x) = g(h(x)) = g(x) = x$$

Thus $g \circ h$ is also in G_x.

Now we consider g in G_x; $g(x) = x$. Since g is a one-to-one correspondence, $x = g^{-1}(x)$. So also g^{-1} is in G_x. This verifies Theorem 2.10(ii). □

As in the previous section for groups, we use $|\ \ |$ to denote the number of elements in a set. Thus $|X_g|$ denotes the number of elements in the fixed-point-set of g. $|[x]|$ denotes the number of elements in the G-equivalence class of x.

Proposition 3.10

Let $(G, \circ)$ be a group of permutations on the set X. Let x be an element of X. Then

$$|G| = |[x]| \cdot |G_x|$$

Example 3.27

Before proving Proposition 3.10, we shall illustrate its statement. Consider Example 3.23 and Example 3.26. In these examples $|G|=4$. Consider $x=1$.

$$|[1]|=|\{1,2\}|=2 \quad \text{and} \quad |G_1|=|\{e,(35)(46)\}|=2$$

$4=2\cdot 2$, as required by Proposition 3.10. △

Proof of Proposition 3.10

By Lagrange's Theorem, $|G|/|G_x|$ equals the number of left cosets of G with respect to G_x. We shall prove Proposition 3.10 by giving a one-to-one correspondence f between the set of left cosets and the elements of $[x]$.

Let gG_x be a left coset. We wish to define f by $f(gG_x)=g(x)$. To see that f is even defined, we must check that $g(x)$ is independent of the choice g made for the element of gG_x. Any element of gG_x can be written in the form $g\circ s$, with s in G_x. Then

$$(g\circ s)(x)=g(s(x))=g(x)$$

since s is in the stabilizer of x. So f is defined independently of the choice of the element in the coset. The definition of G-equivalence gives $x\sim g(x)$. So the image of f is in $[x]$, as desired.

We shall now show that f is a one-to-one correspondence. Let g_1G_x and g_2G_x be cosets such that $f(g_1G_x)=f(g_2G_x)$. Then $g_1(x)=g_2(x)$. Applying $g_2{}^{-1}$ to both sides gives $(g_2{}^{-1}\circ g_1)(x)=(g_2{}^{-1}\circ g_2)(x)=e(x)=x$. So $g_2{}^{-1}\circ g_1$ fixes x and so is in G_x. Let s denote $g_2{}^{-1}\circ g_1$. Then $s=g_2{}^{-1}\circ g_1$.

$$g_2\circ s=g_2\circ g_2{}^{-1}\circ g_1=e\circ g_1=g_1$$

So $g_2\sim g_1$. Then, since cosets are equivalence classes, $g_1G_x=g_2G_x$. That is, f is one-to-one.

Suppose that $x\sim y$. Then there exists g in G such that $y=g(x)$. Then $f(gG_x)=g(x)=y$. So f is onto. So f is the desired one-to-one correspondence. □

Example 3.28

Let $X=\{1,2,3,4,5\}$. Let $(G,\circ)$ consist of the following permutations on X:

$$e,\ (13),\ (13)(25),\ (25)$$

Table 3.5 gives $[x]$, $|[x]|$, G_x, and $|G_x|$ for each x in X. We observe that, as required by Proposition 3.10, $|[x]|\cdot|G_x|=4=|G|$ for all x. △

Theorem 3.11

(*Burnside's Theorem*) Let $(G,\circ)$ be a group of permutations on the set X. Let k denote the number of G-equivalence classes. Then

$$k=\frac{1}{|G|}\sum|X_g|$$

Table 3.5 Proposition 3.10 for Example 3.28

x	$[x]$	$\lvert [x] \rvert$	G_x	$\lvert G_x \rvert$
1	$\{1,3\}$	2	$\{e, (25)\}$	2
2	$\{2,5\}$	2	$\{e, (13)\}$	2
3	$\{1,3\}$	2	$\{e, (25)\}$	2
4	$\{4\}$	1	G	4
5	$\{2,5\}$	2	$\{e, (13)\}$	2

where the sum $\sum$ is taken over all elements g of G, and X_g is the fixed-point-set of g.

Before proving Theorem 3.11, we shall illustrate both its statement and its proof.

Example 3.29

We continue with Examples 3.23 and 3.26. From Example 3.23, it is known that $k=2$. In Table 3.6, for each element g of G, we list X_g and $|X_g|$. Adding up the $|X_g|$ column gives 8.

$$|G|=4$$

$8/4=2=k$, as required by Theorem 3.11. △

Table 3.6 Computation for Burnside's theorem

g	X_g	$\lvert X_g \rvert$
e	X	6
(12)(3456)	$\varnothing$	0
(35)(46)	$\{1,2\}$	2
(12)(3654)	$\varnothing$	0

Example 3.30

We shall illustrate the counting argument, which will be used in the proof of Theorem 3.11. We continue with Examples 3.23 and 3.26. Table 3.7 lists

Table 3.7 Stabilizers

x	G_x	$\lvert G_x \rvert$
1	$\{e, (35)(46)\}$	2
2	$\{e, (35)(46)\}$	2
3	$\{e\}$	1
4	$\{e\}$	1
5	$\{e\}$	1
6	$\{e\}$	1

each element x of X, G_x, and $|G_x|$. Observe that the sum of the $|G_x|$ column in Table 3.7 is 8, the same as the sum of the $|X_g|$ column in Table 3.6. △

Proof of Theorem 3.11

There are two ways to count all of the fixed points of all of the elements of G. First, we may count the fixed points $|X_g|$ for each g in G and then add up the $|X_g|$. Alternatively, we may count the group elements $|G_x|$ that fix a point x in X and then add up the $|G_x|$. The two methods must give the same answer. So

$$\sum_{g \in G} |X_g| = \sum_{x \in X} |G_x| \tag{3.13}$$

Let us examine the sum on the right side of (3.13). By Proposition 3.10,

$$|G_x| = |G|/|[x]| \tag{3.14}$$

Suppose that $x \sim y$. Then $[x]=[y]$. So also $|[x]|=|[y]|$. Hence from (3.14), $|G_x|=|G_y|$. The number of y's that are equivalent to x equals $|[x]|$. So summing (3.14) over the equivalence class of x gives $|[x]|$ equal summands as follows:

$$\sum_{y \in [x]} |G_y| = \sum_{y \in [x]} |G_x| = \sum_{y \in [x]} |G|/|[x]| = |[x]| \cdot |G|/|[x]| = |G| \tag{3.15}$$

(3.15) says that each equivalence class of elements in X contributes all together the sum $|G|$ towards the sum in the right side of (3.13). The number of equivalence classes is k. So the right side of (3.13) equals $k \cdot |G|$. So also the left side of (3.13) equals $k \cdot |G|$:

$$\sum_{g \in G} |X_g| = k \cdot |G| \tag{3.16}$$

Solving (3.16) for k gives Theorem 3.11. ◇

Example 3.31

Let us apply Burnside's Theorem to count the number of different, or inequivalent, ways that the vertices of a square may be colored with the two colors *White* and *Red*. We say that two colorings are equivalent if a symmetry of the square changes one to the other. Figure 3.6, for instance, shows colorings that are equivalent via a reflection.

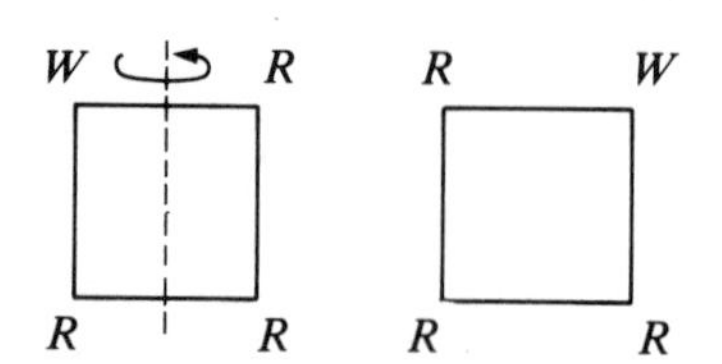

Figure 3.6 Equivalent colorings

The symmetries of the square are listed in Figure 2.7. The set of vertices is $X=\{G,H,I,J\}$. The permutations of the vertices are given by

$$\begin{array}{ll} h_1=e & h_2=(GHIJ) \\ h_3=(GI)(HJ) & h_4=(GJIH) \\ h_5=(GH)(IJ) & h_6=(GJ)(HI) \\ h_7=(GI) & h_8=(HJ) \end{array} \tag{3.17}$$

Let $(H,\circ)$ denote the group of permutations given in (3.17). Let $\mathscr{F}$ be the set of functions from the set X of vertices to the set $Y=\{W,R\}$ of colors. Each h in (3.17) induces a permutation h' of $\mathscr{F}$ given formally by

$$\text{for } f \text{ in } \mathscr{F}, \quad h'(f)=f\circ h \tag{3.18}$$

For example, in Figure 3.6, the reflection is h_5. (3.18) becomes

$$\begin{array}{rcccc} h_5: & G\to H & H\to G & I\to J & J\to I \\ f: & G\to W & H\to R & I\to R & J\to R \\ h'(f)=f\circ h_5: & G\to R & H\to W & I\to R & J\to R \end{array}$$

The set of all such h' is a permutation group G on $\mathscr{F}$. We are looking for the number of G-equivalence classes.

To apply Burnside's Theorem, we compute the $|\mathscr{F}_{h'}|$. The identity is e. So e' is also the identity. Then

$$\mathscr{F}_{e'}=\mathscr{F} \quad \text{and} \quad |\mathscr{F}|=2^4=16$$

$\mathscr{F}_{(GHIJ)'}$ consists of all f in $\mathscr{F}$ Such that f is unchanged via the permutation $G\to H$, $H\to I$, $I\to J$, $J\to K$. That is, $f(G)=f(H)$, $f(H)=f(I)$, $f(I)=f(J)$, $f(J)=f(G)$. That is, f is constant. The map f may be constantly W or constantly R. So $|\mathscr{F}_{(GHIJ)'}|=2$.

We look at $\mathscr{F}_{(GI)(HJ)'}$. A map f in $\mathscr{F}_{(GI)(HJ)'}$ must have the same value on G and I, as well as the same value on H and J. There are two independent choices for each value. So $|\mathscr{F}_{(GI)(HJ)'}|=2\cdot 2=4$.

The computation for $|\mathscr{F}_{(GJIH)'}|$ is the same as for $|\mathscr{F}_{(GHIJ)'}|$. The values $|\mathscr{F}_{(GH)(IJ)'}|$ and $|\mathscr{F}_{(GJ)(HI)'}|$ are computed as was $|\mathscr{F}_{(GI)(HJ)'}|$. The computations for $|\mathscr{F}_{(GI)'}|$ and $|\mathscr{F}_{(HJ)'}|$ are the same; we do $|\mathscr{F}_{(GI)'}|$. An f in $\mathscr{F}_{(GI)'}$ must have the same value on G and I, yielding two choices. There are no restrictions on the values of f in $\mathscr{F}_{(GI)'}$ for H and J; yielding two choices in each case. In all, $|\mathscr{F}_{(GI)'}|=|\mathscr{F}_{(HJ)'}|=2\cdot 2\cdot 2=8$.

Applying Burnside's Theorem to the h' corresponding to (3.17):

$$k=\frac{1}{8}(16+2+4+2+4+4+8+8)=6 \qquad \triangle$$

It is convenient to formalize the counting argument used in Example 3.31. We leave the proof of the following Proposition as an exercise.

Proposition 3.12

Let $\mathscr{F}$ be the set of all functions from the set X to the set Y. Let g be a permutation of X. Then g induces the following permutation g' of $\mathscr{F}$:

$$\text{for } f \text{ in } \mathscr{F}, \quad g'(f) = f \circ g$$

Let c be the number of cycles in the cycle decomposition of g. Then

$$|\mathscr{F}_{g'}| = |Y|^c \qquad \diamond$$

Example 3.32

Let $X = \{1,2,3,4,5,6,7\}$. Let $Y = \{A,B,C\}$. Also let $g = (13)(245) = (13)(245)(6)(7)$. Then $c = 4$. Any f in $\mathscr{F}_{g'}$ must have the same value on each cycle in g. There are $|Y| = 3$ choices for this same value. So $|\mathscr{F}_{g'}| = 3^4 = 81$. △

Example 3.33

In how many different ways can we color the vertices of a square using three different colors? We proceed as in Example 3.31. The cycle decompositions of the symmetries are given in (3.17). In Example 3.33, $|Y| = 3$, rather than 2, as in Example 3.31. By Burnside's Theorem and Proposition 3.12, the answer is

$$\frac{1}{8}(3^4 + 3^1 + 3^2 + 3^1 + 3^2 + 3^2 + 3^3 + 3^3) = 21 \qquad \triangle$$

Example 3.34

In how many different ways can we color the faces of a cube using two different colors? To apply Burnside's Theorem and Proposition 3.12, we must find the symmetries of the cube and list them by their cycle decompositions. Omitting details, there are 48 symmetries of the cube, 24 of which are reflections. We shall not consider the reflections in this problem since they may not be realized by a physical movement. Figure 3.7 gives a numbering of the faces of a cube. With this numbering, the 24

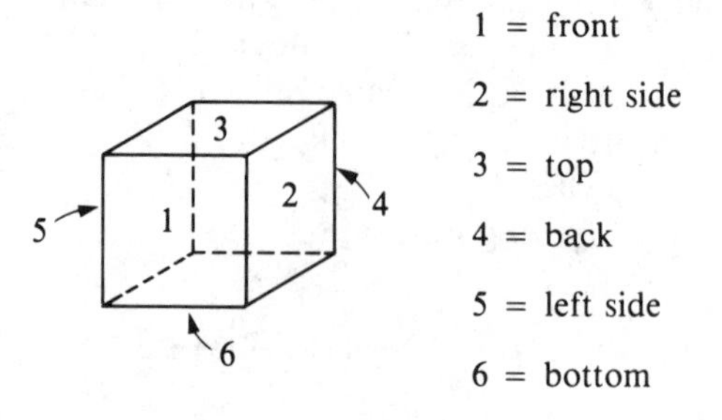

Figure 3.7 The faces of the cube

Figure 3.8 The physical symmetries of the cube

e
This is the identity map.

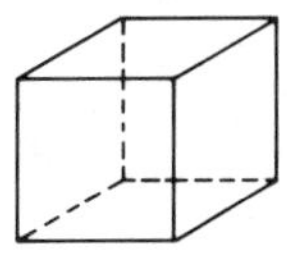

(1245), (14)(52), (1542)
These are rotations of 90°, 180°, and 270° about a vertical axis, as shown. There are similar rotations about axes through the centers of faces 1,4 and faces 2,5.

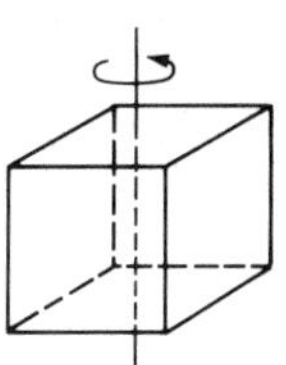

(14)(26)(35)
This is a rotation of 180° about the shown axis. There are five other similar rotations about the axes through the centers of opposite edges.

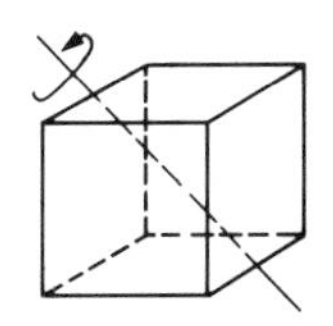

(135)(246), (153)(264)
These are rotations of 120° and 240° about the shown axis. There are three other similar axes through opposite vertices.

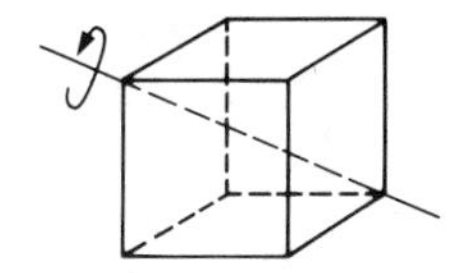

(physical) symmetries of the cube may be described for our purposes in Figure 3.8.

The symmetry e has $|\mathscr{F}_{e'}| = 2^6$

The symmetries (1245) and (1542) have $|\mathscr{F}_{(1245)'}| = |\mathscr{F}_{(1542)'}| = 2^3$. There are $2 \cdot 3 = 6$ such symmetries.

The symmetry (14)(52) has $|\mathscr{F}_{(14)(52)'}| = 2^4$. There are three such symmetries.

$|\mathscr{F}_{(14)(26)(35)'}| = 2^3$. There are six such symmetries.

$|\mathscr{F}_{(135)(246)'}| = 2^2$. There are eight such symmetries.

In all, there are just

$$\frac{1}{24}(2^6 + 6 \cdot 2^3 + 3 \cdot 2^4 + 6 \cdot 2^3 + 8 \cdot 2^2) = 10$$

inequivalent colorings of the faces of the cube using two colors. △

Example 3.35

How many different switching functions are there of the three variables (x, y, z) if we consider a permutation of the variables as giving an equivalent function?

Observe that a permutation of $\{x, y, z\}$ is *not* a permutation of the type in Proposition 3.12 because a function f in $\mathscr{F}_3$ is a function from the *set of values* for (x,y,z) and not a function from the *set* $\{x,y,z\}$. For example, we consider the permutation (xyz) on the set $\{x,y,z\}$. Figure 3.9 illustrates its effect on $\mathscr{F}_3$; the function $f(x,y,z)$ is permuted to the function $f(z,x,y)$. In terms of the composition of maps, we may see this as follows: Think of (xyz) as the map

$$\begin{pmatrix} x & y & z \\ Y & Z & X \end{pmatrix} \tag{3.19}$$

where x,y,z are the independent variables and X,Y,Z are the dependent variables. Then (3.19) may also be written

$$X=z, \quad Y=x, \quad Z=y \tag{3.20}$$

Thus composing the function $f(X,Y,Z)$ with (3.20) gives $f(z,x,y)$.

In terms of input values, the permutation (xyz) permutes, say, $(0,0,1)$ to $(1,0,0)$. This may be seen either from Figure 3.9 or from (3.20). Similarly, (xyz) permutes $(1,0,0)$ to $(0,1,0)$ and $(0,1,0)$ back to $(0,0,1)$. Let X be the set of values for the binary 3-tuple (x,y,z). We have just computed a cycle in the cycle decomposition of the permutation on X that corresponds to (xyz).

A compact notation for X is $X=\{0,1,2,3,4,5,6,7\}$ with

$$\begin{array}{llll} 0\to(0,0,0) & 1\to(0,0,1) & 2\to(0,1,0) & 3\to(0,1,1) \\ 4\to(1,0,0) & 5\to(1,0,1) & 6\to(1,1,0) & 7\to(1,1,1) \end{array}$$

The six permutations of $\{x,y,z\}$ then correspond to the following permutations of X:

$$\begin{aligned} e &\to e \\ (xy) &\to (0)(1)(24)(35)(6)(7) \\ (xz) &\to (0)(14)(2)(36)(5)(7) \\ (yz) &\to (0)(12)(3)(4)(56)(7) \\ (xyz) &\to (0)(142)(356)(7) \\ (xzy) &\to (0)(124)(365)(7) \end{aligned} \tag{3.21}$$

$\mathscr{F}_3$ may be thought of as all functions from X to $Y=\{0,1\}$. Equivalence is via the permutation group in (3.21). So there are

$$\frac{1}{6}(2^8+3\cdot 2^6+2\cdot 2^4)=80$$

essentially different switching functions of three variables. △

Figure 3.9 Permuting the inputs via (xyz)

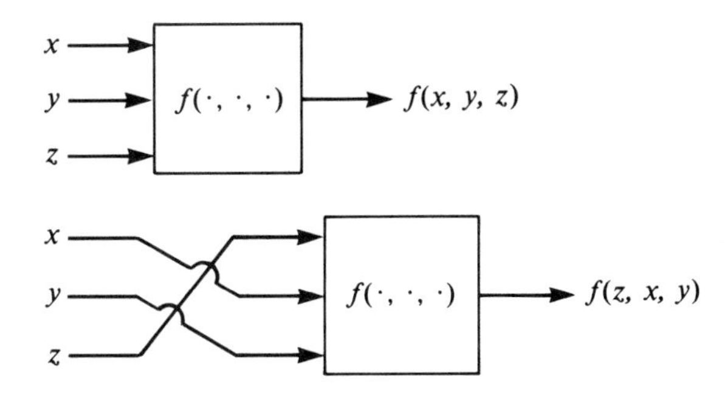

Figure 3.10 Permuting and inverting inputs

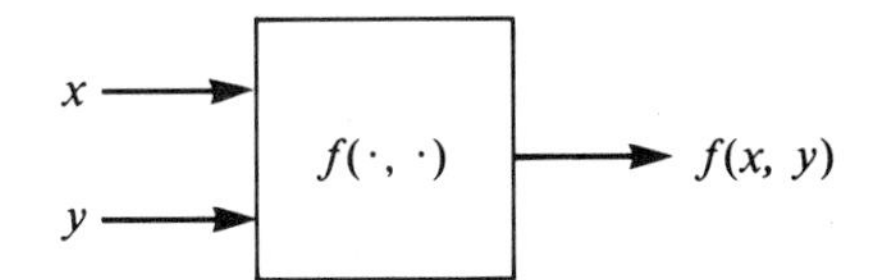

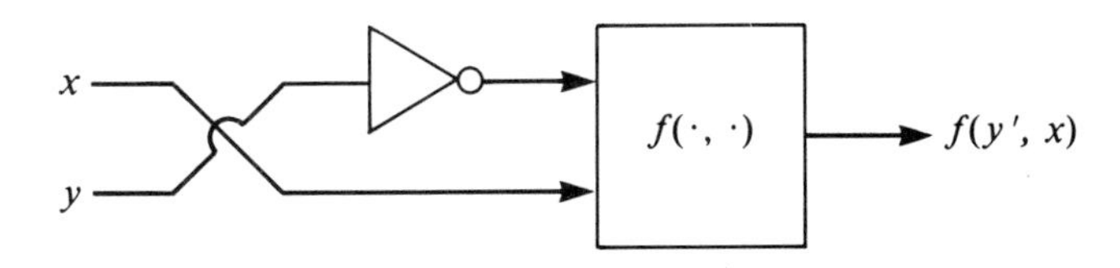

Example 3.36

Now we shall complete Example 3.25, the computation of the number of equivalence classes of functions in $\mathscr{F}_2$ via both permutations and inversions of the variables (x,y). Figure 3.10 shows the effect of first permuting the input variables and then inverting the (new) first variable. In the notation corresponding to that of (3.20), Figure 3.10 corresponds to

$$X = y' \qquad Y = x$$

For example, Figure 3.10 permutes the input (1,0) to (1,1) and (1,1) is permuted to (0,1).

Let X be the set of values for the binary 2-tuple (x,y). $X = \{0,1,2,3\}$ with

$$0 \to (0,0) \qquad 1 \to (0,1) \qquad 2 \to (1,0) \qquad 3 \to (1,1)$$

The allowed permutations and inversions of (x,y) yield the following permutations of X:

$$
\begin{aligned}
&X=x,\ \ Y=y \rightarrow e\\
&X=x',\ Y=y \rightarrow (02)(13)\\
&X=x,\ \ Y=y' = (01)(23)\\
&X=x',\ Y=y' \rightarrow (03)(12)\\
&X=y,\ \ Y=x \rightarrow (12)\\
&X=y',\ Y=x \rightarrow (0231)\\
&X=y,\ \ Y=x' \rightarrow (0132)\\
&X=y',\ Y=x' \rightarrow (03)
\end{aligned}
\qquad \textbf{(3.22)}
$$

By Burnside's Theorem and Proposition 3.12, the desired number of equivalence classes via (3.22) is

$$\frac{1}{8}(2^4+2^2+2^2+2^2+2^3+2^1+2^1+2^3)=6 \qquad \triangle$$

Exercises 3.3

1. Compute all X_g and all G_x for the following permutation groups.
   a. $X=\{1,2,3\}$, $G=S_3=\{e, (12), (23), (13), (123), (132)\}$
   b. $X=\{1,2,3,4,5,6\}$, $G=\{e, (12), (345), (354), (12)(345), (12)(354)\}$
2. For Exercises 1(a) and 1(b),
   i. Compute the G-equivalence class decomposition of X.
   ii. For each x in X, verify that $|G|=|[x]|\cdot|G_x|$
3. Use Exercises 1(a) and 2(i) to give an example of a permutation group $(G,\circ)$ on a set X and two elements x and y of X such that $x \sim y$, but $G_x \neq G_y$.
4. Compute the number of G-equivalence classes in Exercise 1 using Burnside's Theorem. Then check your answer against your computation for Exercise 2.
5. How many different ways can the vertices of an equilateral triangle be colored with three different colors?
6. How many different ways can the vertices of a rectangle be colored with three different colors?
7. A necklace consists of five rubies and/or diamonds connected by gold chains of equal length. How many different such necklaces can exist? (Do not consider the size of the jewels.)
8. How many equivalence classes of switching functions are there in $\mathcal{F}_4$ if the input variables w,x,y,z may be permuted via the subgroup of S_4 that is generated by $(wxyz)$?

9. The vertices of a square are colored either *Blue* or *Red*.
   a. Explain why equivalent colorings have the same number of *Blue* vertices.
   b. List explicitly six inequivalent colorings.
10. a. Let f and g be switching functions of two variables that are equivalent via permutations and inversions of the variables. Show that f and g equal 0 the same number of times.
    b. Explicitly list six inequivalent switching functions of two variables.
11. Another way economically to reduce the number of needed different switching functions is to allow inversions of the functions, as well as of the variables. Show that permutations and inversions then lead to four equivalence classes of functions in $\mathscr{F}_2$.
12. a. Explain why a symmetry of a polygon is determined by its effect on the sides of the polygon.

       Hint: Vertices are determined by adjacent sides.
    b. How many different ways can the sides of a rectangle be colored with three different colors?
13. Let $X=\{x,y,z\}$. Let $(G,\circ)=(S_3,\circ)$ be the group of all permutations of X.
    a. Find G_y and the coset decomposition of G with respect to G_y.
    b. Show by explicit calculation that, if g_1 and g_2 are in the same coset, then $g_1(y)=g_2(y)$.
14. Compute as follows the number of equivalence classes of functions in $\mathscr{F}_3$ via permutations and inversions of the variables (x,y,z). Number the eight values for (x,y,z) as in Example 3.35.
    a. As in (3.21), list the eight permutations that come from inverting, but not permuting, the variables.
    b. We need only consider the type of cycle decomposition for the composition of permutations and pure inversions. So compose the answers from part (a) with (xy) and with (xyz) of (3.21).
    c. Finish the computation using Burnside's Theorem and Proposition 3.12.
15. Compute how many different ways there are to color the faces of a cube so that two faces are red, two are white, and two are blue.

    Hint: Proposition 3.12 does not apply. Use Burnside's Theorem and Figure 3.8 anyway.

3.4 Partial Orders

In Section 3.1 equivalence relations, which describe how one object is to be considered the same as another object, were introduced. This section concerns partial orders, which describe how one object may be considered to be smaller than another object. Partial orders are common in mathematics and its applications.

Example 3.37

Any two real numbers r and s may always be compared in the sense that exactly one of the following three conditions holds:

$$r=s \qquad r<s \qquad \text{or} \qquad s<r \tag{3.23}$$

It turns out for the purposes here to be easier to deal with $\leq$, rather than with $<$. So (3.23) becomes: Given two real numbers r and s,

$$r \leq s \quad \text{or} \quad s \leq r$$

and both hold if and only if $r=s$. The symbol $\leq$ gives what will be called a **total order** on the real numbers. △

Example 3.38

Let $Y=\{a,b,c\}$. The eight subsets of Y are

$$\varnothing \qquad \{a\} \qquad \{b\} \qquad \{c\}$$
$$\{a,b\} \qquad \{a,c\} \qquad \{b,c\} \qquad \{a,b,c\}$$

How can we compare subsets of Y? One way would be to compare the number of elements, but this loses information about the nature of the elements. Instead, we shall use set inclusion: $A \subset B$ means that every element of A is also an element of B. $A \not\subset B$ means that $A \subset B$ is false. For example,

$$\{a\} \subset \{a,c\} \qquad \varnothing \subset \{b,c\} \qquad \{a\} \not\subset \{b,c\} \qquad \{b,c\} \not\subset \{a\}$$
$$\{a,c\} \subset \{a,c\} \qquad Y \not\subset \{a,c\}$$

Observe that, in contrast to $\leq$ of Example 3.37, *not every* pair of subsets of Y may be successfully compared; there is no inclusion, for example, between $\{a\}$ and $\{b,c\}$. In other ways, however, $\subset$ acts very much like $\leq$. Thus we shall call $\subset$ a **partial order** on X, the set of subsets of Y. △

Definition 3.8

Let R be a relation on the set X. R is a **partial order** if R is reflexive, antisymmetric, and transitive. The symbol $\leq$, rather than R, will usually be used to denote a partial order. A **partially ordered set**, or **poset**, $(X, \leq)$ is a set X with a partial order $\leq$.

A partial order $\leq$ on a set X is a **total** (or **linear**) **order** if, for all x, y in X, it is always true that $x \leq y$ and/or $y \leq x$. ○

Example 3.39

Let Y be as in Example 3.38. Let X, also as in Example 3.38, be the set of all subsets of Y. X is called the **power set** of Y and is often denoted by $\mathbb{P}(Y)$. Let us see that indeed $\subset$ is a partial order on X in the sense of Definition 3.8 and Definition 3.2.

Reflexivity requires that $A \subset A$ for all elements of X, that is, for all subsets A of Y. This is true.

Antisymmetry. Suppose that $A \subset B$ and $B \subset A$. Then indeed $A = B$.

Transitivity. Suppose that $A \subset B$ and $B \subset C$. Then also $A \subset C$, as required. △

Example 3.40

Let $\mathbb{P} = \{1,2,3,4,5,\ldots\}$ be the set of positive integers. Let $|$ be the relation on $\mathbb{P}$ given by $x|y$ if x divides y, that is, if y/x is an integer. Thus $3|6$, $7|14$, $10|50$, $4|6$, and $3|26$. Let us show that $|$ is a partial order.

Reflexivity. $\frac{x}{x} = 1$. So $x|x$.

Antisymmetry. If $x|y$ and $y|x$, then $x \leq y$ and $y \leq x$. So $x = y$.

Transitivity. $x|y$ implies that y/x is an integer.

$y|z$ implies that z/y is an integer. So $\frac{y}{x} \cdot \frac{z}{y} = \frac{z}{x}$ is also an integer. So $x|z$. △

Partial orders for finite sets can often be conveniently described via the following concepts and pictures: Let $(X, \leq)$ be a poset. Say that $x < y$ if $x \leq y$ and $x \neq y$. Say that $x > y$ if $y < x$. It is left to the exercises to verify that $<$ and $>$ are transitive relations on X. Say that x **covers** y if $x > y$ and there does not exist z such that $x > z > y$. That is, x covers y means that x is just larger than y. Using the partial order $|$ of Example 3.40, it can be seen that 4 covers 2. Eight does not cover 2 since $2|4$ and $4|8$. For $(\mathbb{Z}, \leq)$, the integers $\mathbb{Z}$ with the usual $\leq$, x covers y means that $x = y + 1$.

Proposition 3.13

Let $(X, \leq)$ be a finite poset. Then the covering relation on X determines $\leq$ as follows: Given $x \neq y$ in X, $x \leq y$ if and only if there exist elements $z_1, z_2, \ldots, z_m$ in X such that y covers z_m, z_m covers $z_{m-1}, \ldots, z_2$ covers z_1, z_1 covers x.

Proof of Proposition 3.13

Suppose that $z_1, \ldots, z_m$ exist. Then $y > z_m$, $z_m > z_{m-1}, \ldots, z_1 > x$. By transitivity, $y > x$.

Now suppose that $x \neq y$ and $x \leq y$. We must show that the z_i can be found. We are given that $y > x$. If y covers x, then the z_i are not needed. (Take $m = 0$.) Otherwise, by the definition of "covers," there exists z such that $y > z > x$. If y covers z and z covers x, then the proof is complete. If not, we insert a z' between y and z or between z and x; that is, we find z' such that $y > z' > z > x$ or $y > z > z' > x$. We keep inserting such z's for as long as possible. Since X is finite, the process must terminate. When no more z's may be inserted, all of the desired covering relations hold. □

Example 3.41 Let $X = \{1,2,3,\dots,23,24\}$. For the partial order $|$ on X, we find $z_1,\dots,z_m$ as in Proposition 3.8 when $x=1$, $y=24$:

$$1 \mid 6 \mid 24$$

$$1 \mid 3 \mid 6 \mid 12 \mid 24$$

$z_1=3$, $z_2=6$, $z_3=12$.

We observe that the z_i are not uniquely determined:

$$1 \mid 8 \mid 24$$

$$1 \mid 4 \mid 8 \mid 24$$

$$1 \mid 2 \mid 4 \mid 8 \mid 24$$

$z_1=2$, $z_2=4$, $z_3=8$. △

Example 3.42 Let $(\mathbb{R}, \leq)$ be the real numbers $\mathbb{R}$ with the usual $\leq$. Suppose that $x > y$. Then $x > \frac{x+y}{2} > y$. So x never covers y. The covering relation does not determine the partial order $\leq$ in this case. Of course, $\mathbb{R}$ is infinite, so Proposition 3.13 does not apply. △

The covering relation for a finite poset is conveniently displayed by a Hasse diagram, defined as follows: Represent the elements of X as points in the plane. If y covers x, draw an arrow from x to y. To simplify the Hasse diagram further, arrange so that if y covers x, then y lies above x on the paper; so all arrows point upwards and the arrowheads may be omitted. Figure 3.11 is the Hasse diagram for $(X,|)$ with $X = \{2,3,4,\dots,11,12\}$. Figure 3.12 is the Hasse diagram for Example 3.38. If $(X,\leq)$ is given by a Hasse diagram, then $x \leq y$ simply means that either $x = y$, or else that x may be connected to y via a constantly upwards path. In the exercise set, it is shown that every Hasse diagram necessarily yields a partial order. So a finite set has many partial orders.

Figure 3.13 is the Hasse diagram for $(X,\leq)$ with $X = \{0,1,2,3,4\}$ and $\leq$ the usual less-than-or-equal-to. Observe that $\leq$ is a total order on X. The Hasse diagram is just a vertical line. All total orders have Hasse diagrams of this type.

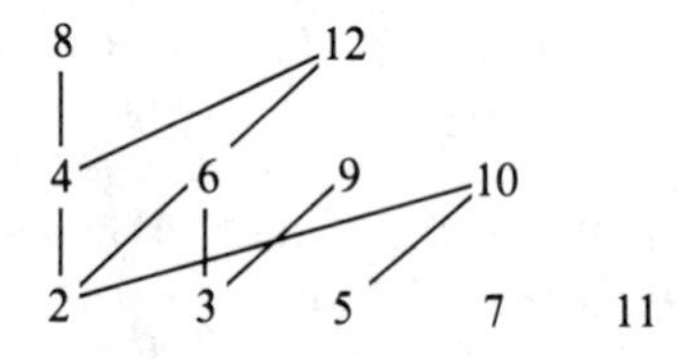

Figure 3.11 Hasse diagram for $(X,|)$

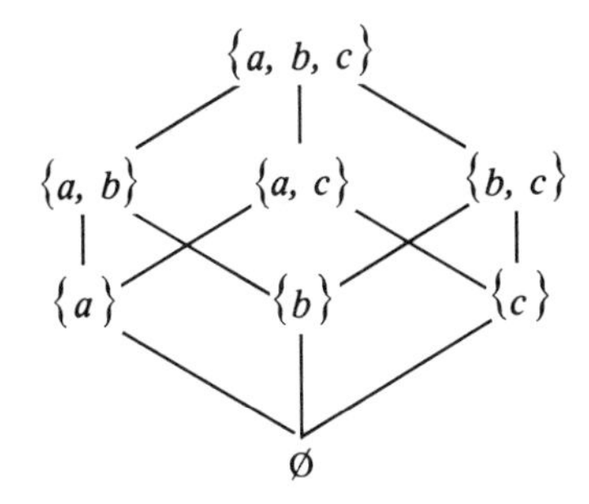

Figure 3.12 Hasse diagram for $(\mathbb{P}(\{a,b,c\}), \subset)$

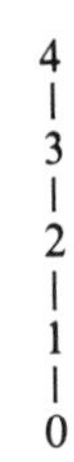

Figure 3.13 Hasse diagram for $(\{0,1,2,3,4\}, \leq)$

Proposition 3.13 has the following algebraic reformulation. Let R be a relation on the finite set X. Let n be the number of elements in X. Then R may be given as a binary $n \times n$ matrix called $G(R)$. The rows and columns of $G(R)$ are labeled by the elements of X. If xRy, place a 1 in the x-row, y-column of $G(R)$; otherwise, place a 0 in the x-row, y-column. Table 3.8 gives $G(R)$ for Example 3.38. The matrix $G(R)$ is essentially the graph of the relation R, that is, all points in $X \times X$ that are in R. Indeed, the entry places in the matrix correspond to points of $X \times X$. An entry of 1 indicates that the point is in R; an entry of 0 indicates that the point is not in R.

If $(X, \leq)$ is a finite poset, $G(>)$ is obtained from $G(\leq)$ by changing all of the diagonal entries in $G(\leq)$ from 1 to 0 and then interchanging rows and columns (**transposing** the matrix). Table 3.9 gives $G(>)$ for Table 3.8; $\supsetneqq$ is the usual symbol for $>$ in this context. Let $C(\leq)$ denote the **covering**

Table 3.8 Relation matrix for $(\mathbb{P}(\{a,b,c\}, \subset)$

	$\varnothing$	$\{a\}$	$\{b\}$	$\{c\}$	$\{a,b\}$	$\{a,c\}$	$\{b,c\}$	$\{a,b,c\}$
$\varnothing$	1	1	1	1	1	1	1	1
$\{a\}$	0	1	0	0	1	1	0	1
$\{b\}$	0	0	1	0	1	0	1	1
$\{c\}$	0	0	0	1	0	1	1	1
$\{a,b\}$	0	0	0	0	1	0	0	1
$\{a,c\}$	0	0	0	0	0	1	0	1
$\{b,c\}$	0	0	0	0	0	0	1	1
$\{a,b,c\}$	0	0	0	0	0	0	0	1

Table 3.9 Relation matrix for $(\mathbb{P}\{a,b,c\}, \supsetneqq)$

	$\varnothing$	$\{a\}$	$\{b\}$	$\{c\}$	$\{a,b\}$	$\{a,c\}$	$\{b,c\}$	$\{a,b,c\}$
$\varnothing$	0	0	0	0	0	0	0	0
$\{a\}$	1	0	0	0	0	0	0	0
$\{b\}$	1	0	0	0	0	0	0	0
$\{c\}$	1	0	0	0	0	0	0	0
$\{a,b\}$	1	1	1	0	0	0	0	0
$\{a,c\}$	1	1	0	1	0	0	0	0
$\{b,c\}$	1	0	1	1	0	0	0	0
$\{a,b,c\}$	1	1	1	1	1	1	1	0

Table 3.10 Covering matrix for Tables 3.8 and 3.9

	$\varnothing$	$\{a\}$	$\{b\}$	$\{c\}$	$\{a,b\}$	$\{a,c\}$	$\{b,c\}$	$\{a,b,c\}$
$\varnothing$	0	0	0	0	0	0	0	0
$\{a\}$	1	0	0	0	0	0	0	0
$\{b\}$	1	0	0	0	0	0	0	0
$\{c\}$	1	0	0	0	0	0	0	0
$\{a,b\}$	0	1	1	0	0	0	0	0
$\{a,c\}$	0	1	0	1	0	0	0	0
$\{b,c\}$	0	0	1	1	0	0	0	0
$\{a,b,c\}$	0	0	0	0	1	1	1	0

matrix for $(X, \leq)$, that is, the matrix for the relation "x covers y" on X. Then $C(\leq)$ is obtained from $G(>)$ by changing from 1 to 0 those (x,y) entries in $G(>)$ such that there is a z with $(x,z) = (z,y) = 1$. Table 3.10 gives $C(\subset)$ for Table 3.8 and Table 3.9.

Tables 3.8 and 3.10 contain the same information, but observe how many fewer 1's there are in Table 3.10 than there are in Table 3.8. So Table 3.10 might require less storage space in a computer than does Table 3.8.

How can we algebraically recover $\leq$ from $C(\leq)$? Recall the multiplication of binary matrices from Chapter 1, Section 1.4. There, we multiplied binary matrices like real matrices except that addition and multiplication were defined in $\mathbb{Z}_2$: Table 1.5 and Table 1.10. Table 3.11 gives another addition and multiplication for $\{0,1\}$. In Table 3.11, think of addition as "maximum" and multiplication as "minimum." We shall see Table 3.11 again, essentially as Table 5.2, in the chapter on Boolean algebras. The operations of Table 3.11 are called **Boolean addition** and **Boolean multiplication**.

Table 3.11 Boolean addition and multiplication

+	0	1
0	0	1
1	1	1

·	0	1
0	0	0
1	0	1

Proposition 3.14

Let $(X, \leq)$ be a finite poset. Let $m \geq 1$. Let $[C(\leq)]^{m+1}$ be given by matrix multiplication using Boolean addition and multiplication. Then the y-row, x-column entry in $[C(\leq)]^{m+1}$ is 1 if and only if there exist elements $z_1, z_2, \ldots, z_m$ in X such that y covers z_m, z_m covers z_{m-1}, ..., z_2 covers z_1, z_1 covers x.

Example 3.43

Before proving Proposition 3.14, we shall illustrate its statement. Let $X = \{a,b,c,d\}$. Let the partial order $\leq$ be given by the Hasse diagram of Figure 3.14. Then

$$C(\leq) = \begin{array}{c|cccc} & a & b & c & d \\ \hline a & 0 & 0 & 0 & 0 \\ b & 1 & 0 & 0 & 0 \\ c & 1 & 0 & 0 & 0 \\ d & 0 & 1 & 1 & 0 \end{array} \quad \text{or just} \quad C(\leq) = \begin{pmatrix} 0 & 0 & 0 & 0 \\ 1 & 0 & 0 & 0 \\ 1 & 0 & 0 & 0 \\ 0 & 1 & 1 & 0 \end{pmatrix}$$

$[C(\leq)]^2$ is given below in (3.25). In (3.25), we underline the d-row and the a-column in the first and second factors respectively. This row and column multiply to give the only non-0 entry in $[C(\leq)]^2$, as follows:

$$(0 \quad 1 \quad 1 \quad 0) \cdot \begin{pmatrix} 0 \\ 1 \\ 1 \\ 0 \end{pmatrix} = 0 \cdot 0 + 1 \cdot 1 + 1 \cdot 1 + 0 \cdot 0 = 0 + 1 + 1 + 0 = 1 \tag{3.24}$$

by Table 3.11.

$$\begin{pmatrix} 0 & 0 & 0 & 0 \\ 1 & 0 & 0 & 0 \\ 1 & 0 & 0 & 0 \\ \underline{0} & \underline{1} & \underline{1} & \underline{0} \end{pmatrix} \cdot \begin{pmatrix} \underline{0} & 0 & 0 & 0 \\ \underline{1} & 0 & 0 & 0 \\ \underline{1} & 0 & 0 & 0 \\ \underline{0} & 1 & 1 & 0 \end{pmatrix} = \begin{pmatrix} 0 & 0 & 0 & 0 \\ 0 & 0 & 0 & 0 \\ 0 & 0 & 0 & 0 \\ \underline{1} & 0 & 0 & 0 \end{pmatrix} \tag{3.25}$$

We observe from Figure 3.14 that indeed d covers b and b covers a. △

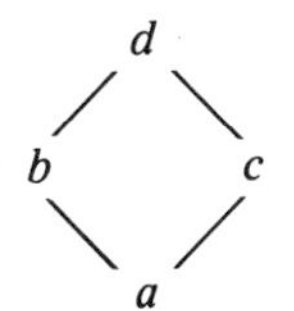

Figure 3.14 Hasse diagram

Proof of Proposition 3.14

First we consider $m=1$, or $[C(\leq)]^2$. Consider the entry at the y-row, x-column of $[C(\leq)]^2$. This entry is computed as a sum of products, as in (3.24). By Table 3.11, thinking of $+$ as maximum, this sum is 1 precisely when at least one of the products equals 1. A product is 1 precisely when both factors equal 1. In all, the (y,x) entry in $[C(\leq)]^2$ equals 1 precisely when there is a z such that the (y,z) and (z,x) entries in $C(\leq)$ equal 1. Then y covers z and z covers x. So $[C(\leq)]^2$ is as claimed.

To do the $m=3$ case, we write

$$[C(\leq)]^3=[C(\leq)]\cdot[C(\leq)]^2 \tag{3.26}$$

Proposition 3.14 is now known for $[C(\leq)]^2$ in (3.26). Applying the argument for the proof of $[C(\leq)]^2$ to (3.26) proves Proposition 3.14 for $m=3$. We continue the argument for all positive integral m. (This is really a proof by mathematical induction. See the appendix for a discussion of induction.) □

Example 3.44

We compute $[C(\leq)]^2$, $[C(\leq)]^3$, and $[C(\leq)]^4$ for Example 3.38. Figure 3.12 gives the Hasse diagram. Table 3.10 gives $C(\leq)$.

$$[C(\leq)]^2=\begin{pmatrix} 0&0&0&0&0&0&0&0\\ 1&0&0&0&0&0&0&0\\ 1&0&0&0&0&0&0&0\\ 1&0&0&0&0&0&0&0\\ 0&1&1&0&0&0&0&0\\ 0&1&0&1&0&0&0&0\\ 0&0&1&1&0&0&0&0\\ 0&0&0&0&1&1&1&0 \end{pmatrix}\cdot$$

$$\begin{pmatrix} 0&0&0&0&0&0&0&0\\ 1&0&0&0&0&0&0&0\\ 1&0&0&0&0&0&0&0\\ 1&0&0&0&0&0&0&0\\ 0&1&1&0&0&0&0&0\\ 0&1&0&1&0&0&0&0\\ 0&0&1&1&0&0&0&0\\ 0&0&0&0&1&1&1&0 \end{pmatrix}$$

$$
= \begin{pmatrix} 0&0&0&0&0&0&0&0\\ 0&0&0&0&0&0&0&0\\ 0&0&0&0&0&0&0&0\\ 0&0&0&0&0&0&0&0\\ 1&0&0&0&0&0&0&0\\ 1&0&0&0&0&0&0&0\\ 1&0&0&0&0&0&0&0\\ 0&1&1&1&0&0&0&0 \end{pmatrix}
$$

$$
[C(\leq)]^3 = C(\leq)\cdot[C(\leq)]^2 = \begin{pmatrix} 0&0&0&0&0&0&0&0\\ 1&0&0&0&0&0&0&0\\ 1&0&0&0&0&0&0&0\\ 1&0&0&0&0&0&0&0\\ 0&1&1&0&0&0&0&0\\ 0&1&0&1&0&0&0&0\\ 0&0&1&1&0&0&0&0\\ 0&0&0&0&1&1&1&0 \end{pmatrix} \cdot
$$

$$
\cdot \begin{pmatrix} 0&0&0&0&0&0&0&0\\ 0&0&0&0&0&0&0&0\\ 0&0&0&0&0&0&0&0\\ 0&0&0&0&0&0&0&0\\ 1&0&0&0&0&0&0&0\\ 1&0&0&0&0&0&0&0\\ 1&0&0&0&0&0&0&0\\ 0&1&1&1&0&0&0&0 \end{pmatrix}
$$

$$
= \begin{pmatrix} 0&0&0&0&0&0&0&0\\ 0&0&0&0&0&0&0&0\\ 0&0&0&0&0&0&0&0\\ 0&0&0&0&0&0&0&0\\ 0&0&0&0&0&0&0&0\\ 0&0&0&0&0&0&0&0\\ 0&0&0&0&0&0&0&0\\ 1&0&0&0&0&0&0&0 \end{pmatrix}
$$

All entries in $[C(\leq)]^4$ are 0. It is easy to see from Figure 3.12 that all of the entries in the matrices are as required by Proposition 3.14. △

If $(X, \leq)$ is a poset, the relation $\geq$ on X is defined by $x \geq y$ if $y \leq x$. It is very easy to see that $\geq$ is a partial order and that there are no real differences between $\leq$ and $\geq$. Recall that the identity $n \times n$ matrix I has 1's only along the main diagonal. The illustration and proof of the following Proposition are left as an exercise.

Proposition 3.15 Let $(X, \leq)$ be a finite poset. Let n be the number of elements in X. Then, using Boolean addition and multiplication,

$$G(\geq) = I + C(\leq) + [C(\leq)]^2 + \cdots + [C(\leq)]^{n-1} \qquad \square$$

Exercises 3.4

1. Let $X = \{1,2,3,4,5\}$. Decide which of the following relations on X are partial orders. Decide which of the partial orders are total orders.
   a. $\neq$ b. $\geq$ c. $>$ d. $x + y$ is even
   e. R is given by xRx for all x in X and $2R5$.
2. Draw the Hasse diagram for $\{3,5,7,9,15\}$ under the partial order $|$.
3. Let $Y = \{a,b\}$. Draw the Hasse diagram for $(\mathbb{P}(Y), \subset)$.
4. For each of the following Hasse diagrams, decide which of the indicated relations are true.

a. 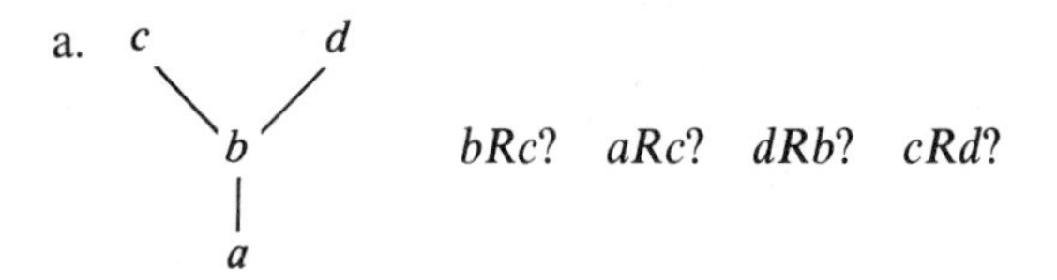

b. 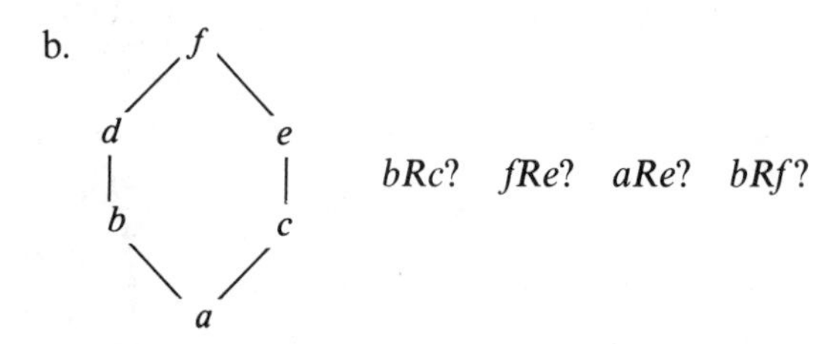

5. Let Y be a set. Consider the covering relation on $(\mathbb{P}(Y), \subset)$. Explain why A covers B if and only if the elements of A consist of the elements of B plus one additional element.
6. Consider the partial order $|$ on $\mathbb{P} = \{1,2,3,4,\ldots\}$. Explain why x covers y if and only if x/y is a prime number.
7. Let $(X, \leq)$ be a poset. Show that $\geq$ is a partial order on X.

8. Let $(X, \leq)$ be a poset. Suppose that $a \leq b$, $b \leq c$, and $c \leq a$. Show that $a = b = c$.

   Hint: $a \leq b$ and $b \leq a$.
9. Let $(X, \leq)$ be a poset. Show that $<$ is a transitive relation on X.
10. Write xCy if x covers y. A Hasse diagram for a finite poset $(X, \leq)$ indicates when xCy is true. A sequence

$$\underline{x_1}Cx_2, x_2Cx_3, \ldots, x_{n-1}Cx_n, x_nC\underline{x_1}$$

   never occurs. Now consider a relation C on a finite set X that satisfies the above condition. Define the relation $x \leq y$ to mean that either $x = y$ or that there exist $z_1, z_2, \ldots, z_m$ in X such that $yCz_m, z_mCz_{m-1}, \ldots, z_2Cz_1, z_1Cx$. Show that $\leq$ is a partial order on X.
11. Let R be a relation on the finite set X.
    a. Show that R is reflexive if and only if $G(R)$ has only 1's along the main diagonal.
    b. Show that R is symmetric if and only if for all x, y in X, the (x, y) entry in $G(R)$ equals the (y, x) entry in $G(R)$.
    c. Show that R is antisymmetric if and only if, given that $x \neq y$ in X, the (x, y) and (y, x) entries in $G(R)$ cannot both be 1.
12. Let M be an $n \times n$ matrix. Define M^t, the transpose of M, to be that $n \times n$ matrix such that the (x, y) entry in M^t equals the (y, x) entry in M. Let $(X, \leq)$ be a finite poset. Show that $G(\geq) = [G(\leq)]^t$.
13. a. Compute the covering matrix $C(|)$ for the set $X = \{2, 3, 4, 6, 8\}$ with the partial order $|$.
    b. Compute $C(|)^2$, $C(|)^3$, ... until $C(|)^m$ has only 0 entries.
    c. Compute $I + C(|) + C(|)^2 + \cdots + C(|)^4$.
    d. Check the answer to part (c) against the predicted result from Proposition 3.15.
14. Let R be a relation on the set X. The *transitive closure* R^+ of R is that relation on X given by xR^+y if, with $x = z_1$ and $y = z_m$, there exist $z_1, z_2, \ldots, z_m$ in X such that $z_1Rz_2, z_2Rz_3, \ldots, z_{m-1}Rz_m$.
    a. Show that R^+ is a transitive relation on X.
    b. Let X be a finite set with n elements. Using Boolean addition and multiplication, show that

$$G(R^+) = G(R) + [G(R)]^2 + \cdots + [G(R)]^n$$

4 Graph Theory

The word "graph" denotes, in general, some diagrammatic representation of information. There are graphs of functions in calculus. Numbers and percentages are often represented by bar graphs and circular graphs. This chapter considers mathematical graphs that consist of vertices and edges, in various guises. Some data present themselves naturally in this form. Thus a typical graph might come from a road map, where the vertices are towns or intersections and the edges are roads. Many more examples are given in the text.

This chapter should be considered as only a brief introduction to graph theory. The basic terminology of graphs and trees is given and illustrated. Also, some representative theorems and applications are discussed.

We have already seen examples of graphs in the Hasse diagrams of the previous chapter. Informal use of graphs will also occur in the later chapters on fast algorithms, on machines, and on formal languages.

The Appendix to this text gives a general discussion of mathematical induction. This chapter makes nontrivial use of induction in several proofs.

4.1 Graphs; Directed Graphs

This section begins with some examples of typical graphs from outside of mathematics. Then the formal definitions for graphs and related objects will be given. Graphs may be directed or undirected, and may be labeled or unlabeled. The choice of graph type is usually determined naturally by the problem at hand.

The terminology for graph theory is not completely standardized. The names used in this book for objects are among the most common names, but do check the definitions in other texts before skimming them.

Example 4.1

In chemistry, the structure of a molecule is often described as a graph (or a multigraph). The atoms serve as vertices. Each edge represents a chemical bond between different atoms. The number of bonds associated to a given atom is called its **valence**. Different atoms of the same chemical element often have the same valence. Figure 4.1 gives diagrams for some simple compounds of hydrogen, denoted by H, and carbon, denoted by C. Observe in all of the molecules that each hydrogen atom has a valence of 1 and that each carbon atom has a valence of 4.

Molecules such as *n*-butane and isobutane, which contain similar atoms but have different graphs, are called **isomers**. Isomers have different chemical and physical properties, but only slightly so in the case of *n*-butane and isobutane. △

Figure 4.1 Some molecules

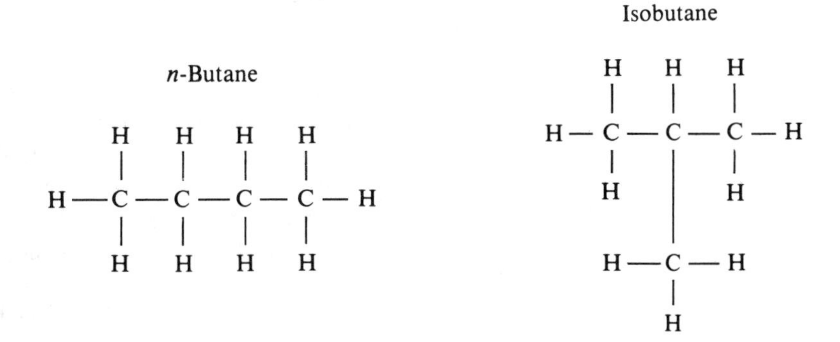

Benzene

H
H C H
C C
C C
H C H
H

Example 4.2

Family trees are graphs. In fact, family trees are often trees in the sense of graph theory. Some authors use the common terminology for family trees as their terminology for mathematical trees. In family trees, the vertices are people. An edge connects two people if one is the parent of the other. Family trees are usually arranged so that parents are listed above their children.

Figure 4.2 is a partial family tree that lists some of the descendents of King George V of Great Britain. Titles are largely omitted in Figure 4.2. Also, to save space, many descendents are indicated by only a dash in Figure 4.2. △

The reader may also be familiar with the graphs that come from electrical diagrams and from flow charts. Specific examples are not included.

In this chapter all graphs will be finite. Infinite "graphs" will be occasionally useful, however.

Definition 4.1

A **graph** G consists of a finite set V of **vertices** and a finite set E of **edges**, such that each edge e is associated with a pair of distinct vertices v_1 and v_2, called the **endpoints** of e, and such that different edges have different pairs of endpoints. ○

In a graph, we may think of a vertex as a point and an edge as a curve that connects two vertices. There is no preference for the order in listing the endpoints of an edge. Observe from Definition 4.1 that an edge in a graph is completely specified by its endpoints. Of course, not every pair of distinct vertices is required to be the endpoints of an edge. Figure 4.3 gives a typical graph. There, edge b has endpoints 2, 3; the endpoints of edge d are 4, 3. If edge e has vertex v as an endpoint, we say that e is **incident** at v. In Figure 4.3, edge c is incident at vertices 1 and 4, but not at vertices

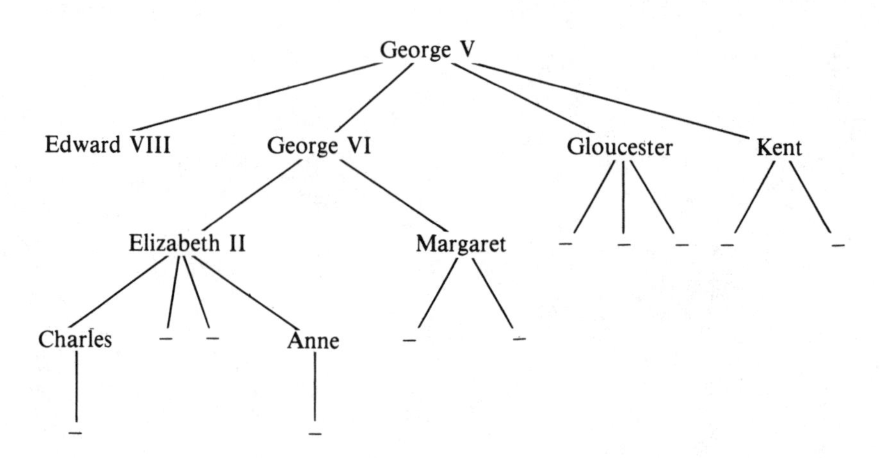

Figure 4.2 A partial family tree

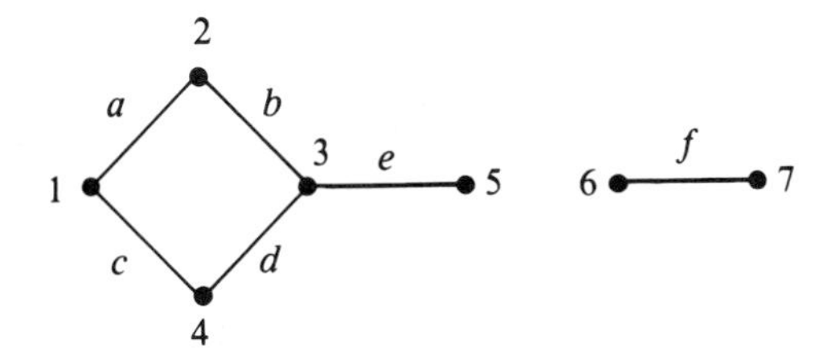

Figure 4.3 A typical graph

Vertices: 1, 2, 3, 4, 5, 6, 7
Edges: a, b, c, d, e, f

2,3,5,6, and 7. Two vertices that are the endpoints of the same edge are called **adjacent**. In Figure 4.3, 3 and 5 are adjacent vertices. Vertices 1 and 3 are not adjacent.

Eliminating the requirements in Definition 4.1 that edges have distinct endpoints and that different edges have different pairs of endpoints gives the definition of a **multigraph**. Figure 4.4 is a typical multigraph. Observe in Figure 4.4 that both edge a and edge b have vertices 1,2 as endpoints. This is not allowed in a graph. Also in Figure 4.4, the endpoints of edge d coincide. Such an edge is called a **loop**. Loops are not allowed in graphs. Multigraphs, as distinct from graphs, occur naturally as highway maps where more than one road may connect two towns. We shall also need multigraphs for the machine diagrams of Chapter 7. This chapter will be devoted to graphs. However, most of the definitions and results may be applied to multigraphs with only minor modifications.

The information in a graph may be given numerically as described in Definition 4.2, which follows. Recall the notation that $|S|$ equals the number of elements in the set S.

Definition 4.2 Let G be a graph with $n=|V|$ vertices. Let the vertices be numbered $v_1, v_2, \ldots, v_n$. The **adjacency matrix** A for G is the $n \times n$ matrix whose (i,j)-entry A_{ij} equals 1 or 0 according to whether there is or is not an edge with v_i and v_j as endpoints. ○

Observe that in an adjacency matrix A, A_{ij} equals 1 when vertices v_i and v_j are adjacent. Otherwise, A_{ij} equals 0.

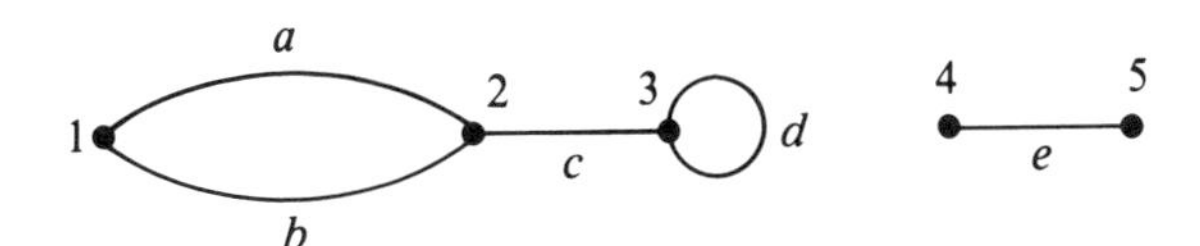

Figure 4.4 A typical multigraph

Vertices: 1, 2, 3, 4, 5
Edges: a, b, c, d

Example 4.3

Here is the adjacency matrix for the graph of Figure 4.3. Of course, $v_i = i$.

$$\begin{pmatrix} 0 & 1 & 0 & 1 & 0 & 0 & 0 \\ 1 & 0 & 1 & 0 & 0 & 0 & 0 \\ 0 & 1 & 0 & 1 & 1 & 0 & 0 \\ 1 & 0 & 1 & 0 & 0 & 0 & 0 \\ 0 & 0 & 1 & 0 & 0 & 0 & 0 \\ 0 & 0 & 0 & 0 & 0 & 0 & 1 \\ 0 & 0 & 0 & 0 & 0 & 1 & 0 \end{pmatrix}$$

△

Suppose that an edge e in a graph has v_i and v_j as endpoints. Then we may also say that e has v_j and v_i as endpoints. So each edge creates a 1 in both an A_{ij} and an A_{ji} entry in A of Definition 4.2. For all i,j, $A_{ij} = A_{ji}$; that is, A is a symmetric matrix.

Example 4.4

Consider the matrix A of (4.1). A has only 0 and 1 as entries, is symmetric, and has entries only of 0 along the main diagonal. Any such matrix is the adjacency matrix for a uniquely specified graph. Figure 4.5 gives a (nonunique) drawing of the graph for (4.1).

$$\begin{pmatrix} 0 & 0 & 1 & 0 & 0 & 0 \\ 0 & 0 & 0 & 0 & 1 & 0 \\ 1 & 0 & 0 & 1 & 1 & 0 \\ 0 & 0 & 1 & 0 & 1 & 0 \\ 0 & 1 & 1 & 1 & 0 & 1 \\ 0 & 0 & 0 & 0 & 1 & 0 \end{pmatrix} \tag{4.1}$$

△

Definition 4.3

Let G be a graph. A **path** of **length** n, $n \geq 0$, consists of an alternating sequence $v_0, e_1, v_1, e_2, \ldots, v_{n-1}, e_n, v_n$ of $n+1$ vertices and n edges such that e_i

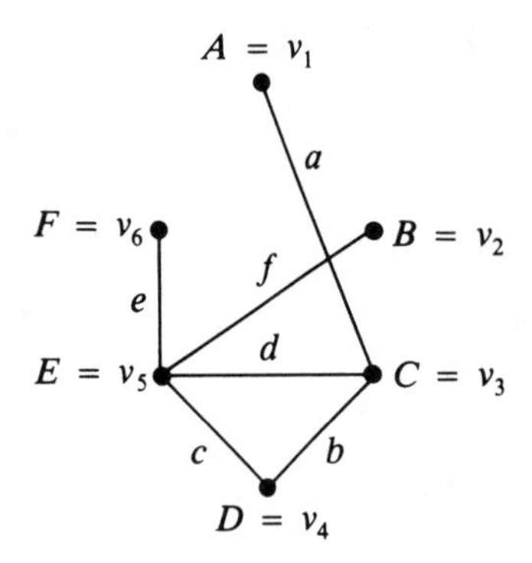

Figure 4.5 Graph for (4.1)

has v_{i-1} and v_i as endpoints. A path of length n **connects** the vertices v_0 and v_n. A graph is **connected** if all pairs of vertices may be connected by paths. A path of length n is **simple** if, except possibly for v_0 and v_n, all of the v_i and all of the e_i in the path are distinct. ○

Observe that each vertex v of a graph is a (simple) path of length 0. A path of length 1, also necessarily simple, is just an edge connecting its endpoints.

Example 4.5

Here are some paths for the graph of Figure 4.5. Vertices are named with capital letters; edges with small letters.

F,e,E,d,C,a,A	length 3, simple
F,e,E,d,C,b,D,c,E	length 4, not simple
D	length 0, simple
C,d,E,c,D,b,C	length 3, simple
A,a,C,a,A	length 2, not simple

△

Geometrically, we may think of a path as a route that traverses some points in the drawing of the graph. Simple paths then have no duplications of points, except possibly for the first and last points.

Example 4.6

Figure 4.6 gives some connected graphs. Examples of nonconnected graphs are given in Figure 4.7. Observe in Figure 4.7 that the nonconnected graphs (ii) and (iii) are redrawn as (ii)′ and (iii)′, respectively, to separate geometrically those vertices that may be connected to each other. △

Figure 4.6 Four connected graphs

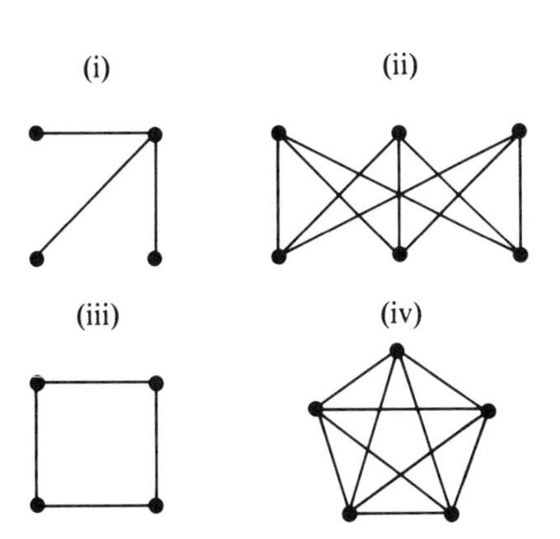

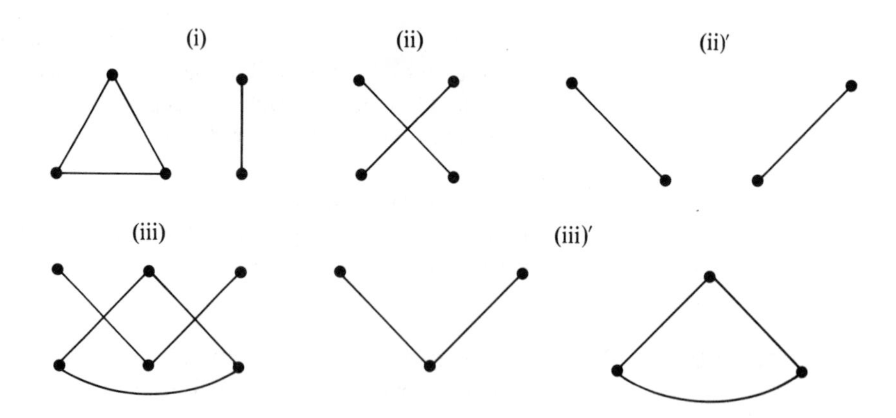

Figure 4.7 Three nonconnected graphs

Example 4.7

Let us look at the vertices B and F of Figure 4.5. The vertices B and F may be connected by the nonsimple path

$$B, f, E, \underline{d, C, b, D, c, E,} e, F \tag{4.2}$$

B and F may also, obviously, be connected by a simple path. One way to get such a simple path is to start with the nonsimple path of (4.2). Vertex E is duplicated in (4.2). So we delete the extra E and those edges that connect the two E's. These are underlined in (4.2). This yields (4.3), a shorter path that connects B and E.

$$B, f, E, e, F \tag{4.3}$$

(4.3) happens to be a simple path. But were it not, we could repeat the simplification of the previous paragraph. Eventually, we would reach a simple path. △

The argument of Example 4.7 is perfectly general. So, without further proof, we state the result.

Proposition 4.1

Let v and v' be vertices of a graph that may be connected by a path. Then v and v' may be connected by a simple path. □

Definition 4.4

Let G be a graph with vertices V and edges E. A **subgraph** G' of G is a graph with vertices V' and edges E' such that V' and E' are subsets of V and E respectively. ○

To check that subsets V' and E' do give a subgraph, we need only check that the endpoints of each edge in E' are vertices in V' (rather than just in V). Figure 4.8 gives a graph and some of its subgraphs. Figure 4.9

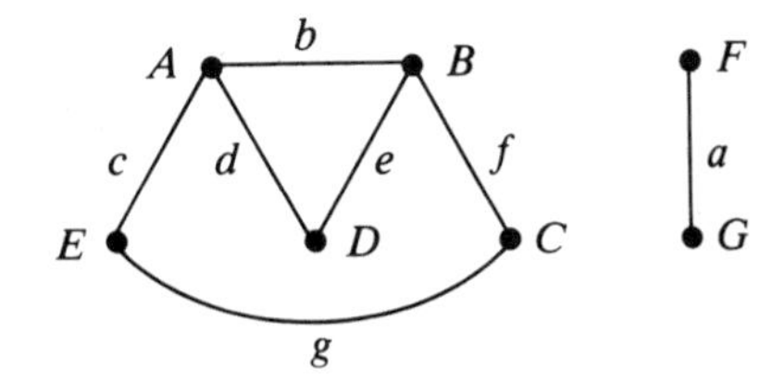

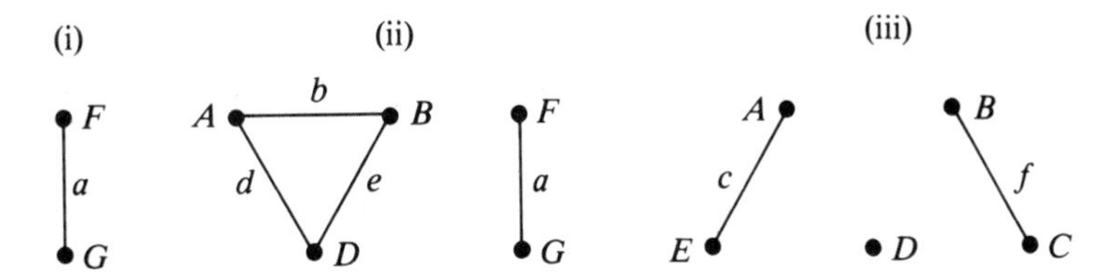

Figure 4.8 Graph and three subgraphs

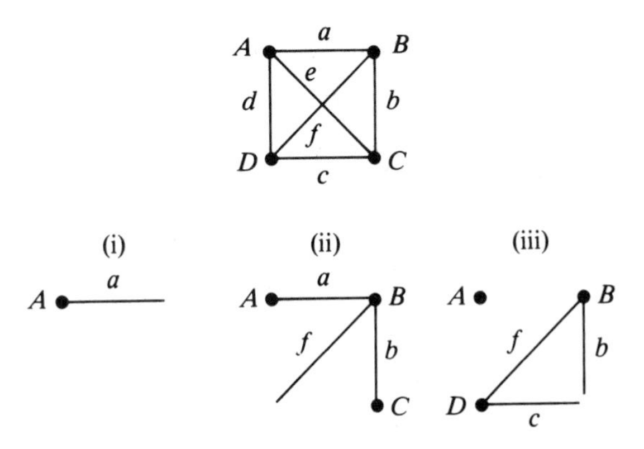

Figure 4.9 Graph and three subnongraphs

gives a graph and some subsets of vertices and edges that are not subgraphs.

Let G be a graph. It is easy to see that the vertices and edges that may appear in paths that begin with a given vertex v_0 form a subgraph G_0 of G. The subgraph G_0 is connected and is called the **connected component** of G containing v_0. We can partition G into connected components. This was done, for example, in Figure 4.7 in going from (ii) to (ii)′ and from (iii) to (iii)′. More examples and details may be found in the exercises.

As in Figure 4.8, we often assign names to the vertices and edges of a graph so that we may discuss them. But often, as in Figure 4.1, vertices (or edges) may have natural information, as distinct from names, associated with them. Such graphs are said to be **labeled**. A typical edge labeling would be the distances along the roads of a map.

Very often in a graph, there is a preferred direction along each of the edges. For example, in Figure 4.2, each edge connects a parent to a child. In many road maps, each lane has a one-way direction. Such graphs are said to be directed. Most of the concepts above have easy analogs for directed graphs. Formally, we have Definition 4.5.

Definition 4.5

A **directed graph** G consists of a finite set V of **vertices** (or **nodes**) and a finite set E of **directed edges** (or **arcs**) such that each directed edge e is associated to an **initial** (or **tail**) vertex v_1 and a **terminal** (or **head**) vertex v_2, $v_1 \neq v_2$. Also, different directed edges have different initial and/or terminal vertices. ○

As with undirected graphs, we may think of the vertices of a directed graph as points. The directed edges are curves that start at the initial vertices and end at the terminal vertices. On the curves we put arrows that point at the terminal vertices. Figure 4.10 is thus a typical directed graph. Observe in Figure 4.10 that e_5 has v_4 as initial vertex and v_2 as terminal vertex, while e_6 has v_2 as initial vertex and v_4 as terminal vertex.

We shall usually refer to the directed edges of a directed graph as edges.

Definition 4.6

Let G be a directed graph with $n = |V|$ vertices. Let the vertices be numbered $v_1, v_2, \ldots, v_n$. The **adjacency matrix** A for G is the $n \times n$ matrix with (i,j)-entry A_{ij} equal to 1 or 0 according to whether there is or is not an edge with v_i as initial vertex and v_j as terminal vertex. ○

Example 4.8

Here is the adjacency matrix for the directed graph of Figure 4.10:

$$A = \begin{pmatrix} 0 & 0 & 0 & 0 & 0 \\ 1 & 0 & 0 & 1 & 1 \\ 0 & 1 & 0 & 0 & 1 \\ 0 & 1 & 0 & 0 & 0 \\ 0 & 0 & 0 & 0 & 0 \end{pmatrix}$$

△

Definition 4.7

Let G be a directed graph. A **directed path** of length n, $n \geq 0$, consists of an alternating sequence $v_0, e_1, v_1, e_2, \ldots, v_{n-1}, e_n, v_n$ of $n+1$ vertices and n edges

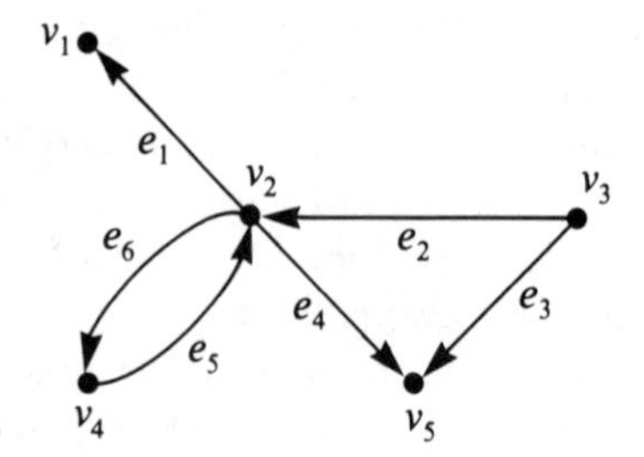

Figure 4.10 A directed graph

such that e_i has v_{i-1} as its initial vertex and v_i as its terminal vertex. Such a directed path **connects** v_0 to v_n and shows that v_n is **accessible** from v_0. ○

Example 4.9 Consider Figure 4.10. Here is a list of the accessible vertices from a given vertex.

Initial vertex	Accessible vertices
v_1	v_1
v_2	v_1, v_2, v_4, v_5
v_3	v_1, v_2, v_3, v_4, v_5
v_4	v_1, v_2, v_4, v_5
v_5	v_5

△

Let v_0 be a vertex of the directed graph G. It is shown in the exercises that the edges and vertices that may appear in the directed paths which begin at v_0 form a directed subgraph of G.

The adjacency matrix A of a directed graph G contains all the information in the directed graph. Let us see how accessibility may be computed from A by usual matrix multiplication. We define A^0 to be I, the $n \times n$ identity matrix.

Theorem 4.2 Let A be the adjacency matrix of the directed graph G. Let $A_{ij}{}^m$ denote the (i,j)-entry in A^m, $m \geq 0$. Then $A_{ij}{}^m$ equals the number of directed paths of length m from v_i to v_j.

Example 4.10 Before proving Theorem 4.2, we will illustrate its statement. Consider A of Example 4.8 and Figure 4.10.

$$A^0 = I = \begin{pmatrix} 1 & 0 & 0 & 0 & 0 \\ 0 & 1 & 0 & 0 & 0 \\ 0 & 0 & 1 & 0 & 0 \\ 0 & 0 & 0 & 1 & 0 \\ 0 & 0 & 0 & 0 & 1 \end{pmatrix}$$

Indeed, a path of length 0 just connects a vertex to itself.

Paths of length 1 just show that the terminal vertex of an edge is accessible from the initial vertex. So the theorem is correct for $m=1$. A matrix multiplication shows that

$$A^2 = \begin{pmatrix} 0 & 0 & 0 & 0 & 0 \\ 0 & 1 & 0 & 0 & 0 \\ 1 & 0 & 0 & 1 & 1 \\ 1 & 0 & 0 & 1 & 1 \\ 0 & 0 & 0 & 0 & 0 \end{pmatrix}$$

${A_{31}}^2$ corresponds to the path v_3, e_2, v_2, e_1, v_1.
${A_{22}}^2$ corresponds to the path v_2, e_6, v_4, e_5, v_2.
${A_{32}}^2 = 0$. Indeed, while there is a path of length 1 from v_3 to v_2, there is no path of length 2 from v_3 to v_2. △

Proof of Theorem 4.2

The proof will be by mathematical induction (see the Appendix) on m. The cases of $m=0$ and $m=1$ are proved by the observations in Example 4.10, preceding. So we shall assume Theorem 4.2 for m and prove it for $m+1$.

$$A^{m+1} = A \cdot A^m$$

To simplify the notation, let $B = A^m$ and $C = A^{m+1}$. Then

$$C = A \cdot B$$

From the definition of matrix multiplication,

$$C_{ik} = A_{i1} \cdot B_{1k} + \cdots + A_{ij} \cdot B_{jk} + \cdots + A_{in} \cdot B_{nk} \tag{4.4}$$

We interpret the term $A_{ij} \cdot B_{jk}$ in (4.4). We know that A_{ij} equals the number of paths of length 1 from v_i to v_j. By the induction hypothesis, B_{jk} equals the number of paths of length m from v_j to v_k. So $A_{ij} \cdot B_{jk}$ equals the number of paths from v_i to v_k of length $m+1$ that initially go through v_j. So (4.4) does count all of the paths of length $m+1$ from v_i to v_k. Observe that no path is counted twice in (4.4) because all vertices v_j are different for the $A_{ij} \cdot B_{jk}$. ◇

Exercises 4.1

1. Give the adjacency matrix for each of the graphs in Figure 4.11.
2. Draw a picture of a graph corresponding to each of the following adjacency matrices. Be sure to name each of the vertices on the graph.

a. $\begin{pmatrix} 0 & 1 & 1 \\ 1 & 0 & 1 \\ 1 & 1 & 0 \end{pmatrix}$ b. $\begin{pmatrix} 0 & 0 & 1 & 1 \\ 0 & 0 & 0 & 1 \\ 1 & 0 & 0 & 1 \\ 1 & 1 & 1 & 0 \end{pmatrix}$

c. $\begin{pmatrix} 0 & 1 & 1 & 0 & 0 \\ 1 & 0 & 0 & 1 & 1 \\ 1 & 0 & 0 & 1 & 0 \\ 0 & 1 & 1 & 0 & 0 \\ 0 & 1 & 0 & 0 & 0 \end{pmatrix}$ d. $\begin{pmatrix} 0 & 1 & 0 & 1 & 0 \\ 1 & 0 & 1 & 0 & 0 \\ 0 & 1 & 0 & 0 & 1 \\ 1 & 0 & 0 & 0 & 1 \\ 0 & 0 & 1 & 1 & 0 \end{pmatrix}$

3. Classify the graphs of Figure 4.12 as connected or nonconnected. For the nonconnected graphs, draw the subgraphs that are the connected components.

4. Give the adjacency matrix for each of the directed graphs in Figure 4.13.

Figure 4.11

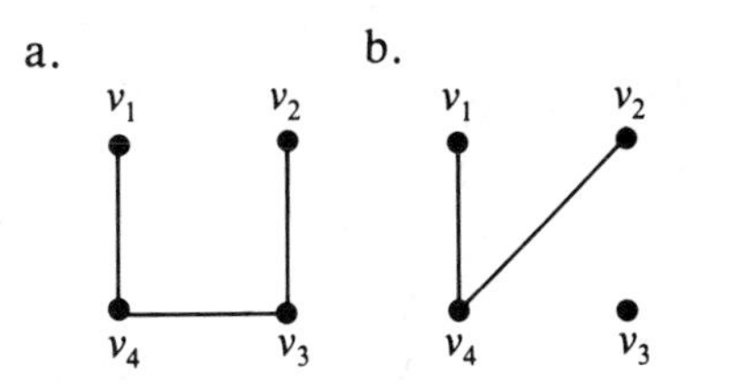

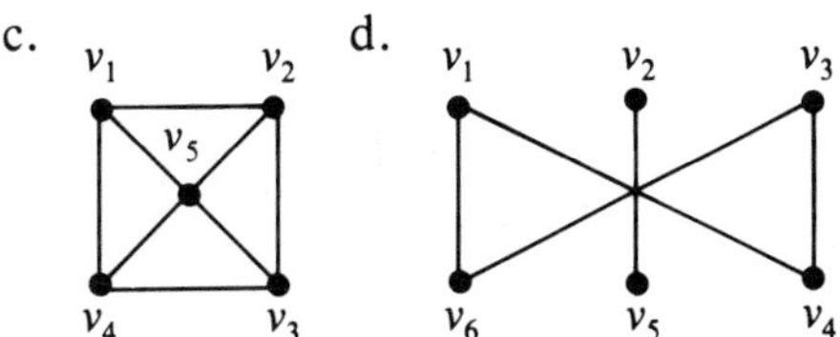

Figure 4.12

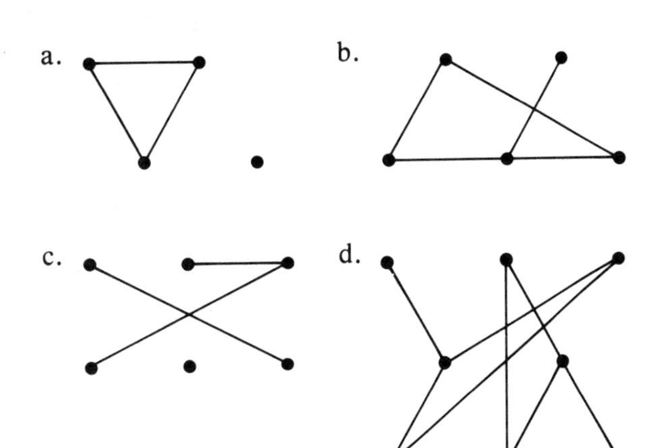

Figure 4.13

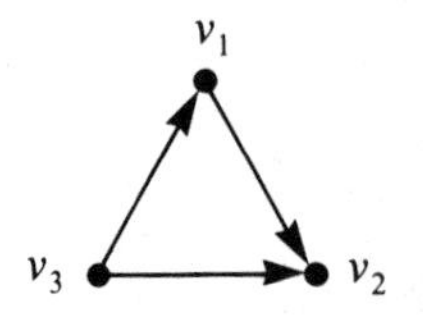

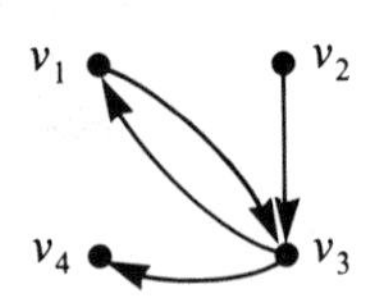

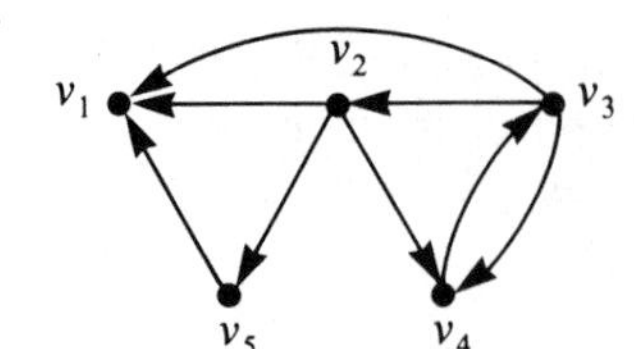

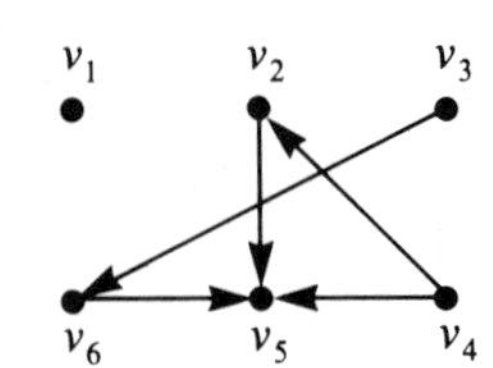

5. Draw the directed graphs that correspond to each of the following adjacency matrices. Be sure to name the vertices on each of the graphs.

a. $\begin{pmatrix} 0 & 0 & 1 \\ 0 & 0 & 1 \\ 0 & 0 & 0 \end{pmatrix}$ b. $\begin{pmatrix} 0 & 0 & 0 & 0 \\ 1 & 0 & 1 & 0 \\ 0 & 0 & 0 & 0 \\ 0 & 1 & 0 & 0 \end{pmatrix}$

c. $\begin{pmatrix} 0 & 1 & 0 & 0 \\ 1 & 0 & 0 & 1 \\ 0 & 1 & 0 & 0 \\ 0 & 0 & 1 & 0 \end{pmatrix}$ d. $\begin{pmatrix} 0 & 1 & 0 & 1 & 0 \\ 1 & 0 & 0 & 0 & 1 \\ 0 & 0 & 0 & 1 & 0 \\ 1 & 1 & 0 & 0 & 0 \\ 1 & 0 & 0 & 0 & 0 \end{pmatrix}$

6. For each directed graph in Figure 4.13, give a table as in Example 4.9 showing which vertices are accessible from other vertices.
7. Explain why the adjacency matrix of Definition 4.2 may also be thought of as the relation matrix, as in Table 3.8, for the relation "v_i is adjacent to v_j."
8. Let A be the adjacency matrix for the graph G. Show that the sum of all of the entries in A equals twice the number of edges in G.
9. Let G' and G'' be subgraphs of G with vertices V', V'' and edges E', E'' respectively. Show that $V' \cup V''$ and $E' \cup E''$ are the vertices and edges for a subgraph of G.
10. Let G be a graph with vertices V and edges E.
    a. Show that "v_1 may be connected to v_2" is an equivalence relation $\sim$ on V.
    b. Suppose that the edge e is incident at vertices v_1 and v_2. Explain why $v_1 \sim v_2$.
    c. Let $V' = [v]$ be an equivalence class. Let E' consist of all edges e

such that e is incident at elements in V'. Show that V' and E' give a *connected subgraph* G' of G.

d. Show that all of the E' from part (c) form a partition of E.

e. Let G' be as in part (c). Let G'' be a subgraph of G such that $V' \subset V''$ and $E' \subset E''$, with $V' \neq V''$ and/or $E' \neq E''$. Show that G'' is not connected.

11. Let V be the set of vertices for a directed graph G. Explain why "v_2 is accessible from v_1" is not in general an equivalence relation.
12. Explain how Theorem 4.2 may be used to prove Proposition 3.14.

4.2 Trees

The previous section introduced the general notion of a graph. This section is devoted to the special kind of undirected graph called a *tree*. Trees are very important in studying general graphs.

Definition 4.8

Let G be a graph. A path of length n, $n \geq 1$, is **closed** if $v_0 = v_n$. A simple, closed path is a **cycle** (or **circuit**). ○

Example 4.11

Look at the graph of Figure 4.14. Here are some closed paths that are not simple, and so are not cycles:

$$A, a, B, a, A$$

$$B, c, C, e, F, g, E, f, D, d, C, e, F, g, E, b, B$$

$$E, b, B, a, A, h, F, g, E, b, B, a, A, h, F, g, E$$

Here are two cycles on the graph of Figure 4.14:

$$B, c, C, e, F, g, E, b, B$$

$$A, a, B, c, C, d, D, f, E, g, F, h, A \qquad \textbf{(4.5)}$$

We observe that cycle (4.5) may be redrawn as a quadralateral, as in Figure 4.15 on p. 176. △

Definition 4.9

A **tree** is a connected graph with no cycles. ○

Figure 4.14

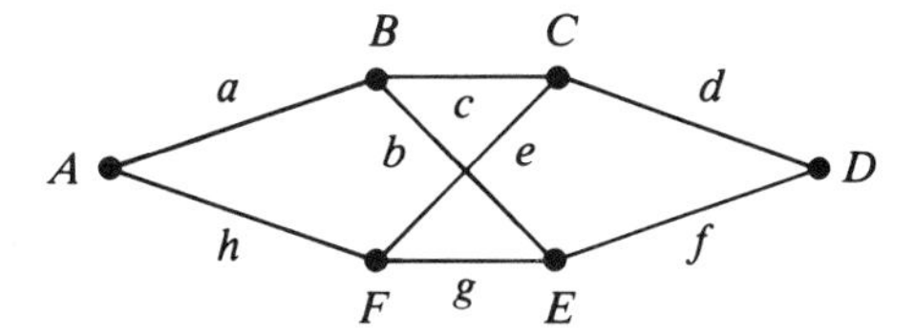

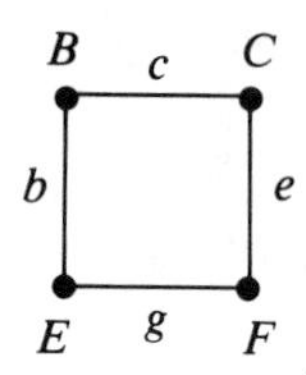

Figure 4.15 A cycle

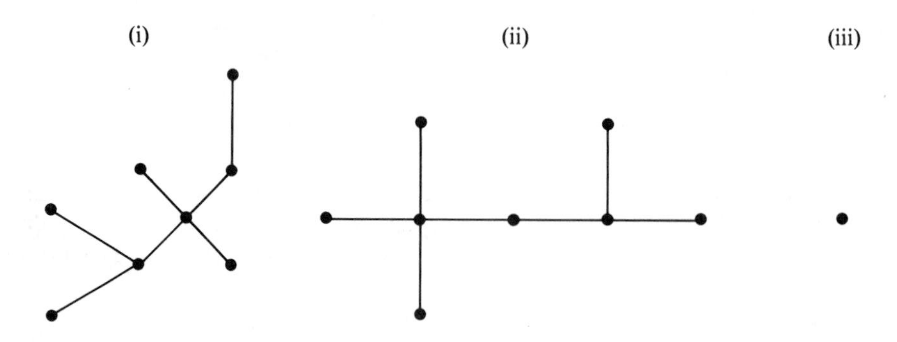

Figure 4.16 Trees

The partial family tree of Figure 4.2 is then also a tree in the sense of Definition 4.9; we are neglecting any directions on the edges. Figure 4.14 is not a tree, since it has cycles as in Example 4.11. Figure 4.16 gives some more trees. Observe that Figure 4.16(iii), with one vertex and no edges, is a tree.

Theorem 4.3 Let v and v' be vertices of a tree. Then there is a unique simple path connecting v and v'.

Before proving Theorem 4.3, we illustrate its statement and part of its proof.

Example 4.12 The reader may easily verify that unique simple paths exist between vertices in each of the trees of Figure 4.16. △

Example 4.13 Consider vertices B and C of Figure 4.14. Then

$$B,c,C \quad \text{and} \tag{4.6}$$

$$B,a,A,h,F,e,C \tag{4.7}$$

are two different simple paths connecting B and C. Traversing first (4.6) and then (4.7) in reverse order gives the cycle

$$B,c,C,e,F,h,A,a,B$$

Of course, Figure 4.14 does not represent a tree. △

Proof of Theorem 4.3

A tree is given to be a connected graph. So by Proposition 4.1, there is a simple path connecting v and v'. We shall show that the existence of more than one simple path leads to the existence of a cycle, and so contradicts Definition 4.9.

If $v=v'$, then the simple path of length 0 that consists solely of v connects v to itself. Any other simple path would be a cycle. So we may assume that $v \neq v'$.

Suppose that there are two different simple paths, P_1 and P_2, connecting the distinct vertices v and v'. Using v's and w's for vertices and e's and f's for edges, we may denote P_1 and P_2 as follows:

$$\begin{aligned} &P_1: v=v_0, e_1, v_1, \ldots, v_{n-1}, e_n, v_n=v' \\ &P_2: v=w_0, f_1, w_1, \ldots, w_{m-1}, f_m, w_m=v' \end{aligned} \tag{4.8}$$

Since $P_1 \neq P_2$, there is a first edge or vertex in which they differ. Since edges determine their endpoints, P_1 and P_2 must in fact first differ in an edge, say $e_i \neq f_i$. $v_{i-1}=w_{i-1}$. So by replacing P_1 and P_2 by possibly shorter paths starting at $v_{i-1}=w_{i-1}$, we may assume in (4.8) that $e_1 \neq f_1$; see Figure 4.17. Should some v_j, $j<n$, equal a w_k, $k<m$, then we may replace P_1 and P_2 by possibly shorter paths that end at $v_j=w_k$; see Figure 4.18. So in (4.8) we may assume that, except for $v_0=w_0$ and $v_n=w_m$, all of the vertices v_i and w_j are distinct. Since an edge determines its endpoints, all of the edges e_i and w_j in (4.8) must also be distinct, unless possibly $n=m=1$. But $e_1 \neq f_1$, so the case $n=m=1$ cannot happen. We now get a cycle, and our desired contradiction, by following P_1 in (4.8) by P_2 in reverse order:

$$v=v_0, e_1, v_1, \ldots, e_n, v_n=v'=w_m, f_m, w_{m-1}, \ldots, w_1, f_1, w_0=v \qquad \diamond$$

Suppose that we have a system of telephone cables that connects a collection of towns. Suppose that, possibly for emergency planning, a minimal subsystem of cables must be found that still connects all of the towns. In a cycle of cables, any single cable may be deleted, while still retaining connectivity. So what is called for is a spanning tree, as in

Figure 4.17

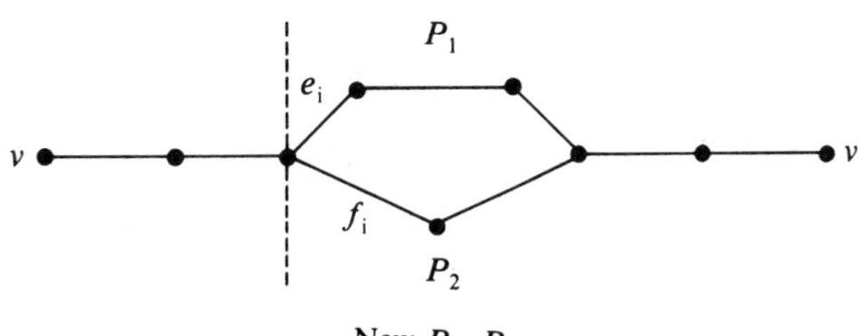

New P_1, P_2

Figure 4.18

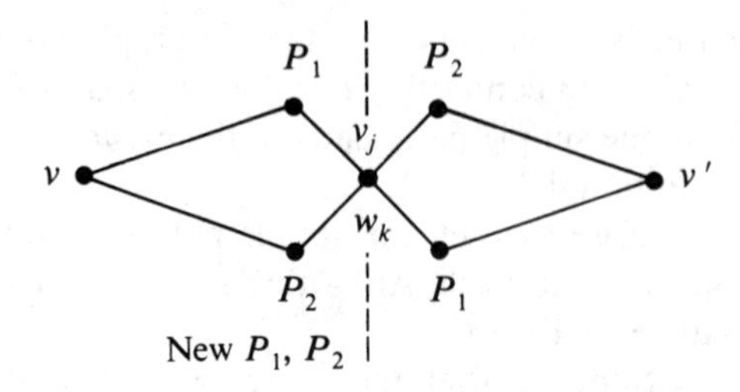

Definition 4.10, which follows. Later we shall consider ways to minimize, say, the cost of the cables in the subsystem.

Definition 4.10

Let G be a connected graph. A **spanning tree** T for G is a subgraph T of G such that T contains all of the vertices of G and such that T is a tree. ○

Example 4.14

Figure 4.19 gives some connected graphs and spanning trees for them. Observe that spanning trees need not be unique. △

It is easy to find a spanning tree for a connected graph G. As in Figure 4.20, one may start with the vertices and then successively add edges that do not create cycles, until all of the vertices are connected. Alternatively, as in Figure 4.21, one may delete edges that are part of cycles until there are no more cycles.

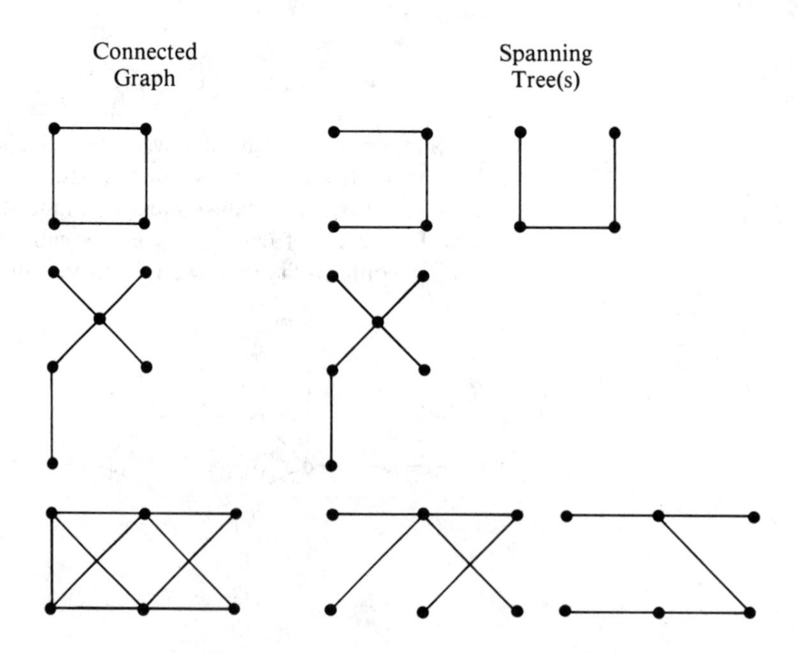

Figure 4.19 Some connected graphs and spanning trees

Figure 4.20 Finding a spanning tree

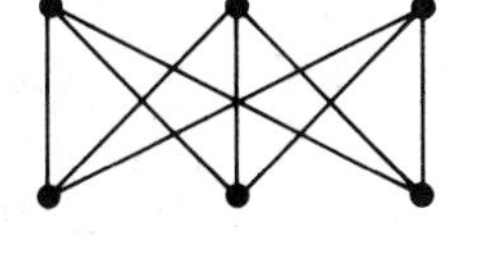

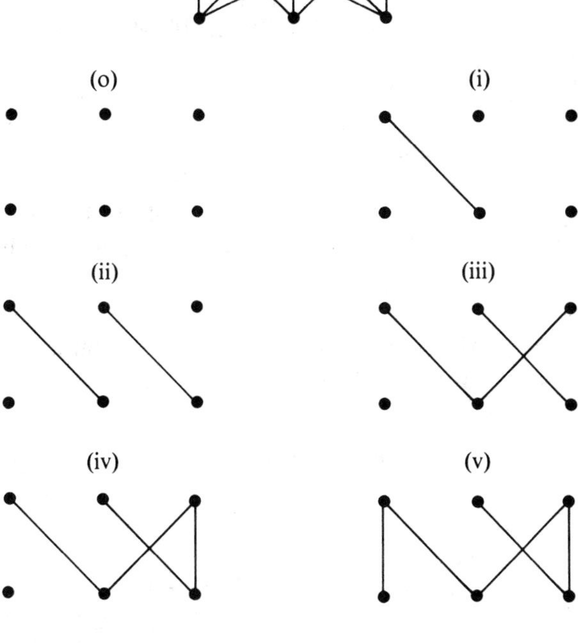

Figure 4.21 Finding a spanning tree

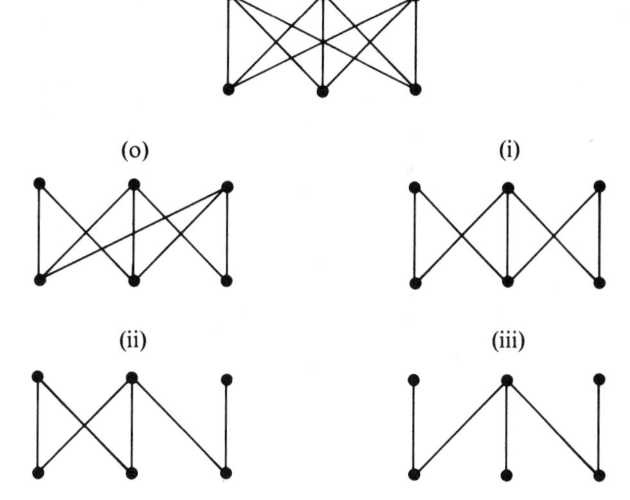

Theorem 4.4 Let G be a connected graph with $|V|$ vertices and $|E|$ edges. Then G is a tree if and only if

$$|V| - |E| = 1$$

Examples 4.15

Before proving Theorem 4.4, we shall illustrate its statement. Figure 4.22 gives a tree with $|V|=6$ vertices and $|E|=5$ edges. Indeed, $6-5=1$. △

In the connected graph of Figure 4.23, $|V|=6$ and $|E|=9$.

$$|V|-|E|=6-9=-3\neq 1$$

The graph of Figure 4.23 is not a tree. △

In the graph of Figure 4.24, $|V|=5$ and $|E|=4$. Then $|V|-|E|=1$. But this graph is not a tree. Theorem 4.4 only applies to connected graphs. △

Proof of Theorem 4.4 The proof will be by mathematical induction on $|V|$, the number of vertices in the graph G.

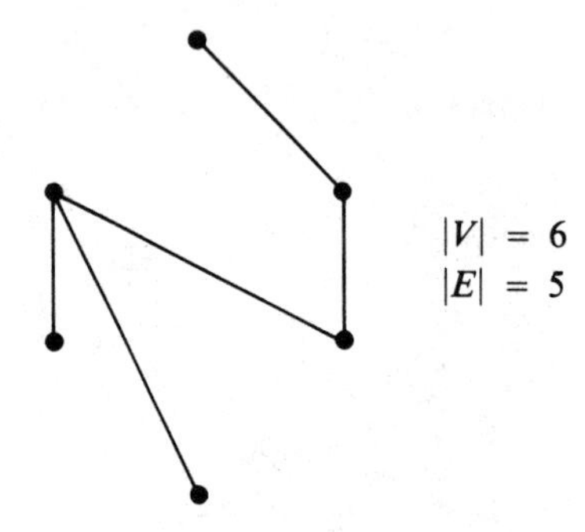

Figure 4.22 A tree

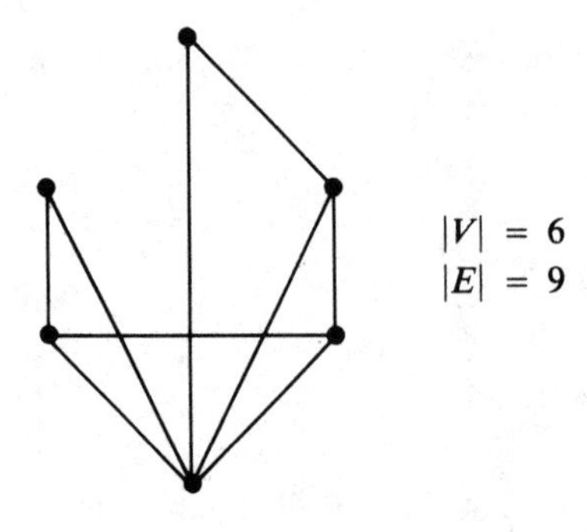

Figure 4.23 A connected graph

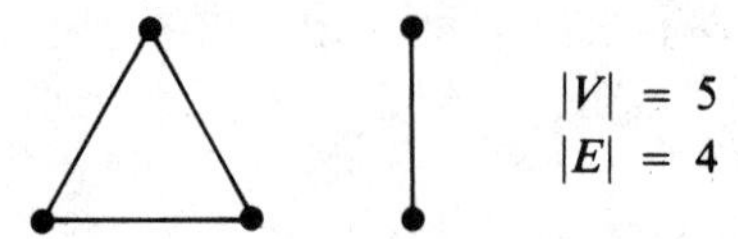

Figure 4.24 A nonconnected graph

For a graph with just one vertex, the only possible edges are loops. Loops are not allowed in Definition 4.1. So $|E|=0$ and the graph is automatically a tree.

So we assume Theorem 4.4 for all connected graphs with $n=|V|$ vertices. We must prove it for each connected graph G with $n+1$ vertices. Suppose first that G is a tree. Let v be a vertex of G. We construct a simple path P_1,

$$P_1 : v = v_0, e_1, v_1, \ldots, v_{m-1}, e_m, v_m$$

with length m as large as possible. Then e_m must be the only edge incident at v_m because, if $e \neq e_m$ were incident at v_m, then we could extend P_1 by e (and e's other endpoint) and get a longer simple path. Then removing e_m and v_m from G gives a subgraph G' with only n vertices.

$$\begin{aligned} |V'| &= |V| - 1 \\ |E'| &= |E| - 1 \end{aligned} \qquad \textbf{(4.9)}$$

Since G has no cycles, certainly G' has no cycles. Since e_m is incident only at v_m and since G is connected, G' is also connected. So G' is a tree. By the induction hypothesis,

$$|V'| - |E'| = 1$$

By (4.9), also

$$|V| - |E| = 1 \qquad \textbf{(4.10)}$$

Now suppose that (4.10) holds. We must show that G is a tree. Let T be a spanning tree for G. Then T and G have the same $n+1$ vertices. By the already proved part of the induction step, T has n edges. By (4.10), with $|V|=n+1$, G also has n edges. So T is in fact all of G and G is a tree.

◇

Now consider a connected graph G that has a cost $c(e)$ associated to each edge e. This cost might be, for example, the length of the roads between towns. The **cost** of a subgraph is the sum of the costs of the edges in the subgraph. We are looking for a connected subgraph G' such that G' has all of the vertices of G and as low a cost as possible. If all of the costs are positive (or nonnegative), we can delete any excess edges from G'. So G' will be a tree. A **minimum-cost** spanning tree T is a spanning tree T for G such that the cost for T is as low as possible.

Example 4.16

Graph (i) in Figure 4.25 includes the cost for each edge. The next two graphs in Figure 4.25 are minimum-cost spanning trees for Figure 4.25(i).

Figure 4.25

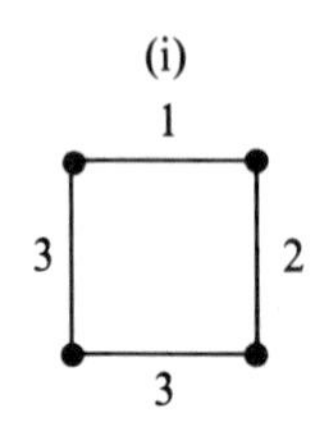

Minimum-Cost Spanning Trees for (i)

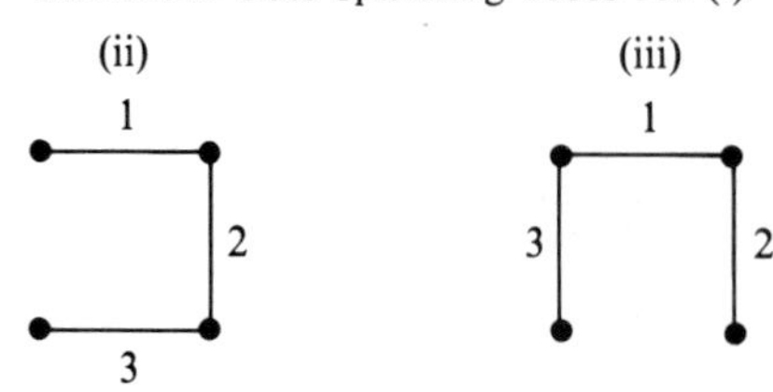

Observe that while Figures 4.25(ii) and 4.25(iii) necessarily have the same cost, they are different subgraphs of Figure 4.25(i). So minimum-cost spanning trees need not be unique. It is true, however, that the costs of the edges of a minimum-cost spanning tree are uniquely determined. △

Theorem 4.5

Let G be a connected graph with a cost $c(e)$ for each edge e. List the edges $e_1,e_2,\ldots,e_n$ of G in increasing (or nondecreasing) order of costs. Let T be the spanning tree for G whose edges are given as explained by the following: Successively for $i=1,2,\ldots,n$, add e_i to the list of edges for T if and only if e_i does not create a cycle when added to the current list of edges.

Then T is a minimum-cost spanning tree for G.

Example 4.17

Before proving Theorem 4.5, we shall illustrate its statement. Figure 4.26(i) gives a G for Theorem 4.5. The edges may be numbered as in Figure 4.26(ii). Table 4.1 gives the computation for the edges of T. The spanning tree T is drawn in Figure 4.27. △

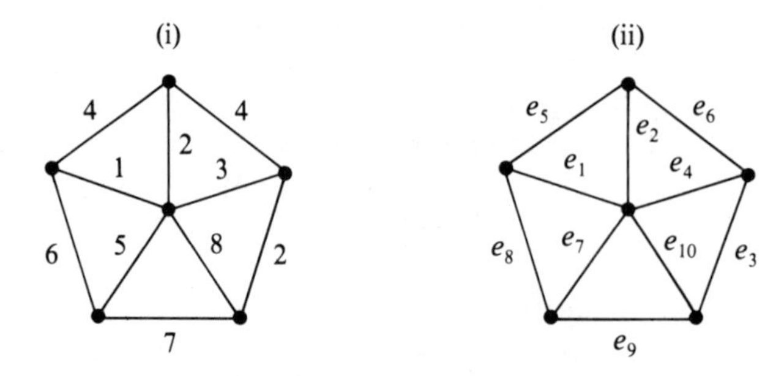

Figure 4.26 Graph with cost function

Table 4.1 Computation of a minimum-cost spanning tree

Edge	Cost	Accept/Reject
e_1	1	Accept
e_2	2	Accept
e_3	2	Accept
e_4	3	Accept
e_5	4	Reject: e_1, e_2, e_5 yields a cycle
e_6	4	Reject: e_2, e_4, e_6 yields a cycle
e_7	5	Accept
We have a spanning tree and may stop. All additional edges must yield cycles.		

Proof of Theorem 4.5

We shall need the following observation: Suppose that T' is a spanning tree for G. Suppose that e is an edge of G that is not an edge of T'. Let v and v' be the endpoints of e. Then there is a simple path P in T' that connects v and v'. Adding the edge e to P creates a cycle C in G. Let e' be an edge in C. Exchanging e' for e in T' gives a new subgraph T'' of G; see Figure 4.28 on p. 184 for an example. T'' is still connected. By Theorem 4.4, T'' is also a tree (and hence a spanning tree for G).

Now consider the first, lowest cost edge e_1. Adding e_1 to the (currently empty) list of edges does not create a cycle. We shall show that there is some minimum-cost spanning tree T_1 that contains e_1. Let T' be any minimum-cost spanning tree. If T' contains e_1, then we are done. Otherwise, as in the first paragraph of this proof, we let P be the simple path in T' that connects the endpoints of e_1. Let C be the cycle formed from P and e_1. Since e_1 has the lowest cost of all edges in G, e_1 may be exchanged in T' for any edge in C to give a new spanning tree T'' with the cost of T'' at most the cost of T'. But T' has minimum cost. So T'' and T' both have minimum cost. Let $T_1 = T''$.

Now let us consider e_2. We know that there is a minimum-cost spanning tree T_1 that contains e_1. Adding e_2 to $\{e_1\}$ cannot create a cycle, by Definition 4.1. Suppose that e_2 is not in T_1. There is a simple path P in T_1 connecting the endpoints of e_2. Adding e_2 to P creates a cycle C. The

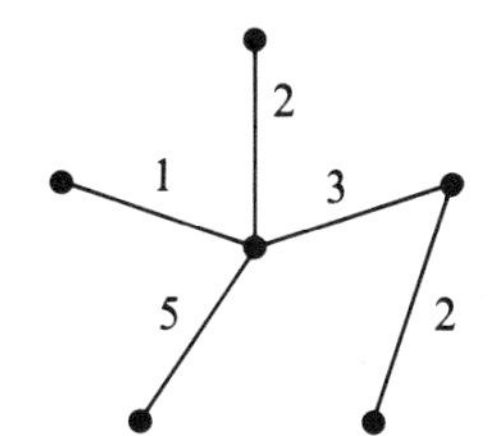

Figure 4.27 Minimum-cost spanning tree for Figure 4.26

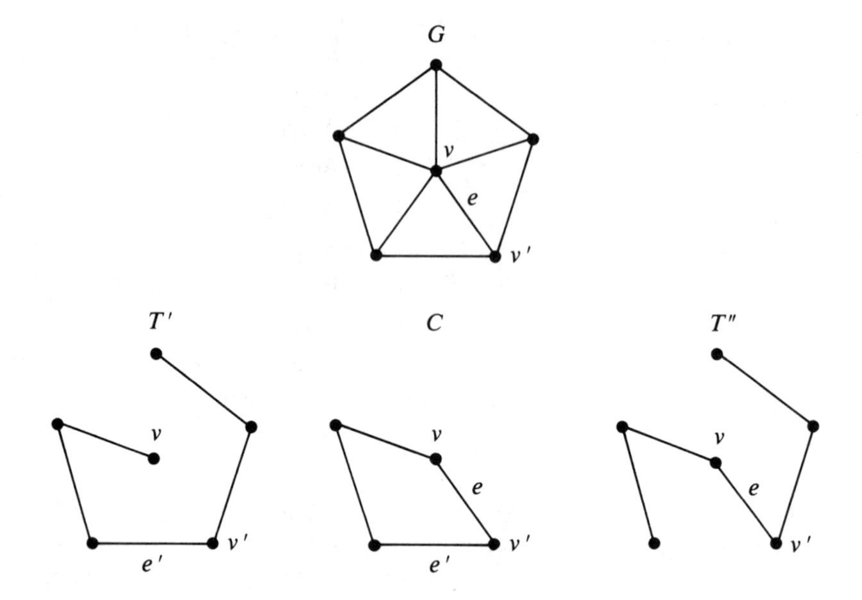

Figure 4.28 Exchanging edges

cycle C cannot consist solely of e_1 and e_2, since e_1 and e_2 do not form a cycle. But e_2 has a cost less than or equal to the cost of all edges besides e_1. So there is an edge $e' \neq e_2$ in C such that $c(e_2) \leq c(e')$. Exchange e' in T_1 for e_2. This creates a spanning tree T_2 with cost at most equal to the cost of T_1. Since T_1 has minimum cost, so does T_2. T_2 contains e_1 and e_2.

Now consider e_3. Suppose that adding e_3 to $\{e_1, e_2\}$ does not create a cycle. Then, as in the previous paragraphs, if e_3 is not already in T_2, we may modify T_2 to create another minimum-cost spanning tree T_3 such that e_3 is in T_3.

Repeating this argument for all of the edges completes the proof of Theorem 4.5. ◇

Example 4.18

Figure 4.29(i) gives a connected graph with a cost function. The rest of Figure 4.29 shows a computation of a minimum-cost spanning tree using Theorem 4.5. The minimum cost is also given.

By Theorem 4.4, in a connected graph with $|V|$ vertices, all spanning trees have $|V| - 1$ edges. So we may stop the computation in Figure 4.29 after accepting $7 - 1 = 6$ edges. △

Exercises 4.2

1. Decide whether or not each of the graphs in Figure 4.30 is a tree.
2. Find three different cycles in the graph of Figure 4.31. Each cycle should have a different set of edges. (The sets of edges need not be disjoint, only different.)

Figure 4.29
Computation of minimum-cost spanning tree

(i) Graph with a Cost Function (ii) Edges Are Ordered

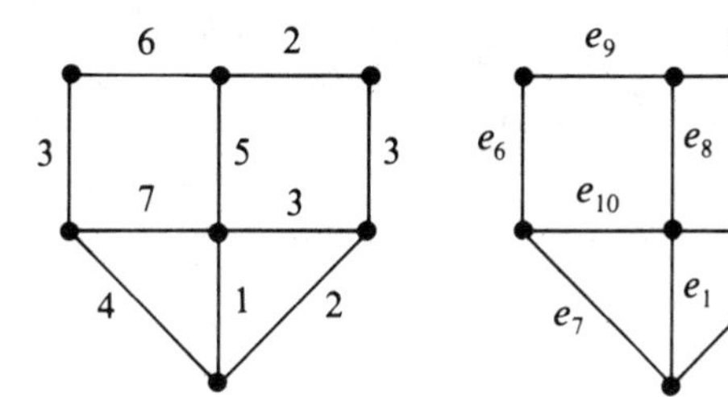

Edge	Cost	A/R
e_1	1	Accept
e_2	2	Accept
e_3	2	Accept
e_4	3	Reject
e_5	3	Accept
e_6	3	Accept
e_7	4	Accept

(iii) Minimum-Cost Spanning Tree

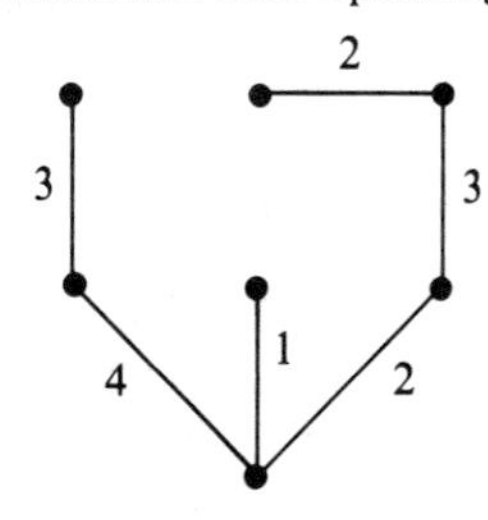

Minimum cost = 15

Figure 4.30

a.
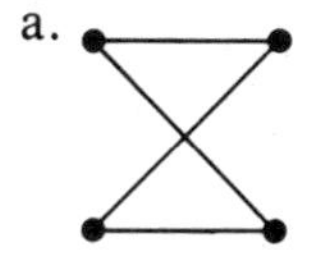

b.
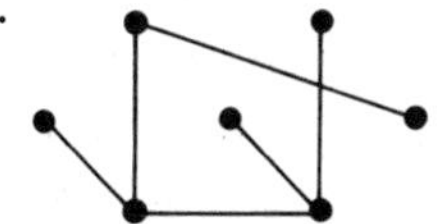

c.
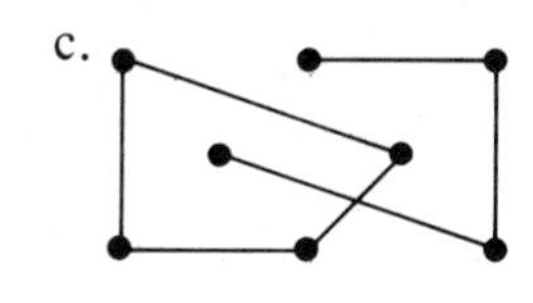

d.

Figure 4.31

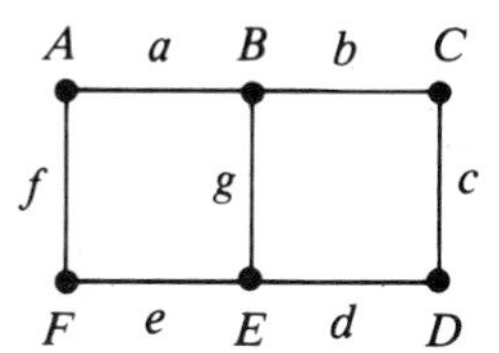

3. Find a minimum-cost spanning tree for each of the graphs in Figure 4.32 on p. 186. Also, give the minimum cost.
4. Let e be an edge in a connected graph G such that removing e from G creates a subgraph that is not connected. Show that e is an edge in every spanning tree for G.

Figure 4.32

a.

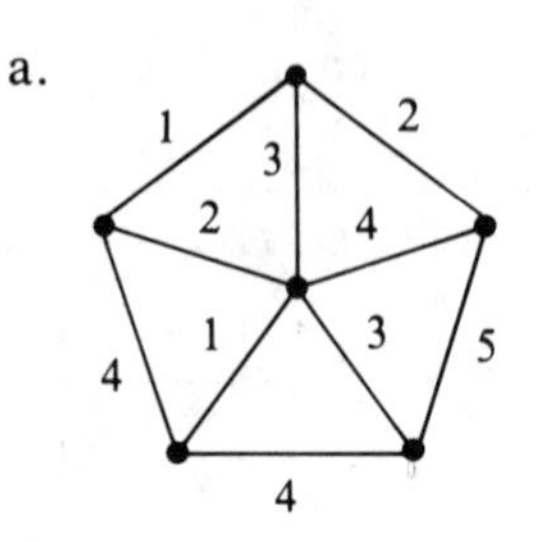

b.

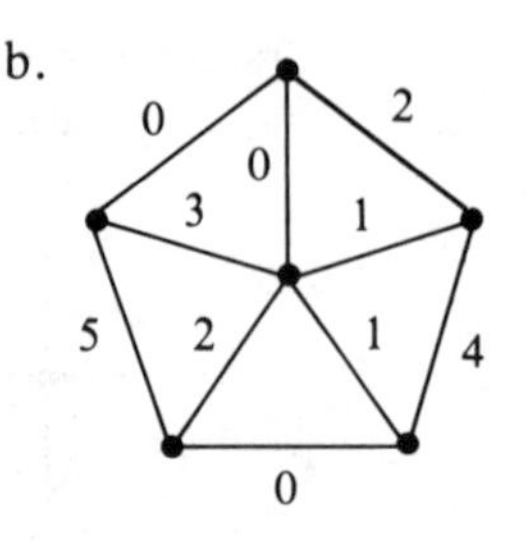

c.

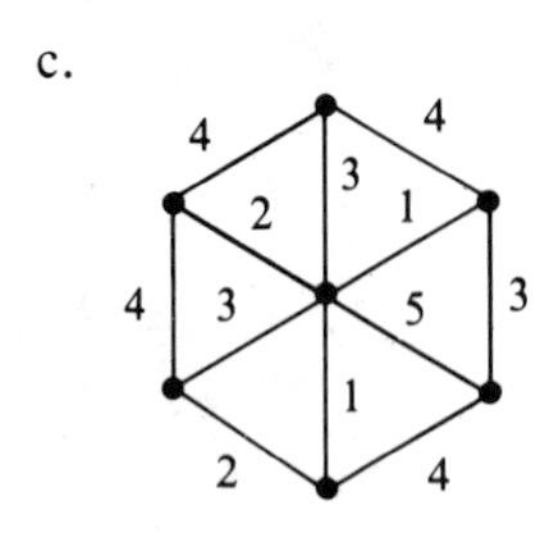

d.

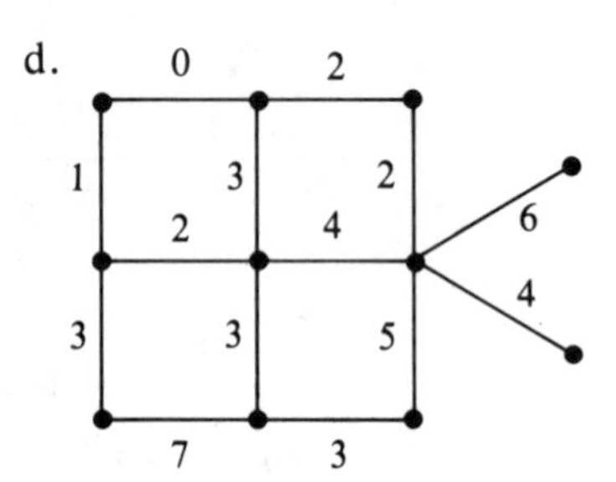

5. Let G be a connected graph. Start with the subgraph that consists of the vertices of G. Explain why successively adding edges that do not yield cycles results in a spanning tree.

   Hint: Let G' be a subgraph of G, without cycles, with vertices v and v' that cannot be connected in G'. Connect v and v' by a simple path P in G. Add a new edge from P.

6. Let G be a connected graph. Explain why successively deleting edges that are parts of cycles creates a spanning tree for G.

   Hint: Let C be a cycle on the connected graph G. Deleting an edge from C cannot make a nonconnected subgraph of G.

7. Let G be a connected graph with a cost function for the edges. Show that the set of costs for any minimum-cost spanning tree T' is uniquely determined.

   Hint: Look at the construction of T from T' in the proof of Theorem 4.5.

4.3 Directed Trees

In this section, we study directed trees. These are the directed graph analogs of the trees of the previous section. We use directed trees for finding the best moves in games and for forming an efficient list of words.

Example 4.19

Consider the graph G' in Figure 4.33. Each edge in G' may be made into a directed edge by arbitrarily choosing one endpoint to be the initial vertex and the other endpoint to be the terminal vertex. Making this choice for all

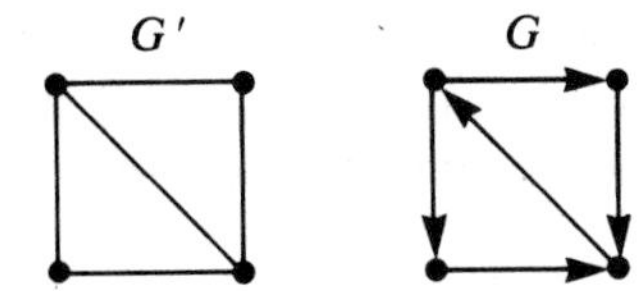

Figure 4.33 Graph G' and directed graph G

of the edges in G' yields a directed graph G. Figure 4.33 gives one such choice for G. △

Definition 4.11

A **directed tree** T (also called a **rooted tree**) is a directed graph formed from a tree T' by

(i) Choosing a vertex r of T', called the **root**, and

(ii) Assigning initial and terminal vertices to the edges of T' so that all vertices of T are accessible from r. ○

Exercise 17 of this section implies that accessibility in Definition 4.11(ii) is always via simple paths. Exercise 18 says that, since we have chosen r in Definition 4.11(i), the assignments in Definition 4.11(ii) are always possible and are unique.

Example 4.20

Figure 4.34 gives some examples of directed trees. The root r is named for each directed tree. Figure 4.35 gives two examples of directed graphs that are not directed trees. In Figure 4.35(i), the underlying graph is a tree, but

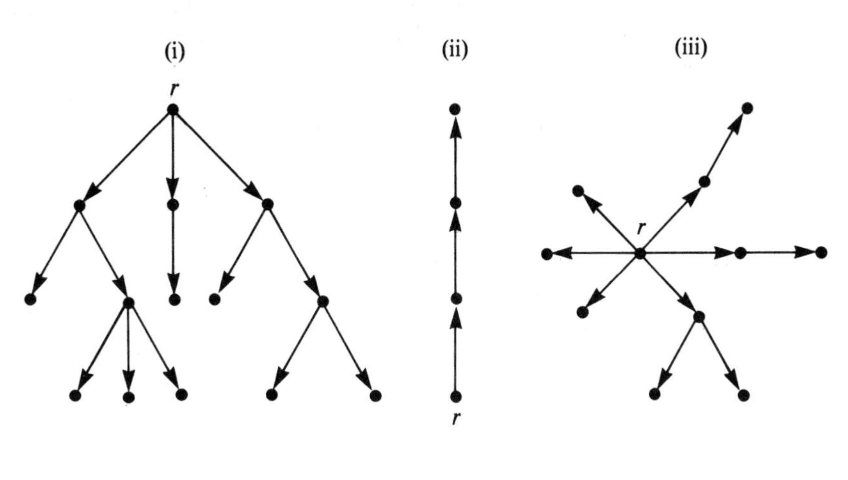

Figure 4.34 Directed trees

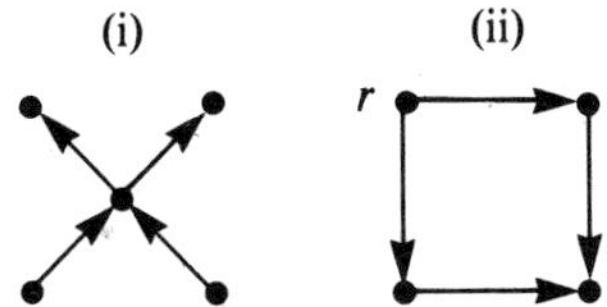

Figure 4.35

the directions on the edges are such that all vertices are not accessible from just a single vertex. In Figure 4.35(ii), all vertices are accessible from the vertex r, but the underlying graph is not a tree. △

Example 4.21

We use a directed tree to calculate an optimal strategy for a simple game. This same tree technique is used in most computer programs to play chess, with larger trees, of course.

Our simple game has two players, A and B. The game begins with four counters. A move consists of the removal of one or two counters. Players alternate moves, with A starting. The player who removes the last counter loses the game.

Figure 4.36, a game tree, describes all possible complete sequences of moves for the game. Namely, the game starts at the top vertex, or root, with four counters and A to move. A has two possible moves, leaving B with the two indicated positions. For each position, B has various moves. Then A has various moves. The label on each vertex gives the number of counters remaining. So the game ends at vertices labeled by 0.

Assuming A's point of view, we wish to assign a value of 1 to positions where A should win and a value of 0 to positions where B should win. The rules of the game give us these values, as listed in Figure 4.37 for those positions in Figure 4.36 with 0 counters.

In assigning values to the unknown entries in Figure 4.37, we assume that each player always makes the best possible move for himself. So, if all moves lead to positions with known values, A chooses a move that maximizes the next value while B chooses a move that minimizes the next value. This maximum or minimum, as appropriate, is the current value.

Figure 4.36 A game tree

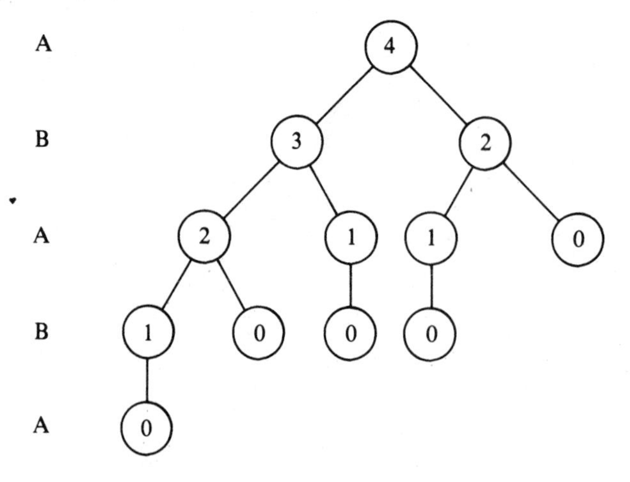

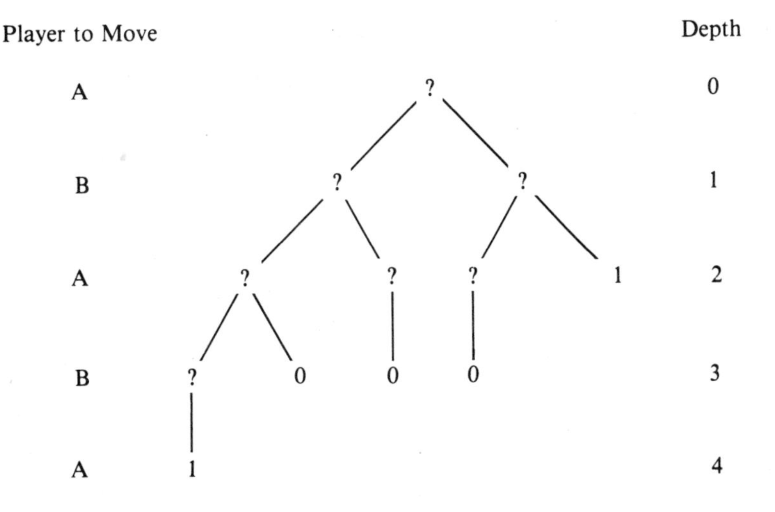

Figure 4.37 Value of the game to A

Theorem 4.3 ensures that there is only one simple path that connects the root of a directed tree to a given vertex, as in Definition 4.11(ii). The **depth** of a vertex in a directed tree is defined as the length of the (unique) simple path that connects the root to the vertex. In Figures 4.36 and 4.37 the vertices are arranged so that all vertices with the same depth appear on the same horizontal line and so the greater depths are lower on the page. One way to compute the desired maximums and minimums, which give the current values of the game, is to start with the greatest depth and to proceed upwards:

Depth 4: All entries are known

Depth 3: B has just one move at the unknown entry.

This brings us to Figure 4.38. For the first unknown entry in Depth 2, A chooses the move that maximizes the position at Depth 3; 1 is this maximum. A has just one move at the other unknown entries in Depth 2 of Figure 4.38. Figure 4.39 gives the results of the complete calculation for all depths.

From Figure 4.39, we see that A should lose this game. B's winning strategy is easily read off from Figure 4.39: B keeps choosing positions of value 0 to A. For example, if A removes one counter from the initial position, B next removes two counters. (This leaves one counter, which A must then remove.) △

Actual computer programs to play chess cannot list all possible sequences of moves; there are too many. Instead, only moves up to a certain depth are listed. Then an evaluation subroutine makes a guess as to

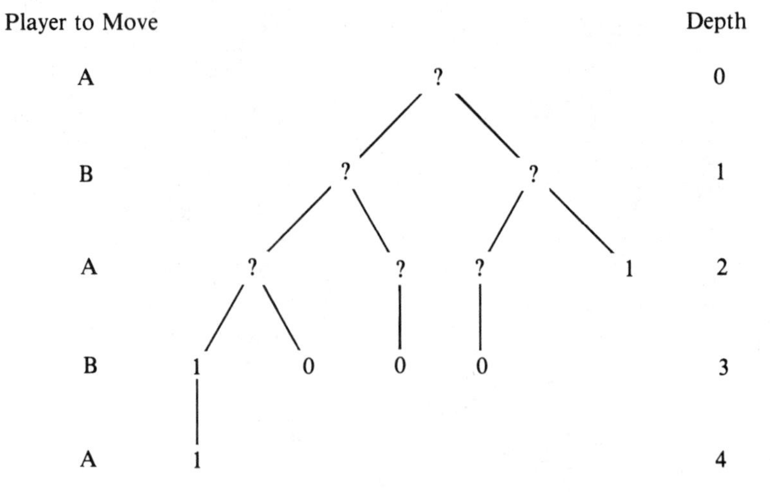

Figure 4.38 Value of the game to A

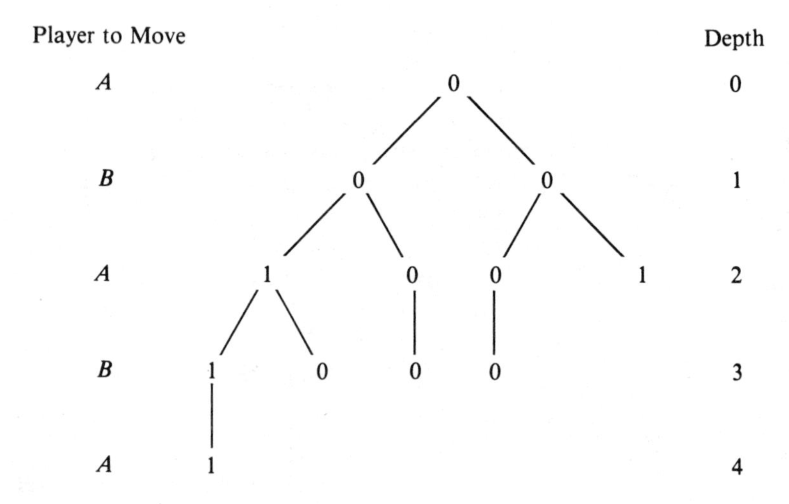

Figure 4.39 Value of the game to A

the relative merit of the resulting position. Also, only "apparently reasonable" moves may be considered, allowing for greater depth in the tree. The order in which we computed maximums and minimums in Example 4.21 requires an excessive amount of storage. Here is a better way.

We are considering a directed tree T with a root r. We will give an efficient order, called **postorder** in Definition 4.13, which follows later, for examining the vertices of T. Start at r and continue along a directed path for as long as possible. The last vertex in the path is the first vertex in postorder. Now backtrack one vertex along the path and attempt to continue the directed path in a different direction. If the attempt is successful, continue the directed path for as long as possible, reaching the second vertex in postorder. If the attempt is not successful, the next-to-the-last vertex in the original path is the second vertex in postorder. To continue this process, avoiding the duplication of vertices, and to be able systematically to continue paths, we need an **order** on T, as in Definition 4.12, which follows.

Definition 4.12 Let T be a directed tree. Let v be a vertex of T. A vertex v' is a **successor** of v if there is a directed edge e in T with v as its initial vertex and v' as its terminal vertex. Then v is a *predecessor* of v'. T is **ordered** if for each vertex v of T there is a total order on the successors of v. ○

Example 4.22 Consider the rooted tree of Figure 4.40. The successors of r are a, b, and c. The vertex b has one successor, g, while j has no successors. The predecessor of i is c. The root r has no predecessors.

The successors to a vertex in Figure 4.40 are listed in order from left to right. Observe that Definition 4.12 does not require any comparison between vertices such as d and h, which are successors to different vertices.

In listing vertices in postorder, as previously defined informally, we continue paths via the smallest unused successor. For Figure 4.40, the first path traverses vertices

$$r,a,d,j \tag{4.11}$$

j is the first vertex in postorder. Backtrack to d in (4.11); d has no other successor besides j, so d is second in postorder. Backtrack to a in (4.11). Continue the path from a, giving a new path through the vertices

$$r,a,e$$

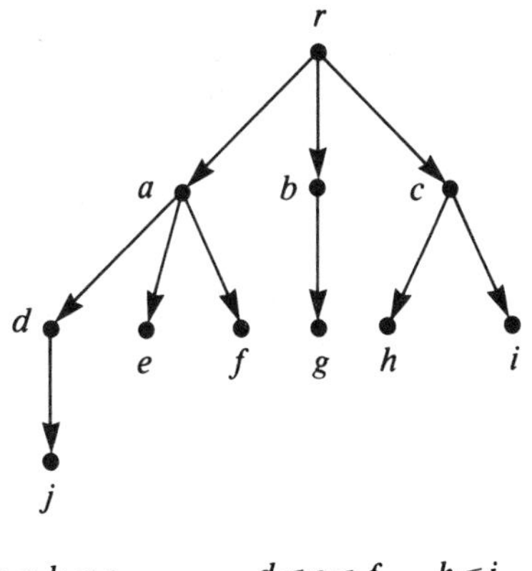

Figure 4.40 An ordered directed tree

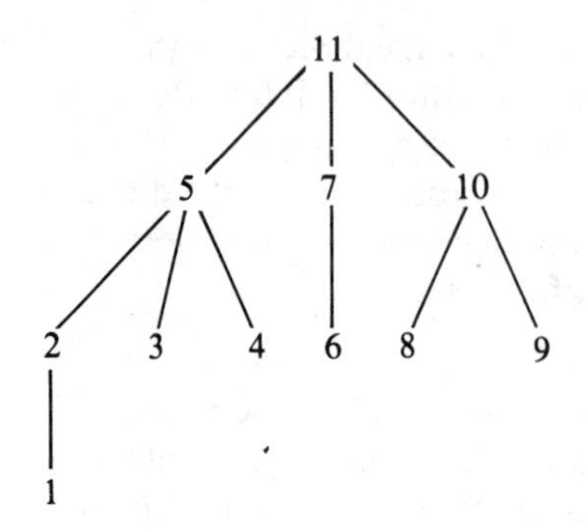

Figure 4.41 Postorder for Figure 4.40

So e is the third vertex in postorder. Figure 4.41 gives a complete numbering of the vertices of Figure 4.40 in postorder. △

Definition 4.13

Let T be an ordered directed tree. The total order **postorder**, $\leq$, on the vertices of T is given as described by the following: Let v and w be vertices of T. Let

$$P_1: r, e_1, v_1, e_2, \ldots, v_{n-1}, e_n, v_n = v \quad \text{and}$$

$$P_2: r, f_1, w_1, f_2, \ldots, w_{m-1}, f_m, w_m = w$$

be the unique simple paths connecting the root r to the vertices v and w respectively.

(i) If v is a vertex in P_2 (that is, if P_1 is a subpath of P_2), then $w \leq v$.

(ii) If $e_i \neq f_i$ is the first edge in which P_1 and P_2 differ, then v_i and w_i are different successors to the vertex $v_{i-1} = w_{i-1}$. Then $v < w$ or $w < v$ according to whether $v_i < w_i$ or $w_i < v_i$, where v_i and w_i are compared via the given order on T. ○

Example 4.23

Order the successors in the directed tree of Figure 4.36 from left to right. Then Figure 4.42 numbers the vertices of Figure 4.36 in postorder. △

Observe that postorder preserves the original order on successors. Thus in Figure 4.40, $a \leq b \leq c$. In Figure 4.41, for postorder, a, b, and c are numbered 5, 7, and 10, respectively.

In computing the values of positions for a game tree, it is efficient to examine the vertices, that is, the game positions, in postorder; the initial ordering of the game tree may be done in any convenient manner. By Definition 4.13(i), the information to compute a maximum or a minimum is always available as needed. More importantly, let v be a vertex in the game tree. Let P be the simple path connecting r to v. *While evaluating position v, the information that must be stored for the evaluation of future*

Figure 4.42 Postorder for Figure 4.36

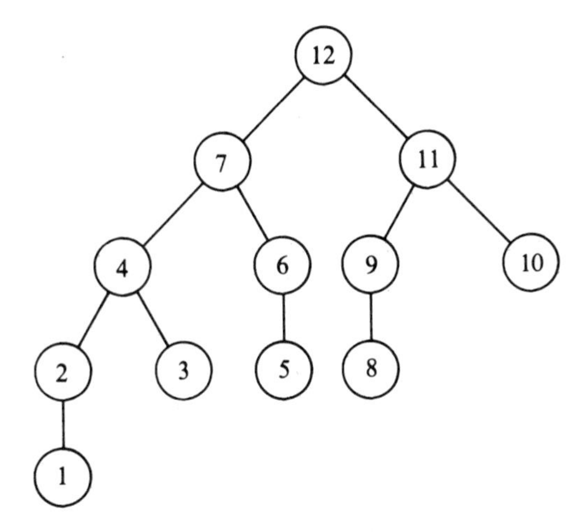

positions is only *the values of previously examined positions that are successors to vertices in P*. This greatly reduces the storage requirements for evaluation over the requirements for the order used in Example 4.21.

Example 4.24

Let T be an ordered directed game tree. Let v be a vertex of T, which we have already evaluated. Let us see how to find and to evaluate the next vertex v' after v in postorder.

Let

$$P: r, e_1, v_1, e_2, \ldots, v_{n-1}, e_n, v_n = v$$

be the simple path connecting r to v. Let

$$w_1 \leq w_2 \leq \cdots \leq w_m$$

denote the successors to v_{n-1}. Then v is one of the w_i; let us say that $v = w_j$.

Case 1. $j = m$; that is, $v = w_m$. Then $v' = v_{n-1}$. The game position for v' is evaluated by taking the maximum or the minimum (as appropriate) over the (known) evaluations of all of the w_i. Also, we may now delete from storage the evaluations of the w_i.

Case 2. $j < m$; that is, $v < w_m$. We find v' by continuing the path from r to w_{j+1} for as long as possible, always choosing the smallest successor. The last vertex in this continuation is v'. The position v' is one that occurs at the end of the game and must be evaluated according to the rules of the game.

Observe that r is the last vertex in postorder. The evaluation of r tells which player should win the game. △

Definition 4.14, which follows, gives another important total order, *preorder*, on the vertices of an ordered directed tree. As does postorder, preorder considers paths that start at r. However, where *post*order starts numbering at the *end* of paths, *pre*order starts numbering at the *beginning* of paths.

Definition 4.14

Let T be an ordered directed tree. The total order **preorder**, $\leq$, on the vertices of T is given as follows: Let v, w, P_1, and P_2 be as in Definition 4.13.

(i) If v is a vertex in P_2, then $v \leq w$.
(ii) Definition 4.13(ii). ○

Example 4.25

Figure 4.43 numbers the vertices of Figure 4.36 in preorder. △

Figure 4.43 Preorder for Figure 4.36

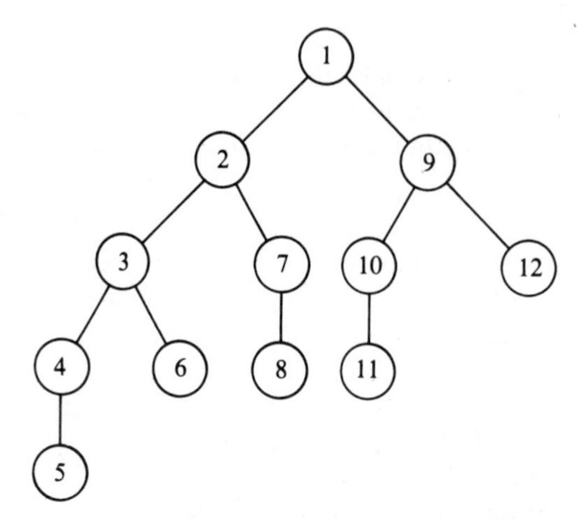

Example 4.26

The line of succession to the throne of the United Kingdom is given by preorder. Successors, that is, children, are ordered by birth, except that males precede females. Figure 4.44 gives the line of succession to King George V in Figure 4.2 (on p. 164). In Figure 4.2, children are ordered from left to right. △

Suppose that we are manipulating a large, changing collection of names. Typical of such collections are the directory of all files in a large computer and the set of labels (and related names) to be compiled in a user's program. These names often come with a natural total order, such as alphabetical order, already on them. Often, it is convenient to store the names in a *binary search tree*, as in Definition 4.17, which follows. The structure of a binary search tree is then convenient for searching for the first name in the tree, for deciding whether a new name is already

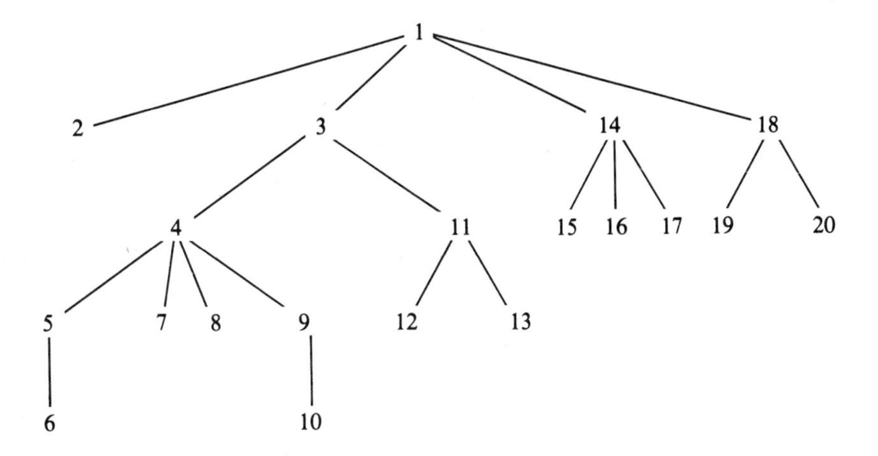

Figure 4.44 Preorder for Figure 4.2

in the tree, for adding a new name to the tree, and for deleting a name from the tree.

Definition 4.15

A **binary tree** T is a directed tree such that

(i) Each vertex v of T has at most two successors.

(ii) Each successor to a vertex v is designated as a left successor, $l(v)$, or as a right successor, $r(v)$. v cannot have two left or two right successors. ○

Example 4.27

Figure 4.45 gives a typical binary tree, with the root at the top. The left successor to a vertex, if any, is drawn at the end of a leftward slanting edge. Similarly, the right successor is drawn at the end of a rightward slanting

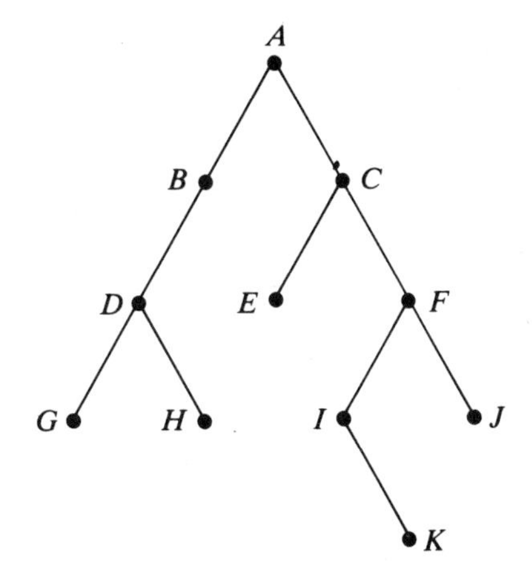

Figure 4.45 A binary tree

edge. Thus in Figure 4.45,

$$l(A)=B, \quad r(A)=C, \quad l(B)=D, \quad r(I)=K$$

I has no left successor, and B has no right successor.

The information in a binary tree is conveniently stored as an array that lists the left and right successors, if any, for each vertex. Table 4.2 gives this successor array for the binary tree of Figure 4.45. Of course, in a computer the array gives the addresses of the successors, rather than their names. △

Table 4.2 Successor array for Figure 4.45

Vertex	A	B	C	D	E	F	G	H	I	K
Left Successor	B	D	E	G	–	I	–	–	–	–
Right Successor	C	–	F	H	–	J	–	–	K	–

Definition 4.16

Let v be a vertex in a binary tree T. The **left subtree** of v consists of all vertices (and connecting edges) of T that are accessible from $l(v)$. The **right subtree** of v consists of all vertices (and connecting edges) of T that are accessible from $r(v)$. ○

Example 4.28

Consider the binary tree of Figure 4.45. Then the left subtree of F has vertices I, K. The right subtree of C has vertices F, I, J, K. The left subtree of I has no vertices at all. △

Definition 4.17

Suppose that the vertices of a binary tree T form a subset of the totally ordered set $(S, \leq)$. Then T is a **binary search tree** if for each vertex v of T

(i) For every vertex u in the left subtree of v, $u<v$, and
(ii) For every vertex u in the right subtree of v, $v<u$. ○

Examples 4.29

Figure 4.46 gives a binary search tree for the distinct words of the sentence "Now is the time for all good men to come to the aid of the party." The (total) order for the words is alphabetical. △

Figure 4.47 gives another binary search tree for the words in Figure 4.46, also with alphabetical order. △

Given a binary tree T, as in Definition 4.15, conditions (i) and (ii) of Definition 4.17 allow only one total order on the vertices of T that is compatible with T being made additionally into a binary search tree. Namely, the root r of T divides the other vertices of T into those that are

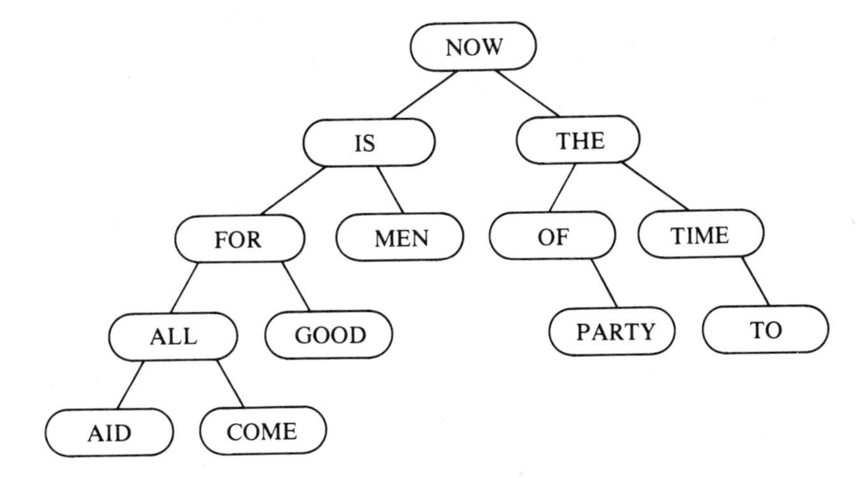

Figure 4.46 A binary search tree

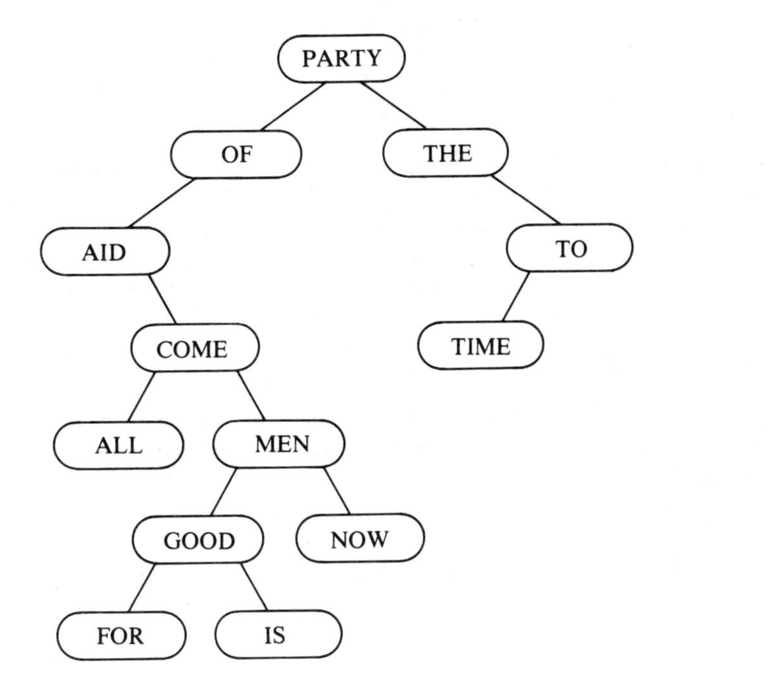

Figure 4.47 A binary search tree

less than r, that is, the left subtree of r, and those that are greater than r, that is, the right subtree of r. Each subtree, in turn, is divided by its root. This order on a binary tree is called **inorder**. Figure 4.48 (p. 198) numbers the vertices of Figure 4.45 in inorder.

We now give algorithms for various operations on data stored in a binary search tree. Each of these algorithms is efficient, in the sense that each requires finding just one directed path in the tree. So each algorithm

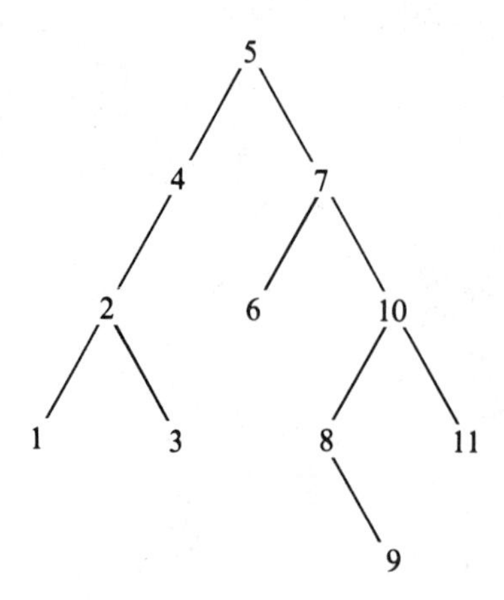

Figure 4.48 Inorder for Figure 4.45

examines only a very small fraction of the entire binary search tree. The proofs that the various algorithms perform as indicated are left as exercises.

Proposition 4.6

Let T be a binary search tree. The smallest vertex in T, with respect to $\leq$ of Definition 4.17, is the final vertex in the directed path that starts at the root r of T and, for as long as possible, continues with left successors.

The largest vertex of T is the final vertex in the directed path that starts at the root of T and, for as long as possible, continues with right successors. □

Examples 4.30

We find some smallest vertices using Proposition 4.6.

In Figure 4.46, the path traverses vertices

NOW, IS, FOR, ALL, AID

and AID is indeed the first word in alphabetical order. △

In Figure 4.47, the path traverses vertices

PARTY, OF, AID △

In Figure 4.48, the path traverses vertices

5, 4, 2, 1 △

Example 4.31

We apply Proposition 4.6 to find the largest vertex in Figure 4.46. The path traverses vertices

NOW, THE, TIME, TO

Indeed, TO is the last word in alphabetical order. △

Proposition 4.7

Let T be a binary search tree. Let s be an element of S, as in Definition 4.17. To see if s is a vertex of T, proceed as follows:

1. Compare s to r, the root of the tree.
2. If $s=r$, then s occurs as a vertex.
3. If $s<r$ and there is no $l(r)$, s is not a vertex.
4. If $s<r$ and there is an $l(r)$, go to Step 1 using $l(r)$ as the root of the left subtree of r.
5. If $s>r$ and there is no $r(r)$, s is not a vertex.
6. If $s>r$ and there is an $r(r)$, go to Step 1 using $r(r)$ as the root of the right subtree of r. □

Examples 4.32

We shall apply Proposition 4.7 to Figure 4.46. Is the word HELP a vertex? Using Proposition 4.7, we successively compare HELP to the vertices NOW, IS, FOR, and GOOD. HELP > GOOD, and GOOD has no right (or even left) successor. So HELP is not a vertex. △

Is NULL a vertex? Using Proposition 4.7, we successively compare NULL to the vertices NOW, THE, and OF. NULL < OF and OF has no left successor. So NULL is not a vertex of Figure 4.46. △

Is MEN a vertex? We successively compare MEN to the vertices NOW, IS, and MEN. MEN = MEN, and MEN is a vertex. △

Proposition 4.8

Let T be a binary search tree. Let s be an element of S that is not a vertex of T. To add s to T so as to form a larger binary search tree, first proceed as in Proposition 4.7. If Proposition 4.7 terminates at Step 3, with $s<v$, then add s to T as $s=l(v)$. If Proposition 4.7 terminates at Step 5, with $s>v$, then add s to T as $s=r(v)$. □

Example 4.33

The binary search tree of Figure 4.46 was formed by starting with the root NOW and then successively adding, using Proposition 4.8, the new words from the sentence "Now is the time for all good men to come to the aid of the party." △

Proposition 4.9

Let v be a vertex of a binary search tree T. Delete v and any edges that are incident at v from T. To obtain a new binary search tree T', reassign successors to the remaining vertices according to the following cases:

1. v has no successors. Successors in T' remain the same as successors in T, except that the predecessor of v in T no longer has v as a successor in T'.
2. v has one successor; call it v'.
   a. If v is the root of T, then v' is the root of T'. Successors in T' remain the same.
   b. If v is not the root of T, let w be its predecessor. In T', let $v' = l(w)$ or $v' = r(w)$ according to whether $v = l(w)$ or $v = r(w)$ in T.
3. v has two successors. Using Proposition 4.6, find u, the largest vertex in the left subtree of v; u necessarily has no right successor in T. In T', let $r(u)$ be $r(v)$ from T. If v is the root of T, then u is the root of T'. Otherwise, let w be the predecessor of v. In T', $u = l(w)$ or $u = r(w)$ according to whether $v = l(w)$ or $v = r(w)$.
   a. Suppose that u has no left successor. In T', let $l(u)$ be given by $l(v)$ from T.
   b. If u has a left successor, use Proposition 4.6 to find t, the smallest vertex in the left subtree of u in T; t necessarily has no left successor in T. In T', let $l(t)$ be $l(v)$ from T. □

Example 4.34

Let us consider the binary search tree of Figure 4.49. The vertices in Figure 4.49 are numbered in their order from S. Figures 4.50–4.54 give the binary search trees that result from using Proposition 4.9 to remove from Figure 4.49 the vertices 2, 1, 7, 3, and 8 respectively. As indicated on the figures, these correspond to the various cases in Proposition 4.9. △

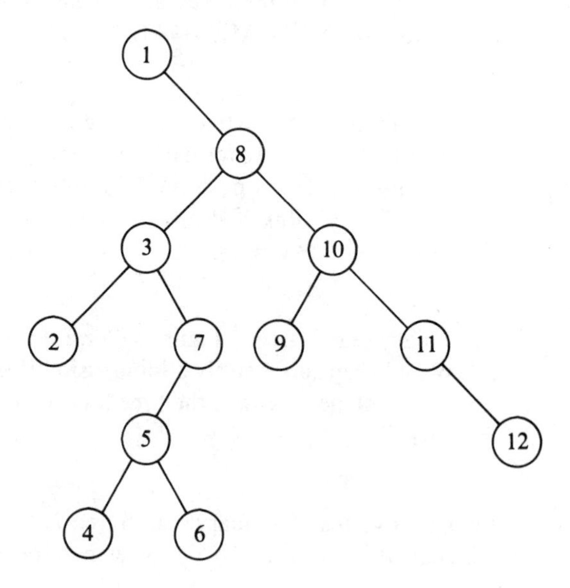

Figure 4.49 A binary search tree

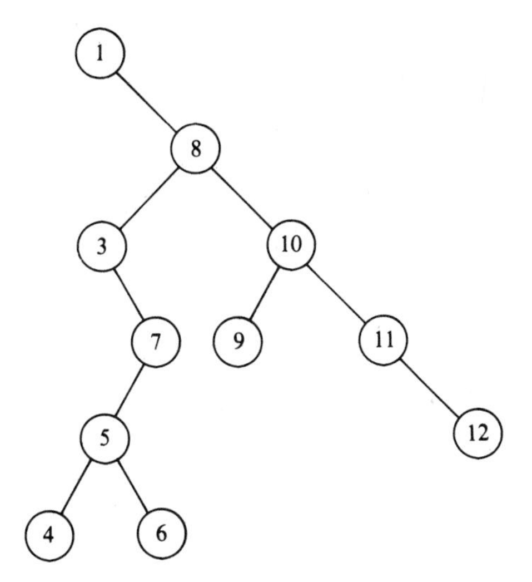

Figure 4.50 Deletion of vertex 2 from Figure 4.49, case 1 of Proposition 4.9

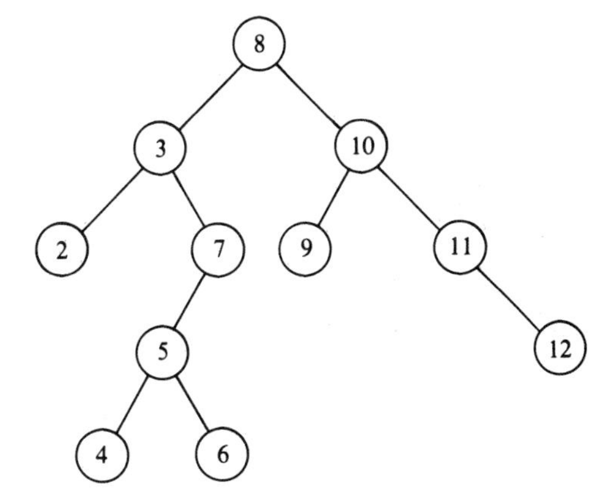

Figure 4.51 Deletion of vertex 1 from Figure 4.49, case 2(a) of Proposition 4.9

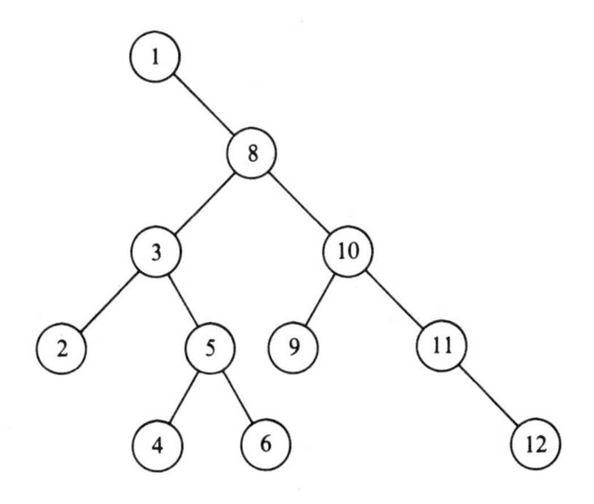

Figure 4.52 Deletion of vertex 7 from Figure 4.49, case 2(b) of Proposition 4.9

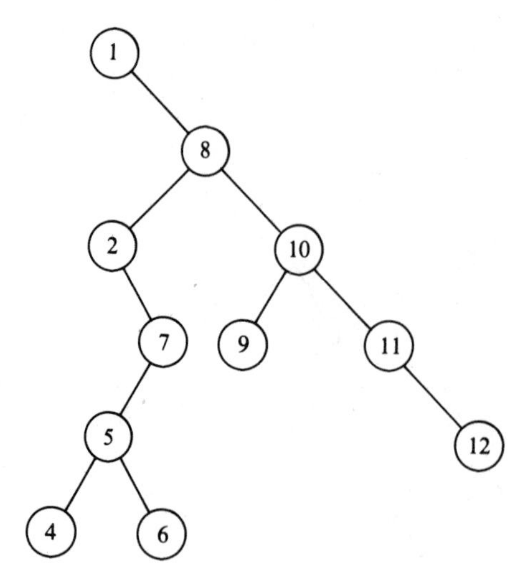

Figure 4.53 Deletion of vertex 3 from Figure 4.49, case 3(a) of Proposition 4.9

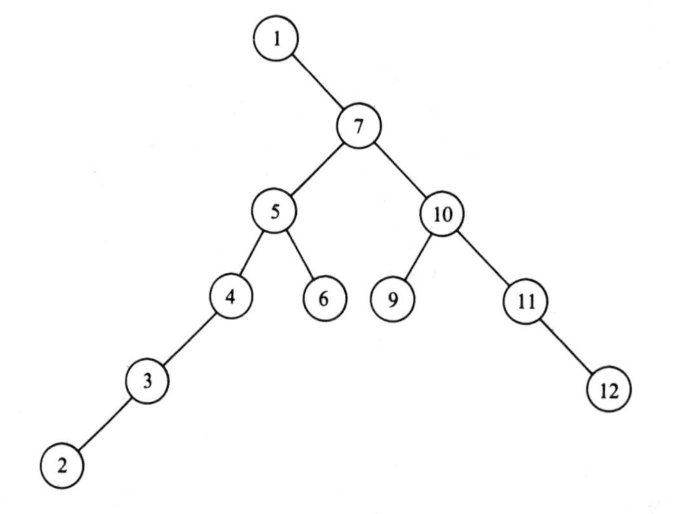

Figure 4.54 Deletion of vertex 8 from Figure 4.49, case 3(b) of Proposition 4.9

Exercises 4.3

1. Decide whether or not each of the directed graphs in Figure 4.55 can be a directed tree. Find the root r in each case where it is possible.

2. Figure 4.56 gives a game tree. Each vertex that represents an end to the game is assigned the value -1, 0, or 1 according to whether A loses, draws, or wins. Assuming the best play by both A and B, assign a value to A for each vertex in Figure 4.56. What should be the outcome of the game?

Figure 4.55

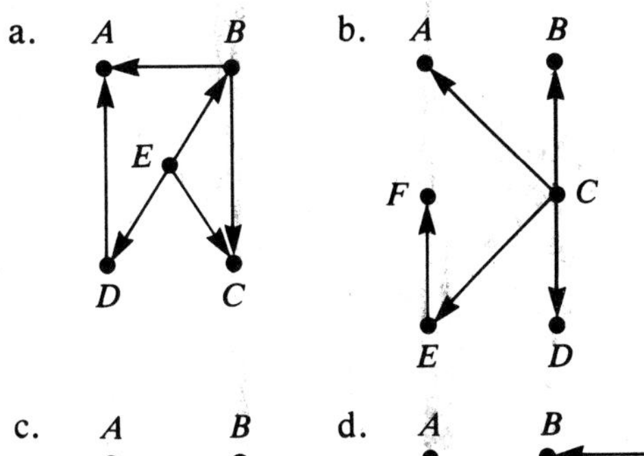

c. A B F C E D

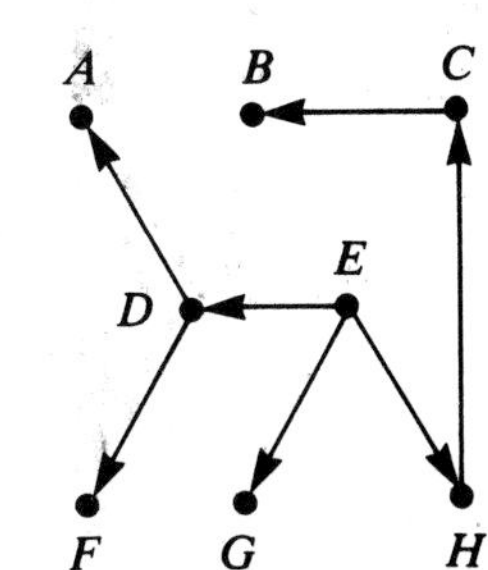

Figure 4.56

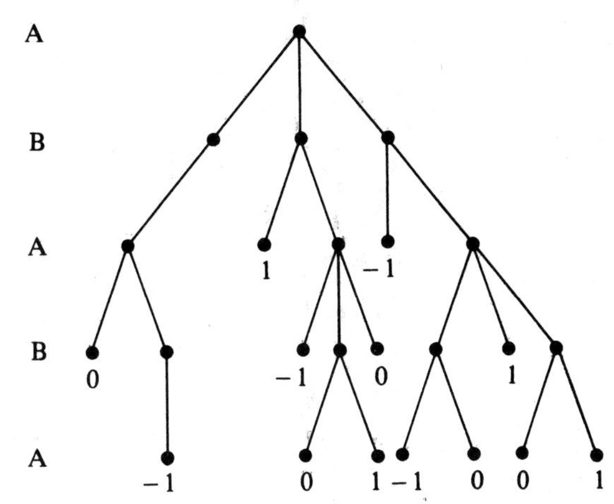

3. Consider the alternate form of the game in Example 4.21, where the player who removes the last counter *wins*. Assuming the best play by both A and B, assign a value to A for each vertex in Figure 4.36. Who should win the game?

4. In each ordered directed graph of Figure 4.57, the root is at the top and the successors of each vertex are ordered from left to right. Number the vertices of each graph in (i) postorder and (ii) preorder.

Figure 4.57

a.

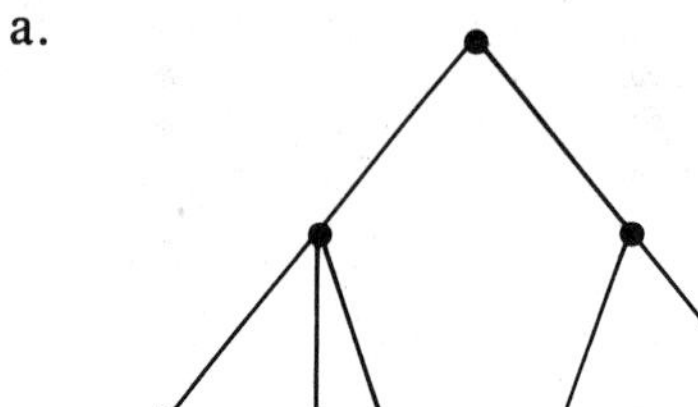

b.

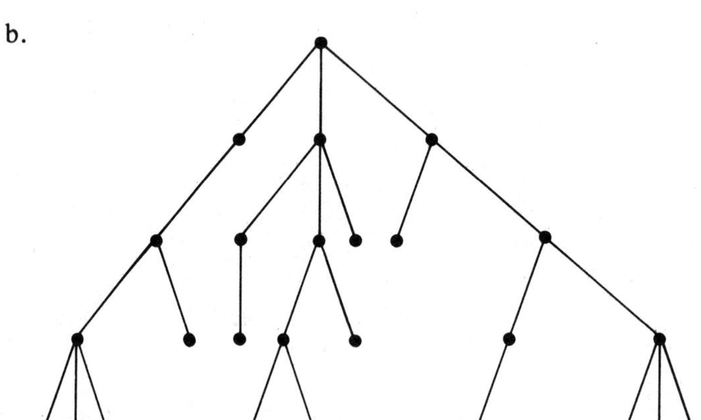

5. Using the algorithm of Proposition 4.8, form a binary search tree for the successive distinct words in the sentence "The quick brown fox jumped over the lazy sleeping dog." Order words alphabetically.

6. Figure 4.58 gives two binary search trees. For each binary search tree, number the vertices in the order from S; that is, number the vertices in inorder.

7. Using the algorithm of Proposition 4.9, remove each of the lettered vertices in Figure 4.58. Retain the numbering from Exercise 6.

8. Let T be a directed graph formed from a tree T' by assigning initial and terminal vertices to the edges of T'. Suppose that r_1 and r_2 are

Figure 4.58

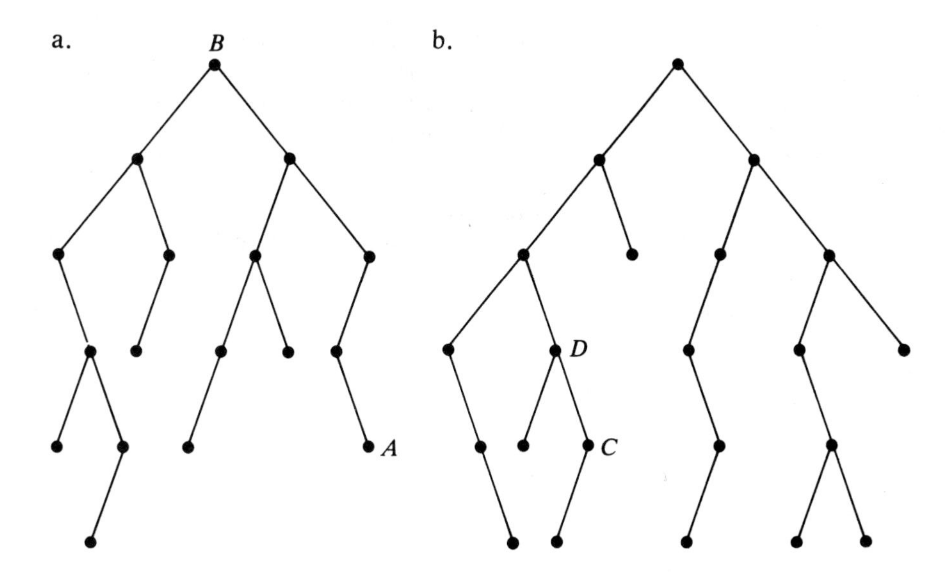

vertices of T such that all vertices of T are accessible from both r_1 and r_2 via simple paths. Show that $r_1 = r_2$.

Hint: Apply Theorem 4.3.

9. Let T be an ordered directed tree. Show that r is the first vertex in preorder. Show that r is the last vertex in postorder.
10. Prove that postorder is a total order on the vertices of an ordered directed tree.

    Hint: Be sure to prove that postorder is a partial order.
11. Prove that preorder is a total order on the vertices of an ordered directed tree.

    Hint: Be sure to prove that preorder is a partial order.
12. Let v and w be vertices of a binary search tree. Let

$$P_1 : r, e_1, v_1, \ldots, v_{n-1}, e_n, v_n = v \quad \text{and}$$

$$P_2 : r, f_1, w_1, \ldots, w_{m-1}, w_m, w_m = w$$

be the simple paths that connect r to v and w, respectively. Specify the order in S between v and w using P_1 and P_2.

13. Prove Proposition 4.6.
14. Prove Proposition 4.7.
15. Prove Proposition 4.8.
16. Prove Proposition 4.9.

17. Let G be a directed graph formed from a tree G' by assigning initial and terminal vertices to the edges of G'. Let v and v' be vertices of G. Show that any directed path that connects v to v' is necessarily simple, and hence unique.

    Hint: Theorem 4.3.

18. Let r be a vertex of the tree T'. Show that there is a unique way to assign initial and terminal endpoints to the edges of T' to form a directed tree T with root r.

5 Boolean Algebras

In the nineteenth century George Boole developed symbolic logic and what is now called **Boolean algebra**. One hundred years later, Shannon and Shestakoff applied Boole's work to the theory of computer design, or **switching theory** as it is sometimes known.

This chapter gives an axiomatic exposition of Boolean algebra. From the point of view of mathematics, the typical Boolean algebra is the power set of a given set. Applications come from suitable interpretations of the standard mathematical terms. For instance, set inclusion corresponds to logical implication. Boolean polynomials correspond to electronic switching circuits. Boolean functions correspond to input/output relationships for switching circuits. We show that every i/o relationship may be achieved by Boolean polynomials, and hence by actual switching circuits.

The last two sections of this chapter are theoretical in nature. We show that every Boolean polynomial is equivalent to a unique Boolean polynomial in disjunctive normal form. We also show that each finite Boolean algebra is isomorphic to the Boolean algebra of a power set.

5.1 Examples and Definitions

Boolean algebras appear naturally in many different forms. So it is useful, as in Definition 5.1, which follows later, to extract their common properties into a set of axioms. Boolean algebras have two laws of composition, just as the integers have addition and multiplication as two laws of composition. Laws of composition apply to *pairs* of elements and so are called **binary** operations. Boolean algebras also have a **unary** operation called **complementation**, which applies to just *single* elements, yielding other single elements. Using the axioms, we introduce a partial order on the elements of a Boolean algebra. This partial order will be very helpful in simplifying later statements about Boolean algebras.

Example 5.1

Let X be the set $\{1,2,3\}$. Here we are solely interested in the fact that X has three elements. Let $\mathscr{P}(X)$, called the **power set of X**, be the set of all subsets of X. Since X has three elements and since each element may either be included or not be included in a subset, X has $2^3 = 8$ distinct subsets. They are

$$\begin{array}{llll} \varnothing & \{1\} & \{2\} & \{3\} \\ \{1,2\} & \{1,3\} & \{2,3\} & \{1,2,3\} \end{array} \qquad \textbf{(5.1)}$$

Sets such as $\{1\}$ and $\{3\}$, having just one element, are called **singletons.** (5.1) lists, of course, the elements of $\mathscr{P}(X)$. There are two binary operations, or laws of composition, for $\mathscr{P}(X)$: union, denoted by $\cup$, and intersection, denoted by $\cap$. Recall, for example, that

$$\{1\}\cup\{3\}=\{1,3\} \qquad \{2,3\}\cup\{1,2\}=\{1,2,3\} \qquad \{2,3\}\cup\varnothing=\{2,3\}$$
$$\{2,3\}\cap\{1,2\}=\{2\} \qquad \{1\}\cap\{3\}=\varnothing \qquad \{1,2\}\cap\{1,2,3\}=\{1,2\}$$

If A is an element of $\mathscr{P}(X)$, the **complement** of A, denoted by $\bar{A}$, is defined as $X-A$, that is, as the set of elements in X that are not in A. Complementation is a unary operation. For example,

$$\overline{\{1\}}=\{2,3\} \qquad \overline{\{1,3\}}=\{2\} \qquad \bar{X}=\overline{\{1,2,3\}}=\varnothing$$

Here are some familiar laws for manipulating these operations on sets.

$$\begin{array}{lll} A\cup B=B\cup A \quad A\cap B=B\cap A & \text{(Commutativity)} & \\ \left.\begin{array}{l} A\cup(B\cap C)=(A\cup B)\cap(A\cup C) \\ A\cap(B\cup C)=(A\cap B)\cup(A\cap C) \end{array}\right\} & \text{(Distributivity)} & \textbf{(5.2)} \\ \overline{A\cup B}=\bar{A}\cap\bar{B} \quad \overline{A\cap B}=\bar{A}\cup\bar{B} & \text{(de Morgan's Laws)} & \end{array}$$

Why are the Distributive Laws given that name? Recall the Distributive Law for ordinary multiplication and addition of integers as follows:

$$a\cdot(b+c)=a\cdot b+a\cdot c \qquad \textbf{(5.3)}$$

With $\cdot$ replacing $\cap$ and $+$ replacing $\cup$, (5.3) is essentially the same as the second Distributive Law in (5.2). The same replacement procedure for the first Distributive Law in (5.2) gives

$$a+(b\cdot c)=(a+b)\cdot(a+c),$$

which is simply not true for arbitrary integers. △

Example 5.2

Let $\mathscr{F}_n$ be the set of all switching functions in n variables; that is, an element of $\mathscr{F}_n$ is a function f from all binary n-tuples to the set $\{0, 1\}$. Each switching function may be thought of as describing a "black box" or module, as in Figure 5.1, which accepts n bits as inputs and produces a single bit as output. Table 5.1, for example, lists all of the elements of $\mathscr{F}_2$.

Table 5.1
$\mathscr{F}_2 = \{$Switching functions with two inputs$\}$

Input	f_0	f_1	f_2	f_3	f_4	f_5	f_6	f_7	f_8	f_9	f_{10}	f_{11}	f_{12}	f_{13}	f_{14}	f_{15}
00	0	0	0	0	0	0	0	0	1	1	1	1	1	1	1	1
01	0	0	0	0	1	1	1	1	0	0	0	0	1	1	1	1
10	0	0	1	1	0	0	1	1	0	0	1	1	0	0	1	1
11	0	1	0	1	0	1	0	1	0	1	0	1	0	1	0	1

We order the output set $\{0,1\}$ in the usual way, $0<1$. Here are two binary operations on $\mathscr{F}_n$. For f and g in $\mathscr{F}_n$, $f \vee g$ is the switching function that assigns to each input the maximum of the outputs for f and g. For example, using the notation of Table 5.1, we have

$$\begin{aligned} f_5 \vee f_6(00) &= \max(f_5(00),\ f_6(00)) = \max(0,0) = 0 \\ f_5 \vee f_6(01) &= \max(f_5(01),\ f_6(01)) = \max(1,1) = 1 \\ f_5 \vee f_6(10) &= \max(f_5(10),\ f_6(10)) = \max(0,1) = 1 \\ f_5 \vee f_6(11) &= \max(f_5(11),\ f_6(11)) = \max(1,0) = 1 \end{aligned} \tag{5.4}$$

Observe that the outputs in (5.4) are the same as for f_7. So $f_5 \vee f_6 = f_7$. Similarly,

$$f_1 \vee f_2 = f_3 \qquad f_5 \vee f_7 = f_7 \qquad f_9 \vee f_6 = f_{15}$$

For f and g in $\mathscr{F}_n$, $f \wedge g$ is the switching function that assigns to each input the minimum of the outputs for f and g. Again using the notation of Table 5.1,

$$\begin{aligned} f_5 \wedge f_6(00) &= \min(f_5(00),\ f_6(00)) = \min(0,0) = 0 \\ f_5 \wedge f_6(01) &= \min(f_5(01),\ f_6(01)) = \min(1,1) = 1 \\ f_5 \wedge f_6(10) &= \min(f_5(10),\ f_6(10)) = \min(0,1) = 0 \\ f_5 \wedge f_6(11) &= \min(f_5(11),\ f_6(11)) = \min(1,0) = 0 \end{aligned} \tag{5.5}$$

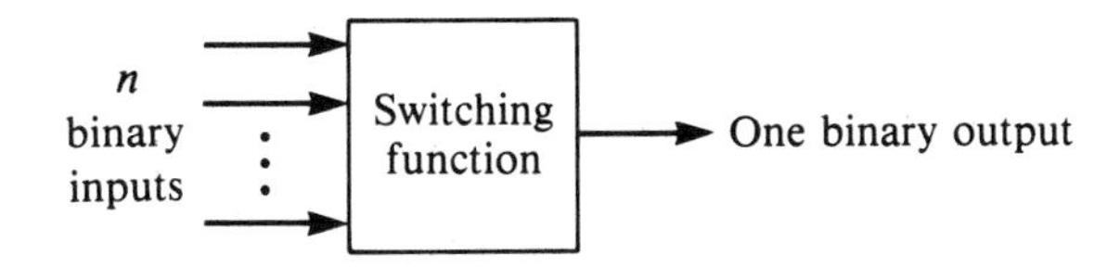

Figure 5.1 A switching function as a module

Observe that the outputs in (5.5) are the same as for f_4. So $f_5 \wedge f_6 = f_4$. Similarly,

$$f_5 \wedge f_9 = f_1 \qquad f_8 \wedge f_7 = f_0 \qquad f_{12} \wedge f_{10} = f_8$$

$\mathscr{F}_n$ also has the unary operation complementation. The complement of f, denoted by f', assigns to each input the output that is the opposite value to that of f. For example, letting $0'$ denote 1 and $1'$ denote 0,

$$\begin{aligned} f_5'(00) &= f_5(00)' = 0' = 1 \\ f_5'(01) &= f_5(01)' = 1' = 0 \\ f_5'(10) &= f_5(10)' = 0' = 1 \\ f_5'(11) &= f_5(11)' = 1' = 0 \end{aligned} \tag{5.6}$$

Since the outputs in (5.6) are the same as for f_{10}, $f_5' = f_{10}$. Similarly,

$$f_0' = f_{15} \qquad f_8' = f_7 \qquad f_7' = f_8$$

△

Both Example 5.1 and Example 5.2 give Boolean algebras, which are defined in general by Definition 5.1.

Definition 5.1

A Boolean algebra B is a set with two laws of composition, $\vee$ and $\wedge$, one unary operation $'$, and two special elements O and I, which satisfy the following axioms. Arbitrary elements of B are denoted by x, y, and z.

(i)	$x \vee x = x \qquad x \wedge x = x$	(Idempotency)
(ii)	$x \vee y = y \vee x \qquad x \wedge y = y \wedge x$	(Commutativity)
(iii)	$x \vee (y \vee z) = (x \vee y) \vee z$ $x \wedge (y \wedge z) = (x \wedge y) \wedge z$	(Associativity)
(iv)	$x \vee (x \wedge y) = x \qquad x \wedge (x \vee y) = x$	(Absorption)
(v)	$x \vee (y \wedge z) = (x \vee y) \wedge (x \vee z)$ $x \wedge (y \vee z) = (x \wedge y) \vee (x \wedge z)$	(Distributivity)
(vi)	$x \wedge O = O \qquad x \vee O = x$ $x \wedge I = x \qquad x \vee I = I$	(Universal Bounds)
(vii)	$x \wedge x' = O \qquad x \vee x' = I$	(Complements)
(viii)	$(x')' = x$	(Involution)
(ix)	$(x \vee y)' = x' \wedge y'$ $(x \wedge y)' = x' \vee y'$	(de Morgan's Laws)

$x \vee y$ is the **join** or **sum** of x and y; $x \wedge y$ is the **meet** or **product** of x and y; x' is the **complement** of x. The **additive identity** is O; I is the **multiplicative identity**. Both O and I are also called **universal bounds**. ○

The axioms of Definition 5.1 have been chosen so that all desired properties of examples such as Examples 5.1 and 5.2 may be deduced from the axioms. To translate Example 5.1 into the notation of Definition 5.1, think of $\cup$ as $\vee$, $\cap$ as $\wedge$, and $\bar{\ }$ as $'$. Think of $\varnothing$ as O and X as I. Then all of the axioms of Definition 5.1 hold for $\mathscr{P}(X)$ via general reasoning about sets. For example, here is a verification of the first absorption law in (iv). Consider x and y as arbitrary subsets of X. Then $x \cap y$ is a subset of x. So $x \cup (x \cap y) = x$. Also, for example, the second part of (vii) simply says that every element of X is contained either in x or in the complement of x.

Example 5.2 also describes a Boolean algebra. One way we may verify the axioms of Definition 5.1 is to observe that each switching function specifies a subset of the set $X = \{00, 01, 10, 11\}$ of inputs as follows: include an input in the subset if the switching function has the value 1 on the input. For example, in the notation of Table 5.1,

$$f_5(00) = 0 \qquad f_5(01) = 1 \qquad f_5(10) = 0 \qquad f_5(11) = 1$$

so f_5 corresponds to the subset $\{01, 11\}$ of X. Then $\vee$ of Example 5.2 corresponds to $\cup$ of Example 5.1, $\wedge$ corresponds to $\cap$, $'$ corresponds to $\bar{\ }$, f_0 corresponds to $\varnothing$, and f_{15} corresponds to X. Since the axioms of Definition 5.1 hold for the set operations of Example 5.1, they also hold for Example 5.2.

Example 5.3

Let $B = \{O, I\}$. Then B is a Boolean algebra when $\vee$, $\wedge$, and $'$ are given as in Table 5.2. One may easily verify the axioms of Definition 5.1 directly from Table 5.2. Alternatively, one may think of O as 0, I as 1, $\vee$ as maximum, $\wedge$ as minimum, and $'$ as "exchange." The axioms then follow from logical considerations. Another interpretation for this Boolean algebra is as $\mathscr{F}_0$, switching functions with no input, that is, with constant output. △

Table 5.2 The Boolean algebra $\{O, I\}$

$\vee$	O	I
O	O	I
I	I	I

$\wedge$	O	I
O	O	O
I	O	I

$'$	O	I
	I	O

Example 5.4

Let X be any set. Since the axioms of Definition 5.1 correspond to set calculations, $\mathscr{P}(X)$ is a Boolean algebra under the usual set operations.

$$O = \varnothing \qquad I = X$$

△

Example 5.5

It turns out, as will be seen in Theorem 5.16, following, that all *finite* Boolean algebras essentially come from Example 5.4, with X finite. Here is an infinite Boolean algebra that does not consist of *all* subsets of some set X. Let $\mathbb{P}$ be the set of all positive integers. We are interested solely in the fact that $\mathbb{P}$ has an infinite number of elements. Let B consist of $\varnothing$, $\mathbb{P}$, and all subsets of $\mathbb{P}$ that are either finite or have finite complements. Here are some typical elements of B and their complements.

$$x = \{1,3,5,11\} \qquad \bar{x} = \{2,4,6,7,8,9,10,12,13,14,15,\ldots\}$$

$$y = \{2,7,9,10,11,12,13,14,\ldots\} \qquad \bar{y} = \{1,3,4,5,6,8\}$$

$\vee$, $\wedge$, and $'$ mean $\cup$, $\cap$, and $\bar{\ }$ as usual. O is $\varnothing$. I is $\mathbb{P}$.

B is a subset of $\mathscr{P}(\mathbb{P})$, a known Boolean algebra. So, as in Theorem 2.10 for subgroups, to show that B is a Boolean algebra, we may simply show that $\cup$, $\cap$, and $\bar{\ }$ are indeed defined in B, that is, that these operations on elements of B yield only elements of B. We shall just verify closure for the operation $\cup$. For x,y in B, consider $x \cup y$. There are essentially two cases.

(i) Both x and y are finite. Then $x \cup y$ is finite and so is in B.
(ii) Suppose that x is infinite. Since x is in B, $\bar{x}$ is finite. Since $\overline{x \cup y} = \bar{x} \cap \bar{y}$ is a subset of the finite set $\bar{x}$, $\overline{x \cup y}$ is finite. Thus $x \cup y$ is also in B.

◇

Example 5.6

Let $X = \{1,2,3\}$. Let $x \vee y$ be the maximum of x and y and let $x \wedge y$ be the minimum of x and y. Let $O = 1$ and let $I = 3$. Then Axioms (i)–(vi) of Definition 5.1 are satisfied, as can be verified. But 2 cannot be assigned a complement $2'$ so as to satisfy (vii). Indeed, (vii) requires that

$$2 \wedge 2' = 1 \quad \text{and} \quad 2 \vee 2' = 3 \tag{5.7}$$

The first equation in (5.7) requires that $2' = 1$; the second requires that $2' = 3$. So $2'$ cannot exist. △

The axioms of Definition 5.1 are a standard choice for Boolean algebras. They are not all independent, in the sense that some axioms may be deduced from the others. However, it will be convenient to have the properties described by the axioms listed and named. The absorption axiom, for example, will be used in the proof of Theorem 5.4, which follows later.

Proposition 5.1

The absorption laws follow from the other axioms.

Proof of Proposition 5.1

We shall only prove that $x \vee (x \wedge y) = x$. The proof for $x \wedge (x \vee y) = x$ is left as an exercise.

$$\begin{aligned} x \vee (x \wedge y) &= (x \wedge I) \vee (x \wedge y), && \text{by universal bounds} \\ &= (x \wedge (y \vee y')) \vee (x \wedge y), && \text{by complements} \\ &= (x \wedge y) \vee (x \wedge y') \vee (x \wedge y), && \text{by distributivity} \\ &= (x \wedge y') \vee (x \wedge y) \vee (x \wedge y), && \text{by commutativity} \\ &= (x \wedge y') \vee (x \wedge y), && \text{by idempotency} \\ &= x \wedge (y' \vee y), && \text{by distributivity} \\ &= x \wedge I, && \text{by complements} \\ &= x, && \text{by universal bounds} \quad \square \end{aligned}$$

Other dependencies among the axioms are given in the exercises. Here is another result that we shall need later.

Proposition 5.2

Let x and y be elements of a Boolean algebra. Then $x \wedge y = x$ if and only if $x \wedge y' = O$.

Example 5.7

Before formally proving Proposition 5.2, we shall illustrate its statement. Let $B = \mathscr{P}(X)$ for some set X. Then $x \wedge y = x$ says that x is a subset of y, as we may easily verify. The equation $x \wedge \bar{y} = \varnothing$ says that no element of X is common to both x and the complement of y; that is, no element of x is in the complement of y. So again x must be a subset of y. So the two conditions are both equivalent to x being a subset of y and so are also equivalent to each other. △

Proof of Proposition 5.2

We first assume that $x \wedge y = x$. We shall show that $x \wedge y' = O$.

$$\begin{aligned} x \wedge y' &= (x \wedge y) \wedge y', && x = x \wedge y \text{ is given} \\ &= x \wedge (y \wedge y'), && \text{by associativity} \\ &= x \wedge O, && \text{by complements} \\ &= O, && \text{by universal bounds} \end{aligned}$$

We now assume that $x \wedge y' = 0$ and show that $x \wedge y = x$.

$$\begin{aligned} x &= x \wedge I, && \text{by universal bounds} \\ &= x \wedge (y \vee y'), && \text{by complements} \\ &= (x \wedge y) \vee (x \wedge y'), && \text{by distributivity} \\ &= (x \wedge y) \vee O, && x \wedge y' = O \text{ is given} \\ &= x \wedge y, && \text{by universal bounds} \quad \square \end{aligned}$$

Recall from Example 5.7 that for Boolean algebras that are power sets, the conditions of Proposition 5.2 are equivalent to x being a subset of y, $x \subset y$. We know from Example 3.39 that $\subset$ is a partial order. We want this partial order to exist in any Boolean algebra. Since the notion of set inclusion is lacking in Definition 5.1, we use instead the conditions of Proposition 5.2.

Definition 5.2

Let B be a Boolean algebra. Let x and y be elements of B. We say that $x \leq y$ if $x \wedge y = x$. ○

Example 5.8

Consider $\mathscr{F}_n$ of Example 5.2. For f and g in $\mathscr{F}_n$, let us interpret the condition $f \leq g$ of Definition 5.2. Applied to an input, $f \wedge g$ gives the minimum of the values of f and g on the same input. So $f \wedge g = f$ requires that this minimum value be the value of f. Thus for $\mathscr{F}_n$, the condition $f \leq g$ of Definition 5.2 is equivalent to: the value of f for each input set is less than or equal to the corresponding value of g. △

Theorem 5.3

The relation $\leq$ of Definition 5.2 is a partial order on B.

Proof of Theorem 5.3

We must verify the three conditions of Definition 3.8.

(i) (*Reflexivity*) We need that $x \wedge x = x$. This is just idempotency for Boolean algebras.
(ii) (*Antisymmetry*) Given that $x \wedge y = x$ and $y \wedge x = y$, we must show that $x = y$. But $x \wedge y = y \wedge x$ by commutativity. So $x = x \wedge y = y \wedge x = y$.
(iii) (*Transitivity*) Given that $x \wedge y = x$ and $y \wedge z = y$, we must show that $x \wedge z = x$.

$$\begin{aligned} x \wedge z &= (x \wedge y) \wedge z, && x = x \wedge y \text{ is given} \\ &= x \wedge (y \wedge z), && \text{by associativity} \\ &= x \wedge y, && y \wedge z = y \text{ is given} \\ &= x, && x \wedge y = x \text{ is given} \end{aligned}$$

◇

Observe from the proof of Theorem 5.3 that only Axioms (i)–(iii) of Definition 5.1 were needed to verify that $\leq$ is a partial order for a Boolean algebra. The other axioms put strong conditions on this partial order.

Example 5.9

We recall some notions about $\mathbb{R}$, the set of real numbers. Consider the subset $S = [0, 3)$ of $\mathbb{R}$. Since for all x in S, $x \leq 4$, we call 4 an **upper bound** for S. Of course, 4 is not the "best" upper bound for S; 3 is. Namely, for x in S, $x \leq 3$ and also, $3 < u$ for *any* other upper bound u for S besides 3. So 3 is called the **least upper bound** for S. Similarly, 0 is the **greatest lower bound** for S. △

Look at Figure 5.2, the Hasse diagram for Example 5.1. The fact that $\emptyset$ is a subset of all other sets translates into the fact that $\emptyset \leq A$ for *all* elements A of the Boolean algebra $\mathscr{P}(X)$. Thus $\emptyset$ is a **universal lower bound**. Similarly, for *all* A in $\mathscr{P}(X)$, $A \leq X$. So X is a **universal upper bound**. Axiom (vi) of Definition 5.1 implies that in any Boolean algebra, $O \leq x$ and $x \leq I$ for all elements x. So O is a universal lower bound and I is a universal upper bound, justifying the terminology at the end of Definition 5.1.

Definition 5.3

Let $\leq$ be a partial order on a set B. Let $S = \{x_1, \ldots, x_n\}$ be a set of elements of B. The element y in B is an *upper bound* for S if $x_i \leq y$ for all elements x_i of S. The element y is a *least* upper bound for s if

(i) y is an upper bound for S, and
(ii) For any upper bound z for S, $y \leq z$.

The element y is a *lower bound* for S if $y \leq x_i$ for all elements x_i of S; y is a *greatest lower bound* for S if

(i) y is a lower bound for S, and
(ii) For any lower bound z for S, $z \leq y$. ○

Example 5.10

Let $\mathbb{P}$ be the set of positive integers with $\leq$ the usual less than or equal to. Then 1 is a universal lower bound. There is no universal upper bound. For a (finite) set S, the least upper bound is the maximum of the integers in S and the greatest lower bound is the minimum. △

Example 5.11

Let P be the positive integers with $|$ the partial order: $a \mid b$ if a divides b. Let S be a finite subset of P. Then an upper bound for S is just a common multiple for the elements of S. The least upper bound is the least common multiple. Similarly, the greatest lower bound is the greatest common divisor. △

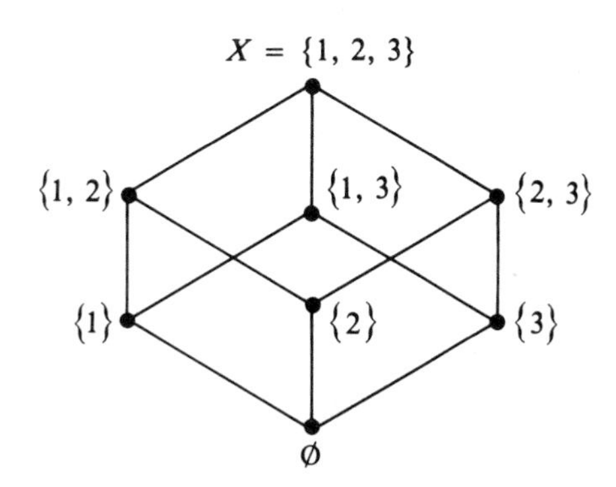

Figure 5.2 Hasse diagram for Example 5.1

Theorem 5.4 Let $S=\{x_1,x_2,\ldots,x_n\}$ be a nonempty finite set of elements in a Boolean algebra B. Then $x_1 \vee x_2 \vee \cdots \vee x_n$ is the least upper bound of S and $x_1 \wedge x_2 \wedge \cdots \wedge x_n$ is the greatest lower bound of S.

Example 5.12 Before proving Theorem 5.4, we shall illustrate its statement. Let $B=\mathscr{P}(X)$ for some set X. Then the least upper bound for a collection S of subsets of X is the union of the sets in S. The greatest lower bound for S is the intersection of the sets in S. △

Proof of Theorem 5.4 Uniqueness for least upper bounds and greatest lower bounds is proved in the exercises. So the two uses of the word "the" are justified in the statement of the theorem. We shall just prove the theorem for least upper bounds; the proof for greatest lower bounds is entirely similar. Let $y=x_1 \vee x_2 \vee \cdots \vee x_n$.

We verify (i) of Definition 5.3. We need to prove that $x_i \wedge y = x_i$ for all x_i. By the commutativity axiom, we may assume in our proof that $x_i = x_1$.

$$
\begin{aligned}
x_1 \wedge y &= x_1 \wedge (x_1 \vee x_2 \vee \cdots \vee x_n), && \text{by the definition of } y \\
&= (x_1 \wedge x_1) \vee (x_1 \wedge (x_2 \vee \cdots \vee x_n)), && \text{by distributivity} \\
&= x_1 \vee (x_1 \wedge (x_2 \vee \cdots \vee x_n)), && \text{by idempotency} \\
&= x_1, && \text{by absorption}
\end{aligned}
$$

We now verify (ii) of Definition 5.3. We are given a z such that $x_i \wedge z = x_i$ for all x_i; that is, z is an upper bound. We need that $y \wedge z = y$.

$$
\begin{aligned}
y \wedge z &= (x_1 \vee x_2 \vee \cdots \vee x_n) \wedge z, && \text{by the definition of } y \\
&= (x_1 \wedge z) \vee (x_2 \wedge z) \vee \cdots \vee (x_n \wedge z), && \\
& && \text{repeated applications of distributivity} \\
&= x_1 \vee x_2 \vee \cdots \vee x_n, && z \text{ is an upper bound} \\
&= y, && \text{by the definition of } y
\end{aligned}
$$

◇

Exercises 5.1

1. Let $X=\{1,2\}$. How many elements has $\mathscr{P}(X)$?
   a. Write out the composition tables for $\cup$ and $\cap$ for $\mathscr{P}(X)$.
   b. Write out the unary operation table for $^{-}$ for $\mathscr{P}(X)$.
2. a. With $\vee$ replaced by $+$ and $\wedge$ replaced by $\cdot$, write out what the absorption "laws" would mean for ordinary addition and multiplication of integers.
   b. Give explicit integer values for x and y that violate the absorption "laws" of part (a).
3. Draw the Hasse diagram for $\mathscr{P}(X)$, with $X=\{1,2\}$.

Figure 5.3

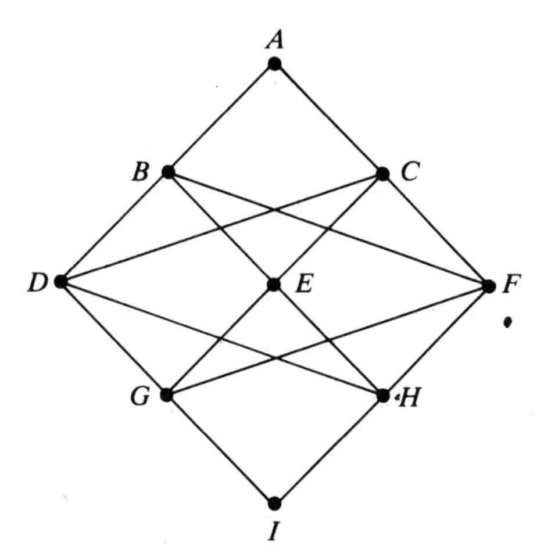

4. In the Hasse diagram of Figure 5.3,
   a. Find the least upper bounds for the sets $\{B,C\}$ and $\{C,E,F,H\}$.
   b. Find the greatest lower bounds for the sets $\{E,G,H\}$ and $\{A,B,C,D\}$.
   c. Find a set of vertices that has no least upper bound and no greatest lower bound.
5. Give reasons for the following steps, which show that the Idempotency Law $x \vee x = x$ may be deduced from the Absorption Laws and substitution.

$$x \vee (x \wedge (x \vee x)) = x$$
$$x \wedge (x \vee x) = x$$
$$x \vee x = x$$

6. Give reasons for the following steps, which show that the absorption law $x \wedge (x \vee y) = x$ follows from the other axioms.

$$\begin{aligned} x \wedge (x \vee y) &= (x \vee O) \wedge (x \vee y) \\ &= (x \vee (y \wedge y')) \wedge (x \vee y) \\ &= (x \vee y) \wedge (x \vee y') \wedge (x \vee y) \\ &= (x \vee y') \wedge (x \vee y) \wedge (x \vee y) \\ &= (x \vee y') \wedge (x \vee y) \\ &= x \vee (y' \wedge y) \\ &= x \vee O \\ &= x \end{aligned}$$

7. Suppose that x and y are elements of a Boolean algebra such that $x \wedge y = O$ and $x \vee y = I$.
   a. Give reasons for the following computation and explain why it shows that $y \leq x'$.

$$\begin{aligned} y &= y \wedge I \\ &= y \wedge (x \vee x') \\ &= (y \wedge x) \vee (y \wedge x') \\ &= O \vee (y \wedge x') \\ &= y \wedge x' \end{aligned}$$

   b. Start with $x = x \vee O$ and conclude, as in part (a), that $x = x \vee y'$. Then conclude that $x' \leq y$.
   c. Show that $y = x'$ and hence that complements are uniquely determined by Definition 5.1(vii).

8. Using Exercise 7, show that in a Boolean algebra,

$$O' = I \quad \text{and} \quad I' = O$$

9. Justify the terminology "O is the *additive identity*; I is the *multiplicative identity*" at the end of Definition 5.1.

10. Let B be a Boolean algebra. Which of the group axioms hold for $(B, \vee)$? for $(B, \wedge)$?

11. Many statements about Boolean algebra come in pairs, such as Theorem 5.4 about upper and lower bounds. These statements involve interchanging $\vee$ with $\wedge$ and O with I. Such pairs of statements are called **duals**.
    a. Show that all of the axioms in Definition 5.1 come in dual pairs. *Note:* (viii) does not involve $\vee$, $\wedge$, O or I. It is said to be self-dual.
    b. The *Duality Principle* for Boolean algebras says that dual statements are either both true or both false. Explain why part (a) justifies the Duality Principle.

12. Show that for any partial order, not necessarily coming from a Boolean algebra, that least upper bounds and greatest lower bounds are unique if they exist.
    Hint: Use antisymmetry.

13. a. Suppose that $O = I$ in some Boolean algebra B. Show that B has just one element.
    b. Suppose that $x = x'$ for some element in a Boolean algebra B. Show that B has just one element.

5.2 Boolean Polynomials, Switching Circuits, and Logic

Recall that ordinary functions, perhaps of more than one variable, are often given by polynomial defining equations. In this section we study similar expressions, called Boolean polynomials, which are suitable for Boolean algebras. Boolean polynomials are used to represent switching circuits and logical propositions. We also see how to construct switching circuits with any desired function from input to output.

(5.8) gives a typical polynomial in the variables x and y with integral coefficients. In (5.8) some multiplications that are traditionally omitted have been included for later clarity.

$$5 \cdot x^2 \cdot y^3 + x \cdot y^2 - 2 \cdot x + 1 \cdot y + 1 \tag{5.8}$$

We may also think of (5.9) as a polynomial in x and y with integral coefficients.

$$y^2 \cdot (5 \cdot x \cdot y + 1) \cdot (x + 1) + y \cdot (1 - 5 \cdot x \cdot y^2 - y) + (x - 1)^2 - x^2 \tag{5.9}$$

An easy calculation shows that (5.9) simplifies to (5.8). So we often think of (5.9) and (5.8) as representing equal polynomials.

Ordinary polynomials, such as (5.8) and (5.9), are formed from constants, such as 0, 1, 5, and -2, variables such as x and y, and operations such as $+$, $-$, and $\cdot$. Boolean polynomials are defined similarly in Definition 5.4, which follows.

Definition 5.4 Let $x_1, x_2, \ldots, x_n$ be a set of symbols, called **Boolean variables**. A **Boolean polynomial** in $x_1, \ldots, x_n$ is an expression formed from the constants O and I and the variables $x_1, \ldots, x_n$ using the operations $\vee$, $\wedge$, and $'$. The formation is as follows:

(i) O, I, and $x_1, x_2, \ldots, x_n$ are Boolean polynomials.

(ii) If f and g are previously defined Boolean polynomials, then $f \vee g$, $f \wedge g$, and f' are also Boolean polynomials. ○

(*Note:* Many authors do not allow O and I to be Boolean polynomials.)

Example 5.13 Here are some Boolean polynomials in the (Boolean) variables x, y, and z.

$$(x \wedge y) \vee (z')$$

$$[x \vee (y \wedge (y'))] \vee [z \wedge I]$$

$$[(x \vee (x')) \vee (O \wedge y)]'$$

△

For ordinary polynomials, we reduce the need for parentheses by using a hierarchy for operations. Namely, exponentiation precedes multiplication, and multiplication precedes both addition and subtraction. For example, the polynomial $x \cdot y + 1$ equals $(x \cdot y) + 1$, rather than $x \cdot (y + 1)$. There is no preference between addition and subtraction, except that these operations are performed from left to right.

We shall use only a small hierarchy for the operations in Boolean polynomials: The complementation operation $'$ is performed before either $\vee$ or $\wedge$, unless parentheses indicate otherwise. There is no preference between $\vee$ and $\wedge$, nor is there an assumed left-to-right order. Thus

$$(x \wedge y) \vee (z') \quad \text{and} \quad (x \wedge y) \vee z'$$

are the same polynomial.

$$[(x \wedge y) \vee z]' \quad \text{and} \quad (x \wedge y) \vee z'$$

are different polynomials.

Just as we may simplify (5.9) to (5.8), we use the axioms of Definition 5.1 to allow "simplification" of Boolean polynomials. The problem immediately arises of when two Boolean polynomials can in fact be transformed into each other. This problem will be solved in Theorems 5.10 and 5.11, which follow later.

Definition 5.5

Two Boolean polynomials f and g in the same variables are **equivalent** (or **equal**) if one may be transformed into the other via the axioms of Definition 5.1. We write $f = g$ to say that f and g are equivalent. ○

We shall often not distinguish between Boolean polynomials that are clearly equivalent. Thus from associativity,

$$(x \vee y) \vee z = x \vee (y \vee z)$$

We shall freely write these two equivalent polynomials as $x \vee y \vee z$.

Examples 5.14

Here are some equivalent polynomials. In this case the manipulations are considered as simplifications, but such an interpretation really depends on the application.

$$\begin{aligned}
[(x \wedge y)' \vee (z \vee z)]' &= [(x \wedge y)' \vee z]', && \text{by idempotency} \\
&= [(x \wedge y)']' \wedge z', && \text{by de Morgan's Laws} \\
&= (x \wedge y) \wedge z', && \text{by involution} \\
&= x \wedge y \wedge z', && \text{by associativity}
\end{aligned}$$

△

$$\begin{aligned}(y \vee y') \wedge (O \vee x \vee x') &= (y \vee y') \wedge [(O \vee x) \vee x'], && \text{by associativity}\\ &= (y \vee y') \wedge (x \vee x'), && \text{by universal bounds}\\ &= I \wedge I, && \text{by complements}\\ &= I, && \text{by universal bounds}\end{aligned}$$ △

Just as ordinary polynomials may be regarded as functions, so also may Boolean polynomials be regarded as (Boolean) functions. Given a Boolean polynomial f in the variables $x_1,\ldots,x_n$, we may evaluate f for any values of the $x_1,\ldots,x_n$ in some Boolean algebra B. For our purposes, it will be sufficient to consider evaluation of a Boolean polynomial only for the variables ranging over the 2-element Boolean algebra $\{O,I\}$, as in Example 5.3. Sometimes, as when we are considering switching functions, we shall use the notation $\{0,1\}$ rather than the notation $\{O,I\}$. At the end of this section, when we shall be considering Boolean polynomials in relation to logic, the notation $O = False$ and $I = True$ will be appropriate.

Example 5.15

Let us evaluate $f(x,y) = (x \vee y') \wedge (x' \vee y)$.

$$\begin{aligned}f(O,O) &= (O \vee O') \wedge (O' \vee O)\\ &= (O \vee I) \wedge (I \vee O)\\ &= I \wedge I\\ &= I\end{aligned}$$

$$\begin{aligned}f(O,I) &= (O \vee I') \wedge (O' \vee I)\\ &= (O \vee O) \wedge (I \vee I)\\ &= O \wedge I\\ &= O\end{aligned}$$

The calculations for $f(I,O)$ and $f(I,I)$ are similar. We summarize the results of the evaluations in Table 5.3, a **function-value** table. △

Table 5.3 Function value table for $f = (x \vee y') \wedge (x' \vee y)$

	(x,y)			
	(O,O)	(O,I)	(I,O)	(I,I)
$f(x,y)$	I	O	O	I

Since elements of a Boolean algebra satisfy the axioms of Definition 5.1, equivalent polynomials in the sense of Definition 5.5 necessarily give the same function values, that is, give the same function. Theorem 5.11 of the next section asserts the converse: that Boolean polynomials that yield the same function are equivalent in the sense of Definition 5.5.

Example 5.16

Let us look at $f(x,y)=(x \vee y') \wedge (x' \vee y)$ of Example 5.15.

$$\begin{aligned}(x \vee y') \wedge (x' \vee y) &= [(x \vee y') \wedge x'] \vee [(x \vee y') \wedge y] \\ &= [(x \wedge x') \vee (y' \wedge x')] \vee [(x \wedge y) \vee (y' \wedge y)] \\ &= O \vee (y' \wedge x') \vee (x \wedge y) \vee O \\ &= (y' \wedge x') \vee (x \wedge y)\end{aligned}$$

So $f(x,y)$ is equivalent to $g(x,y)=(y' \wedge x') \vee (x \wedge y)$. We could easily compute that g also has Table 5.3 as its function-value table; for example

$$\begin{aligned}g(O,O) &= (O' \wedge O') \vee (O \wedge O) \\ &= (I \wedge I) \vee O \\ &= I \vee O \\ &= I\end{aligned}$$

$g(O,I)$, $g(I,O)$ and $g(I,I)$ are computed similarly. △

The evaluation of Boolean polynomials has important interpretations in circuit design and in logic. We shall discuss circuit design first, and then briefly discuss logic.

Bits that are being processed electronically are typically represented by voltages. We shall think of the bit value of 0 as corresponding to 0 volts and the bit value of 1 as corresponding to 1 (physically suitable multiple of a) volt. In doing a computation, these voltages are used to control **gates**, which determine whether some other voltage is 0 or 1. One often thinks of a gate as a possibly complicated switch that is "on" or "off" according to whether the resulting voltage is 1 or 0. Let x be a Boolean variable; we think of O as 0 and of I as 1. Think of the voltage for x as controlling a switch. The switch is open for $x=0$ and closed for $x=1$. See Figure 5.4.

In Figure 5.5, two switches are connected in series. Then an initial voltage of 1 results in a final voltage of 1 if and only if both switches are closed. With the switches controlled by the variables x and y, the series connection results in an output of $x \wedge y$, as given in Table 5.2. Any circuit that produces an output of $x \wedge y$ with inputs x and y is called an **AND**

Figure 5.4 The Boolean variable x controlling a switch

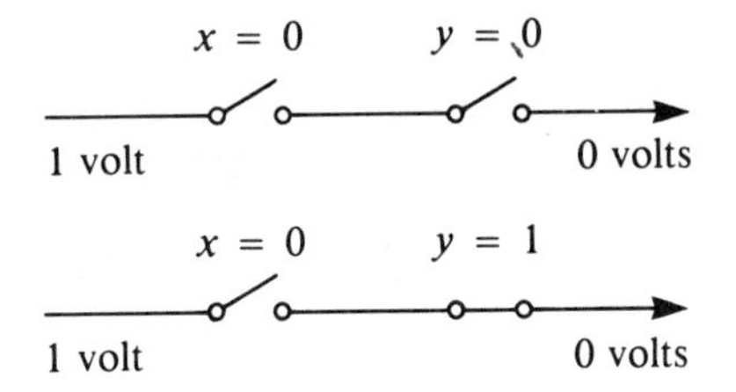

Figure 5.5 $x \wedge y$, a series connection

gate. Figure 5.6 gives the standard symbol for an AND gate. As in Figure 5.7, an AND gate may have multiple inputs. Such AND gates with multiple inputs may be formed from AND gates with just two inputs. For example, Figure 5.8 illustrates an AND gate with three inputs that is constructed from two AND gates with two inputs each.

In Figure 5.9, two switches are connected in parallel. Then an initial voltage of 1 volt results in an output of 1 volt if and only if at least one switch is closed. With the switches controlled by the variables x and y, the parallel connection results in an output of $x \vee y$, as given in Table 5.2. Any circuit that produces an output of $x \vee y$ with inputs x and y is called an **OR gate**. The standard symbol for an OR gate is given in Figure 5.10. As with AND gates, OR gates may have multiple inputs. Such OR gates with multiple inputs may be formed from OR gates with just two inputs.

The Boolean operation of complementation corresponds to a **NOT gate**, also known as an **inverter**. In terms of switches as in Figures 5.5 and 5.9, think of the voltage x as controlling a switch that is normally closed. Then applying a voltage of 1 should open the switch. Figure 5.11 gives the pictures of the circuit. The standard symbol for a NOT gate is given in Figure 5.12. Unlike AND and OR gates, NOT gates are restricted to just one input.

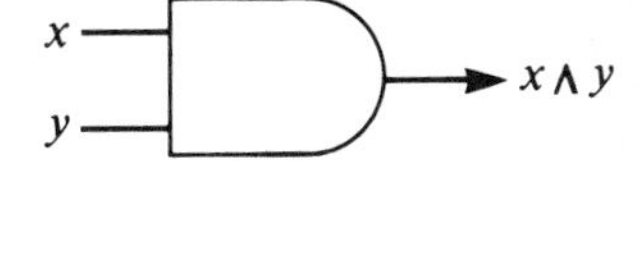

Figure 5.6 An AND gate

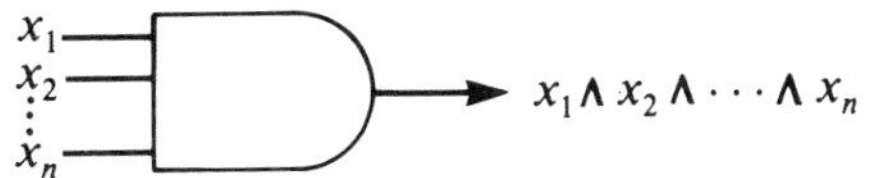

Figure 5.7 A multiple AND gate

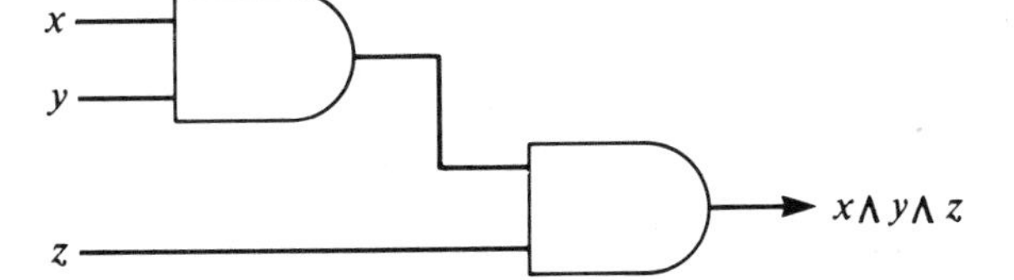

Figure 5.8 An AND gate with three inputs

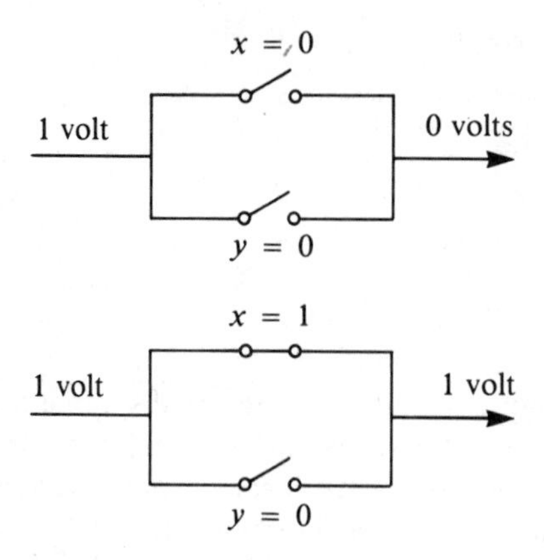

Figure 5.9 $x \vee y$, a parallel connection

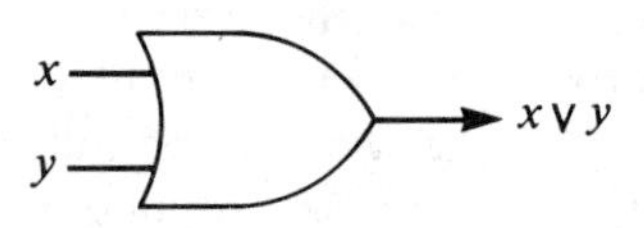

Figure 5.10 An OR gate

Figure 5.11 x' as output

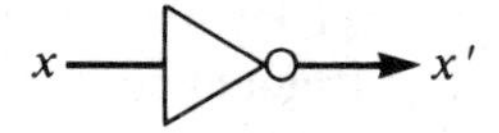

Figure 5.12 A NOT gate

Outputs from AND, OR, and NOT gates may serve as inputs to other such gates, yielding a **switching circuit**. The voltages in a switching circuit are taken to start from the initial inputs and to propagate in the direction of the arrows in Figures 5.6, 5.7, 5.10, and 5.12. We do not allow the propagating voltage to return to a gate once it has passed through the gate.

Example 5.17

Every Boolean polynomial without any O's or I's corresponds directly to a circuit composed of AND, OR, and NOT gates. As explained in the exercises, O's and I's in a Boolean polynomial may also be implemented. How might we build a circuit that "decides" if two inputs are equal? The output should be 1 if both inputs are 0 or if both inputs are 1. One way of writing this desired function is $f(x,y) = (x \wedge y) \vee (x' \wedge y')$. Figure 5.13 gives the corresponding circuit. △

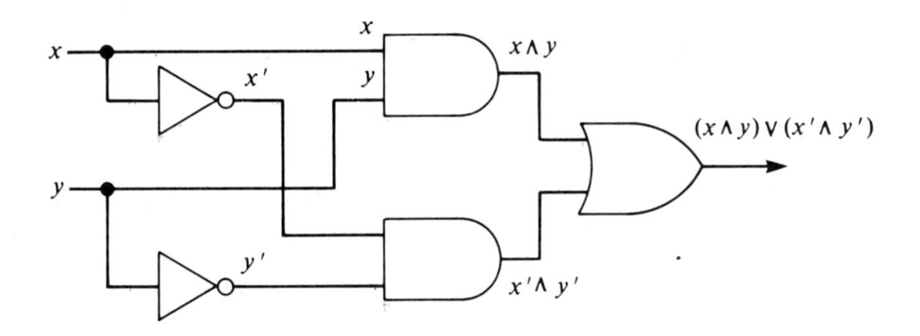

Figure 5.13 Circuit diagram for $(x \wedge y) \vee (x' \wedge y')$

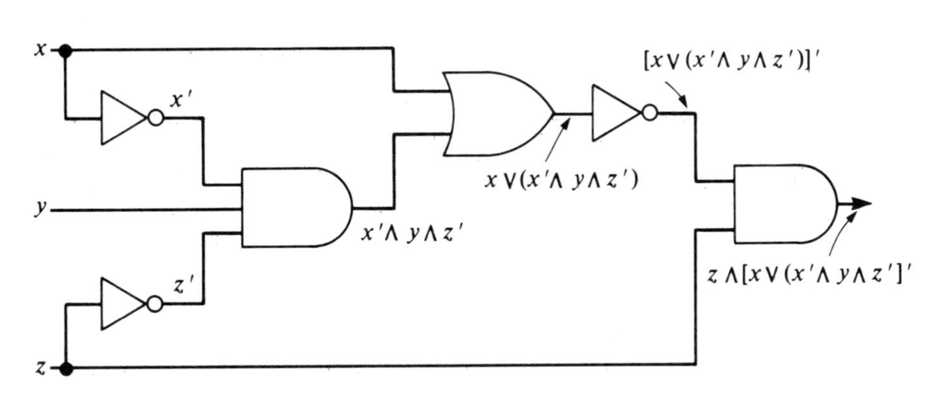

Figure 5.14 From circuit to Boolean polynomial

Example 5.18

Given a switching circuit of AND, OR, and NOT gates, we may form the corresponding Boolean polynomial. Figure 5.14 does this calculation for a rather random circuit. △

Example 5.19

Table 5.1 lists all possible switching, or Boolean, functions of two variables. Regard the first input as x and the second input as y. How may we realize these functions as Boolean polynomials? We are going to use a method that works in general and that illustrates Theorem 5.6, which follows later.

Consider the Boolean polynomial $g(x,y) = x \wedge y$. From Table 5.2, $g(x,y) = 1$ only for $(x,y) = (1,1)$. Otherwise, $g(x,y) = 0$. This gives Table 5.4 as the function-value table for g. Comparing Table 5.4 with the columns of Table 5.1, we see that g gives the same function as f_1 of Table 5.1.

Table 5.4 Function-value table for $g(x,y) = x \wedge y$

(x,y)	$x \wedge y$
(0,0)	0
(0,1)	0
(1,0)	0
(1,1)	1

Observe that just one entry in Table 5.4 equals 1. By additionally considering x' and y', we may form Boolean products whose function-value tables have 1's in any one desired row; see Table 5.5. So in addition to f_1 from above, we have found Boolean polynomials for f_2, f_4, and f_8.

In order to obtain function value tables with more than one 1, we combine the functions of Table 5.5 via $\vee$. For example, f_3 of Table 5.1 equals 1 for $(x,y) = (1,0)$ and for $(x,y) = (1,1)$. From Table 5.5, $x \wedge y'$

Table 5.5 Function-value tables

(x, y)	$x \wedge y$	$x \wedge y'$	$x' \wedge y$	$x' \wedge y'$
(0,0)	0	0	0	1
(0,1)	0	0	1	0
(1,0)	0	1	0	0
(1,1)	1	0	0	0

equals 1 for $(x,y)=(1,0)$ and $x \wedge y$ equals 1 for $(x,y)=(1,1)$. So $f_3=(x \wedge y') \vee (x \wedge y)$, as may also be verified directly. Look at f_{13}; f_{13} is 1 where $x \wedge y$, $x' \wedge y$, and $x' \wedge y'$ are 1. So

$$f_{13}(x,y)=(x \wedge y) \vee (x' \wedge y) \vee (x' \wedge y') \qquad \textbf{(5.10)}$$

The switching circuit for (5.10) is given in Figure 5.15.

This procedure yields Boolean polynomials for all of the functions of Table 5.1 except for f_0, all of whose entries are 0. But $f_0(x,y)=0$ gives the desired polynomial also for f_0. △

Definition 5.6

Consider Boolean polynomials in the variables $x_1, x_2, \ldots, x_n$. Regard the variables as given in the listed order. A **minterm** is a product of the form

$$x_1^{e_1} \wedge x_2^{e_2} \wedge \cdots \wedge x_n^{e_n}$$

where each $x_i^{e_i}$ is either x_i or x_i'. ○

Example 5.20

Let us consider Boolean polynomials in the variables x, y, z. Here are some minterms:

$$x \wedge y \wedge z \qquad x' \wedge y \wedge z' \qquad x' \wedge y' \wedge z \qquad x' \wedge y' \wedge z'$$

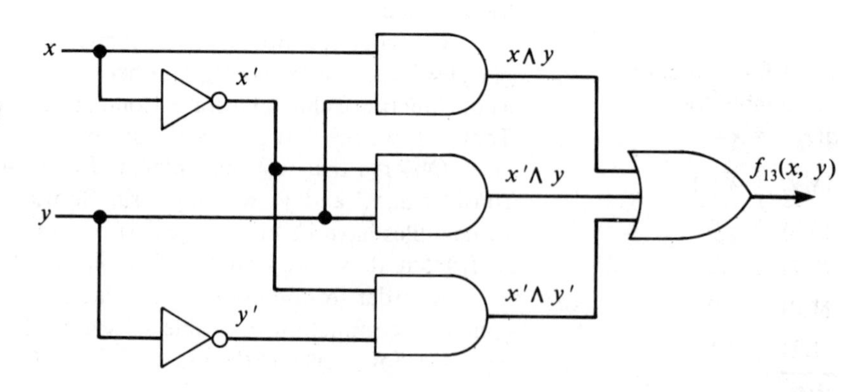

Figure 5.15 Switching circuit for $f_{13}(x,y)=(x \wedge y) \vee (x' \wedge y) \vee (x' \wedge y')$

$x \wedge y$ is not a minterm since the variable z (or z') does not appear. Likewise, $z \wedge y \wedge x$ is not a minterm since the variables are multiplied in the wrong order. Of course, $z \wedge y \wedge x$ is obviously (by commutativity) equivalent to the minterm $x \wedge y \wedge z$. △

In a minterm, each variable or its complement appears. So for n variables, as in Definition 5.6, there are 2^n distinct minterms.

Proposition 5.5

The Boolean function f given by the minterm

$$f(x_1,x_2,\ldots,x_n) = x_1^{e_1} \wedge x_2^{e_2} \wedge \cdots \wedge x_n^{e_n}$$

takes on the value 0 for all but one choice of $(x_1,x_2,\ldots,x_n)$. Thus $f(x_1,x_2,\ldots,x_n) = 1$ for $(x_1,x_2,\ldots,x_n)$, which is given by

$$x_i = 1 \quad \text{if } x_i^{e_i} = x_i$$

$$x_i = 0 \quad \text{if } x_i^{e_i} = x_i'$$

Example 5.21

Before proving Proposition 5.5, we shall illustrate its statement. Let us consider the minterm $f(x,y,z) = x \wedge y' \wedge z'$. Then $f(x,y,z) = 0$ if any of x, y', and z' equals 0. On the other hand, $f(x,y,z) = 1$ only when $x = 1$, $y' = 1$, and $z' = 1$. Since $y' = 1$ is the same as $y = 0$ and $z' = 1$ is the same as $z = 0$, $f(x,y,z) = 1$ only for $x = 1$, $y = 0$, $z = 0$. △

Proof of Proposition 5.5

$f = 0$ if any of the $x_i^{e_i} = 0$. Otherwise, if all of the $x_i^{e_i} = 1$, then $f = 1$.

$$x_i^{e_i} = 1 \quad \text{is} \quad x_i = 1 \quad \text{if } x_i^{e_i} = x_1$$

$$x_i^{e_i} = 1 \quad \text{is} \quad x_i' = 1 \quad \text{if } x_i^{e_i} = x'$$

However, $x_i' = 1$ is equivalent to $x_i = 0$. □

Theorem 5.6

Let f be a Boolean function of the variables $x_1,x_2,\ldots,x_n$. Let $(a_1,a_2,\ldots,a_n)$ be a value for $(x_1,x_2,\ldots,x_n)$ such that $f(a_1,a_2,\ldots,a_n) = 1$. Let the corresponding minterm

$$x_1^{e_1} \wedge x_2^{e_2} \wedge \cdots \wedge x_n^{e_n}$$

be given by

$$x_i^{e_i} = x_i \quad \text{for } a_i = 1$$

$$x_i^{e_i} = x_i' \quad \text{for } a_i = 0$$

Then either f is the 0 function or else f is the sum of all such minterms. In particular, *every* Boolean function may be realized by a Boolean polynomial.

Example 5.22

Before proving Theorem 5.6, we shall illustrate its statement. Let f be f_{13}, as given in Example 5.19 and Table 5.1. From Table 5.1, $f_{13}(x,y)=1$ for (x,y) equal to (0,0), (0,1), and (1,1). The corresponding minterms are

$$(0,0) \to x' \wedge y'$$

$$(0,1) \to x' \wedge y$$

$$(1,1) \to x' \wedge y'$$

So $f(x,y)=(x' \wedge y') \vee (x' \wedge y) \vee (x \wedge y)$. Via commutativity, this is just (5.10) in Example 5.19. △

Proof of Theorem 5.6

By Proposition 5.5, the minterm

$$x_1^{e_1} \wedge x_2^{e_2} \wedge \cdots \wedge x_n^{e_n}$$

has the value 1 at $(a_1,a_2,\ldots,a_n)$ and the value 0 elsewhere. So the value of the minterm agrees with the value of f at $(x_1,x_2,\ldots,x_n)=(a_1,a_2,\ldots,a_n)$. Adding the minterms corresponds to taking the maximum of their values. So the sum gives the same function as f. ◇

Example 5.23

Let the Boolean function $f(x,y,z)$ have the function-value table

	(x,y,z)							
	(0,0,0)	(0,0,1)	(0,1,0)	(0,1,1)	(1,0,0)	(1,0,1)	(1,1,0)	(1,1,1)
$f(x,y,z)$	0	1	1	0	1	1	0	0

The needed minterms are

$$(0,0,1) \to x' \wedge y' \wedge z$$

$$(0,1,0) \to x' \wedge y \wedge z$$

$$(1,0,0) \to x \wedge y' \wedge z'$$

$$(1,0,1) \to x \wedge y' \wedge z$$

$$f(x,y,z)=(x' \wedge y' \wedge z) \vee (x' \wedge y \wedge z) \vee (x \wedge y' \wedge z') \vee (x \wedge y' \wedge z)$$ △

Example 5.24

The Boolean polynomial given by Theorem 5.6 is often not the "simplest" polynomial that represents the function. Look at f_{13} in Example 5.22; $f_{13}(x,y)=0$ only for (1,0). So the minterm $x \wedge y'$ takes on the opposite values from f_{13}. Thus

$$\begin{aligned} f_{13}(x,y) &= (x \wedge y')' \\ &= x' \vee (y')' \\ &= x' \vee y \end{aligned}$$

We could easily check directly that this last Boolean polynomial also gives the function f_{13}. △

Example 5.25

While every Boolean function may be given by a Boolean polynomial, not every real function of a real variable may be given by a real polynomial. For example, $y=|x|$ cannot be given by a polynomial since it is not differentiable at $x=0$. Neither can $y=e^x$ be given by a polynomial. △

Boolean algebras and Boolean polynomials were invented by George Boole with applications to logic in mind. A very brief description of this application, called the Propositional Calculus, will now be given. **Propositions** are statements, perhaps outside of mathematics and logic, that are either true or false. For example, neglecting trivial objections, "Grass is green" is a true proposition. "Grass is not green" is a false proposition. The element O of the Boolean algebra $\{O,I\}$ is considered to be the truth value *False*; I is given the truth value *True*. Boolean polynomials are called **well-formed formulas**. The variables in a well-formed formula are allowed to take on propositions as values, that is essentially to be either *True* or *False*. The axioms of Definition 5.1 may then be taken as axioms of logic, interpreted as follows.

$\vee$ means "nonexclusive or." That is, let p and q be propositions. The well-formed formula $p \vee q$ has the value *True* if either p is *True* or q is *True*, or if both p and q are *True*. The value for $p \vee q$ is *False* if both p and q are *False*. The $\vee$ table in Table 5.2 agrees with this interpretation.

$\wedge$ means "and." The well-formed formula $p \wedge q$ has the value *True* precisely when both p and q are *True*. The $\wedge$ table in Table 5.2 agrees with this interpretation.

$'$ means "not." That is, p' is *False* when p is *True* and vice-versa.

The axioms of Definition 5.1 then become axioms that propositions must satisfy. The Propositional Calculus also includes two Rules of Inference: substitution and *modus ponens*. Example 5.27, which follows later, describes *modus ponens*. By means of the Rules of Inference, the axioms of Definition 5.1 are equivalent to, but not the same as, the usual axioms for the Propositional Calculus.

For example, axiom (vii) on complements includes the traditional statement of the Law of the Excluded Middle: "A proposition is either *True* or *False*, but not both." Namely, let x be a proposition. By axiom (vii),

$$x \vee x' = I$$

that is, either x is *True* or its negation x' is *True*, and

$$x \wedge x' = O$$

that is, x and its negation x' cannot both be *True*.

A function-value table for a well-formed formula is called a **truth table**, as illustrated in Table 5.6. Theorem 5.11, which follows later, is then interpreted as: If two well-formed formulas have the same truth tables, then they may be deduced from each other via the axioms and the Laws of Inference of the Propositional Calculus. This statement, in turn, leads to a proof of the important theorem in logic called The Completeness of the Propositional Calculus.

Table 5.6 Truth table for $f(x,y) = (x' \vee y) \wedge x$

	(x,y)			
	(T,T)	(T,F)	(F,T)	(F,F)
$(x' \vee y) \wedge x$	T	F	F	F

Example 5.26

What interpretation does $x \leq y$ of Definition 5.2 have for logic? Proposition 5.2 says that $x \leq y$ is equivalent to $x \wedge y' = O$. Starting with the equation $x \wedge y' = O$, take complements of both sides, apply de Morgan's Laws and the involution axiom. Then $x \wedge y' = O$ is equivalent to $x' \vee y = I$. So also $x \leq y$ is equivalent to $x' \vee y = I$. In terms of the Propositional Calculus, $p \leq q$ thus means that either p is False or q is True. Table 5.7 gives the truth table for $p \leq q$. In logic, $p \leq q$ is usually denoted by $p \Rightarrow q$, p **implies** q, for the following reason: "p implies q" should mean that if p is *True*, then also q is *True*. This is consistent with the truth values for $(p,q) = (\text{T},\text{T})$ and $(p,q) = (\text{T},\text{F})$ in Table 5.7. What happens when p is *False*? Table 5.7 requires that $p \Rightarrow q$ must then be *True*, regardless of the truth value of q. This *is* consistent with the normal usage of "*If* ... *then* ..." For example,

Table 5.7 Truth table for $p \leq q$ and for $p \Rightarrow q$

	(p,q)			
	(T,T)	(T,F)	(F,T)	(F,F)
$p \leq q$ $p \Rightarrow q$	T	F	T	T

consider the true statement "*If* this computer program runs the first time *then* I'll eat my hat." There is no danger of the hat being eaten (because experience proves that the program will not run). △

Example 5.27

Modus ponens is a traditional law of logic that says: If $p \Rightarrow q$ and p is *True*, then also q is *True*. We shall "prove" this law in terms of Boolean algebras. We are given that $p \Rightarrow q$ means that $p \leq q$ and that p is *True* means that $p = I$. So, $I \leq q$. But I is a universal upper bound, so $q \leq I$. Since $\leq$ is a partial order, $q = I$; that is, q is True. The exercises give a more direct "proof." △

Exercises 5.2

1. Give reasons for each of the following equivalences between Boolean polynomials.

   a. $z \vee [(x \wedge y) \vee (x \wedge y)] = z \vee (x \wedge y)$
   $= (z \vee x) \wedge (z \vee y)$

   b. $[(x \vee y') \wedge (I \vee x)]' = [(x \vee y') \wedge I]'$
   $= (x \vee y')'$
   $= x' \wedge (y')'$
   $= x' \wedge y$

2. Show equivalence between the Boolean polynomials in each of the following pairs.
   a. $(x \vee x') \wedge (y \vee y)$ and y
   b. $[(x \wedge y)' \vee y]'$ and O
3. For each of the following Boolean polynomials, form a function value table using $\{O,I\}$ as the set of possible values for the variables.
   a. $[(x \wedge y') \vee (x' \wedge x)]'$ b. $[z \wedge (x \vee y')]' \wedge (x' \vee z')$
4. Draw switching circuits corresponding to each of the following Boolean polynomials.
   a. $(x \wedge y')' \wedge (x' \vee x \vee y)$ b. $[x \vee (z' \wedge y)]' \vee (x' \wedge y)'$
5. For each switching circuit in Figure 5.16 on p. 232, give a corresponding Boolean polynomial.
6. For each of the following function value tables, write out a Boolean polynomial, in the form of a sum of minterms, that yields the given function value table.

   a.

	(x,y)			
	(O,O)	(O,I)	(I,O)	(I,I)
$f(x,y)$	I	O	I	O

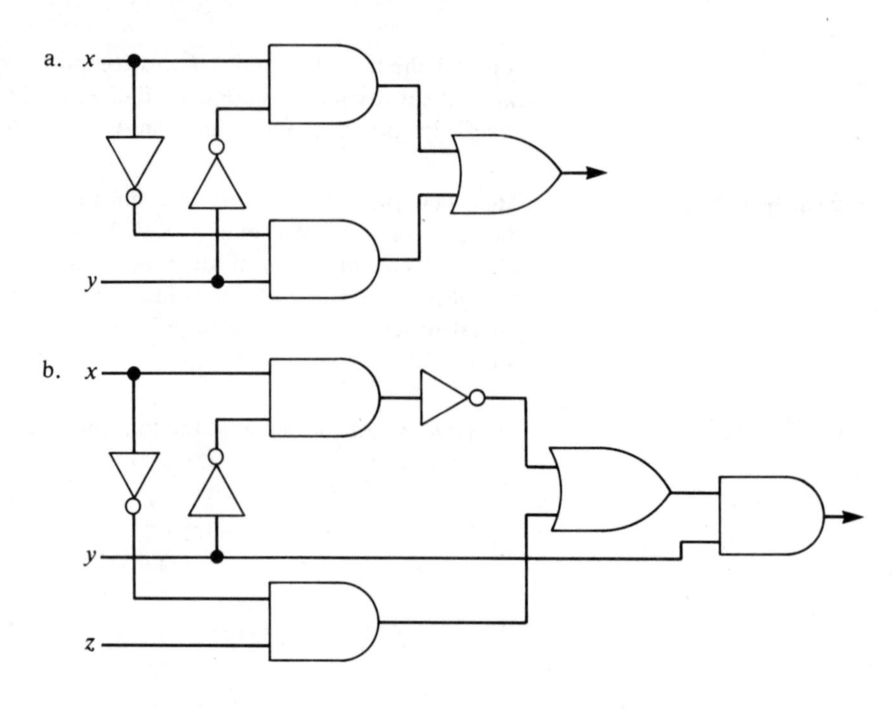

Figure 5.16 Switching circuits

b.

	(x,y,z)							
	(O,O,O)	(O,O,I)	(O,I,O)	(O,I,I)	(I,O,O)	(I,O,I)	(I,I,O)	(I,I,I)
$f(x,y,z)$	O	O	I	O	I	O	O	I

7. The constants 0 and 1 may be introduced into a switching circuit simply by adding input lines that are constantly 0 or 1.
   a. Give the Boolean polynomial that corresponds to the switching circuit of Figure 5.17.

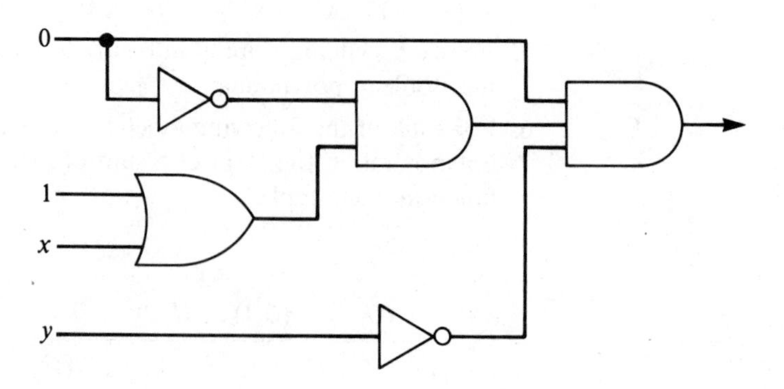

Figure 5.17 A switching circuit

b. Draw the switching circuit, as in Figure 5.17, for the Boolean polynomial $(x \vee y' \vee 0)' \wedge (1 \vee y)$.

8. Compute the truth tables for the following well-formed formulas.

   a. $(p \vee q)' \vee (p' \wedge q')$ b. $[(p' \wedge q') \vee r]'$

9. Explain why Boolean polynomials correspond to switching circuits, while Boolean functions correspond to "black boxes."

10. Show that $=$ is an equivalence relation on Boolean polynomials.

11. a. Explain why the set of all Boolean polynomials in the variables x, y, z is *not* a Boolean algebra.

    Hint: Is $x \vee x$ the same polynomial as x?

    b. Explain why the set of all *equivalence classes* of Boolean polynomials in the variables x, y, z *is* a Boolean algebra.

12. (*Modus ponens*) Suppose that $p \wedge q = p$ and $p = I$. Show that $q = I$.

13. $p \Leftrightarrow q$ means that p and q are either both *True* or both *False*. Show that $p \Leftrightarrow q$ and $(p \Rightarrow q) \wedge (q \Rightarrow p)$ have the same truth tables.

5.3 Disjunctive Normal Form

The previous sections introduced the related, but not identical, concepts of Boolean functions and Boolean polynomials. Recall that each Boolean polynomial yields a Boolean function and that equivalent polynomials yield the same function. Theorem 5.6 showed that every Boolean function may be given by a Boolean polynomial. The polynomials of Theorem 5.6 are the sums of distinct minterms. As formalized in Definition 5.7, which will follow later, such polynomials are said to be in **disjunctive normal form**. In this section, we show that every Boolean polynomial, except O, is equivalent to a unique polynomial in disjunctive normal form. Informally, this implies that the axioms for a Boolean algebra are sufficient to decide whether two Boolean polynomials give the same function. The axioms for a Boolean algebra were taken from set theory and so many others could have been added. But this section implies that additional axioms are unnecessary.

As part of the proof of the theorem on disjunctive normal form, we first show how to rewrite Boolean polynomials so that the operations may be performed in the following order:

(i) complementation $'$
(ii) product $\wedge$
(iii) sum $\vee$

Example 5.28

Let us consider the Boolean polynomial

$$\{[(x \wedge y)' \wedge z]' \vee [(x' \vee z)' \wedge O]\}'$$

We shall find an equivalent polynomial such that $'$ is applied only to variables. Recall from Section 5.1, Exercise 8, that $O'=I$ and $I'=O$.

$$\{[(x \wedge y)' \wedge z]' \vee [(x' \vee z)' \wedge O]\}'$$
$$=\{[(x \wedge y)' \wedge z]'\}' \wedge [(x' \vee z)' \wedge O]', \quad \text{by de Morgan's Laws}$$
$$=[(x \wedge y)' \wedge z] \wedge [(x' \vee z)' \wedge O]', \quad \text{by involution}$$
$$=[(x \wedge y)' \wedge z] \wedge \{[(x' \vee z)']' \vee O'\}, \quad \text{by de Morgan's Laws}$$
$$=[(x \wedge y)' \wedge z] \wedge [(x' \vee z) \vee O'], \quad \text{by involution}$$
$$=[(x \wedge y)' \wedge z] \wedge [(x' \vee z) \vee I], \quad \text{by } O'=I$$
$$=[(x' \vee y') \wedge z] \wedge [(x' \vee z) \vee I], \quad \text{by de Morgan's Laws} \quad \triangle$$

Proposition 5.7 Using involution, de Morgan's Laws, $O'=I$, and $I'=O$, any Boolean polynomial can be shown to be equivalent to a Boolean polynomial for which $'$ is applied only to variables.

Proof of Proposition 5.7 Suppose that $'$ is applied to a Boolean polynomial h. We must show how to simplify h'. Look at Definition 5.4 for a Boolean polynomial. If h comes from (i), we have $O'=I$ and $I'=O$ as simplifications that eliminate the $'$. If $h=x_i$, a variable, then $h'=x_i'$ and we are allowed to keep this term.

If h comes from (ii) of Definition 5.4, we simplify as follows:

For $h=f \vee g$, $h'=(f \vee g)'=f' \wedge g'$, by de Morgan's Laws

For $h=f \wedge g$, $h'=(f \wedge g)'=f' \vee g'$, by de Morgan's Laws

For $h=f'$, $h'=(f')'=f$, by involution.

So the problem of simplifying h' reduces to the problem of simplifying the polynomials f', g', or f. For f' and g', we apply our previous argument to get still simpler polynomials. For f, we look for an outermost $'$ and repeat our argument with h equal to the polynomial on which $'$ operates.

Since a Boolean polynomial has only a finite nesting of operations, the above simplifications always terminate at case (i), with $'$ applied only to variables. □

Example 5.29 Consider the Boolean polynomial

$$f=x \wedge (z \wedge (x' \vee y))$$

f has been chosen so that $'$ applies only to variables. We want to simplify f so that $\wedge$ never applies to a term involving $\vee$. Moreover, we shall not do any manipulations involving $'$; x' will be preserved as a symbol.

$$x \wedge (z \wedge (x' \vee y)) = (x \wedge z) \wedge (x' \vee y), \quad \text{by associativity}$$
$$= [(x \wedge z) \wedge x'] \vee [(x \wedge z) \wedge y], \quad \text{by distributivity}$$

The last polynomial is in the desired form. Using associativity, we may write f more simply as

$$f = (x \wedge z \wedge x') \vee (x \wedge z \wedge y)$$

More simplifications are available, but we shall not make them. △

Example 5.30 Let

$$f = (x \vee y') \wedge [z \wedge (O \vee y)]$$

We shall rewrite f as in Example 5.29.

$$(x \vee y') \wedge [z \wedge (O \vee y)]$$
$$= \{x \wedge [z \wedge (O \vee y)]\} \vee \{y' \wedge [z \wedge (O \vee y)]\}, \quad \text{by distributivity}$$
$$= \{(x \wedge z) \wedge (O \vee y)\} \vee \{(y' \wedge z) \wedge (O \vee y)\}, \quad \text{by associativity}$$
$$= \{[(x \wedge z) \wedge O] \vee [(x \wedge z) \wedge y]\}$$
$$\vee \{[(y' \wedge z) \wedge O] \vee [(y' \wedge z) \wedge y]\}, \quad \text{by distributivity}$$

Eliminating excess parentheses, we find that

$$f = (x \wedge z \wedge O) \vee (x \wedge z \wedge y) \vee (y' \wedge z \wedge O) \vee (y' \wedge z \wedge y)$$ △

Proposition 5.8 Let f be a Boolean polynomial with $'$ applied only to variables. Then, using the commutative, associative, and distributive laws, we may rewrite f into an equivalent Boolean polynomial that is the sum of products. Each product has only O, I, the x_i, and the x_i' as factors. We accept as products O, I, x_i, or x_i' alone.

Proof of Proposition 5.8 Examples 5.29 and 5.30 illustrate the techniques that we wish to use. But we must show that these techniques work in general.

We start with the Boolean polynomial f. If f has no $\vee$ or $\wedge$ in it, then f is O, I, x_i, or x_i' and the proof is complete. Otherwise, we take an outermost $\vee$ or $\wedge$. If we are in the case $f = g \vee h$, it suffices to put the simpler polynomials g and h into the desired form.

So it suffices to consider the case that $f = g \wedge h$, where g and h are simpler (i.e. have fewer operations) than f. If the operation $\vee$ does not occur in g or in h, then f is already a product and the proof is complete. So let us suppose that $\vee$ occurs somewhere in h. (The case of $\vee$ in g is entirely similar; or we may use commutativity to interchange g and h.) Let us choose an outermost $\wedge$ or $\vee$ in h.

Case a. $h = s \wedge t$
Then $f = g \wedge h = g \wedge s \wedge t$. The $\vee$ in h must occur in either s or t. So by associativity and commutativity, we may write in all cases, $f = (g \wedge s) \wedge t$ with $\vee$ occurring in t. t has fewer operations than has h. So the original decomposition $f = g \wedge h$ for f may be replaced by $f = (g \wedge s) \wedge t$, with the $\vee$ occurring in the simpler polynomial t, rather than in h. Continuing this argument, we see that eventually the $\vee$ must be outermost. So we end up in case (b), which follows.

Case b. $h = s \vee t$.
So $f = g \wedge h = g \wedge (s \vee t)$. But $g \wedge (s \vee t) = (g \wedge s) \vee (g \wedge t)$ by distributivity. Since both s and t have fewer operations than has h, both $(g \wedge s)$ and $(g \wedge t)$ have fewer operations than has $f = g \wedge h$. So, as in the second paragraph of the proof, we have simplified the problem.

Repeating the simplifications of case (a) and case (b) as often as necessary, we obtain the desired polynomial that is equivalent to f. □

Example 5.31

To reach disjunctive normal form from Propositions 5.7 and 5.8, we must still rewrite the product terms. Here are some obvious simplifications:

$O \wedge x = O$,	by universal bounds
$x' \wedge I = x'$,	by universal bounds
$x \wedge y \wedge x' = x \wedge x' \wedge y$,	by commutativity
$= O \wedge y$,	by complements
$= O$,	by universal bounds
$x \wedge y \wedge x = x \wedge y$,	by commutativity and idempotency △

Example 5.32

Sums may also be simplified.

$(x \wedge y) \vee (x \wedge y) = x \wedge y$,	by idempotency
$x \vee x' = y \vee y'$,	since both equal I. △

Proposition 5.9

Let f be a Boolean polynomial in the variables $x_1, \ldots, x_n$. Suppose that f is a product, with each factor either O, I, an x_i, or an x_i'. Then either $f = 0$ or else f is equivalent to a sum of minterms from Definition 5.6.

Examples 5.33 We shall illustrate the proof of Proposition 5.9, which follows.

$$\begin{aligned} f(x,y,z) &= x \wedge y \wedge x' \wedge z \\ &= x \wedge x' \wedge y \wedge z, && \text{by commutativity} \\ &= O \wedge y \wedge z, && \text{by complements} \\ &= O, && \text{by universal bounds} \end{aligned}$$

△

$$f(x,y,z) = x' \wedge y$$

which is not a minterm since z or z' is lacking.

$$\begin{aligned} x' \wedge y &= x' \wedge y \wedge I, && \text{by universal bounds} \\ &= x' \wedge y \wedge (z \vee z'), && \text{by complements} \\ &= (x' \wedge y \wedge z) \vee (x' \wedge y \wedge z'), && \text{by distributivity} \end{aligned}$$

△

$f(x,y,z) = y \wedge x' \wedge z$ is not a minterm since the order of the variables in the product is not as in Definition 5.6. Via the commutativity axiom,

$$y \wedge x' \wedge z = x' \wedge y \wedge z$$

which is a minterm. △

Proof of Proposition 5.9 If any factor of f is 0, then the product is O by the universal bounds axiom. If $f = I$, replace f by $x_1 \vee x_1'$. If f otherwise has a factor of I, we delete that factor by the universal bounds axiom. If f contains both x_i and x_i' as factors, then $f = O$ by the commutativity, complements, and universal bounds axioms. So we may assume that each factor of f is either an x_i or an x_i', but that both do not occur. Multiple factors of x_i or of x_i' may be deleted by idempotency.

Suppose that some variable x_j or its complement x_j' is lacking in the product f. Then

$$\begin{aligned} f &= f \wedge I, && \text{by universal bounds} \\ &= f \wedge (x_j \vee x_j'), && \text{by complements} \qquad \textbf{(5.11)} \\ &= (f \wedge x_j) \vee (f \wedge x_j'), && \text{by distributivity} \end{aligned}$$

Suppose that some other variable x_k or its complement x_k' is lacking in the products $f \wedge x_j$ and $f \wedge x_j'$. Repeat the argument of (5.11) to introduce x_k and x_k' as factors. Eventually, we write f as the sum of products, such that each product contains each variable or its complement as a factor.

Each product can fail to be a minterm from Definition 5.6 only because the order of the factors may not be as required. Apply the commutativity axiom to rearrange the order of multiplication. □

Example 5.34 We write $f(w,x,y,z) = x \wedge y$ as a sum of minterms.

$$\begin{aligned} x \wedge y &= x \wedge y \wedge I \wedge I \\ &= x \wedge y \wedge (w \vee w') \wedge (z \vee z') \\ &= [(x \wedge y \wedge w) \vee (x \wedge y \wedge w')] \wedge (z \vee z') \\ &= (x \wedge y \wedge w \wedge z) \vee (x \wedge y \wedge w' \wedge z) \\ &\quad \vee (x \wedge y \wedge w \wedge z') \vee (x \wedge y \wedge w' \wedge z') \\ &= (w \wedge x \wedge y \wedge z) \vee (w' \wedge x \wedge y \wedge z) \\ &\quad \vee (w \wedge x \wedge y \wedge z') \vee (w' \wedge x \wedge y \wedge z') \end{aligned}$$

△

Definition 5.7 A Boolean polynomial f is in **disjunctive normal form** if either f is O or f is written as the sum of distinct minterms. ○

Examples 5.35 The polynomial

$$f(x,y,z) = (x' \wedge y \wedge z') \vee (x \wedge y \wedge z')$$

is in disjunctive normal form. △

$$f(x,y,z) = (x \wedge y \wedge z') \vee (x \wedge y \wedge z') \vee (x' \wedge y' \wedge z)$$

is not in disjunctive normal form since the product $x \wedge y \wedge z'$ is duplicated. △

$$f(x,y,z) = (x \wedge y) \vee (x' \wedge y)$$

is not in disjunctive normal form since $x \wedge y$ and also $x' \wedge y$ are not minterms for the full set of variables x,y,z. △

Theorem 5.10 Every Boolean polynomial f is equivalent to a Boolean polynomial g in disjunctive normal form. The minterms in g, but not the order of their sum, are uniquely determined by f.

Example 5.36 We shall illustrate part of the proof of Theorem 5.10, which follows. Apply all of the above techniques to $f(x,y,z) = [(x \wedge y') \vee z]' \wedge y$.

$$\begin{aligned} &[(x \wedge y') \vee z]' \wedge y \\ &\qquad = [(x \wedge y')' \wedge z'] \wedge y \\ &\qquad = [(x' \vee (y')') \wedge z'] \wedge y \\ &\qquad = [(x' \vee y) \wedge z'] \wedge y, && \text{finished with } ' \\ &\qquad = (x' \vee y) \wedge (z' \wedge y) \end{aligned}$$

$$=(x' \wedge z' \wedge y) \vee (y \wedge z' \wedge y), \quad \text{a sum of products}$$
$$=(x' \wedge z' \wedge y) \vee (y \wedge z')$$
$$=(x' \wedge z' \wedge y) \vee (y \wedge z' \wedge (x \vee x'))$$
$$=(x' \wedge z' \wedge y) \vee (y \wedge z' \wedge x) \vee (y \wedge z' \wedge x')$$
$$=(x' \wedge y \wedge z') \vee (x \wedge y \wedge z') \vee (x' \wedge y \wedge z'), \quad \text{minterms}$$
$$=(x' \wedge y \wedge z') \vee (x \wedge y \wedge z'), \quad \text{no duplications}$$

△

Proof of Theorem 5.10

By Propositions 5.7, 5.8, and 5.9, either $f=O$ or else f may be written as the sum of minterms. By idempotency, we may eliminate any duplications among the minterms and still have an equivalent polynomial g. What we must show is that, except for the order of addition of the minterms, the choice of the minterms is unique. Look at the minterm

$$m=x_1^{e_1} \wedge x_2^{e_2} \wedge \cdots \wedge x_n^{e_n}$$

Then, as a Boolean function, $m=I$ only for $x_i=O$ if $x_i^{e_i}=x_i'$ and $x_i=I$ for $x_i^{e_i}=x_i$. Since equivalent Boolean polynomials give the same Boolean function, m occurs in g if and only if f equals I for the above choices for the x_i values. ◇

Theorem 5.11

Let f and g be Boolean polynomials that give the same Boolean function. Then f and g are equivalent polynomials in the sense of Definition 5.5. In particular, every Boolean polynomial f is equivalent to the corresponding Boolean polynomial given in Theorem 5.6 from the function value table for f.

Example 5.37

Before proving Theorem 5.11, we shall illustrate its statement. Consider f of Example 5.36. Table 5.8 is its table of function values.

$$f(O,I,O)=I \quad \text{and} \quad f(I,I,O)=I$$

Then

$$f(x,y,z)=(x' \wedge y \wedge z') \vee (x \wedge y \wedge z')$$

in agreement with Example 5.36. △

Table 5.8 $f(x,y,z)=[(x \wedge y') \vee z]' \wedge y$

	(x,y,z)							
	(O,O,O)	(O,O,I)	(O,I,O)	(O,I,I)	(I,O,O)	(I,O,I)	(I,I,O)	(I,I,I)
$f(x,y,z)$	O	O	I	O	O	O	I	O

Proof of Theorem 5.11

Consider f and g. Since f and g have the same function values, their corresponding Boolean polynomials from Theorem 5.6 are the same. Since $=$ from Definition 5.5 is an equivalence relation, to prove this theorem, we need only prove that f (and so similarly g) is equivalent to the polynomial from Theorem 5.6.

Theorem 5.10 implies that f is equivalent to a polynomial, call it h, in disjunctive normal form. Moreover, the proof of Theorem 5.10 shows that the minterms of h are uniquely determined as corresponding to the function values of I for f. Since the sum of minterms in Theorem 5.6 has no duplications and gives the correct function values, except possibly for the order of the sum of the minterms, this sum must be h. ◇

Exercises 5.3

1. Rewrite each of the following Boolean polynomials into an equivalent polynomial for which $'$ is applied only to variables.
   a. $[(x \vee y')' \vee z']' \wedge (x' \vee y)'$
   b. $\{[(x' \wedge y')' \vee z]' \vee x\}'$
2. Rewrite each of the following Boolean polynomials into an equivalent polynomial that is a sum of products. Also, $'$ should apply only to variables.
   a. $(x \vee y) \wedge (y' \vee x)$
   b. $[(x \wedge y') \vee (y \wedge z)] \wedge x'$
   c. $(x \vee y) \wedge [(x' \vee z) \wedge y]$
3. Rewrite each of the following products into an equivalent polynomial that is the sum of minterms. The variables are x, y, z in all cases.
   a. $x \wedge y$ b. $x' \wedge y \wedge I$ c. $I \wedge x \wedge y \wedge x \wedge z'$
4. Rewrite each of the following Boolean polynomials into an equivalent polynomial in disjunctive normal form in two different ways: (i) via equivalences from Definition 5.5, as in Theorem 5.10; (ii) via function values, as in Theorem 5.11.
   a. $(x \vee y') \wedge x$,   variables x, y
   b. $(x' \vee z)' \vee y$,   variables x, y, z
   c. $((x \wedge y)' \wedge x')'$,   variables x, y, z
5. We are considering Boolean polynomials in the variables x, y.
   a. Using the technique of the proof of Theorem 5.10, rewrite the polynomials x and $x \vee (x \wedge y)$ so that they are in disjunctive normal form.
   b. How does part (a) relate to the proof of Proposition 5.1?
6. a. What is the general nature of a switching circuit that corresponds to a Boolean polynomial in disjunctive normal form?
   b. Using multiple AND and OR gates, what is the maximum number of AND gates and OR gates that are required to implement a

Boolean polynomial of the variables $x_1,x_2,\ldots,x_n$ that is in disjunctive normal form?

7. A **maxterm** in the variables $x_1,x_2,\ldots,x_n$ is an expression of the form

$$x_1^{e_1} \vee x_2^{e_2} \vee \cdots \vee x_n^{e_n}$$

A Boolean polynomial is in **conjunctive normal form** if it is the product of distinct maxterms. Without proof, state the analogs of Theorems 5.10 and 5.11 for conjunctive normal form.

8. Consider real polynomials of one real variable x. Explain why polynomials of the type

$$a_nx^n + a_{n-1}x^{n-1} + \cdots + a_1x + a_0, \qquad a_n \neq 0$$

can be thought of as normal forms. (Omit proofs.)

5.4 Finite Boolean Algebras

In the first section of this chapter the general notion of a Boolean algebra was introduced. We saw that the power set of a set formed a Boolean algebra under the usual set operations of union, intersection, and complement. We also saw that each switching function could be regarded, through its values of 1, as choosing a subset of the values of the input variables. This made the Boolean algebra $\mathscr{F}_n$ essentially the power set of the input values. Theorems 5.10 and 5.11 of the previous section show that the equivalence classes of Boolean polynomials in the variables $x_1,x_2,\ldots,x_n$ are essentially the switching functions in $\mathscr{F}_n$. In summary, we have seen that $\mathscr{F}_n$ and the power set Boolean algebra for the n input values and the Boolean algebra of equivalence classes of Boolean polynomials in n variables are all essentially the same Boolean algebra. In this section, we prove that *all* finite Boolean algebras essentially come from power sets.

Example 5.38

Let X be a finite set. Recall that singletons are sets with just one element. Since every set consists of its elements, every subset of X, except for $\varnothing$, can be written as the union of singletons. Here are some easy examples with $X = \{1,2,3,4\}$.

$$\{1,2,3\} = \{1\} \cup \{3\} \cup \{2\} \tag{5.12}$$

$$\{2,4\} = \{2\} \cup \{4\} \cup \{4\} \tag{5.13}$$

$$\{3\} = \{3\} \tag{5.14}$$

Moreover, if we avoid duplications, for example, if we allow (5.12) and (5.14) but not (5.13), the singletons are unique except for the order in which they are given. Singletons may be characterized as those sets s such that $s \neq \varnothing$ and such that the only subsets of s are s and $\varnothing$. △

For an arbitrary Boolean algebra, Definition 5.8 (which follows) for an **atom** generalizes the notion of a singleton for a power set. For a finite Boolean algebra, we shall show in Theorem 5.15, which follows later, that, as for sets, all non-O elements can be formed from atoms. Atoms, though, have no smaller pieces. Recall that $\leq$ for Boolean algebras was defined in Definition 5.2.

Definition 5.8 Let B be a Boolean algebra. An element s of B is an **atom** if

(i) $s \neq O$, and
(ii) for $x \leq s$, either $x = s$ or $x = O$. ○

Example 5.39 As proved in the Exercises of Section 5.3, the atoms of a Boolean algebra are exactly the elements that cover O in the sense of posets. In terms of the Hasse diagram, the atoms are those elements that lie immediately above O. Thus in Figure 5.2, $\{1\}$, $\{2\}$, and $\{3\}$ are the atoms. △

Example 5.40 Which are the atoms in Example 5.2? The additive identity $O = f_0$ takes on only the value 0. Let f and g be switching functions. The condition $f \leq g$ is explained in Example 5.6. For f to be an atom, f must be just bigger than f_0. That is, f should have the value 1 for just one input; the other values of f should all be 0. In Table 5.1, the atoms are f_1, f_2, f_4, and f_8. △

Example 5.41 Consider the Boolean algebra of equivalence classes of Boolean polynomials. Let us see that (the equivalence class of) a minterm

$$m = x_1^{e_1} \wedge x_2^{e_2} \wedge \cdots \wedge x_n^{e_n}$$

is an atom. Since m and O have different function values, $m \neq O$. Suppose that a Boolean polynomial f satisfies $f \wedge m = f$, that is, $f \leq m$. We may take f to be written in disjunctive normal form

$$f = m_1 \vee m_2 \vee \cdots \vee m_k$$

with each m_i a minterm. Then, by distributivity,

$$f \wedge m = (m_1 \wedge m) \vee (m_2 \wedge m) \vee \cdots \vee (m_k \wedge m) \quad \textbf{(5.15)}$$

But $m_i \wedge m = O$, unless $m_i = m$, since m and m_i are both minterms. So in (5.15), $f \wedge m$ is either O or m. Since $f \wedge m = f$ is given, f is either O or m. This concludes the verification of Definition 5.8. △

Proposition 5.12 Let s and t be atoms in a Boolean algebra such that $s \neq t$. Then $s \wedge t = O$.

Example 5.42 Before proving Proposition 5.12, we shall illustrate its statement. Let $B = \mathscr{P}(X)$ for some set X. Then s and t are singletons with different elements, and $s \cap t = \varnothing$. △

Proof of Proposition 5.12 By Theorem 5.4, $s \wedge t$ is the greatest lower bound for s and t. In particular, $s \wedge t \leq s$. From Definition 5.8, either $s \wedge t = s$ or $s \wedge t = O$. We need to show that $s \wedge t = s$ leads to a contradiction and so cannot happen. The condition $s \wedge t = s$ means that $s \leq t$. However, t is given to be an atom. So either $s = t$, which is assumed not to happen, or $s = O$, which contradicts Definition 5.8(i). This is the desired contradiction. □

Proposition 5.13 Let B be a finite Boolean algebra. Let x be an element of B such that $x \neq O$. Then there exists an atom s in B such that $s \leq x$.

Example 5.43 Before proving Proposition 5.13, we shall illustrate its statement. Let $B = \mathscr{P}(X)$. Let $x \neq \varnothing$ be a subset of X. Since x is not empty, it has an element e. Let $s = \{e\}$.

Proof of Proposition 5.13 $O \leq x$ by the universal lower bound property of O. By assumption, $O \neq x$. Theorem 5.3 says that $\leq$ is a partial order. Since B is given to be a finite set, Proposition 3.13 applies to show that there is an element s of B such that $O < s \leq x$ and such that s covers O. Then, as will be shown in the exercises, s is an atom. □

Proposition 5.14 Let B be a Boolean algebra. Let $x = s_1 \vee s_2 \vee \cdots \vee s_n$ be a sum of atoms. Let s be an atom. Then $s \leq x$ if and only if $s = s_i$ for some s_i.

Example 5.44 Before proving Proposition 5.14, we shall illustrate its statement. Consider $B = \mathscr{P}(X)$. Let the singleton s_i have e_i as its element. Then $x = \{e_1, e_2, \ldots, e_n\}$. Let $s = \{e\}$. Then $s \subset x$ means that e equals some e_i. △

Proof of Proposition 5.14 By commutativity, changing the order in which the s_i are listed does not change x. By idempotency, x is also unchanged if we delete excess copies of the same s_i. So we may assume that all of the s_i in the theorem are distinct.

$$\begin{aligned} s \wedge x &= s \wedge (s_1 \vee s_2 \vee \cdots \vee s_i \vee \cdots \vee s_n) \\ &= (s \wedge s_1) \vee (s \wedge s_2) \vee \cdots \vee (s \wedge s_i) \vee \cdots \vee (s \wedge s_n) \end{aligned} \tag{5.16}$$

by repeated applications of distributivity. By Proposition 5.12, each term $(s \wedge s_i)$ in (5.16) is either O or s, with $s \wedge s_i = s$ occurring only for $s = s_i$. By the universal bounds property, O makes no contribution to the sum in (5.16). So

$$s \wedge x = \begin{cases} O & \text{if } s \text{ equals no } s_i \\ s_i & \text{if } s \text{ equals } s_i \text{ for some } s_i \end{cases} \tag{5.17}$$

$s \leq x$ is equivalent to $s \wedge x = s$. Also, $s \neq O$ since s is an atom. So the first case in (5.17) corresponds to $s \leq x$ being false. The second case in (5.17), where $s \wedge x = s_i = s$, corresponds to $s \leq x$ being true. □

Theorem 5.15

Let x be an element of the finite Boolean algebra B. Then either $x = O$ or else there is a uniquely determined nonempty set $S = \{s_1, s_2, \ldots, s_n\}$ of atoms such that $x = s_1 \vee s_2 \vee \cdots \vee s_n$.

Example 5.45

Before proving Theorem 5.15, we shall illustrate its statement. Again, let $B = \mathscr{P}(X)$, with X a finite set. A non-O element x of B is a nonempty subset of X. Let $x = \{e_1, e_2, \ldots, e_n\}$. Then $s_1 = \{e_1\}$, $s_2 = \{e_2\}, \ldots, s_n = \{e_n\}$.

$$\{e_1, e_2, \ldots, e_n\} = \{e_1\} \cup \{e_2\} \cup \ldots \cup \{e_n\}.$$

△

Proof of Theorem 5.15

We first show that the desired set S of atoms exists. We shall show later that S is uniquely determined by x. Let S be the set of atoms s_i such that $s_i \leq x$. Proposition 5.13 implies that at least one such s_i exists. So $S \neq \varnothing$. Also, since S is a subset of the finite set B, S is finite. So we may write $S = \{s_1, s_2, \ldots, s_n\}$. Let $y = s_1 \vee s_2 \vee \cdots \vee s_n$. We need to show that $y = x$. We shall show that $y = x$ by showing that $y \leq x$ and $x \leq y$. Antisymmetry for the partial order then implies that $y = x$.

$s_i \leq x$ for each s_i by our choice of the s_i. So x is an upper bound for S. By Theorem 5.4, $y = s_1 \vee s_2 \vee \cdots \vee s_n$ is the least upper bound for S. So $y \leq x$.

By Proposition 5.2, $x \leq y$ is equivalent to $x \wedge y' = O$. By Proposition 5.14, if $s \leq (x \wedge y')$ is false for every atom s, then $x \wedge y' = O$. The condition $s \leq (x \wedge y')$ is equivalent to $s \wedge (x \wedge y') = s$. Therefore, to show that $x \leq y$, it suffices to show that $s \wedge (x \wedge y') = O$ for every atom s in B.

There are two cases, (i) s is an s_i such that $s_i \leq x$ and (ii) $s \leq x$ is not true.

Case (i). Since $s_i \leq x$, $s_i \leq y$. Then by Proposition 5.2, $s_i \wedge y' = O$. Then $s_i \wedge (x \wedge y') = x \wedge (s_i \wedge y') = x \wedge O = O$.
Case (ii). Since $s \wedge x \leq s$, by Definition 5.4, $s \wedge x$ is either O or s. Since $s \leq x$ is assumed false, it must be true that $s \wedge x = O$. Then also $s \wedge (x \wedge y') = (s \wedge x) \wedge y' = O \wedge y' = O$.

We have shown so far that choosing S to be the set of all atoms s_i such that $s_i \leq x$ works for forming x. Now suppose that we have a possibly different set of atoms $T=\{t_1,t_2,\ldots,t_m\}$ such that also

$$x=t_1 \vee t_2 \vee \cdots \vee t_m \tag{5.18}$$

To prove uniqueness, we need that $T=S$. But for an atom s, by Proposition 5.14 and (5.18), $s \leq x$ if and only if s equals one of the t_j. That is, s is in S if and only if s is in T. So $S=T$. ◇

Example 5.46 Let $\mathscr{F}_n$ be the switching algebra of Example 5.2. The atoms s_i in $\mathscr{F}_n$ are, as noted in Example 5.40, those switching functions that have the value 1 for just one input. Let f be an arbitrary switching function. Then Theorem 5.15 and its proof say that f is the sum of those switching functions whose output is 1 for some input where f has output 1. We have already seen this in Example 5.19. △

Example 5.47 Consider the Boolean algebra of equivalence classes of Boolean polynomials in n variables. Example 5.41 shows that (the equivalence class of) a minterm is an atom. Theorem 5.10 says that every Boolean polynomial is equivalent either to O or to the sum of atoms that are minterms. So, by Theorem 5.15, there are no other atoms besides the (equivalence classes of) minterms. Roughly speaking, Theorem 5.15 *is* the Theorem on Disjunctive Normal Form for a general finite Boolean algebra. △

Informally, two Boolean algebras B_1 and B_2 are **isomorphic** if they are the same except for the names of their elements. Here is the formal definition; in Definition 5.9, the map f translates the names of the elements.

Definition 5.9 A one-to-one correspondence $f: B_1 \rightarrow B_2$ between the Boolean algebras B_1 and B_2 is an **isomorphism** if

(i) For all x,y in B_1, $f(x \vee y)=f(x) \vee f(y)$
(ii) For all x,y in B_1, $f(x \wedge y)=f(x) \wedge f(y)$
(iii) For all x in B_1, $f(x')=[f(x)]'$ ○

Example 5.48 Let $B_1=\mathscr{P}(\{a,b,c\})$ and let $B_2=\mathscr{P}(\{1,2,3\})$. It is easy to see that the map $f: B_1 \rightarrow B_2$ given by

$$\varnothing \rightarrow \varnothing \qquad \{a\} \rightarrow \{1\} \qquad \{b\} \rightarrow \{2\} \qquad \{c\} \rightarrow \{3\}$$

$$\{a,b\} \rightarrow \{1,3\} \qquad \{a,c\} \rightarrow \{1,3\} \qquad \{b,c\} \rightarrow \{2,3\} \qquad \{a,b,c\} \rightarrow \{1,2,3\}$$

is an isomorphism. △

Example 5.49

Let $\mathscr{F}_2$ be the switching algebra whose elements are given in Table 5.1. $\mathscr{F}_2$ has $16=2^4$ elements. Let $X=\{00,01,10,11\}$ be the set of possible inputs. X has $4=2^2$ elements. $\mathscr{P}(X)$ has $2^4=16$ elements. An isomorphism between $\mathscr{F}_2$ and $\mathscr{F}(X)$ may be given by renaming each f_i in $\mathscr{F}_2$ to that subset of X which has an output of 1. That is

$$f_0 \to \varnothing \qquad f_1 \to \{11\} \qquad f_2 \to \{10\} \qquad f_3 \to \{10,11\}$$
$$f_4 \to \{01\} \qquad f_5 \to \{01,11\} \qquad f_6 \to \{01,10\} \qquad f_7 \to \{01,10,11\}$$
$$\cdots$$

The operations $\vee$, $\wedge$, and $'$ in $\mathscr{F}_2$ are renamed to the operations $\cup$, $\cap$, and $\bar{}$ in $\mathscr{P}(X)$ respectively. △

Theorem 5.16

Let B be a finite Boolean algebra such that $O \neq I$. Let X be the set of atoms of B. Then the map $f: B \to \mathscr{P}(X)$, defined by $f(x)$ equals S from Theorem 5.15, is an isomorphism between B and $\mathscr{P}(X)$.

Proof of Theorem 5.16

Let x and y be elements of the finite Boolean algebra B.

$$x = s_1 \vee s_2 \vee \cdots \vee s_n \qquad S = f(x) = \{s_1, s_2, \ldots, s_n\} \tag{5.19}$$

$$y = t_1 \vee t_2 \vee \cdots \vee t_m \qquad T = f(y) = \{t_1, t_2, \ldots, t_m\} \tag{5.20}$$

where the s_i and the t_j are atoms. We must verify the specifications of Definition 5.9. Let us first see that f is a one-to-one correspondence. If $f(x)=f(y)$, then $x=y$ by commutativity and associativity. So f is one-to-one. Also, f is onto because, given any subset S of the atoms of B, we can just define x by (5.19). Then $f(x)=S$.

We now verify the three conditions of Definition 5.9.

Definition 5.9(i) By (5.19) and (5.20),

$$x \vee y = s_1 \vee s_2 \vee \cdots \vee s_n \vee t_1 \vee \cdots \vee t_m \tag{5.21}$$

By commutativity and idempotency, we may eliminate any duplicate atoms from the sum in (5.21). Then we will have written $x \vee y$ as a sum of distinct atoms. Theorem 5.15 implies that there is only one way to do this. That is,

$$f(x \vee y) = S \cup T = f(x) \cup f(y)$$

Definition 5.9(ii) By (5.19) and (5.20),

$$x \wedge y = (s_1 \vee s_2 \vee \cdots \vee s_n) \wedge (t_1 \vee \cdots \vee t_m) \tag{5.22}$$

By many applications of distributivity, (5.22) becomes

$$\begin{aligned} x \wedge y = &(s_1 \wedge t_1) \vee (s_1 \wedge t_2) \vee \cdots \vee (s_1 \wedge t_m) \\ &\vee (s_2 \wedge t_1) \vee (s_2 \wedge t_2) \vee \cdots \vee (s_2 \wedge t_m) \\ &\cdots \\ &\vee (s_n \wedge t_1) \vee (s_n \wedge t_2) \vee \cdots \vee (s_n \wedge t_m) \end{aligned} \tag{5.23}$$

Look at a term $s_i \wedge t_j$ in (5.23). By Proposition 5.12, either $s_i = t_j$ and so $s_i \wedge t_j = s_i = t_j$, or $s_i \neq t_j$ and $s_i \wedge t_j = O$. Terms of O may be eliminated from (5.23), leaving $x \wedge y$ as the sum of atoms. The atoms that do occur in the sum (5.23) must be common to both x and y. That is, $f(x \wedge y) = S \cap T = f(x) \wedge f(y)$.

Definition 5.9(iii) By Definition 5.8, $f(O) = \varnothing$; that is, there are no atoms s such that $s \leq 0$. By the universal bounds axiom, $s \leq I$ for all atoms. So, $f(I) = X$. Now consider $f(x')$. By the already proved conditions (i) and (ii),

$$f(x) \vee f(x') = f(x \vee x') = f(I) = X \quad \text{and}$$

$$f(x) \wedge f(x') = f(x \wedge x') = f(O) = \varnothing$$

By Section 5.1, Exercise 7, $f(x)$ and $f(x')$ are complements in the Boolean algebra $\mathscr{P}(X)$. That is, $f(x') = [f(x)]'$. ◇

The proofs of the following two corollaries of Theorem 5.16 are left to the exercises.

Corollary 5.17 Let B be a finite Boolean algebra. Let $|B|$ denote the number of elements in B. Then for some nonnegative integer n,

$$|B| = 2^n$$

Corollary 5.18 Let B_1 and B_2 be finite Boolean algebras. Then B_1 and B_2 are isomorphic if and only if they have the same number of elements.

Exercises 5.4

1. Let s be an element of the Boolean algebra B. Show that s is an atom in the sense of Definition 5.8 if and only if, using Definition 5.2, s covers O in the sense of Chapter 3, Section 3.4.
2. Let X be a finite set. Make $\mathscr{P}(X)$ into a Boolean algebra using the following nonstandard notation:

$\vee$ = the set operation $\cap$

$\wedge$ = the set operation $\cup$

$'$ = the set operation $^{-}$

What are the atoms in this Boolean algebra?

3. Let m_1 and m_2 be distinct minterms. Show that $m_1 \wedge m_2 = O$.

   Hint: For some i, x_i and x_i' occur in m_1 and m_2.

4. Show that isomorphism, as in Definition 5.9, is an equivalence relation on any set of Boolean algebras.

5. Let $f: B_1 \to B_2$ be an isomorphism of Boolean algebras. With the obvious notation, show that $f(O_1) = O_2$ and that $f(I_1) = I_2$.

   Hint: Consider $x \wedge x'$ and $x \vee x'$.

6. Suppose that $f: B_1 \to B_2$ is a map between Boolean algebras that satisfies Definition 5.9(i), Definition 5.9(ii), $f(O_1) = O_2$, and $f(I_1) = I_2$. Show that f also satisfies Definition 5.9(iii).

   Hint: Apply Section 5.1, Exercise 7.

7. Prove Corollary 5.17.

8. Prove Corollary 5.18.

9. Let X be an infinite set.

   a. Explain why the atoms in $\mathscr{P}(X)$ are the singletons.

   b. Explain why X in $\mathscr{P}(X)$ cannot be written as the (finite) sum of atoms.

6 Fast Sorting and Fast Addition

Modern computers execute each machine instruction very rapidly and very inexpensively. Nonetheless, many important computations require the execution of so many instructions that their total running time is large or excessive. Other computations are easy, but are done so often that low cost or high speed is very desirable. So, despite the low component cost of integrated circuits, good algorithms and efficient circuit design are needed.

This chapter begins with a discussion of sorting, describing, and comparing bubble, bucket, and merge sorts. A bubble sort is slow for sorting a large list, but ease of programming makes it preferable for sorting a small list. For sorting a large, arbitrary list, a merge sort is about as fast as is theoretically possible. For sorting a list with special properties, a bucket sort may be the fastest.

Sorting algorithms (or procedures) are judged by means of the following general paradigm: We show how the inherent difficulty in sorting a list, that is, the number of simple computations required to complete the sort, may be estimated in terms of the number of elements to be sorted. The **time complexity** of an algorithm is the function that expresses the completion time for the algorithm in terms of the size of the problem, for example, the number of elements to be sorted. A good sorting algorithm thus has a time complexity about as large as the estimate for the inherent difficulty of the sorting problem. As longer lists are sorted, the **asymptotic** complexity of the algorithm, that is, its behavior for large amounts of data, becomes more important in determining costs than does its simplicity for programming purposes.

The bulk of this chapter is devoted to the much more algebraic, much more complicated problem of finding good switching circuits to perform addition in $(\mathbb{Z}_N, +)$. These circuits are evaluated via a paradigm similar to the one above for sorting algorithms. Namely, under various assumptions about the nature of the circuit, we estimate theoretically the number of components and the time required to complete the addition. We then compare the circuit values to the theoretical estimates. The usual method for binary addition turns out to minimize the required number of circuit modules. By allowing many more components and hence the simultaneous execution of many operations, we construct a parallel adder whose asymptotic completion time is of the same order of magnitude as the theoretical minimum. Using somewhat sophisticated group theory, we also see that for the purposes of addition in $(\mathbb{Z}_{2^n}, +)$, the usual binary representation for integers is as efficient as any other possible representation.

When N is not a power of a prime, the results about fast addition circuits are rather different than for $N = 2^n$. The usual method of representation, such as is used for decimal numbers, is no longer as efficient as possible. The Chinese Remainder Theorem, as discussed in the last section, provides a better representation. In Chapter 9, we shall use the Chinese Remainder representation in the Schönhage-Strassen algorithm for the fast multiplication of very large ordinary integers. It should be noted that representing numbers via the Chinese Remainder Theorem is not usually done in actual practice since it provides no advantages for comparing two numbers or for detecting overflows.

The discussion of the Chinese Remainder Theorem leads to formal definitions of group homomorphism and group isomorphism. Homomorphisms for machines will be important in the next chapter.

6.1 Sorting

Very often a list of N names must be alphabetized, or a list of N numbers must be rearranged into ascending order. Such an alphabetization or rearrangement is called a **sort**. In this section, we give a lower bound for how much computation is required to sort an arbitrary list of N integers. We also use a sorting technique, called a **merge sort**, which is as efficient as this lower bound. Although we only examine sorting explicitly for lists of integers, the discussion applies readily to sorting lists from any totally ordered set. To simplify the discussion, we shall assume that all of the integers in the list are distinct.

Example 6.1

We wish to sort a given list of N distinct integers into ascending order. The list is supposed to be given to us in a very random order. Also, the integers in the list may be very large with respect to N. One way to sort the N integers is to form a second, sorted list as follows:

1. Start the sorted list with $m = 0$ elements.
2. Compare the $(m+1)$st element of the given list sequentially with the m elements of the sorted list.
3. Place the $(m+1)$st element of the given list appropriately in the sorted list.
4. If $m+1 = N$, stop. Otherwise, replace m by $m+1$ and go to Step 2.

For example, this procedure sorts the list

$$5, 0, 80, 40, 13 \quad \textbf{(6.1)}$$

as follows:

	$m=0$	$m=1$	$m=2$	$m=3$	$m=4$
$(m+1)$st element:	5	0	80	40	13
Comparisons:	–	$0<5$	$80>0$ $80>5$	$40>0$ $40>5$ $40<80$	$13>0$ $13>5$ $13<40$
New sorted list:	5	0,5	0,5,80	0,5,40,80	0,5,13,40,80

△

Example 6.2

Here is an improvement of Example 6.1 called a **bubble sort**. A bubble sort is much simpler to program on a computer than is the sort of Example 6.1. Again, we wish to sort a given list of N distinct integers into ascending order. Instead of forming a new sorted list, we shall rearrange the given list. So let $A(i)$, $1 \leq i \leq N$, denote the current integer in place i of the list.

1. For j starting at 1 and successively increasing to $2,3,\ldots,N-1$, bring the jth smallest integer to the jth place on the list by:
   2. For i starting at N and successively decreasing to $N-1$, $N-2,\ldots,j+1$, compare $A(i)$ to $A(i-1)$.
      3. If $A(i)<A(i-1)$, then interchange the values of $A(i)$ and $A(i-1)$.
      4. If $A(i)>A(i-1)$, retain the values of $A(i)$ and $A(i-1)$.

For example, a bubble sort for the list (6.1) proceeds as follows: $A(i)$ and $A(i-1)$ are underlined at each step below.

		Current List
$j=1$	$i=5$	5, 0, 80, $\underline{40}$, 13
	$i=4$	5, 0, $\underline{80}$, $\underline{13}$, 40
	$i=3$	5, $\underline{0}$, $\underline{13}$, 80, 40
	$i=2$	$\underline{5}$, $\underline{0}$, 13, 80, 40
$j=2$	$i=5$	0, 5, 13, $\underline{80}$, $\underline{40}$
	$i=4$	0, 5, $\underline{13}$, $\underline{40}$, 80
	$i=3$	0, $\underline{5}$, $\underline{13}$, 40, 80
$j=3$	$i=5$	0, 5, 13, $\underline{40}$, $\underline{80}$
	$i=4$	0, 5, $\underline{13}$, $\underline{40}$, 80
$j=4$	$i=5$	0, 5, 13, $\underline{40}$, $\underline{80}$
		0, 5, 13, 40, 80

Observe that the list was correctly sorted already after $j=2$, $i=5$. However, were the initial list in decreasing order,

80, 40, 13, 5, 0

the bubble sort would require all values of j and i. △

Example 6.3

We wish to sort a list of N distinct integers, which are *given* to range from at least 1 to at most R. A **bucket sort** will suffice, as follows: Let $A(i), 1 \leq i \leq N$, denote the ith integer in the given list. $B(i), 1 \leq i \leq N$, will becomes the ith integer in the sorted list. $C(j)$, $1 \leq j \leq R$, are binary variables.

1. Set all of the $C(j)$ to 0.
2. For $i=1,2,\ldots,N$, let $j=A(i)$. Reset $C(j)$ to 1.
3. Let I be a variable. Start I at 1. For $j=1,2,\ldots,R$,
   4. If $C(j)=1$, let $B(I)=j$. Replace I by $I+1$.
   5. If $C(j)=0$, just replace I by $I+1$.

For example, consider a bucket sort of the list

5, 7, 1, 2, 4

with R given to be 10. Then after Step 2 above, the $C(j)$ are given by

$$\begin{array}{rcccccccccc} j: & 1 & 2 & 3 & 4 & 5 & 6 & 7 & 8 & 9 & 10 \\ C(j): & 1 & 1 & 0 & 1 & 1 & 0 & 1 & 0 & 0 & 0 \end{array} \qquad (6.2)$$

Looking at the 1's in (6.2) gives the desired sorted list

1, 2, 4, 5, 7 △

We need measures for the efficiency of a sorting procedure. Preferably, such measures should be independent of any computer that implements the procedure. For sorts, such as in Examples 6.1 and 6.2, which only compare the sizes of the integers, we let $M_{\max}(N)$, or just $M(N)$, denote the *maximum* number of comparisons that are needed to sort a list of N integers. For some applications, it is preferable to use $N_{\mathrm{av}}(N)$, the *average* number of comparisons that a sorting procedure uses to sort a list with N elements. $M(N)$ and $M_{\mathrm{av}}(N)$ are ways to express the time complexity of a procedure (or algorithm).

Example 6.4

We compute $M(N)$ for the sorting procedure of Example 6.1. Comparisons occur in Step 2. The $(m+1)$st element of the given list may be larger than all of the m elements of the sorted list. So Step 2 may involve at most m comparisons each time it is used. In Step 4, m varies from 0 through $N-1$. So, summing the arithmetic progression,

$$M(N)=0+1+2+\cdots+(N-1)=\frac{N(N-1)}{2}$$

It is easy also to compute $M_{av}(N)$ for this sorting procedure. We are assuming a random distribution of lists. So in Step 2, we expect the $(m+1)$st element to fit into the middle of the sorted list, on the average. So only about half as many comparisons are needed for $M_{av}(N)$ as are needed for $M(N)$.

$$M_{av}(N)\approx\frac{N(N-1)}{4}$$ △

It is easy to see that the bubble sort of Example 6.2 always requires $\frac{N(N-1)}{2}$ comparisons. A bubble sort is usually more efficient than a sort from Example 6.1, even though the latter generally uses fewer comparisons, because the bubble sort requires many fewer steps for other operations besides comparisons.

Example 6.5

How shall we measure the time T needed to execute a bucket search, as in Example 6.3? Steps 1 and 3 each require R different values for j. Step 2 requires N different values for i. So, for large N and R, there should be constants a and b, which depend on the machine, such that

$$T\approx aN+bR \tag{6.3}$$ △

Which sort is faster, a bubble sort or a bucket sort? The answer is that it depends. The running time for a bubble sort is approximately proportional to $\frac{N(N-1)}{2}$, which should be compared to $aN+bR$ from (6.3) for the bucket sort. For R much larger than N^2, the bubble sort is faster. For R much smaller that N^2, say with R comparable with N, the bucket sort is faster.

For the remainder of this section, we shall consider only sorts that use comparisons between integers as a basis for sorting a list L. We think of such a sort as proceeding as follows: An initial comparison is made between two integers on the list, call them a_1 and b_1. If $a_1\le b_1$ is true, then the sort proceeds in one manner. If $a_1\le b_1$ is false, then the sort proceeds in another manner. In either case, another comparison is made, say between a_2 and b_2. The choice of a_2 and b_2 will usually depend on the truth of $a_1 \leq b_1$. Depending on the truth of $a_2 \leq b_2$, the sort continues. This is indicated schematically as a binary tree in Figure 6.1. In Figure 6.1, each decision is represented by a solid disc. Each decision leads below it to two lines, which represent the two possible continuations of the sort. Eventually, depending on the list L, the sorting procedure terminates. Termination is represented by a circle in Figure 6.1. At termination, the sorting procedure has permuted the given list L into ascending order. Since only comparative size information about the integers in L is used, each termination in Figure 6.1 may also be thought of as a suitable permutation of the *positions* in the list L.

As in Figure 6.1, consider sorting all lists with N distinct integers. There are $N!$ possible permutations of the positions of the integers. Each such permutation must be represented by at least one termination in Figure 6.1, since all lists have to be sorted correctly. So there are at least $N!$ terminations. In Figure 6.1, the number of decisions needed to reach a given termination is found by counting the number of decisions from the initial decision $a_1 \leq b_1$? to the given termination. For example, p_1 and p_2 need two decisions; p_3 and p_4 need three decisions; p_{11} needs six decisions. Each decision level $a_i \leq b_i$? doubles the number of possible terminations. Since there are at least $N!$ terminations, we have proved the following theorem.

Figure 6.1 A sort

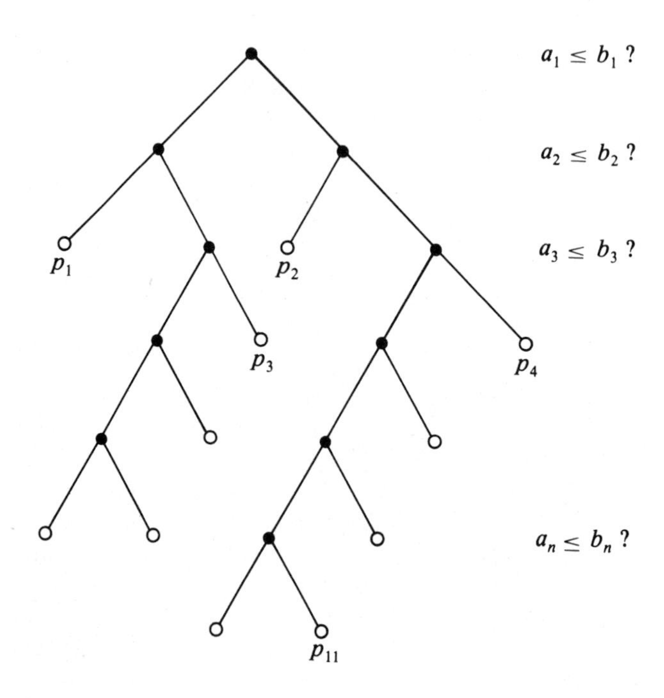

Theorem 6.1

Let M be the maximum number of comparisons via $\leq$ that a sorting procedure needs to sort a list of N elements. Then

$$2^M \leq N! \qquad \diamond$$

The estimate of Theorem 6.1 may be rewritten, as follows, into a more usable form. Formula (6.4), which follows, known as Stirling's Formula, is an approximation for $N!$ We shall not prove (6.4); some numerical examples for (6.4) are discussed in the exercises at the end of this section.

$$N! \sim \sqrt{2\pi}\, e^{-N} N^{N+(1/2)} \tag{6.4}$$

In (6.4), $\sim$ means that the ratio of the two sides approaches 1 as N approaches infinity. Intuitively, $\sim$ means that the two sides have the same growth rate. The symbol $\sim$ is read "is asymptotic to."

We take $\log_2$ of both sides of Theorem 6.1 and obtain

$$M \geq \log_2(N!) \tag{6.5}$$

From (6.4),

$$\begin{aligned}\log_2 N! &\sim \log_2\sqrt{2\pi} - N\log_2 e + (N+\tfrac{1}{2})\log_2 N \\ &\sim N\log_2 N\end{aligned} \tag{6.6}$$

From (6.5) and (6.6), we may say that, *roughly, at least $N\log_2 N$ comparisons are needed in order to be able to sort all lists of N elements.*

Recall that $M(N) = \frac{N(N-1)}{2}$ for both a bubble sort and the sort of Example 6.1. Recall from the Calculus that $\frac{N(N-1)}{2}$ grows much more rapidly as a function of N than does the $N\log_2 N$ estimate from above. This correctly suggests that, at least for large N, much more efficient sorts are available. A **merge sort**, as in the next example, does as well as allowed by Theorem 6.1.

Example 6.6

(A **merge sort**) We wish to sort a list of N distinct integers. In order to simplify things a little, we shall assume that $N = 2^n$, for some integer n.

Suppose that we have a pair of lists, each with m elements, which are already sorted. We may *merge* the two sorted lists into one sorted list of $2m$ elements by successively adding elements of the first list to the appropriate position in the second list.

Now let us return to our given list of $N = 2^n$ elements. We wish to merge sorted lists. We start with each element as a sorted list with $m=1$ element. We pair off the elements and merge them into sorted lists with $2m=2$ elements. Now we pair off the sorted lists of $m=2$ elements and merge them into sorted lists with $2m=4$ elements. We continue this process. After i merges, each sorted list has 2^i elements. So, after n merges, all $N=2^n$ elements on the list are sorted. Figure 6.2 illustrates a merge sort with $N=16$.

In order to estimate $M(N)$ for a merge sort, we must first estimate how many comparisons may be needed to merge two lists of m integers each. We consider, for example, merging the lists

$$36, 42, 53, 71 \quad \text{and} \quad 3, 11, 52, 60 \tag{6.7}$$

from Figure 6.2. We add elements of the first list in (6.7) to the second list in (6.7) via the following comparisons:

$$\begin{array}{ll} & \textit{New List} \\ 36>3,\ 36>11,\ 36<52 & 3,11,\underline{36},52,60 \\ 42<52 & 3,11,36,\underline{42},52,60 \\ 53>52,\ 53<60 & 3,11,36,42,52,\underline{53},60 \\ 71>60 & 3,11,36,42,52,53,60,\underline{71} \end{array} \tag{6.8}$$

Observe in (6.8) that each successive comparison $a<b$ has either a or b increasing in position by 1. This is true in general. So *at most* $(2m-1)$ *comparisons are needed to merge two sorted lists of* m *elements each.*

We can now complete our calculation of $M(N)$. $N=2^n$. A merge sort, as in Figure 6.2, starts with 2^{n-1} pairs of lists, each with 1 element. Each pair requires 1 comparison for merging. So the first level, as in Figure 6.2,

Figure 6.2 A merge sort for $N=16=2^4$

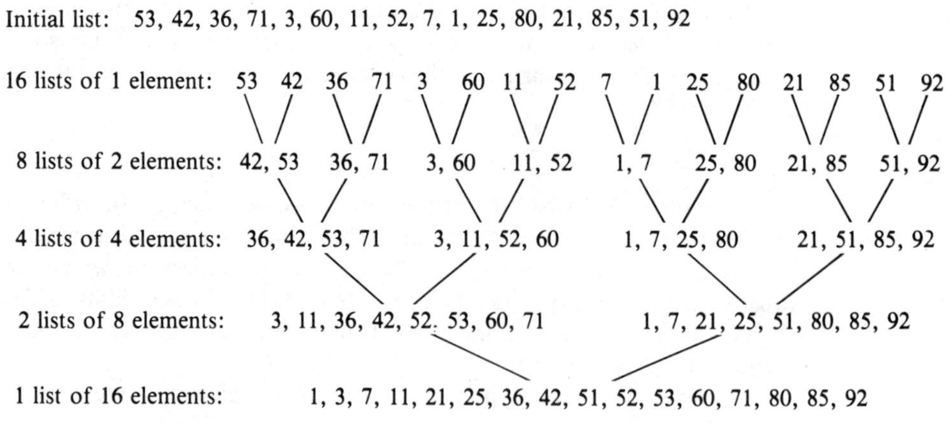

Initial list: 53, 42, 36, 71, 3, 60, 11, 52, 7, 1, 25, 80, 21, 85, 51, 92

16 lists of 1 element: 53 42 36 71 3 60 11 52 7 1 25 80 21 85 51 92

8 lists of 2 elements: 42, 53 36, 71 3, 60 11, 52 1, 7 25, 80 21, 85 51, 92

4 lists of 4 elements: 36, 42, 53, 71 3, 11, 52, 60 1, 7, 25, 80 21, 51, 85, 92

2 lists of 8 elements: 3, 11, 36, 42, 52, 53, 60, 71 1, 7, 21, 25, 51, 80, 85, 92

1 list of 16 elements: 1, 3, 7, 11, 21, 25, 36, 42, 51, 52, 53, 60, 71, 80, 85, 92

requires

$$2^{n-1}\cdot 1$$

comparisons in all. Next, there are 2^{n-2} pairs of lists, each with 2 elements. Merging each pair takes $2\cdot 2-1=3$ comparisons. In all,

$$2^{n-2}\cdot 3$$

comparisons are needed. For the ith level in a merge sort, there are 2^{n-i} pairs of lists, each with 2^{i-1} elements.

$$2^{n-i}\cdot(2\cdot 2^{i-1}-1)=2^{n-i}(2^i-1) \quad \textbf{(6.9)}$$

comparisons are needed for all of the mergers. Summing (6.9), we see that a merge sort requires at most

$$2^{n-1}\cdot 1+2^{n-2}\cdot 3+\cdots+2^{n-i}(2^i-1)+\cdots+1\cdot(2^n-1) \quad \textbf{(6.10)}$$

comparisons. Each product term in (6.10) is less than

$$2^{n-i}\cdot 2^i=2^n$$

(6.10) is the sum of n terms. In all, for a merge sort,

$$M(2^n)<n\cdot 2^n$$

With $N=2^n$,

$$M(N)<N\log_2 N \quad \textbf{(6.11)}$$

That is, the asymptotic behavior of a merge sort is as good as possible, by Theorem 6.1. △

Exercises 6.1

1. Consider the sorting procedure of Example 6.1.
   a. What value does Example 6.4 give for $M(5)$?
   b. Give an explicit list of five integers that requires this maximum number of comparisons for a sort.
2. Do a merge sort, as in Figure 6.2, for the list

   21, 13, 52, 7, 2, 43, 77, 56, 3, 98, 15, 34, 11, 90, 65, 64

3. a. From (6.10), what is $M(64)$ for a merge sort?
   b. Compare the answer from part (a) to $M(64)$ for a bubble sort.

4. a. Give two sorted lists, each with eight integers, such that merging as in (6.8) requires $2 \cdot 8 - 1 = 15$ comparisons.
   b. Give a list of 16 integers that requires the maximum number of comparisons for sorting via a merge sort.
5. Complete the following table, which gives numerical computations for Stirling's Formula.

n	$n!$	$\sqrt{2\pi} e^{-n} n^{n+(1/2)}$	Error	Percentage error
1	1	0.9221	0.0779	7.8%
4	24	23.506	0.494	2.1%
7	–	4,980.4	–	–
10	3,628,800	3,598,695.6	–	0.83%
13	6,227,020,800	6,187,239,477.	–	–

6. Consider sorting a list of N distinct integers, which are given to range from at least 1 to at most R. Which is faster, a bucket sort or a merge sort?

   Hint: Consider R as a function of N.
7. Justify the step

$$\log_2 \sqrt{2\pi} - N \log_2 e + (N + \tfrac{1}{2}) \log_2 N \sim N \log_2 N$$

   in (6.6).
8. Consider merging two sorted lists, each having m elements.
   a. Show that any diagram such as Figure 6.1 for any merging procedure must have at least $\dfrac{(2m)!}{m!\,m!}$ terminations.

      Hint: In the $2m$ positions for the merged list, you must choose the m positions for the first list.
   b. Using Stirling's Formula, as in the text, show that asymptotically, at least $2m$ comparisons via $\leq$ are needed to merge two sorted lists of m elements each.
9. The following procedure, called a **QUIK sort**, is used very often because its *average* running time on most digital computers is among the least of all known sorting procedures (for "arbitrary" lists).

   1. Pick an integer s at random from the given list.
   2. Divide the given list into three sublists consisting of elements: less than s, equal to s, greater than s.

3. Repeat Steps 1 and 2 on the first and third sublists until all sublists have just one element.

Suppose that a list has N distinct elements and that s always turns out to be the largest element. Show that $\frac{N(N-1)}{2}$ comparisons are made using $\leq$.

6.2 Series and Parallel Adders

In this section, we compare the usual series method of binary addition with a more sophisticated parallel method of binary addition. Especially for large numbers, electronic parallel addition is much faster than series addition. Parallel addition does have the disadvantage that it requires a much larger circuit to implement electronically.

Example 6.7

Let us add in the usual way the numbers 10100111 and 01110101, which are given in the usual binary notation. As in (6.12) below, we start by adding the rightmost, or units places, giving a sum of 0 and a carry of 1. We next add the 2's places and the carry from the units places, giving a sum of 0 and a carry of 1. Next, add the 4's places, taking the carry from the 2's places into account. We continue, finally adding the 128's places, and we are finished. Any final carry goes into the 256's place of the sum.

$$\begin{array}{lccccccccc} \text{Carry:} & 1 & 1 & 1 & 0 & 0 & 1 & 1 & 1 & - \\ 10100111: & & 1 & 0 & 1 & 0 & 0 & 1 & 1 & 1 \\ 01110101: & & 0 & 1 & 1 & 1 & 0 & 1 & 0 & 1 \\ \hline \text{Sum:} & 1 & 0 & 0 & 0 & 1 & 1 & 1 & 0 & 0 \end{array} \tag{6.12}$$

△

The addition method of Example 6.7 is called **series addition** because the places are added one at a time, after each other. With series addition, we do not compute the higher places of the sum until we know the carries from the lower places. We measure time in units given as follows: One time unit is the time needed to add three bits. Then, as in Example 6.7, adding two eight-bit numbers via series addition takes eight time units. In general *with series addition, it takes as many time units to do the addition as there are bits in the larger of the two addends.*

Example 6.8

We translate the series addition scheme of Example 6.7 into the outline of a switching circuit, as given in Figure 6.3. Each square, or **module**, in Figure 6.3 is itself a switching circuit, but of a relatively simple type. The top module in Figure 6.3 on p. 260 accepts two binary inputs and yields their two-bit binary sum. The 2's place of this sum becomes the carry for the

Figure 6.3 A series adder

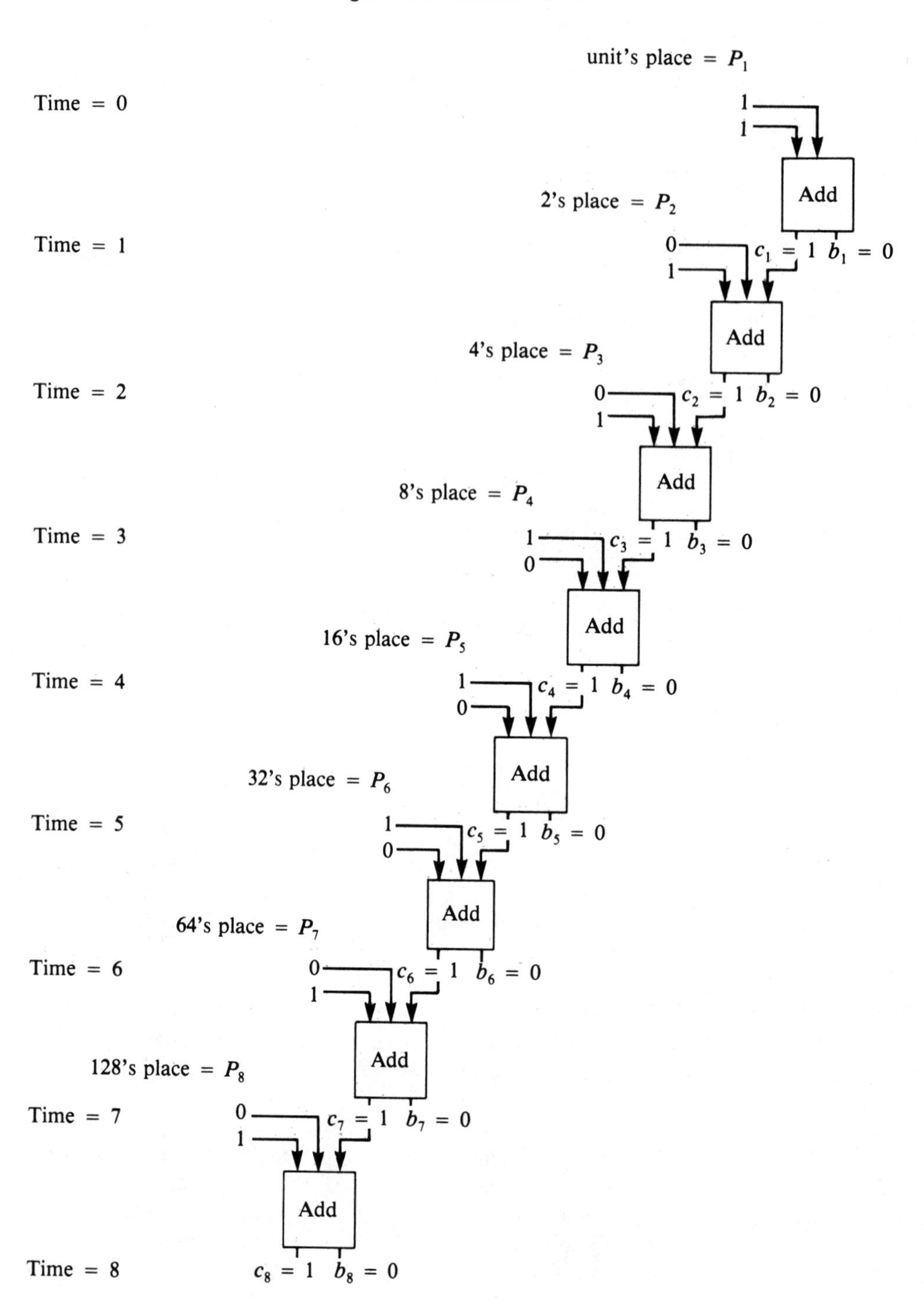

next module. All of the other modules in Figure 6.3 are the same: They accept three binary inputs and yield their two-bit binary sum. We shall thus call the modules of Figure 6.3 **adders**. One possible internal configuration of the adders is discussed in the exercises at the end of this section. In general, a **module** is a simple switching circuit that is part of a larger switching circuit.

In Figure 6.3, we add the two eight-bit numbers 00111001 and 11000111. These two numbers were chosen so that the carry from the units place would influence as many subsequent places as possible:

$$00111001 + 11000111 = 100000000$$

The diagram of Figure 6.3 is, of course, capable of adding *all* pairs of eight-bit numbers.

Observe that the number of time units needed to perform addition via Figure 6.3 equals the maximum number of modules that lie between an input and an output. In Figure 6.3, this maximum of 8 occurs between the inputs P_1 and the outputs c_8 and b_8. △

A series adder as in Figure 6.3 is quite simple and cheap to build. But by constructing a more complicated circuit, is it possible to add in fewer time units, that is, to have fewer levels of modules between the inputs and the outputs? Yes, it is possible. One standard method is given in Figures 6.4, 6.5, and 6.6. As explained later, this type of adder is called a **parallel**

Figure 6.4

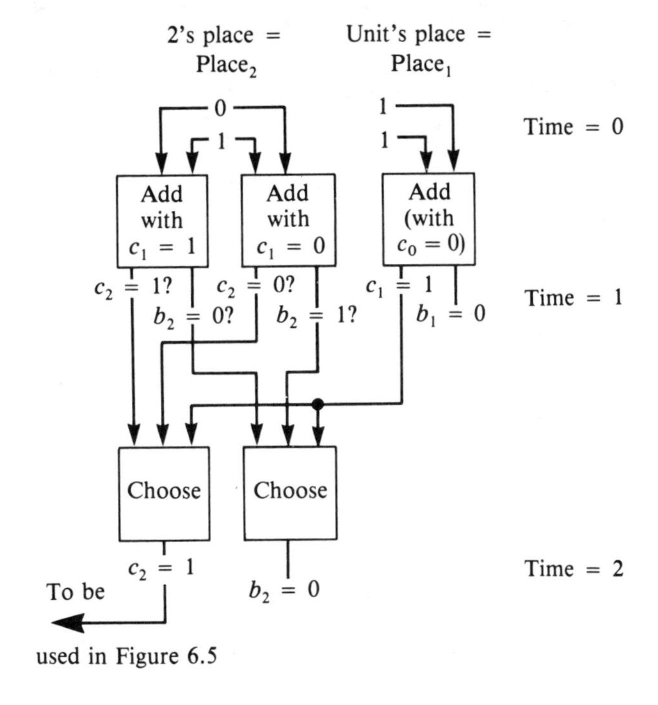

Figure 6.5

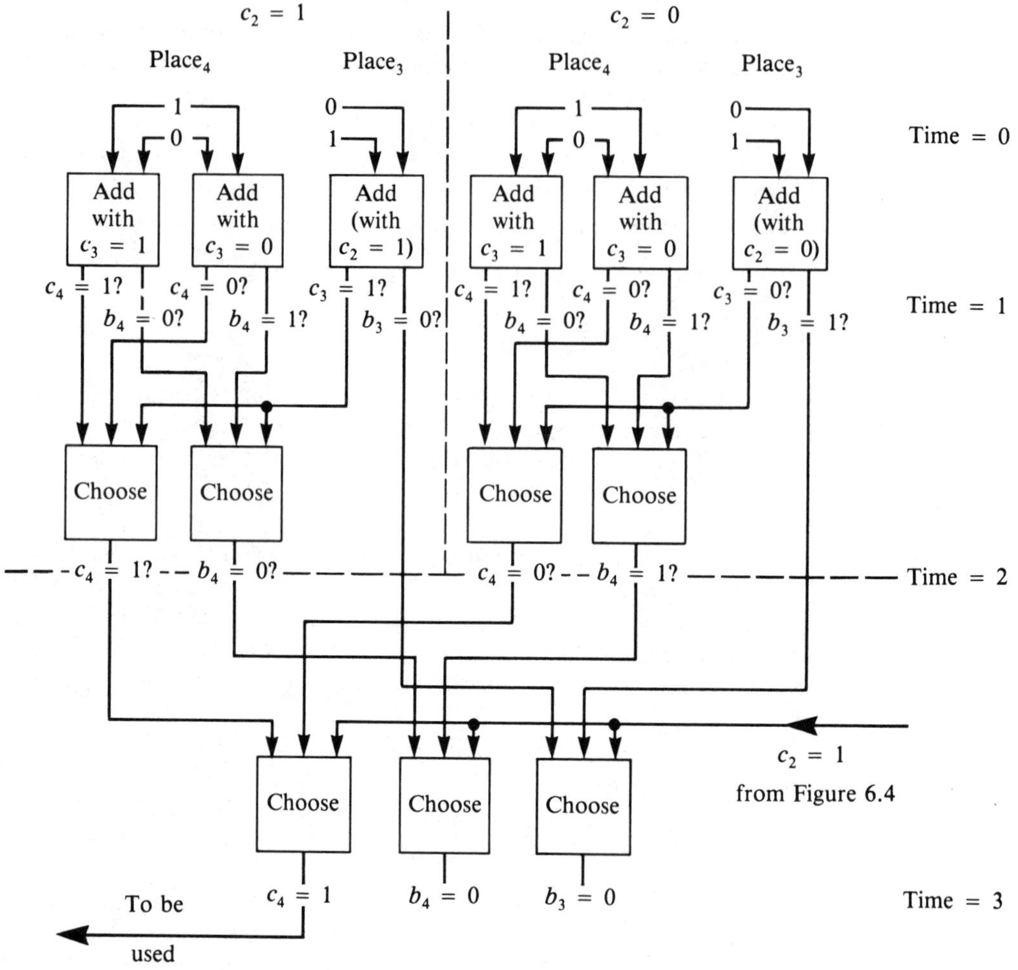

adder. In our parallel adder, we have strived for relative simplicity, at a small cost in efficiency. The modules of the parallel adder are of roughly two types: There are adders, as in Figure 6.3, with either two or three binary inputs. There are also logic circuits with three binary inputs; the third input tells which of the first two inputs will be the output of the module. One possible internal structure of such a logic module is discussed in the exercises at the end of this section.

Example 6.9

Here is a rough description of how the parallel adder works. Consider the sum in (6.12). Group the eight bit places into two sets of four each. *Simultaneously*, perform the following three additions (p. 264):

Figure 6.6

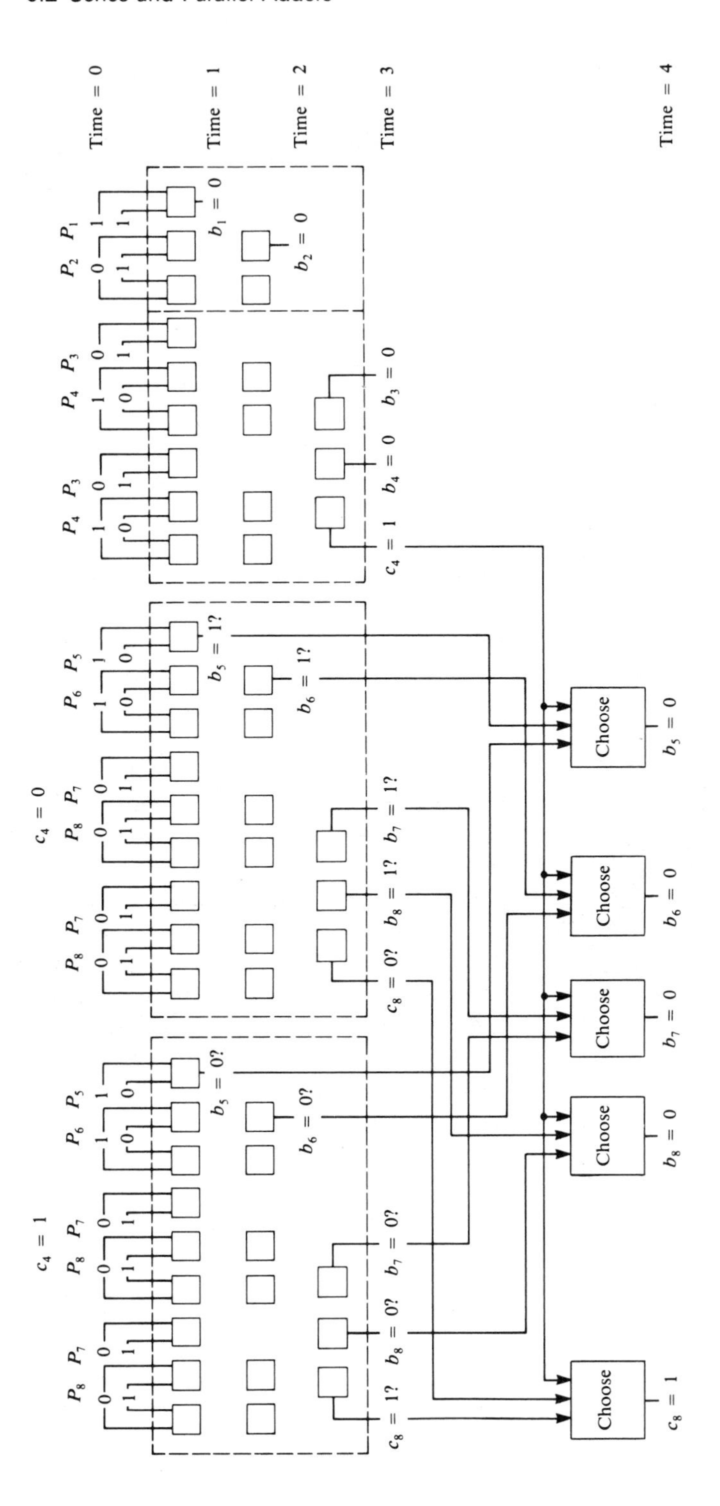
Time = 0
Time = 1
Time = 2
Time = 3
Time = 4
P_2 P_1
P_4 P_3
P_4 P_3
P_6 P_5
P_8 P_7
P_8 P_7
P_6 P_5
P_8 P_7
P_8 P_7
$c_4 = 0$
$c_4 = 1$
$b_1 = 0$
$b_2 = 0$
$c_4 = 1$ $b_4 = 0$ $b_3 = 0$
$b_5 = 1?$
$b_6 = 1?$
$c_8 = 0?$ $b_8 = 1?$ $b_7 = 1?$
$b_5 = 0?$
$b_6 = 0?$
$c_8 = 1?$ $b_8 = 0?$ $b_7 = 0?$
Choose
Choose
Choose
Choose
Choose
$b_5 = 0$
$b_6 = 0$
$b_7 = 0$
$b_8 = 0$
$c_8 = 1$

$$
\begin{array}{rrrrr}
 & & \text{(iii)} & & \\
 & & & & 1 \\
 & 1 & 0 & 1 & 0 \\
 & 0 & 1 & 1 & 1 \\
\hline
1 & 0 & 0 & 1 & 0
\end{array}
\qquad
\begin{array}{rrrrr}
 & & \text{(ii)} & & \\
 & & & & 0 \\
 & 1 & 0 & 1 & 0 \\
 & 0 & 1 & 1 & 1 \\
\hline
1 & 0 & 0 & 0 & 1
\end{array}
\qquad
\begin{array}{rrrrr}
 & & \text{(i)} & & \\
 & & & & \\
 & 0 & 1 & 1 & 1 \\
 & 0 & 1 & 0 & 1 \\
\hline
0 & 1 & 1 & 0 & 0
\end{array}
\qquad \textbf{(6.13)}
$$

Sum (i) in (6.13) is the usual sum for the rightmost four bit places in (6.12). Observe that the final carry in (6.13)(i) is 0. Sums (ii) and (iii) in (6.13) are the sums for the leftmost four bit places in (6.12), assuming respective carries from (6.13)(i) of 0 and 1. Observe that, in preparation for receiving the carry from (6.13)(i), the sums of (6.13)(ii) and (iii) may be computed at the same time as (6.13)(i). Having completed (6.13), the parallel adder uses the final carry of 0 from (6.13)(i) to choose (6.13)(ii) as the appropriate computation for the leftmost four bit places. (6.3)(iii) is ignored. Disregarding the carry from (6.13)(i), we get the correct sum of 100011100.

Notice that after the completion of (6.13), only one additional time unit was required to complete the sum. A series adder uses another four time units for the last four bits. In the complete parallel adder, the four-bit sums of (6.13) are also divided into simultaneous smaller sums, of two bits. The two bit sums, in turn, are divided into one bit sums. △

In Example 6.9, we described the workings of the parallel adder in the reverse order of execution. The one bit sums must be done first. They are all computed at the same time, which is why the adder is called a *parallel* adder. Each one-bit addition is done in two ways: with a carry of 0 and with a carry of 1. The function of the rest of the parallel adder is to decide, for each bit, whether the addition with a carry of 0 or the addition with a carry of 1 was the appropriate addition. Each of the modules in the parallel adder takes approximately the same amount of time to perform its function, once its inputs are available. So as with the series adder, we may measure the time needed to produce an output by the maximum number of modules that lie between the output and any input that is connected to the output. Figures 6.4, 6.5, and 6.6 are arranged so that outputs that require the same time for computation appear on the same horizontal line.

Let us now examine in detail how the parallel adder works. The addends used as an example in Figures 6.4, 6.5, and 6.6 are 00111001 and 11000111, the same addends that were used in the series adder of Figure 6.3. We start with Figure 6.4, where we are adding the units places and the 2's places. The units bits, 1 and 1, are accepted by an adder, producing a sum of 10. The units place, 0, of 10 becomes b_1, the units place of the overall sum. The 2's place, 1, of 10 becomes c_1, the carry for the addition of the next place. At the same time that the above calculation takes place, the 2's bits, 0 and 1, of 00111001 and 11000111 are accepted by each of two adders. One adder assumes that $c_1 = 1$, yielding a possible sum, b_2, of 0 and a possible carry, c_2, of 1. The other adder assumes that $c_1 = 0$, yielding a possible b_2 of 1 and a possible c_2 of 0. This completes the calculations that are done after one time unit in Figure 6.4.

We now look at the second time interval in Figure 6.4; c_1 and the two possible values for b_2 are accepted by a logic circuit. The value of c_1 determines which b_2 should be the output. In the example in Figure 6.4, $c_1 = 1$, so the b_2 from the adder "Add with $c_1 = 1$" is the output. Also, c_1 and the two possible values for c_2 are accepted by a similar logic circuit. Again, since $c_1 = 1$, the value of c_2 from the adder "Add with $c_1 = 1$" becomes the output. Of course, sometimes the value of c_2 does not depend on c_1, but the parallel adder must do all cases and so the logic circuits are needed. So far, by Time = 2 in Figure 6.4, we know b_1, b_2, and c_2.

Now look at Figure 6.5, which is the part of the parallel adder that sums the 4's place, also called Place_3, and the 8's place, also called Place_4. The part of Figure 6.5 that operates until Time = 2 is essentially two copies of the circuit of Figure 6.4. The right copy in Figure 6.5 assumes that $c_2 = 0$. The left "copy" in Figure 6.5 differs from the right copy only in that it assumes that $c_2 = 1$. So the two copies differ only in the adder "Add (with $c_2 = 0$)" versus "Add (with $c_2 = 1$)." Observe that the bit values in Place_3 are accepted by two adders. The bit values in Place_4 are accepted by four adders. As we may check, but essentially because the two halves of the circuit in Figure 6.5 are each the same as our previously analyzed Figure 6.4, by the second time unit, each half of Figure 6.5 has produced possible values for b_3, b_4, and c_4. One half assumes $c_2 = 1$; the other half assumes $c_2 = 0$. *But by Time = 2, the true value of* c_2 *is available from Figure 6.4.* So the parallel adder uses the third time interval to select the correct values for b_3, b_4, and c_4. In our numerical example, $c_2 = 1$. So the values of b_3, b_4, and c_4 are chosen from the half of the circuit in Figure 6.5 that assumes that $c_2 = 1$. So by Time = 3, the parallel adder has computed b_3, b_4, and c_4 (in addition to b_2 and b_1, which were computed earlier). The circuits of Figure 6.4 and Figure 6.5 must be connected, as indicated by the arrows at the $c_2 = 1$ output. The combined circuit is indicated sketchily in the rightmost rectangle of Figure 6.6 and is also drawn again in Figure 6.8.

So far, we have a circuit to compute b_1, b_2, b_3, b_4, and c_4. To compute b_5, b_6, b_7, b_8, and c_8, we first make two copies of the rightmost rectangle in Figure 6.6. The left copy assumes $c_4 = 1$ and the right copy assumes $c_4 = 0$. Thus the "copies" differ in just one adder. These copies accept values in places P_5, P_6, P_7, and P_8. As before, by Time = 3, we get two tentative values, depending on c_4, for b_5, b_6, b_7, b_8, and c_8. However, by Time = 3, the true value of c_4 is available from the rightmost rectangle of Figure 6.6. We use this value of c_4 to choose between each of the two tentative values for b_5, b_6, b_7, b_8, and c_8. Thus by Time = 4, we have completed the addition of the two summands 00111001 and 11000111.

Example 6.10

We continue the construction of Figure 6.6 to construct parallel adders for larger summands. To add two 16-bit numbers, we make two additional copies of the circuit of Figure 6.6. The unmodified copy assumes a c_8 of 0. Modify the other copy in its rightmost adder so that it assumes a c_8 of 1. The two copies each accept as inputs the bit values of the summands in places P_9 through P_{16}. By Time = 4, the two copies have produced two tentative values for $b_9,\ldots,b_{16}$, and c_{16}. Use the c_8 output of Figure 6.6, which is available after Time = 4, to choose between each of the two values. This gives the 16-bit sum by Time = 5.

The general scheme is drawn in Figure 6.7. We already have an adder for N-bit summands. A parallel adder for $2N$-bit summands is formed by adjoining two "copies" of the N-bit adder. This gives a parallel adder that takes one more time unit to compute a $2N$-bit sum than was needed to compute an N-bit sum. △

Example 6.11

What are the comparative speeds of the series adder and the parallel adder? For eight-bit addends, the series adder of Figure 6.3 needs eight time units to produce the sum. The parallel adder of Figure 6.6 needs four time units to produce the same sum.

The real speed superiority of the parallel adder appears, however, when we wish to add much larger numbers. From Example 6.10, doubling the number of bits in the summands increases the computation time of the parallel adder only by 1. So, in general, the scheme of Figure 6.7 will add summands with 2^m bits in $m+1$ time units. The series adder scheme of Figure 6.3 requires 2^m time units to add summands with 2^m bits. As

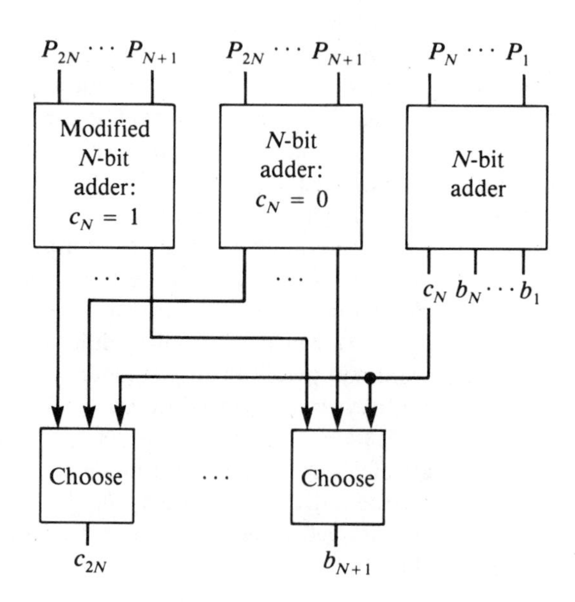

Figure 6.7 A $2N$-bit adder

functions of m, $m+1$ grows much more slowly than 2^m. So for large summands, the parallel adder is much faster than the series adder. △

Example 6.12

How much more complicated is the parallel adder than the series adder? It is convenient to measure complexity by the number of modules, since all of the modules are of approximately equal simplicity. Modules are represented by squares in Figures 6.3 through 6.6. The series adder of Figure 6.3 uses 2^m modules to add summands with 2^m bits.

Looking at Figure 6.6, we can count the number of modules needed by the parallel adder to add summands with $1=2^0$, $2=2^1$, $4=2^2$, and $8=2^3$ bits. To add summands with 16 bits, we must, as in Figure 6.7, triple the circuit of Figure 6.6 and then add logic modules for outputs $b_9,\ldots,b_{16}$, and c_{16}. In general, to increase the exponent m by 1, we first triple the number of modules and then add 2^m+1 logic modules. The first few values for the number of modules for a parallel adder are given in Table 6.1.

Table 6.1 Number of modules needed by a parallel adder to add two 2^m-bit summands

m	2^m	Number of modules
0	1	1
1	2	5
2	4	18
3	8	59
4	16	186
5	32	575

It will be shown in the exercises at the end of the section that the number of modules needed by a parallel adder that accepts 2^m-bit summands is approximately $\frac{5}{2}\cdot 3^m$. As a function of m, $\frac{5}{2}\cdot 3^m$ grows much more rapidly than does 2^m, which is the number of modules needed by the series adder for the same calculation. △

In this section, we measured the execution time for the series and parallel adders in terms of the *number of levels* of modules between inputs and outputs. This is correct when considering electronic switching circuits. However, a diagram of modules, such as Figures 6.3 and 6.6, may also be thought of as implementing some underlying algorithm on bits. This algorithm may be programmed on a general-purpose computer. Most computers have little parallel processing capability, at least as compared to what we are allowing in large parallel adders. So the program execution time for the underlying algorithm is measured appropriately by the *total number* of modules.

Exercises 6.2

1. For each of the following sums, draw a series adder, as in Figure 6.3, which does the addition. Indicate all of the values for the inputs and the outputs, including the carries.

   a. 110 + 011 b. 11010 + 01101 c. 11101111 + 10111011

2. For each of the following sums, redraw Figure 6.4 with the corresponding outputs. Include all intermediate outputs, that is, outputs in Figure 6.4 that are followed by "?".

   a. 01 + 01 b. 10 + 11 c. 00 + 10

3. Figures 6.4 and 6.5 are combined into Figure 6.8. For each of the following sums, redraw Figure 6.8 and indicate all of the outputs of all of the modules.

   a. 1010 + 1110 b. 0111 + 1001

4. Draw a circuit equivalent to Figure 6.5 with two fewer modules. *Hint:* The adders "Add with $c_3 = 1$" and "Add with $c_3 = 0$" appear twice in Figure 6.5.

Figure 6.8

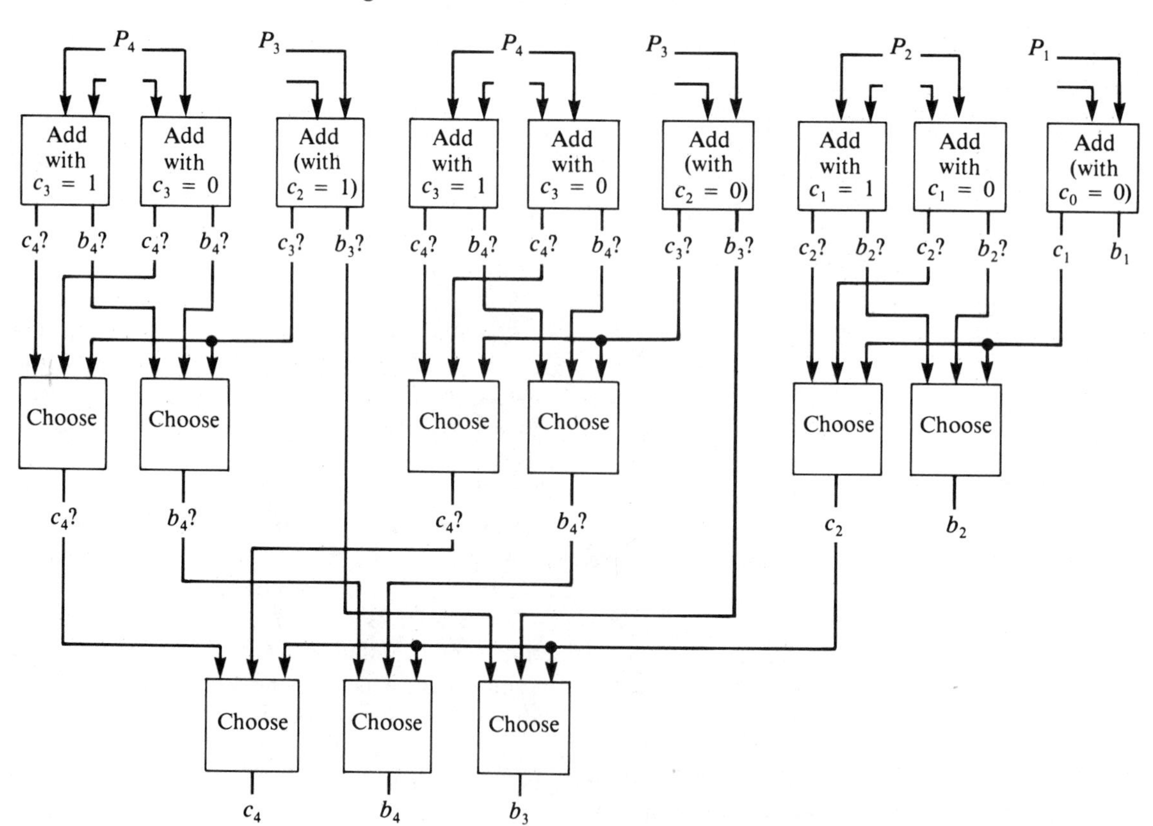

5. In building a parallel adder for 16-bit summands, which output in Figure 6.6 will be accepted by other parts of the circuit? How many logic modules will accept this output?
6. Explain how Figure 6.4 may be thought of as Figure 6.7 with $N=1$.
7. Continue Table 6.1 to $m=6$ and $m=7$.
8. Compute 3^m for $m=0,1,2,3,4,5,6,7$. Divide the "Number of Modules" column of Table 6.1 by 3^m. Does the quotient seem to be approaching $\frac{5}{2}$?
9. Compute as follows that N_m, the number of modules in a 2^m-bit parallel adder, is approximately $\frac{5}{2}\cdot 3^m$.
   a. Explain why $N_{m+1}=3N_m+2^m+1$.
   b. Let $S_m=N_m/3^m$. From part (a), derive a formula for S_{m+1} in terms of S_m.
   c. Observe that $S_0=1$ and that S_m is a partial sum for an infinite series. Sum the series.
10. Consider a 1-bit adder, as in Figure 6.4, which assumes a carry of 0.
    a. Write out a table that gives the relation between the two bits of input and the two bits of output for the adder.
    b. Using Theorem 5.6, write out Boolean polynomials $c(x,y)$ and $b(x,y)$ that give the carry and the bit output respectively for the adder; x and y are the input variables.
    c. Draw a switching circuit that performs the function of the adder.
11. Consider a logic module, as in Figure 6.4, that accepts x, y, and z as inputs and produces x or y as output, according to whether $z=0$ or $z=1$.
    a. Show that the Boolean polynomial $f=(x \wedge z') \vee (y \wedge z)$ correctly expresses the input/output function of the logic module.
    b. Draw a switching circuit that performs the function of the logic module.

6.3 How Good Are the Adders?

Consider the addition of two N-bit numbers, $N=2^m$. In the previous section, we exhibited a series adder and a parallel adder. The series adder requires only N modules to perform the addition but takes longer than the parallel adder, which requires $m+1$ time units to produce the sum. In this section, we see that, under rather mild restrictions about the nature of the adder's circuit, no adder may have fewer modules than has the series adder or exhibit a substantial time improvement over the parallel adder.

We must first describe the type of adder circuits that we are comparing. We assume that our adders are constructed out of smaller modules, as in Figures 6.3 through 6.6. We also assume that the output from a given module never eventually leads back into the same given module. We must put some constraints on the modules; otherwise we could just build the adder out of a single module! The important constraint is to limit the number of inputs to, say, r inputs per module. For example, in Figures 6.3 through 6.6, $r = 3$. We restrict the modules to binary inputs and outputs. Theorem 5.6 then shows how to build a module with any possible relationship between inputs and a single output. Moreover, the construction of Theorem 5.6 shows that r limits the needed internal complexity of the single-output module. So limiting the number of inputs is a good constraint to put on the modules. With r inputs and multiple outputs, a module could become very complicated internally. It will turn out, however, that allowing more than two outputs does not reduce the minimum number of modules needed to produce a sum. When we try to minimize time, by allowing as many modules as we wish, a module with multiple outputs could be replaced, if desired, by multiple modules (one for each output) with single outputs. So we shall always allow multiple outputs for the modules. Finally, in an adder, we allow an input or a module output to be accepted by more than one module.

Definition 6.1 Let p be an input bit and let b be an output bit for a circuit that is described by modules. Then b **depends** on p if there is a sequence of modules, in the direction of the input/output arrows, that connects p to b. ○

Example 6.13 In both Figure 6.3 and Figure 6.4, output b_2 depends on the P_1 and P_2 inputs. Output b_1 depends only on the P_1 inputs, and not on the P_2 inputs. Similarly, in Figure 6.3 and in Figure 6.6 (with the understood lines included), b_4 depends on all of the input bits in P_1, P_2, P_3, and P_4 but on none of the bits in P_5, P_6, P_7, and P_8. These dependency statements correspond, of course, to the fact that in binary addition, the value of a place in the sum depends only on the places in the summands up to and including that place. △

When we are describing a circuit by its function, for example, that the circuit adds two binary numbers, we do not have a circuit diagram to use for checking dependence in the sense of Definition 6.1. Nonetheless, in many cases we can be sure that an output bit b depends on an input bit p. Namely, start with some particular input set of bits for all of the inputs to the circuit. Now change the value of the input bit p. If the value of the output bit b also changes, then b must depend on p.

Example 6.14 We are adding 8-bit numbers. We wish to show that for *any* adder, b_8, the 128's place of the sum, depends on p, the 4's place of the first summand. In the following two additions b_8 and p are underlined. Observe that changing p results in a change for b_8.

$$\begin{array}{rr} & 00000\underline{1}00 \\ + & 01111100 \\ \hline & \underline{1}0000000 \end{array} \qquad \begin{array}{rr} & 00000\underline{0}00 \\ + & 01111100 \\ \hline & \underline{0}1111100 \end{array}$$

△

As we know, all output bits must depend on the units place of the first summand. We can see this by means of the following two additions. The changed places are underlined.

$$\begin{array}{rr} & 0000000\underline{1} \\ + & 01111111 \\ \hline & \underline{10000000} \end{array} \qquad \begin{array}{rr} & 0000000\underline{0} \\ + & 01111111 \\ \hline & \underline{01111111} \end{array}$$

Further sums easily show that the highest place, b_8, of the output depends on all of the input bits. △

Example 6.15

Suppose that a circuit has two binary inputs (x, y) and one binary output b, which are related as in Table 6.2; $b = b(x, y)$. What are the dependencies?

$$b(0,\underline{0}) = \underline{0}, \quad \text{while } b(0,\underline{1}) = \underline{1}$$

So b depends on y.

$$b(\underline{0},0) = b(\underline{1},0) = 0 \quad \text{and}$$
$$b(\underline{0},1) = b(\underline{1},1) = 1$$

So we cannot say whether or not b depends on x without additional information about the circuit. Of course, we may *design* a circuit where b does not depend on x, but this is a different question. △

Table 6.2 A black box

	Input (x, y)			
	00	01	10	11
Output b	0	1	0	1

The following Proposition implies that the series adder of Figure 6.3 is as efficient as possible with regard to the number of modules.

Proposition 6.2

Suppose that a circuit is composed of 3-input modules. Suppose that the inputs to the circuit consist of two n-bit binary numbers and that the output from the circuit is b_n, the nth bit place for the sum of the inputs. Then the circuit consists of at least n modules.

Proof of Proposition 6.2

Suppose that, as in Figure 6.9, there is a module M in the circuit such that b_n does not depend on any output from M. Then we may remove M from the circuit and still have a circuit that produces b_n as output. So, in proving Proposition 6.2, we may assume that for each module, either b_n is an output for that module or else depends on at least one output from the module. Moreover, we may take b_n to be the output from just one module.

Let x denote the number of modules in the circuit; b_n is the output for 1 of these modules. For each of the remaining $x-1$ modules, at least one output must be accepted by some other module (or else b_n cannot depend on some output from the module). As observed in Examples 6.14, b_n depends on all $2n$ input bits. So the x modules must also accept all $2n$ input bits. In all, we have accounted for

$$(x-1)+2n$$

distinct inputs to the modules. Each module has at most 3 inputs. So

$$3x \geq \text{ total number of module inputs } \geq (x-1)+2n \tag{6.14}$$

Solving the outer inequality in (6.14) for x yields

$$x \geq -\frac{1}{2}+n$$

Since x and n are whole numbers,

$$x \geq n$$

□

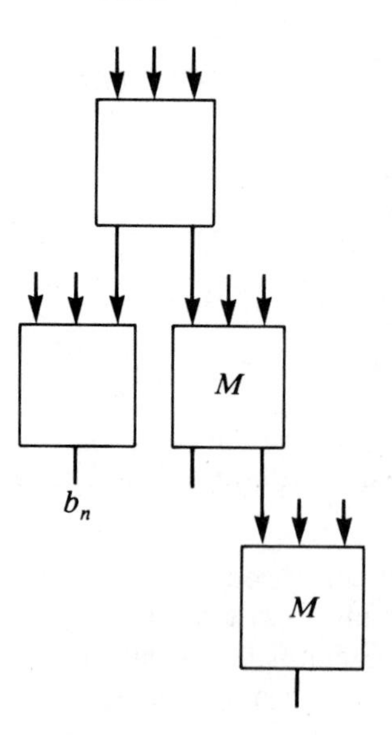

Figure 6.9 Discard the modules labeled with M

We now allow many modules and look for estimates on the time needed for addition. We measure the time required by an adder by finding the maximum number of modules that lie between an input and an output.

Theorem 6.3

Suppose that an adder is composed of r-input modules. Suppose that the inputs to the adder consist of two n-bit binary numbers. Suppose that the output of the adder consists of the n-bit sum, without the final carry. Then the time needed by the adder to compute the sum is at least $\log_r(2n)$ time units. Computation of the final carry also requires at least $\log_r(2n)$ time units.

Proof of Theorem 6.3

We look at b_n, the highest place of the output. As we observed in Examples 6.14, b_n depends on all of the input bits. There are $2n$ input bits, n from each summand. Each module has at most r inputs. So the module that produces b_n accepts inputs from at most r different modules. Each of these at most r modules accepts inputs from at most r modules. So b_n can now be influenced by the output of at most r^2 additional modules. These r^2 additional modules can have a total of r^3 inputs. We continue. In general, as we go up another level above b_n in the diagram for the adder, we multiply the number of inputs available to b_n by r. See Figure 6.10.

Let t denote the time needed by the adder to perform the addition.

Figure 6.10 Fanning in of inputs. $r=3$ $t=3$

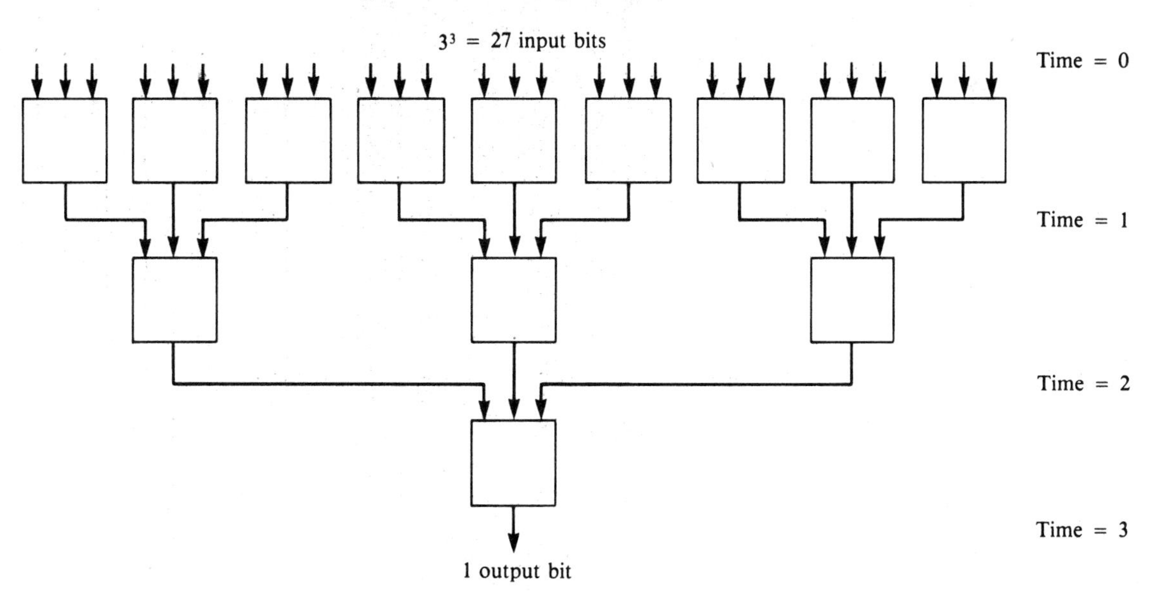

Then there are at most t levels of modules between b_n and the $2n$ inputs on which b_n depends. Then

$$r^t \geq 2n \qquad \textbf{(6.15)}$$

Taking logarithms, base r, of both sides of (6.15) gives Theorem 6.3 for the sum.

The argument for the time needed to compute the final carry is entirely similar. ◇

Example 6.16

How close to optimal is the parallel adder of Section 6.2? In the parallel adder, $r=3$ and $n=2^m$. By Theorem 6.3, at least $\log_3(2.2^m)$ time units are needed for the computation. The parallel adder actually uses $m+1$ time units. So we must compare $\log_3(2 \cdot 2^m)$ with $m+1$:

$$\begin{aligned} \log_3(2\cdot 2^m) = \log_3(2^{m+1}) &= (m+1)\cdot \log_3{}^2 \\ &= 0.6309\cdot(m+1) \quad \text{or} \\ m+1 &= 1.5850\cdot \log_3(2\cdot 2^m) \end{aligned}$$

In other words, the parallel adder of Section 6.2 takes just 58% more time than is estimated in Theorem 6.3, *for all m*. This is quite good. For a slow adder, such as the series adder, the ratio of the time needed by the adder to the estimate of Theorem 6.3 becomes unbounded as m approaches infinity. △

Example 6.17

We may turn Example 6.16 around and use it as follows to measure the preciseness of Theorem 6.3. Theorem 6.3 gives only a minimum needed time for a binary adder. But perhaps this is, in fact, a very poor estimate; perhaps no adder can come even close to doing an addition in the time suggested by Theorem 6.3. However, the parallel adder of Section 6.2 shows that the $\log_r(2n)$ estimate of Theorem 6.3 cannot be increased substantially for all n. △

The proofs of Proposition 6.2 and Theorem 6.3 are really general counting arguments that use the fact that the output b_n depends on all of the inputs. The proofs thus apply to Theorem 6.4, which follows. (To generalize Proposition 6.2 to r-input modules, replace 3 by r in (6.14).)

Theorem 6.4

Let a circuit be composed of r-input modules. Suppose that an output depends on n inputs. Then the circuit has at least $\dfrac{n-1}{r-1}$ modules. Also, the time needed to compute the output is at least $\log_r n$ time units. ◇

Example 6.18

We wish to design a circuit that accepts 2^m bits as input and that yields as output the parity of the number of 1's among the 2^m input bits. An output of 0 stands for even parity; an output of 1 stands for odd parity. Using 2-input modules, how many modules and how many time units are required for the computation?

Changing an input bit changes the parity of the set of input bits. So the output bit must depend on all 2^m input bits. By Theorem 6.4, at least

$$\frac{2^m - 1}{2 - 1} = 2^m - 1$$

modules and at least $\log_2(2^m) = m$ time units are needed.

If we use 2-input modules that produce the parity of the two input bits, then Figure 6.11(i) gives a circuit that achieves the minimums just estimated for both the number of modules and the execution time. Using the same 2-input modules, Figure 6.11(ii) achieves the minimum number of modules, but not the minimum electronic execution time. However, the underlying algorithm for Figure 6.11(ii) is much easier to program than is the underlying algorithm for Figure 6.11(i). △

Exercises 6.3

1. In Figure 6.10, on how many inputs does the output bit depend?
2. A circuit has (x, y, z) as binary inputs and $b = b(x, y, z)$ as its output bit; $b(x, y, z)$ is given by

(x, y, z)	000	001	010	011	100	101	110	111
$b(x, y, z)$	0	0	1	1	1	1	0	0

   Show that b must depend on input bits x and y.
3. Draw a picture similar to Figure 6.10 for $r = 4$ and $t = 2$.
4. Give integer-valued estimates, using Theorem 6.4, for the minimum number of modules and the minimum time needed to compute an output for a circuit that satisfies each of the following conditions. The circuit consists of r-input modules. The output depends on n inputs.

   a. $r = 3, n = 9$ b. $r = 3, n = 16$ c. $r = 3, n = 25$
   d. $r = 3, n = 45$ e. $r = 4, n = 100$ f. $r = 5, n = 1000$
5. Suppose that a circuit is composed of 1-input modules. On how many inputs can an output depend?
6. How many essentially different modules are there with r binary inputs and 1 binary output?

   Hint: Think of a module as a switching function.

Figure 6.11 Parity check circuits

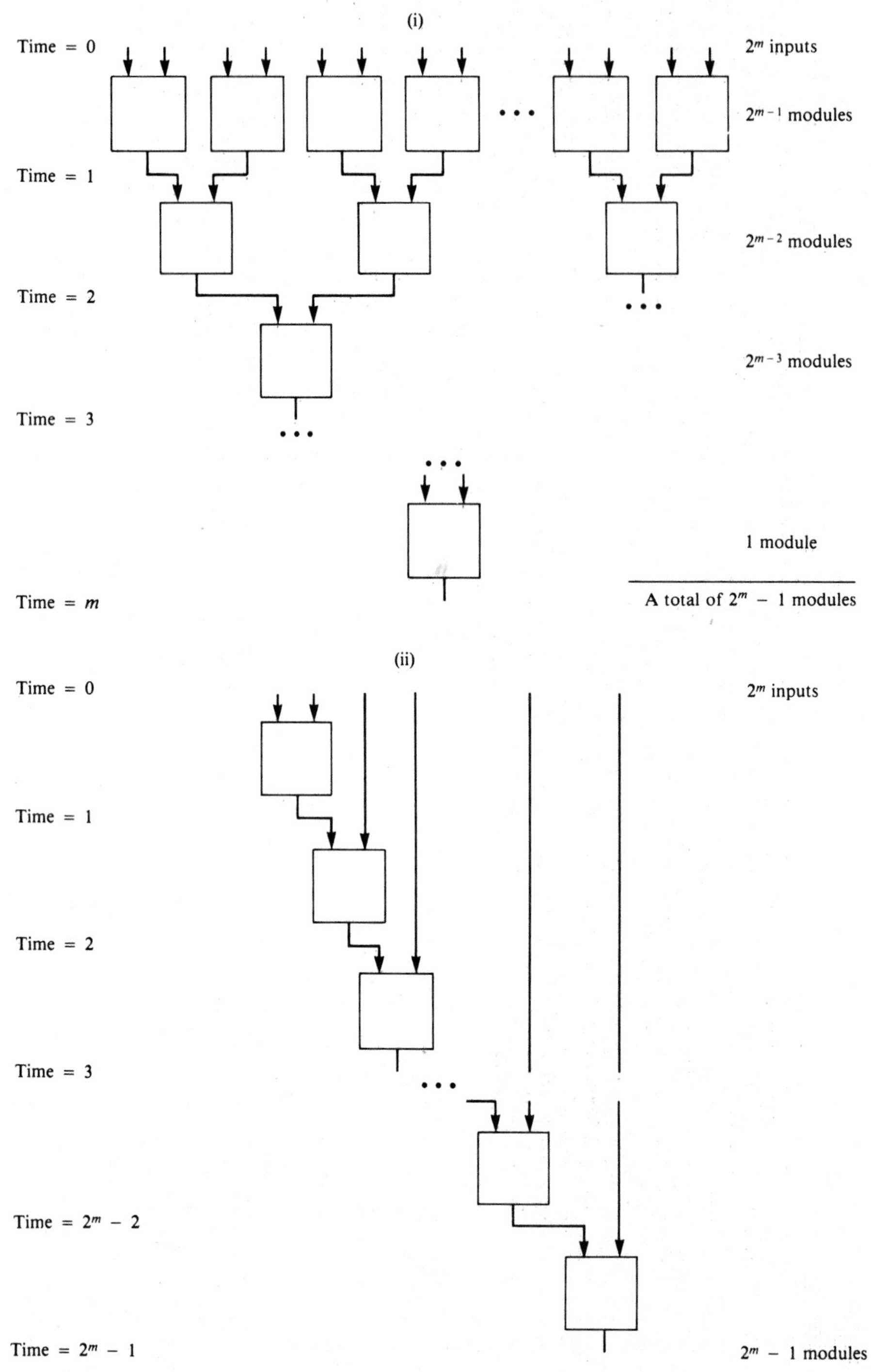

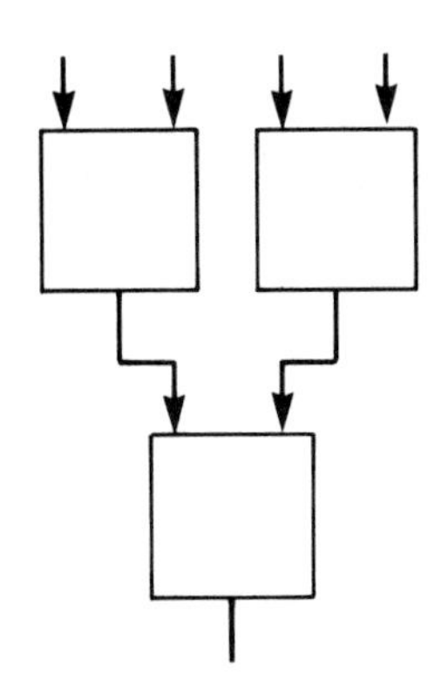

Figure 6.12 An attempt to simulate a 4-input module

7. a. Using Exercise 6, explain why not all 4-input, 1-output modules can be replaced by three 2-input, 1-output modules as in Figure 6.12.
   b. What time estimate does Theorem 6.4 give for $r=2$, $n=4$?
   c. Why must there be relationships between inputs and output that cannot be computed in the minimum time estimate of Theorem 6.4?
8. For x a real number, let the **ceiling** of x, denoted by $\lceil x \rceil$, be the least integer at least equal to x; for example, $\lceil 7 \rceil = 7$, $\lceil 2.5 \rceil = 3$. Using AND, OR, and NOT gates, we wish to construct an r-input, 1-output module with a given input/output relationship. Show how to construct such a module so that the time needed for the module to compute its output is at most $1 + \lceil \log_2 r \rceil + r$ time units. Measure time by the maximum number of gates in a path between an input and an output.

   Hint: Write the corresponding switching function in disjunctive normal form.
9. A circuit accepts two 2^m-bit binary numbers and produces an output of 1 or 0 according to whether or not the two numbers are equal.
   a. Show that the output bit depends on each of the $2 \cdot 2^m$ input bits.
   b. If the circuit is composed of r-input modules, what are the estimates given by Theorem 6.4?
   c. Using 2-input modules, design an efficient circuit that tells whether or not two 2^m-bit binary numbers are equal.

6.4 Addition in $\mathbb{Z}_N$

In the previous sections methods for computing sums and carries for binary numbers with n bits were described. The numbers that can be represented by n bits range from 0 through $2^n - 1$. Let $N = 2^n$. Then, if we disregard the final carry, we are doing addition in $(\mathbb{Z}_N, +)$. This is essentially fixed point addition for a digital computer. This section begins the discussion of addition in $(\mathbb{Z}_N, +)$ for arbitrary N. With N a power of a prime, we obtain module number and time estimates for addition in $(\mathbb{Z}_N, +)$ that are entirely similar to those of the previous section. We also see that the usual binary representation for $\mathbb{Z}_N$ with $N = 2^n$ is as efficient as any other possible representation for the purposes of addition. In the exercises at the end of this section, we describe circuits for addition in $(\mathbb{Z}_N, +)$, with N arbitrary. The discussion of addition in $(\mathbb{Z}_N, +)$, with N not a power of a prime, will conclude in the next section.

Example 6.19

We start to add two three-place decimal numbers; $N = 1000$. Assuming binary inputs and outputs, how shall we represent elements of $\mathbb{Z}_{1000}$, that is, three-place decimal numbers?

There are two likely schemes: $2^{10} = 1024$, which is greater than 1000. So every (decimal) number from 0 through 999 can be represented in binary notation using 10 bits. Alternatively, the digits 0 through 9 can all be represented in binary notation using 4 bits. Then the three digits require $3 \cdot 4 = 12$ bits. Here are the two different representations for 185 and for 942.

$185 = 0010111001$ (base 2)

$185 = 0001 \quad 1000 \quad 0101$ using $1 = 0001 \quad 8 = 1000 \quad 5 = 0101$

$942 = 1110101110$ (base 2)

$942 = 1001 \quad 0100 \quad 0010$ using $9 = 1001 \quad 4 = 0100 \quad 2 = 0010$

Is one representation superior to the other for addition? Theorem 6.4 suggests that we see on how many input bits the output bits depend. A direct analysis is too long for $\mathbb{Z}_{1000}$. So we stop here and go on to a simpler example. △

Table 6.3 Addition table for $(\mathbb{Z}_6, +)$

	0	1	2	3	4	5
0	0	1	2	3	4	5
1	1	2	3	4	5	0
2	2	3	4	5	0	1
3	3	4	5	0	1	2
4	4	5	0	1	2	3
5	5	0	1	2	3	4

Example 6.20

We consider addition in $(\mathbb{Z}_6, +)$. $\mathbb{Z}_6 = \{0,1,2,3,4,5\}$. Table 6.3 is the usual addition table for $(\mathbb{Z}_6, +)$. Instead of writing the elements of $\mathbb{Z}_6$ in decimal notation, we may write them in binary notation. This gives Table 6.4 as well as the addition table for $(\mathbb{Z}_6, +)$.

Table 6.4 Addition table for $(\mathbb{Z}_{110}, +)$, in binary

	000	001	010	011	100	101
000	000	001	010	011	100	101
001	001	010	011	100	101	000
010	010	011	100	101	000	001
011	011	100	101	000	001	010
100	100	101	000	001	010	011
101	101	000	001	010	011	100

Let us see that b_3, the 4's bit of the output, depends on all six of the input bits. It suffices to show that b_3 depends on each of the three bits in, say, the first summand. The following three pairs of additions show this dependence by each changing only one input bit while also changing b_3. The changed bits are underlined. Recall that all additions are in $(\mathbb{Z}_6, +)$, as given in Table 6.4.

$$10\underline{0}+001=\underline{1}01 \qquad 10\underline{1}+001=\underline{0}00$$

$$0\underline{0}0+010=\underline{0}10 \qquad 0\underline{1}0+010=\underline{1}00$$

$$\underline{1}00+001=\underline{1}01 \qquad \underline{0}00+001=\underline{0}01$$

△

Example 6.21

We now consider a rather different 3-bit representation for $\mathbb{Z}_6 = \{0,1,2,3,4,5\}$. Recall that, as in Example 2.24, $(\mathbb{Z}_6, +)$ is isomorphic to $(\mathbb{Z}_3 \times \mathbb{Z}_2, +)$ via the renaming (2.10). Represent elements of $\mathbb{Z}_3$ and of $\mathbb{Z}_2$ in the usual binary notation as follows:

For $\mathbb{Z}_3 : 0 = 00, \quad 1 = 01, \quad 2 = 10$

For $\mathbb{Z}_2 : 0 = 0, \quad 1 = 1$

Combined with (2.10), this gives the representation (6.16) for elements of $\mathbb{Z}_6$.

$$\begin{array}{lll} 0 \to 000 & 1 \to 011 & 2 \to 100 \\ 3 \to 001 & 4 \to 010 & 5 \to 101 \end{array} \qquad \textbf{(6.16)}$$

The notation of (6.16) yields Table 6.5 as the addition table for $(\mathbb{Z}_6, +)$. In contrast with Table 6.4, each output bit for Table 6.5 need depend on only at most four of the six bits. How do we see this?

Output bit b_1 depends on inputs in Place_1 as given in Table 6.6. Table 6.6 is verified by a case-by-case check from Table 6.5. For example, from Table 6.5,

Table 6.5 Another addition table for $(\mathbb{Z}_6, +)$

+	000	011	100	001	010	101
000	000	011	100	001	010	101
011	011	100	001	010	101	000
100	100	001	010	101	000	011
001	001	010	101	000	011	100
010	010	101	000	011	100	001
101	101	000	011	100	001	010

Table 6.6 b_1 dependence on Place$_1$

	0	1
0	0	1
1	1	0

Table 6.7 b_3b_2 dependence on Place$_3$Place$_2$

	00	01	10
00	00	01	10
01	01	10	00
10	10	00	01

$$01\underline{0}+00\underline{1}=01\underline{1} \tag{6.17}$$

This agrees with Table 6.6, which says that Place$_1$ inputs of 0 and 1 yield $b_1=1$. Similarly,

$$10\underline{0}+01\underline{1}=00\underline{1}$$

As in (6.17), Place$_1$ inputs of 0 and 1 yield $b_1=1$. Since (6.16) came via (2.10), Table 6.6 may also be thought of as the addition table for $(\mathbb{Z}_2,+)$.

Output bits b_3 and b_2 depend on inputs in Place$_3$ and Place$_2$, as given in Table 6.7. Again, we can verify Table 6.7 by a case-by-case check from Table 6.5. For example, from Table 6.5,

$$\underline{01}1+\underline{10}0=\underline{00}1 \quad \text{and} \quad \underline{01}0+\underline{10}1=\underline{00}1$$

$$\underline{10}0+\underline{10}0=\underline{01}0 \quad \text{and} \quad \underline{10}1+\underline{10}0=\underline{01}1$$

Table 6.7 says that Place$_3$ Place$_2$ input bits of 01 and 10 should yield $b_3b_2=00$. Similarly, Place$_3$ Place$_2$ inputs of 10,10 yield $b_3b_2=01$. Again, since (6.16) came via (2.10), Table 6.7 may also be thought of as the addition table for $(\mathbb{Z}_3,+)$. △

It is easy to see that, under certain conditions, the representation (6.16) for $\mathbb{Z}_6$ may result in faster addition than the binary representation of Table 6.4: Consider building an adder for $(\mathbb{Z}_6,+)$ out of 4-input modules. Using (6.16), two 4-input modules in parallel, given by Tables 6.6 and 6.7, perform addition in just one time unit. As shown in Example 6.20, b_3 of the binary representation depends on all six input bits. So, by Theorem 6.4, at least two time units are required for addition using 4-input modules and the usual binary representation.

The previous paragraph suggests that, in order to maximize the efficiency of addition in $(\mathbb{Z}_N,+)$, we allow arbitrary representations of the elements of $\mathbb{Z}_N$. We do continue to assume that each element of $\mathbb{Z}_N$ is represented by a unique sequence of bits. To get our estimates for the number of modules and for the time needed for addition in $(\mathbb{Z}_N,+)$, we shall make nontrivial use of group theory.

Recall Chapter 2, Section 2.5, especially the notation of (2.28), Theorem 2.11, and Theorem 2.12. Recall also that $-y$ denotes the inverse to y in $(\mathbb{Z}_N,+)$. We introduce $-$ as a binary operation on $\mathbb{Z}_N$ in the usual way:

$$x-y=x+(-y)$$

For example, in $\mathbb{Z}_6$,

$$-4=2 \qquad 1-4=1+(-4)=1+2=3$$

$$-3=3 \qquad 5-3=5+(-3)=5+3=2$$

Theorem 6.5

Let the elements of $\mathbb{Z}_N$ have some representation using bits. Suppose that an adder circuit does addition in $(\mathbb{Z}_N, +)$ using this representation. Let x and y be elements of $\mathbb{Z}_N$ whose representations are the same in all of the input bits of the first summand on which place b_i of the output depends. Then the representations of all of the elements of the subgroup $\langle x-y \rangle$ have the same bit value in Place_i.

Examples 6.22

Before proving Theorem 6.5, we shall give some illustrations of its statement. Let the circuit be the series adder of Figure 6.3. Let $b_i = b_2$ be the 2's place of the output. In Theorem 6.5, $i=2$; b_2 depends on Place_1 and Place_2 of the summands. So x and y must agree in Place_1 and Place_2, that is, in the units and 2's places. Let us take, for example,

$$x = 011011\underline{10} \quad \text{and} \quad y = 110110\underline{10}$$

Then

$$\begin{aligned} -y &= 00100110 \\ \hline x-y &= 100101\underline{00} \end{aligned}$$

Since $x-y$ has 0's in both the units and 2's places, all multiples of $x-y$ also have 0's in both the units and 2's place. Theorem 6.5 just says that $\langle x-y \rangle$; that is, all multiples of $x-y$, have the same value, 0, in Place_2, the 2's place. △

Suppose that we use representation (6.16) for $\mathbb{Z}_6$. Let b_2 be the output bit under consideration; $i=2$. Suppose that, as in Table 6.7, we have a circuit in which b_2 depends only on input bits in Place_3 and Place_2. Take

$$x = \underline{01}1 \quad \text{and} \quad y = \underline{01}0$$

From Table 6.5, $-y = 100$ and $x-y = 001$. We compute $\langle 001 \rangle$ as in Example 2.38.

$$\begin{aligned} 001 &= 001 \\ 2 \cdot 001 &= 000, \qquad \text{the identity} \end{aligned}$$

$\langle x-y \rangle = \langle 001 \rangle = \{001, 000\}$. Theorem 6.5 then implies that $0\underline{0}1$ and $0\underline{0}0$ must agree in Place_2, which they do.

By Example 6.21, b_3 also need depend only on Place_3 and Place_2. Then Theorem 6.5 also implies that the elements of $\langle x-y \rangle$ must agree in Place_3, which they do. △

Proof of Theorem 6.5

$+$ denotes addition in $(\mathbb{Z}_N, +)$. For any element z in $\mathbb{Z}_N$:

$$\begin{aligned} (x-y)+z &= (x+(-y))+z, && \text{by the definition of } - \\ &= x+((-y)+z), && \text{by associativity} \end{aligned} \qquad \textbf{(6.18)}$$

$$\begin{aligned} y+((-y)+z) &= (y+(-y))+z, && \text{by associativity} \\ &= 0+z, && \text{by the definition of } -y \\ &= z, && \text{by the definition of } 0 \end{aligned} \qquad \textbf{(6.19)}$$

Since x and y are given to agree in all bits (of the first summand) on which b_i depends, adding x is the same as adding y so far as b_i is concerned. For g, an element of $\mathbb{Z}_N$, we let $[g]_i$ denote Place$_i$ of its representation. Then, adding x and y to $(-y)+z$,

$$[x+((-y)+z)]_i = [y+((-y)+z)]_i \qquad \textbf{(6.20)}$$

We substitute (6.18) into the left side of (6.20) and substitute (6.19) into the right side of (6.20) yielding:

$$[(x-y)+z]_i = [z]_i \qquad \textbf{(6.21)}$$

In equation (6.21), first we let $z = x-y$. Then, since $(x-y)+(x-y) = 2\cdot(x-y)$,

$$[2\cdot(x-y)]_i = [x-y]_i$$

That is, $x-y$ and $2\cdot(x-y)$ have the same bit value in Place$_i$.

Now we let $z = 2\cdot(x-y)$ in (6.21) and proceed as follows:

$$[3\cdot(x-y)]_i = [2\cdot(x-y)]_i$$

That is, $3\cdot(x-y)$ and $2\cdot(x-y)$ have the same bit value in Place$_i$. But we already know that $2\cdot(x-y)$ and $x-y$ agree in Place$_i$. So also $3\cdot(x-y)$ has the same bit in Place$_i$ as has $x-y$.

Letting $z = 3\cdot(x-y)$ in (6.21) gives $4\cdot(x-y)$ with the same bit in Place$_i$ as $x-y$. We continue. All multiples of $x-y$, that is, all elements of $\langle x-y \rangle$, have the same bit value in Place$_i$. ◇

Definition 6.2

Let $(G, \circ)$ be a group. An element u of G is **ubiquitous** if

(i) u is not the identity element e of G.

(ii) For every element g in G such that $g \neq e$, u is an element of $\langle g \rangle$. ○

Informally, we can say that, except for the trivial cases, a ubiquitous element is a power (or multiple) of every group element. Let N be a prime power. We shall see by means of Theorems 6.6 and 6.7, which will follow, that a ubiquitous element in $(Z_N, +)$ limits the speed of adders for $(\mathbb{Z}_N, +)$.

Example 6.23 We look for ubiquitous elements in $(\mathbb{Z}_9, +)$. With $g \neq 0$, a straightforward computation of the $\langle g \rangle$ yields

$$\begin{aligned} \langle 1 \rangle = \langle 2 \rangle = \langle 4 \rangle = \langle 5 \rangle = \langle 7 \rangle = \langle 8 \rangle \\ = \{0,1,2,3,4,5,6,7,8\} \\ \langle 3 \rangle = \langle 6 \rangle = \{0,3,6\} \end{aligned}$$

By Definition 6.2(ii), a ubiquitous element must be in both of these subgroups. By Definition 6.2(i), 0 is excluded as a ubiquitous element. So 3 and 6 are the ubiquitous elements in $\mathbb{Z}_9$. △

Example 6.24 We show that $(\mathbb{Z}_6, +)$ does not have a ubiquitous element. Consider

$$\langle 2 \rangle = \{0,2,4\} \quad \text{and}$$
$$\langle 3 \rangle = \{0,3\}$$

0 is the only element of $\mathbb{Z}_6$ that is common to both of these subgroups. But 0 is not a candidate for a ubiquitous element. So $(\mathbb{Z}_6, +)$ has no ubiquitous element. △

Theorem 6.6 Let $N = p^n$, with p a prime number. Then p^{n-1} is a ubiquitous element in $(\mathbb{Z}_N, +)$.

We shall only prove Theorem 6.6 for the case $p = 2$. A proof for all primes is outlined in the exercises. Before the partial proof however, let us illustrate the statement of Theorem 6.6.

Examples 6.25 Let $N = 8 = 2^3$. We check that $2^2 = 4$ is ubiquitous.

$$\begin{aligned} \langle 1 \rangle = \langle 3 \rangle = \langle 5 \rangle = \langle 7 \rangle = \{0,1,2,3,4,5,6,7\} \\ \langle 2 \rangle = \langle 6 \rangle = \{0,2,4,6\} \\ \langle 4 \rangle = \{0,4\} \end{aligned}$$

Indeed, 4 is in all of these subgroups. △

Look at Example 6.23. $9=3^2$. Theorem 6.6 implies that $3^1=3$ is ubiquitous in $(\mathbb{Z}_9,+)$. By Example 6.23, both 3 and 6 are ubiquitous. △

Proof of Theorem 6.6 with p=2

2^{n-1} has order 2 in $(\mathbb{Z}_{2^n},+)$; that is, computing in $(\mathbb{Z}_{2^n},+)$,

$$2\cdot 2^{n-1}=2^{n-1}+2^{n-1}=0$$

In fact, 2^{n-1} is the *unique* element u in $\mathbb{Z}_{2^n}$ of order 2. Namely, let us suppose that $2\cdot u=u+u=0$ in $\mathbb{Z}_{2^n}$. Then, if we compute in $\mathbb{Z}$, 2^n divides $2u$. So 2^{n-1} divides u. But $1\leq u\leq 2^n-1$. Hence $u=2^{n-1}$.

Now let us consider an element $g\neq 0$ in $\mathbb{Z}_{2^n}$. Let m be the order of g.

$$\langle g\rangle=\{g,2\cdot g,3\cdot g,\ldots,m\cdot g=0\} \quad \textbf{(6.22)}$$

If we compute in $\mathbb{Z}$, 2^n divides mg. Since $1\leq g\leq 2^n-1$, 2 divides m; $\frac{m}{2}$ is an integer. So $\frac{m}{2}\cdot g$ is an element of $\langle g\rangle$ from (6.22) and $\frac{m}{2}\cdot g\neq 0$. $2\cdot\frac{m}{2}\cdot g=m\cdot g=0$ in $\mathbb{Z}_{2^n}$. So $\frac{m}{2}\cdot g$ has order 2 in $\mathbb{Z}_{2^n}$. Then, as just shown, $\frac{m}{2}\cdot g=2^{n-1}$. ◇

Theorem 6.7

Let $N=p^n$, with p a prime number. Let the elements of $\mathbb{Z}_N$ have some representation using bits. Suppose that an adder circuit does addition in $(\mathbb{Z}_N,+)$. Suppose that the adder circuit is composed of r-input modules. Then the adder circuit consists of at least

$$\frac{(2\cdot\log_2 N)-1}{r-1}$$

modules. Also, the time needed to compute a sum is at least $\log_r(2\cdot\log_2 N)$ time units.

Example 6.26

Before proving Theorem 6.7, we shall discuss its statement and proof in the special case that $N=2^n$. Then addition in $(\mathbb{Z}_N,+)$ can be realized as the addition of n-bit binary numbers (without a final carry). Since $N=2^n$, $\log_2 N=n$. So with $r=3$, the estimate in Theorem 6.7 for the number of modules is the same as the estimate in Proposition 6.2. Also, the time estimate of Theorem 6.7 is the same as the estimate of Theorem 6.3. But Proposition 6.2 and Theorem 6.3 require the *usual binary* representation. Theorem 6.7, on the other hand, allows *arbitrary* bit representations. Recall that, as observed prior to Proposition 6.2 for the series adder and as discussed in Example 6.17 for the parallel adder, the estimates of Proposition 6.2 and Theorem 6.3, and hence also of Theorem 6.7, are really quite good. So the moral of Theorem 6.7 in the case $N=2^n$ is that the usual binary representation is as suitable as *any* other representation for the purpose of addition.

Recall that the proofs of Proposition 6.2 and Theorem 6.3 were based primarily on the observation that b_n, the highest order output bit, must depend on all $2n$ inputs. Observe that 2^{n-1}, the ubiquitous element in $\mathbb{Z}_{2^n}$, has a 1 in this Place$_n$ and that 0, which is in every subgroup of $\mathbb{Z}_{2^n}$, has a 0 in Place$_n$. The proof of Theorem 6.7 exploits in a general context these differing bits in Place$_n$. △

Proof of Theorem 6.7

p^{n-1} is different from 0. So the representations for p^{n-1} and 0 must differ in some bit, call it Place$_i$. We claim that the ith output bit, b_i, depends on at least $\log_2 N$ input bits for each summand and show this as follows: Let us suppose that b_i depends on m input bits for say, the first summand. By assuming that $m<\log_2 N$, we shall reach a contradiction. With $m<\log_2 N$, $2^m<N$. So m bits are not enough to distinguish between all of the N elements of $\mathbb{Z}_N$. So there are two different elements, call them x and y, of $\mathbb{Z}_N$ that are the same in all of the m input bits of the first summand on which b_i depends. By Theorem 6.5, all elements of the subgroup $\langle x-y\rangle$ have the same bit value in Place$_i$.

Since $x\neq y$, $x-y\neq 0$. Then p^{n-1}, which is ubiquitous by Theorem 6.6, is an element of $\langle x-y\rangle$. The identity element 0 is necessarily also an element of $\langle x-y\rangle$. Hence, by the previous paragraph, p^{n-1} and 0 have the same bit value in Place$_i$. But i was specifically chosen so that p^{n-1} and 0 had different bit values in Place$_i$. This is the desired contradiction; $m<\log_2 N$ is false.

So b_i depends on at least $\log_2 N$ inputs of the first summand. Similarly, b_i depends on at least $\log_2 N$ inputs of the second summand. This gives $2\cdot\log_2 N$ inputs in all. Theorem 6.4 now gives the conclusion of Theorem 6.7. ◇

Exercises 6.4

1. Write out the composition table for $(\mathbb{Z}_3, +)$ using
   a. the usual binary notation $0\to 00$, $1\to 01$, $2\to 10$
   b. $0\to 00$, $1\to 10$, $2\to 11$
2. In Exercise 1(a) and 1(b), show that b_2 (Place$_2$) of the output depends on all four input bits.
3. Draw a schematic diagram, as in Figure 6.4, to compute composition as given by Table 6.5. Use one 2-input, 1-output module and two 4-input, 1-output modules. The computation should be completed in just one time unit.

4. Compute $\langle g\rangle$ for $(\mathbb{Z}_N,+)$ in each of the following cases.

   a. $g=2, N=5$ b. $g=6, N=9$

   c. $g=4, N=5$ d. $g=4, N=7$

5. In the representation (6.16) for $\mathbb{Z}_6$, consider $x=100$ and $y=101$. Observe that x and y agree in Place_2 and Place_3. By direct computation from Table 6.5, show that all elements of $\langle x-y\rangle$ agree in Place_2.

6. In the representation (6.16) for $\mathbb{Z}_6$, consider $x=011$ and $y=101$. Observe that x and y agree in Place_1. By direct computation from Table 6.5, show that all elements of $\langle x-y\rangle$ agree in Place_1.

7. Whenever possible, write each of the following numbers in the form p^n, with p a prime.

   a. 10 b. 8 c. 125 d. 1000 e. 729

8. Recall the definition of $\lceil x\rceil$, from Section 6.3, Exercise 8. Explain why the proof of Theorem 6.7 really yields the estimates $\left\lceil \frac{(2\cdot\lceil\log_2 N\rceil)-1}{r-1}\right\rceil$ and $\lceil\log_r(2\cdot\lceil\log_2 N\rceil)\rceil$.

9. Using Exercise 8, estimate the minimum number of modules and the minimum time needed to add in $(\mathbb{Z}_N,+)$ for each of the following values of r and N.

   a. $r=3, N=3^4$ b. $r=2, N=3^4$

   c. $r=4, N=5^3$ d. $r=4, N=5^4$

10. Suppose that the representation in Theorem 6.7 has the additional property that 0 in $(\mathbb{Z}_N,+)$ is represented by having all 0 bits. Show that the common bit value in Place_i for elements of $\langle x-y\rangle$ must be 0.

    Hint: 0 is in $\langle x-y\rangle$.

11. Show that $(\mathbb{Z}_{10},+)$ does not have a ubiquitous element.

    Hint: Look at $\langle 2\rangle$ and $\langle 5\rangle$.

12. Show that $(\mathbb{Z}_{30},+)$ does not have a ubiquitous element.

    Hint: Look at $\langle 5\rangle$ and $\langle 6\rangle$.

13. Suppose that N is not equal to a power of a prime. Show that $(\mathbb{Z}_N,+)$ does not have a ubiquitous element.

14. Prove Theorem 6.6 for an arbitrary prime p by showing:

    a. $p^{n-1}, 2p^{n-1}, \ldots, (p-1)p^{n-1}$ are the elements of $\mathbb{Z}_N$ that have order p.

    b. Let m be the order of the element $g\neq 0$ in $\mathbb{Z}_N$. Then p divides m.

    c. $p^{n-1}, 2p^{n-1}, \ldots, (p-1)p^{n-1}$ are the ubiquitous elements in $\mathbb{Z}_N$.

15. Let $u\neq e$ be an element in the group $(G,\circ)$. Show that u is ubiquitous if and only if u is an element of all subgroups H of G such that $H\neq\{e\}$.

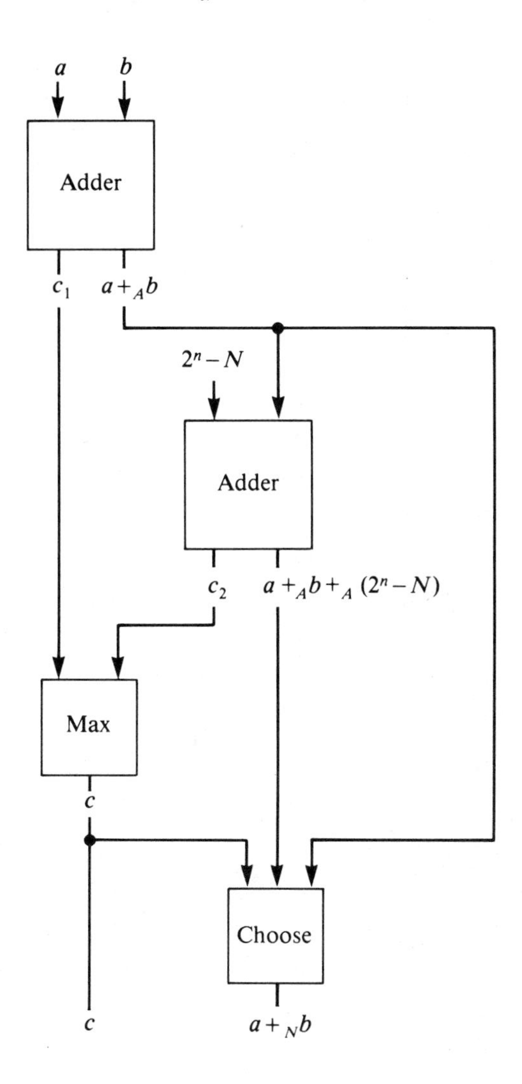

Figure 6.13 Addition in $(\mathbb{Z}_N, +)$

16. We wish to exhibit reasonably efficient circuits to perform addition in $(\mathbb{Z}_N, +)$ with N not a power of 2. Take n such that $2^n > N$. Represent elements of $\mathbb{Z}_N$ in the usual binary notation, using n bits. The adder in Figure 6.13 may be either the n-bit series adder or the n-bit parallel adder from Section 6.2.
    a. Let $a +_A b$ denote addition using the adder. Explain why the circuit of Figure 6.13 performs addition in $(\mathbb{Z}_N, +)$, as well as producing the correct value for c, the final carry (or overflow). In Figure 6.13, the Choose module produces the sum $a +_A b$ if $c = 0$ and the sum $a +_A b +_A (2^n - N)$ if $c = 1$.

Hint: Let $+$ denote the usual addition for integers. Then $a +_A b = a+b$ if $a+b<2^n$, while $a+_A b = a+b-2^n$ if $a+b \geq 2^n$.

b. Show that if the adder of Figure 6.13 is the series adder, then there are $3n+1$ 2- or 3-input modules in the full circuit of Figure 6.13.

c. Show that if the adder of Figure 6.13 is the parallel adder, then the circuit of Figure 6.13 requires approximately $4+2\cdot\log_2(\log_2 N)$ time units to produce its output.

In Exercises 17, 18, and 19 we are considering $\mathbb{Z}_N$ with N an arbitrary positive integer. The elements of $\mathbb{Z}_N$ have some given bit representation. In each exercise the given circuit is composed of r-input modules. The circuit accepts two elements, a and b, of $\mathbb{Z}_N$ and produces one bit of output, as specified in the exercise. In each exercise, show that the circuit consists of at least $\dfrac{(2\cdot\log_2 N)-1}{r-1}$ modules and requires at least $\log_r(2\cdot\log_2 N)$ time units to produce its output.

17. The output is 1 or 0 according to whether $a=b$ or $a\neq b$.

    Hint: Suppose that the output depends on less than $\log_2 N$ bits for the first element. Let $a\neq b$ be elements of $\mathbb{Z}_N$ that agree in these bits.

18. The output is 1 or 0 according to whether or not $a<b$.

    Hint: Start as in Exercise 17. Consider the inputs (a,b) and (b,a).

19. The output is 1 or 0 according to whether $a+b\geq N$ or $a+b<N$, that is, according to whether or not there is an overflow in addition.

    Hint: Start as in Exercise 17. Take $a<b$. Let $c=N-b$. Consider the inputs (a,c) and (b,c).

20. With N not assumed to be a power of a prime, let the elements of $\mathbb{Z}_N$ have some (*unique*) representation using bits. Consider an adder circuit for $(\mathbb{Z}_N,+)$ that is composed of r-input modules.

    a. Show that at least $\log_2 N$ bits of each summand are accepted by the modules of the circuit.

       Hint: If not, let $x\neq y$ be elements of $\mathbb{Z}_N$ that agree in the bits of the first summand that are accepted by the modules. Then x and y differ in some bits that directly become output bits. Use the adder to evaluate $x+(-x)$ and $y+(-y)$ in $(\mathbb{Z}_N,+)$. Reach a contradiction by seeing that 0 in $\mathbb{Z}_N$ must have two different bit representations.

    b. From part (a), conclude that the adder circuit contains at least $\dfrac{(2\cdot\log_2 N)-1}{r-1}$ modules.

    c. Use part (b) and Exercise 16(b) to conclude that the scheme of Figure 6.13, with the series adder, comes "close" to minimizing the number of modules for addition in $(\mathbb{Z}_N,+)$, for all N.

6.5 The Chinese Remainder Theorem

Consider addition in $(\mathbb{Z}_N, +)$. For N a power of a prime, we saw in the previous section that the speed for addition is limited by the fact that $(\mathbb{Z}_N, +)$ has a ubiquitous element. In this section, we state and prove the Chinese Remainder Theorem, which enables a more rapid addition for N not a power of a prime. The Chinese Remainder Theorem is so named because it was first known to the ancient Chinese. Our attempt to "improve" the Chinese Remainder Theorem leads to a group homomorphism, rather than to an isomorphism. We shall use the concept of homomorphism in the next chapter, when we study machine simulations and monoids.

Recall from Example 6.21 that since $(\mathbb{Z}_6, +)$ is isomorphic to $(\mathbb{Z}_3 \times \mathbb{Z}_2, +)$, we may add in $\mathbb{Z}_6$ by simultaneously adding in $\mathbb{Z}_3$ and in $\mathbb{Z}_2$. Observe that $6 = 3 \cdot 2$. This suggests that for arbitrary N, we factor N as $N = Q_1 \cdot Q_2 \cdot \cdots \cdot Q_k$ and see if $(\mathbb{Z}_N, +)$ is isomorphic to $(\mathbb{Z}_{Q_1} \times \mathbb{Z}_{Q_2} \times \cdots \times \mathbb{Z}_{Q_k}, +)$. Recall, however, Example 2.25: while $4 = 2 \cdot 2$, $(\mathbb{Z}_4, +)$ is *not* isomorphic to $(\mathbb{Z}_2 \times \mathbb{Z}_2, +)$.

The desired factorization of N is found as in Examples 6.27 below. We must briefly review unique prime factorization for integers. Recall that a number may be factored into primes by continually factoring it into smaller factors (which are at least 2) for as long as possible.

Examples 6.27

Consider the number 60. There are several ways to find a prime factorization.

$$60 = 3 \cdot 20 = 3 \cdot 5 \cdot 4 = 3 \cdot 5 \cdot 2 \cdot 2$$

$$60 = 2 \cdot 30 = 2 \cdot 3 \cdot 10 = 2 \cdot 3 \cdot 5 \cdot 2$$

$$60 = 6 \cdot 10 = 2 \cdot 3 \cdot 10 = 2 \cdot 3 \cdot 2 \cdot 5$$

$$60 = 5 \cdot 12 = 5 \cdot 4 \cdot 3 = 5 \cdot 2 \cdot 2 \cdot 3$$

Observe that, except for the order of multiplication, the final, prime factorizations are all the same. △

We now find the prime factorization of 100:

$$100 = 10 \cdot 10 = 2 \cdot 5 \cdot 10 = 2 \cdot 5 \cdot 2 \cdot 5$$

$$100 = 2 \cdot 50 = 2 \cdot 2 \cdot 25 = 2 \cdot 2 \cdot 5 \cdot 5$$

$$100 = 5 \cdot 20 = 5 \cdot 4 \cdot 5 = 5 \cdot 2 \cdot 2 \cdot 5$$

As with 60, the final, prime factorizations are all the same. △

The Fundamental Theorem of Arithmetic, which we shall prove in the Exercises of Section 9.1, states that the factorization of a number into prime factors is always unique, except for the order of the prime factors.

The Fundamental Theorem of Arithmetic was illustrated above in Examples 6.27. In order to simplify the statement of the Fundamental Theorem of Arithmetic, 1 is not considered to be a prime because if 1 were considered to be prime, a prime factorization of a number could have as many 1's as desired and so would not be unique.

Having completely factored a number into prime factors, we may then group together identical prime factors. The product of these equal primes is, of course, a power of the prime. This results in factoring the original number into a (unique) product of powers of distinct primes. It is convenient, but not necessary, to arrange the primes into increasing order of size. Then from Examples 6.27,

$$60 = 2^2 \cdot 3 \cdot 5$$
$$100 = 2^2 \cdot 5^2$$

The reader may easily check the following examples:

$$40 = 2^3 \cdot 5 \qquad 27 = 3^3 \qquad 41 = 41 \text{ (41 is prime)} \qquad 99 = 3^2 \cdot 11$$

Theorem 6.8

Let $Q_1, Q_2, \ldots, Q_k$ be powers of distinct primes. Then $(\mathbb{Z}_{Q_1} \times \mathbb{Z}_{Q_2} \times \cdots \times \mathbb{Z}_{Q_k}, +)$ is a cyclic group with $(1,1,\ldots,1)$ as a generator.

Example 6.28

Before proving Theorem 6.8, we shall illustrate its statement and proof. Let $Q_1 = 2^2 = 4$ and $Q_2 = 3$; $k = 2$. Then in $(\mathbb{Z}_4 \times \mathbb{Z}_3, +)$, the cyclic subgroup generated by $(1,1)$ should be all of $\mathbb{Z}_4 \times \mathbb{Z}_3$. Indeed, computing in $(\mathbb{Z}_4 \times \mathbb{Z}_3, +)$,

$$\begin{array}{lll} 1 \cdot (1,1) = (1,1) & 2 \cdot (1,1) = (2,2) & 3 \cdot (1,1) = (3,0) \\ 4 \cdot (1,1) = (0,1) & 5 \cdot (1,1) = (1,2) & 6 \cdot (1,1) = (2,0) \\ 7 \cdot (1,1) = (3,1) & 8 \cdot (1,1) = (0,2) & 9 \cdot (1,1) = (1,0) \\ 10 \cdot (1,1) = (2,1) & 11 \cdot (1,1) = (3,2) & 12 \cdot (1,1) = (0,0) \end{array}$$

So $(1,1)$ has order 12. $\mathbb{Z}_4 \times \mathbb{Z}_3$ has 12 elements. △

Proof of Theorem 6.8

Look at $1 \cdot (1,1,\ldots,1)$, $2 \cdot (1,1,\ldots,1)$, $3 \cdot (1,1,\ldots,1)$, ... For an integer m, let m_i denote its remainder after division by Q_i. Then, since each factor is added independently in $(\mathbb{Z}_{Q_1} \times \mathbb{Z}_{Q_2} \times \cdots \times \mathbb{Z}_{Q_k}, +)$,

$$m \cdot (1,1,\ldots,1) = (m_1, m_2, \ldots, m_k) \qquad \textbf{(6.23)}$$

$(m_1, m_2, \ldots, m_k) = (0,0,\ldots,0)$, the identity in $\mathbb{Z}_{Q_1} \times \mathbb{Z}_{Q_2} \times \cdots \times \mathbb{Z}_{Q_k}$, exactly when m is a multiple of each of the Q_i. Since the Q_i are powers of *distinct* primes, their least common multiple is their product $Q_1 \cdot Q_2 \cdot \dots \cdot Q_k$. So $(1,1,\dots,1)$ has order $Q_1 \cdot Q_2 \cdot \dots \cdot Q_k$. But $\mathbb{Z}_{Q_1} \times \mathbb{Z}_{Q_2} \times \dots \times \mathbb{Z}_{Q_k}$ has exactly $Q_1 \cdot Q_2 \cdot \dots \cdot Q_k$ elements. So $(1,1,\dots,1)$ is all of $\mathbb{Z}_{Q_1} \times \mathbb{Z}_{Q_2} \times \dots \times \mathbb{Z}_{Q_k}$. ◇

Example 6.29

Let us see what may happen in Theorem 6.8 if the Q_i are not powers of distinct primes. Take $Q_1 = 3$ and $Q_2 = 3^2 = 9$. Then, computing in $(\mathbb{Z}_3 \times \mathbb{Z}_9, +)$,

$$1 \cdot (1,1) = (1,1) \qquad 2 \cdot (1,1) = (2,2) \qquad 3 \cdot (1,1) = (0,3)$$

$$4 \cdot (1,1) = (1,4) \qquad 5 \cdot (1,1) = (2,5) \qquad 6 \cdot (1,1) = (0,6)$$

$$7 \cdot (1,1) = (1,7) \qquad 8 \cdot (1,1) = (2,8) \qquad 9 \cdot (1,1) = (0,0)$$

(6.23) still holds. But $(1,1)$ has only order 9; $\mathbb{Z}_3 \times \mathbb{Z}_9$ has 27 elements. △

A cyclic group $(G, +)$ with N elements is isomorphic to $(\mathbb{Z}_N, +)$. Moreover, if g generates $(G, +)$, the isomorphism from $\mathbb{Z}_N$ to G may be given by renaming m in $\mathbb{Z}_N$ to $m \cdot g$ in G, as in (6.23). So we may combine Theorem 6.8 with the Fundamental Theorem of Arithmetic to get the following statement of the Chinese Remainder Theorem. A more traditional version is given in the exercises.

Theorem 6.9. (The Chinese Remainder Theorem)

Let N be an integer at least equal to 2. Write N as

$$N = Q_1 \cdot Q_2 \cdot Q_3 \cdot \dots \cdot Q_k$$

with each Q_i a power of a different prime. Then $(\mathbb{Z}_N, +)$ is isomorphic to $(\mathbb{Z}_{Q_1} \times \mathbb{Z}_{Q_2} \times \mathbb{Z}_{Q_3} \times \dots \times \mathbb{Z}_{Q_k}, +)$ via the map f that takes m in $\mathbb{Z}_N$ to its remainders after division by $Q_1, Q_2, Q_3, \dots, Q_k$. ◇

Example 6.30

Let us take $N = 60$ to illustrate Theorem 6.9. Then

$$60 = 2^2 \cdot 3 \cdot 5$$

We take

$$Q_1 = 2^2 = 4 \qquad Q_2 = 3 \qquad Q_3 = 5$$

Theorem 6.9 implies that $(\mathbb{Z}_{60}, +)$ is isomorphic to $(\mathbb{Z}_4 \times \mathbb{Z}_3 \times \mathbb{Z}_5, +)$. Let us compute the renaming f of Theorem 6.9 for a few elements of $\mathbb{Z}_{60}$:

$$f(12) = (0,0,2)$$

$$f(18) = (2,0,3)$$

$$f(25)=(1,1,0)$$

$$f(47)=(3,2,2)$$

△

Example 6.31

In Figure 6.13, we gave a rather simple way of using the parallel adder of Section 6.2 to perform addition in $(\mathbb{Z}_N,+)$ for arbitrary N. Neglecting final carries, let us compare the needed times for addition in $(\mathbb{Z}_{60},+)$ using the usual binary notation and using the isomorphism with $(\mathbb{Z}_4\times\mathbb{Z}_3\times\mathbb{Z}_5,+)$ given by the Chinese Remainder Theorem.

$2^6=64>60$. So we need 6 bits to represent $\mathbb{Z}_{60}$ in the usual binary notation. A 6-bit adder in Figure 6.13 is just part of a $2^3=8$ bit adder and needs 4 time units for a computation; Figure 6.13 requires two successive uses of the adder and then two more levels of modules. In all, the scheme of Figure 6.13 requires 10 time units for addition in $\mathbb{Z}_{60}$.

Of the groups $\mathbb{Z}_4$, $\mathbb{Z}_3$, and $\mathbb{Z}_5$ in the Chinese Remainder representation for $\mathbb{Z}_{60}$, the group $\mathbb{Z}_5$ will require the longest time for addition. $2^3=8>5$, so we need 3 bits to represent $\mathbb{Z}_5$. A 3-bit adder is just part of a $2^2=4$-bit adder, and needs 3 time units for a computation. Using the scheme of Figure 6.13 then takes $2\cdot3+2=8$ time units for addition in $(\mathbb{Z}_5,+)$. Addition in $(\mathbb{Z}_3,+)$ requires only 6 time units. So addition in $(\mathbb{Z}_4\times\mathbb{Z}_3\times\mathbb{Z}_5,+)$ needs only 8 time units, in contrast with the 10 time units needed for the usual binary representation for $(\mathbb{Z}_{60},+)$.

The addition scheme of Figure 6.13 can be improved upon somewhat. But since we used it for addition in *both* representations, we do have a valid comparison. △

By using an N with very many distinct primes in its prime factorization, it is possible to use the Chinese Remainder Theorem to perform addition in $(\mathbb{Z}_N,+)$ at speeds greatly in excess of the limitation of Theorem 6.7. Section 6.4, Exercises 16 and 20 show that *no* representation for $\mathbb{Z}_N$ can be substantially better than the usual binary representation for the purpose of minimizing the number of modules in an adder for $(\mathbb{Z}_N,+)$. Consider, however, multiplication in $\mathbb{Z}_N$, as discussed in Chapter 2, Section 2.3. As shown in the exercises of this section, the Chinese Remainder representation is also valid for multiplication in $\mathbb{Z}_N$. As well as increasing the speed of multiplication, the Chinese Remainder representation also decreases the number of modules needed for multiplication. But, as shown in Section 6.4, Exercises 17–19, this representation can provide no advantages for some other important computations, such as deciding if two numbers are equal.

In applying the Chinese Remainder Theorem, it is easy enough to compute the map f from $\mathbb{Z}_N$ to $\mathbb{Z}_{Q_1}\times\mathbb{Z}_{Q_2}\times\cdots\times\mathbb{Z}_{Q_k}$. But computing the inverse map f^{-1} from $\mathbb{Z}_{Q_1}\times\mathbb{Z}_{Q_2}\times\cdots\times\mathbb{Z}_{Q_k}$ to $\mathbb{Z}_N$ can be rather difficult. Some shortcuts are available. Think of the elements of $\mathbb{Z}_{Q_1}\times\mathbb{Z}_{Q_2}\times\cdots\times\mathbb{Z}_{Q_k}$ as "vectors" and the map f^{-1} as a linear map. Linear maps are determined by what they do on basis vectors. So knowing f^{-1} on a basis determines f^{-1} for all vectors. Here are some examples.

Example 6.32

Let us look at $f:\mathbb{Z}_{30}\to\mathbb{Z}_2\times\mathbb{Z}_3\times\mathbb{Z}_5$. A "basis" for $\mathbb{Z}_2\times\mathbb{Z}_3\times\mathbb{Z}_5$ may be given by (1,0,0), (0,1,0), and (0,0,1). The reader may easily check that

$$f^{-1}(1,0,0)=15 \qquad f^{-1}(0,1,0)=10 \qquad f^{-1}(0,0,1)=6 \tag{6.24}$$

For our further calculations, it will be convenient to use the notation of the congruence relation $\equiv$ mod 30, of Example 3.5. Recall that $a\equiv b \pmod{30}$ if $\dfrac{a-b}{30}$ is an integer. Equivalently, $a\equiv b \pmod{30}$ requires that a and b leave the same remainder after division by 30. We shall omit the "mod 30" for brevity of notation.

The map f^{-1} is determined from (6.24) as follows: Consider $f^{-1}(1,2,4)$.

$$(1,2,4)=1\cdot(1,0,0)+2\cdot(0,1,0)+4\cdot(0,0,1)$$

Thinking of f^{-1} as a "linear" map:

$$\begin{aligned} f^{-1}(1,2,4)&=1\cdot f^{-1}(1,0,0)+2\cdot f^{-1}(0,1,0)+4\cdot f^{-1}(0,0,1)\\ &=1\cdot 15+2\cdot 10+4\cdot 6, \qquad \text{to be computed in } \mathbb{Z}_{30}\\ &\equiv 15+20+24\\ &\equiv 59\\ &\equiv 29, \qquad \text{in } \mathbb{Z}_{30} \end{aligned}$$

The reader may easily check that indeed $f(29)=(1,2,4)$.

We may compute $f^{-1}(1,0,3)$ similarly as follows:

$$\begin{aligned} f^{-1}(1,0,3)&=1\cdot f^{-1}(1,0,0)+0\cdot f^{-1}(0,1,0)+3\cdot f^{-1}(0,0,1)\\ &=1\cdot 15+0\cdot 10+3\cdot 6\\ &\equiv 15+0+18\\ &\equiv 33\\ &\equiv 3, \qquad \text{in } \mathbb{Z}_{30} \end{aligned}$$

△

Example 6.33

We look at the map f^{-1} from $\mathbb{Z}_4\times\mathbb{Z}_3\times\mathbb{Z}_{25}$ to $\mathbb{Z}_{300}$. One may easily check that

$$f(225)=(1,0,0) \qquad f(100)=(0,1,0) \qquad f(276)=(0,0,1)$$

(A method for finding these equations is given in Example 9.12.) Then, for example,

$$\begin{aligned} f^{-1}(2,1,10) &= 2\cdot f^{-1}(1,0,0) + 1\cdot f^{-1}(0,1,0) + 10\cdot f^{-1}(0,0,1) \\ &= 2\cdot 225 + 1\cdot 100 + 10\cdot 276 \\ &\equiv 450 + 100 + 2760 \\ &\equiv 3310 \\ &\equiv 10, \qquad \text{in } \mathbb{Z}_{300} \end{aligned}$$

Indeed, 10 leaves remainders of 2, 1, and 10 upon division by 4, 3, and 25 respectively. △

Example 6.34

Let us calculate the map f in Theorem 6.9 in a case where the Q_i are not powers of distinct primes. We take $N=9$ and $Q_1=Q_2=3$. Then f is a map from $\mathbb{Z}_9$ to $\mathbb{Z}_3 \times \mathbb{Z}_3$.

$$\begin{array}{lll} f(0)=(0,0) & f(1)=(1,1) & f(2)=(2,2) \\ f(3)=(0,0) & f(4)=(1,1) & f(5)=(2,2) \\ f(6)=(0,0) & f(7)=(1,1) & f(8)=(2,2) \end{array} \tag{6.25}$$

f is certainly not an isomorphism since f is neither one-to-one nor onto. Nonetheless, let us see what the renaming (6.25) does to the composition table for $(\mathbb{Z}_9, +)$. It will be convenient to reorder the elements of $\mathbb{Z}_9$ so that elements with the same image under f are adjacent. Thus we list the elements of $\mathbb{Z}_9$ as 0, 3, 6, 1, 4, 7, 2, 5, 8 and form Table 6.8 as the addition table for $(\mathbb{Z}_9, +)$.

Table 6.8 Addition table for $(\mathbb{Z}_9, +)$

+	0	3	6	1	4	7	2	5	8
0	0	3	6	1	4	7	2	5	8
3	3	6	0	4	7	1	5	8	2
6	6	0	3	7	1	4	8	2	5
1	1	4	7	2	5	8	3	6	0
4	4	7	1	5	8	2	6	0	3
7	7	1	4	8	2	5	0	3	6
2	2	5	8	3	6	0	4	7	1
5	5	8	2	6	0	3	7	1	4
8	8	2	5	0	3	6	1	4	7

Via the renaming of (6.25), Table 6.8 becomes Table 6.9. Dotted lines have been drawn in Table 6.9 to show that it is consistent with itself; for example, $(1,1)+(1,1)=(2,2)$ may be computed from any of the (1,1)-rows and any of the (1,1)-columns. Eliminating the redundancies in Table 6.9 gives Table 6.10. It is easy to check that Table 6.10 is the addition table for the subgroup $\{(0,0), (1,1), (2,2)\}$ of $\mathbb{Z}_3 \times \mathbb{Z}_3$. △

Table 6.9 A renaming for Table 6.8

+	(0,0)	(0,0)	(0,0)	(1,1)	(1,1)	(1,1)	(2,2)	(2,2)	(2,2)
(0,0)	(0,0)	(0,0)	(0,0)	(1,1)	(1,1)	(1,1)	(2,2)	(2,2)	(2,2)
(0,0)	(0,0)	(0,0)	(0,0)	(1,1)	(1,1)	(1,1)	(2,2)	(2,2)	(2,2)
(0,0)	(0,0)	(0,0)	(0,0)	(1,1)	(1,1)	(1,1)	(2,2)	(2,2)	(2,2)
(1,1)	(1,1)	(1,1)	(1,1)	(2,2)	(2,2)	(2,2)	(0,0)	(0,0)	(0,0)
(1,1)	(1,1)	(1,1)	(1,1)	(2,2)	(2,2)	(2,2)	(0,0)	(0,0)	(0,0)
(1,1)	(1,1)	(1,1)	(1,1)	(2,2)	(2,2)	(2,2)	(0,0)	(0,0)	(0,0)
(2,2)	(2,2)	(2,2)	(2,2)	(0,0)	(0,0)	(0,0)	(1,1)	(1,1)	(1,1)
(2,2)	(2,2)	(2,2)	(2,2)	(0,0)	(0,0)	(0,0)	(1,1)	(1,1)	(1,1)
(2,2)	(2,2)	(2,2)	(2,2)	(0,0)	(0,0)	(0,0)	(1,1)	(1,1)	(1,1)

(6.25) is a *homomorphism*. Formally, we have Definition 6.3.

Definition 6.3

Let $(G,\circ)$ and $(H,*)$ be groups. A map $f: G \to H$ is a **homomorphism** if for all elements a,b in G,

$$f(a \circ b) = f(a) * f(b)$$ ○

Table 6.10 A condensation of Table 6.9

+	(0,0)	(1,1)	(2,2)
(0,0)	(0,0)	(1,1)	(2,2)
(1,1)	(1,1)	(2,2)	(0,0)
(2,2)	(2,2)	(0,0)	(1,1)

Why does the condition of Definition 6.3 rename the composition table for $(G,\circ)$ into part of the composition table for $(H,*)$? The entry $a \circ b$ is in the a-row, b-column of G's composition table. Under renaming via f, $f(a \circ b)$ should become the entry in the $f(a)$-row, $f(b)$-column of H's composition table. In the composition table for $(H,*)$, the $f(a)$-row, $f(b)$-column entry must be $f(a)*f(b)$. So for correct renaming, we need that $f(a \circ b) = f(a)*f(b)$. This is Definition 6.3. Since f renames G's composition table to part of H's composition table, the renaming must be consistent, as in Table 6.9.

Example 6.35

Here is a homomorphism f from $(S_3,\circ)$ to $(\mathbb{Z}_2,+)$.

$$\begin{array}{ccc} f(e)=0 & f((123))=0 & f((132))=0 \\ f((12))=1 & f((13))=1 & f((23))=0 \end{array} \qquad \textbf{(6.26)}$$

Let us check Definition 6.3 in two cases:

$$a=(123) \qquad b=(13) \qquad a\circ b=(23) \qquad f(23)=1$$
$$f(a)=0 \qquad f(b)=1 \qquad 0+1=1$$

$$a=(12) \qquad b=(13) \qquad a\circ b=(132) \qquad f((132))=0$$
$$f(a)=1 \qquad f(b)=1 \qquad 1+1=0$$

Table 6.11 gives a complete renaming of the composition table for $(S_3,\circ)$ via (6.26) and so shows that f is a homomorphism. △

Table 6.11 Homomorphism verification

(i) Composition table for $(S_3,\circ)$

$\circ$	e	(123)	(132)	(12)	(13)	(23)
e	e	(123)	(132)	(12)	(13)	(23)
(123)	(123)	(132)	e	(13)	(23)	(12)
(132)	(132)	e	(123)	(23)	(12)	(13)
(12)	(12)	(23)	(13)	e	(132)	(123)
(13)	(13)	(12)	(23)	(123)	e	(132)
(23)	(23)	(13)	(12)	(132)	(123)	e

(ii) Renaming of (i) via (6.25)

+	0	0	0	1	1	1
0	0	0	0	1	1	1
0	0	0	0	1	1	1
0	0	0	0	1	1	1
1	1	1	1	0	0	0
1	1	1	1	0	0	0
1	1	1	1	0	0	0

(iii) Condensation of (ii) = addition table for $(\mathbb{Z}_2,+)$

+	0	1
0	0	1
1	1	0

In combination with the group axioms of Definition 2.3, Definition 6.3 imposes a rather strong condition on a map f for it to be a homomorphism. Some of the important general properties of group homomorphisms are discussed in the exercises.

Let f be a homomorphism, as in Definition 6.3. Then, as just seen, f

renames the elements of G to some of the elements of H in a manner that respects the laws of composition. So, if f is also a one-to-one correspondence, then f is an isomorphism, as informally defined in Chapter 2, Section 2.3. Thus, isomorphisms may be formally defined as in Definition 6.4.

Definition 6.4

Let $(G,\circ)$ and $(H,*)$ be groups. A map $f:G\to H$ is an **isomorphism** if
(i) f is a one-to-one correspondence and
(ii) f is a homomorphism; that is, for all elements a,b in G,

$$f(a\circ b)=f(a)*f(b)$$

Two groups $(G,\circ)$ and $(H,*)$ are **isomorphic** if there is an isomorphism $f:G\to H$. ○

Example 6.36

Sometimes a formal definition, such as Definition 6.4, is easier to use than an informal definition. Let $(G,\circ)$ be a (noncommutative) group. We define the law of composition $\diamond$ on G by, for a,b elements of G,

$$a\diamond b=b\circ a$$

Then the map $f:a\to a^{-1}$ is an isomorphism from $(G,\circ)$ to $(G,\diamond)$: By the existence, Definition 2.3(i), and the uniqueness, Theorem 2.5, of inverses, f is a well-defined map. By Theorem 2.7, f is its own inverse map. By Theorem 2.14, f is a one-to-one correspondence. To verify the homomorphism condition, we need that

$$(a\circ b)^{-1}=a^{-1}\diamond b^{-1} \tag{6.27}$$

Since $a^{-1}\diamond b^{-1}=b^{-1}\circ a^{-1}$, (6.27) is just Theorem 2.6. △

Exercises 6.5

1. Write each of the following numbers as

   (i) The product of primes.
   (ii) The product of powers of distinct primes.

   a. 27 b. 84 c. 146 d. 1024
2. Using the Chinese Remainder Theorem, write each of the following groups as the product of smaller groups.
   a. $(\mathbb{Z}_{24},+)$ b. $(\mathbb{Z}_{50},+)$ c. $(\mathbb{Z}_{75},+)$ d. $(\mathbb{Z}_6\times\mathbb{Z}_{10},+)$

In Exercises 3–8, the map f is the isomorphism from the Chinese Remainder Theorem.

3. $f:\mathbb{Z}_{10}\to\mathbb{Z}_2\times\mathbb{Z}_5$. Give $f(m)$ for all m in $\mathbb{Z}_{10}$.
4. $f:\mathbb{Z}_{160}\to\mathbb{Z}_{32}\times\mathbb{Z}_5$. Compute
   a. $f(34)$ b. $f(65)$ c. $f(100)$ d. $f(134)$
5. $f:\mathbb{Z}_{244}\to\mathbb{Z}_4\times\mathbb{Z}_{61}$. Compute
   a. $f(31)$ b. $f(54)$ c. $f(101)$ d. $f(231)$
6. $f:\mathbb{Z}_{315}\to\mathbb{Z}_5\times\mathbb{Z}_7\times\mathbb{Z}_9$. Compute
   a. $f(23)$ b. $f(41)$ c. $f(231)$ d. $f(300)$
7. $f:\mathbb{Z}_{84}\to\mathbb{Z}_4\times\mathbb{Z}_3\times\mathbb{Z}_7$. $f^{-1}(1,0,0)=21$, $f^{-1}(0,1,0)=28$, $f^{-1}(0,0,1)=36$. Compute
   a. $f^{-1}(1,1,2)$ b. $f^{-1}(3,0,4)$ c. $f^{-1}(2,2,5)$
8. $f:\mathbb{Z}_{220}\to\mathbb{Z}_4\times\mathbb{Z}_5\times\mathbb{Z}_{11}$. $f^{-1}(1,0,0)=165$, $f^{-1}(0,1,0)=176$, $f^{-1}(0,0,1)=100$. Compute
   a. $f^{-1}(2,4,5)$ b. $f^{-1}(0,2,4)$ c. $f^{-1}(1,3,10)$
9. By renaming the entries of the addition table, show that the map $f:\mathbb{Z}_4\to\mathbb{Z}_2\times\mathbb{Z}_2$ given by

   $$f(0)=(0,0),\quad f(1)=(1,1),\quad f(2)=(0,0),\quad f(3)=(1,1)$$

   is a homomorphism.
10. By renaming the entries of the addition table, show that the map $f:\mathbb{Z}_6\to\mathbb{Z}_3$ given by

    $$f(0)=0 \quad f(1)=1 \quad f(2)=2$$
    $$f(3)=0 \quad f(4)=1 \quad f(5)=2$$

    is a homomorphism.
11. Explain why each of the following maps is not a group homomorphism.
    a. $f:\mathbb{Z}_3\to\mathbb{Z}_2$ $0\to0$ $1\to1$ $2\to0$
    b. $f:S_3\to\mathbb{Z}_3$ $e\to0$ $(23)\to1$ $(12)\to2$ $(123)\to0$ $(132)\to1$ $(13)\to2$
    c. $f:\mathbb{Z}_3\to\mathbb{Z}_6$ $0\to0$ $1\to1$ $2\to2$
    d. $f:\mathbb{Z}_4\to\mathbb{Z}_6$ $0\to0$ $1\to1$ $2\to2$ $3\to3$
    e. $f:\mathbb{Z}_8\to\mathbb{Z}_4$ $0\to0$ $1\to0$ $2\to1$ $3\to1$ $4\to2$ $5\to2$ $6\to3$ $7\to3$
12. Show that $(\mathbb{Z}_5\times\mathbb{Z}_6,+)$ is isomorphic to $(\mathbb{Z}_2\times\mathbb{Z}_{15},+)$.
13. Suppose that $a\equiv b \pmod n$ and that $c\equiv d \pmod n$. Show that also $a+c\equiv b+d \pmod n$ and that $a\cdot c\equiv b\cdot d \pmod n$.

14. Let $f:\mathbb{Z}_N \to \mathbb{Z}_{Q_1} \times \mathbb{Z}_{Q_2} \times \cdots \times \mathbb{Z}_{Q_k}$ be the map of the Chinese Remainder Theorem. Show that $f(a \cdot b) = f(a) \cdot f(b)$.
15. The traditional formulation of the Chinese Remainder Theorem is: Let the positive integer n be written $n = n_1 \cdot n_2 \cdot \cdots \cdot n_k$ so that n_i and n_j, $i \neq j$, have no common prime factors. Then, given integers $a_1, a_2, \ldots, a_k$, the simultaneous equations

$$x \equiv a_1 \pmod{n_1}, \quad x \equiv a_2 \pmod{n_2}, \ldots, \quad x \equiv a_k \pmod{n_k}$$

have a unique solution with $0 \leq x < n$. Derive this statement from Theorem 6.9.

In Exercises 16–20, $f:G \to H$ is a homomorphism from the group $(G, \circ)$ to the group $(H, *)$; e_G and e_H denote the identities in G and in H respectively.

16. Give reasons for the following steps, which show that $f(e_G) = e_H$.

$$e_G \circ e_G = e_G$$

$$f(e_G) * f(e_G) = f(e_G)$$

$$f(e_G) * f(e_G) * [f(e_G)]^{-1} = f(e_G) * [f(e_G)]^{-1}$$

$$f(e_G) * e_H = e_H$$

$$f(e_G) = e_H$$

17. Let g be an element of G. Show that $f(g^{-1}) = [f(g)]^{-1}$.
    Hint: Show that $f(g^{-1}) * f(g) = e_H$.
18. Let S be the set of elements h in H such that $h = f(g)$ for some g in G. S is the **image** of f. Show that $(S, *)$ is a subgroup of $(H, *)$.
19. Let K be the set of elements g in G such that $f(g) = e_H$. K is the **kernel** of f. Show that $(K, \circ)$ is a subgroup of $(G, \circ)$.
20. Suppose that the kernel K consists of only e_G. Show that f is a one-to-one map.
    Hint: If $f(a) = f(b)$, consider $f(a \circ b^{-1})$.

7 Finite-State Machines

In this chapter we shall define and use finite-state machines, sometimes also called *finite-state sequential machines* or *finite automata*. Finite-state machines are mathematical objects that are models for digital computers. However, the finite-state machines in the examples will typically have only a few bits of memory, in contrast to the much larger memories of physical machines. These examples thus typify what small components of a real machine might be like. From the theoretical point of view, finite-state machines are special cases of more general objects, such as Turing machines, which are essential in dealing with problems in computability. Finite-state machines will play an important role in the next chapter, on Formal Languages. In turn, the ideas of the next chapter are important in the study of compilers.

The first section of this chapter defines and illustrates finite-state machines by means of tables. The next section gives an alternate description using state diagrams. In the third section, we show that some calculations are not possible using finite-state machines. (This is why more complicated objects such as Turing machines are needed.) Assuming that a finite-state machine can perform a given calculation; that is, that it exhibits a given behavior, we next show how to construct the simplest possible such machine. Section 7.5 shows how one finite-state machine may simulate another. This relates directly to the notion of homomorphism for finite-state machines. In the exercises of Section 7.5 it will also be briefly indicated how the simple machines of the examples may be combined to give more complicated finite-state machines. Section 7.6 is devoted to the algebra of monoids and semigroups. We see in this last section that part of each finite-state machine has a monoid naturally associated with it.

7.1 Definitions and Examples

In this section a formal definition of a finite-state machine is given. A circuit diagram representation for a finite-state machine differs from the switching circuits of the previous chapters primarily by having a memory that allows the reuse of the components of the circuit. Since it is often useful to focus solely on the behavior of the memory, a simpler type of finite-state machine called a finite semiautomaton is introduced.

A **combinatorial network** is a circuit for which the output depends solely on the current, or present, input. That is, the circuit has no internal memory that may influence its output. As in Chapter 5, Section 5.2, the external behavior of a combinatorial network is completely described by the switching, or Boolean, functions that express the output bits in terms of the input bits. The internal behavior of a combinatorial network is often nicely described by Boolean polynomials.

In contrast to a combinatorial network, a **sequential network** is a circuit for which the output may depend on previous inputs besides the current input. That is, a sequential network may have a memory. We shall work out a schematic example of a sequential network later, in Figure 7.3. The behavior of a sequential network is described by a finite-state machine, as will be defined. The execution time of sequential networks is generally much slower than that for equivalent combinatorial networks (if they exist). However, sequential networks are often simpler to build. Most importantly, the memory in sequential networks permits much more complicated relationships between input and output than are possible with combinatorial networks.

Example 7.1

We look again at the series adder of Figure 5.1. For the sake of convenience, Figure 7.1 reproduces the series adder for summands with six bits. Values for the inputs, which are omitted in Figure 7.1, will appear in Figure 7.2. Recall that the series adder of Figure 7.1 does addition in the usual way; it starts with the units places of the two summands and adds them to get the units place of the sum and to yield the value of the carry. Then the 2's place values of the summands and the values of the carry from the units place are all added to get a 2's place value for the sum and a value for the next carry. Next, the 4's place values of the summands and the value of the carry from the 2's place are added to get a 4's place value for the summand and the carry. The series adder continues in this manner, using all of the input bits.

A typical addition of two 6-bit numbers might be

Carry:	1	1	0	1	1	1	–
010101:		0	1	0	1	0	1
110011:		1	1	0	0	1	1
Sum:	1	0	0	1	0	0	0

(7.1)

For the purposes of illustration, we enter the values for the addition in (7.1) into the adder of Figure 7.1. This yields Figure 7.2.

Figure 7.1 is a somewhat complicated combinatorial network. It is

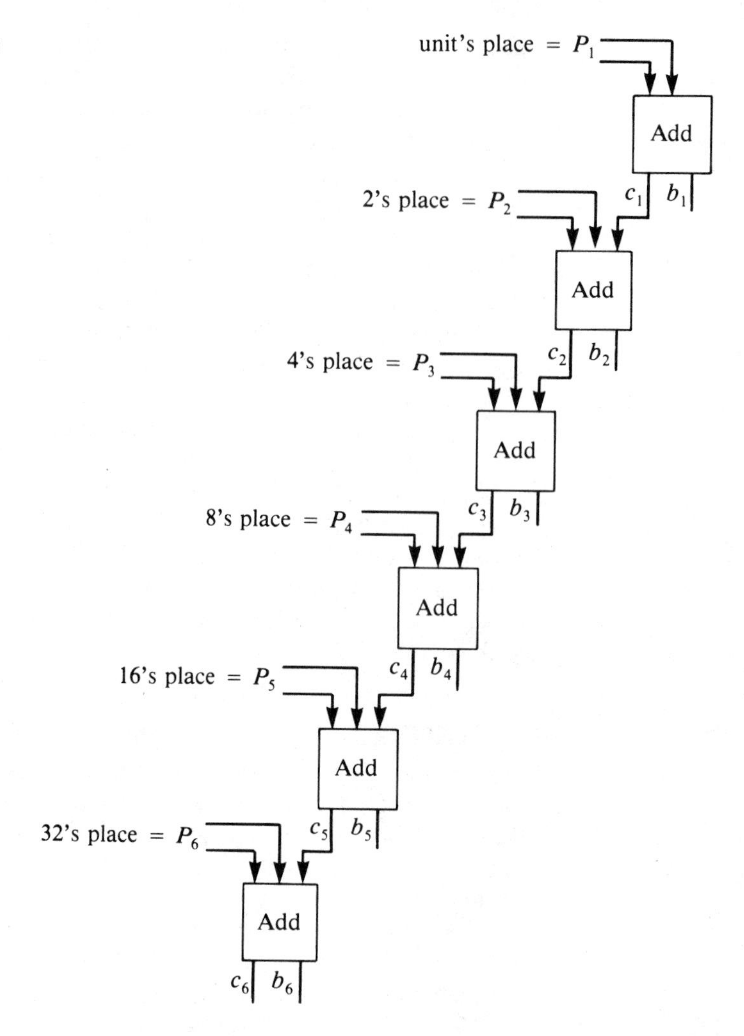

Figure 7.1 A 6-bit series adder

constructed of simpler modules, which are represented by the squares in Figure 7.1. Each module, or adder, in Figure 7.1 accepts binary input bits and produces their binary sum. So each module in Figure 7.1 is itself a combinatorial network. Observe that there are only two types of modules in Figure 7.1, two-input and three-input adders. In fact, as in Figure 7.3, a two-input adder may be replaced by a three-input adder that has one input always set to 0. Table 7.1 (p. 304) gives the relationships between inputs and outputs for a three-input adder. △

Recall that a three-input adder may perform the functions of all of the modules in Figure 7.1. This suggests that rather than using a different module for each place value, we reuse just one module to compute all of

Figure 7.2
010101 + 110011

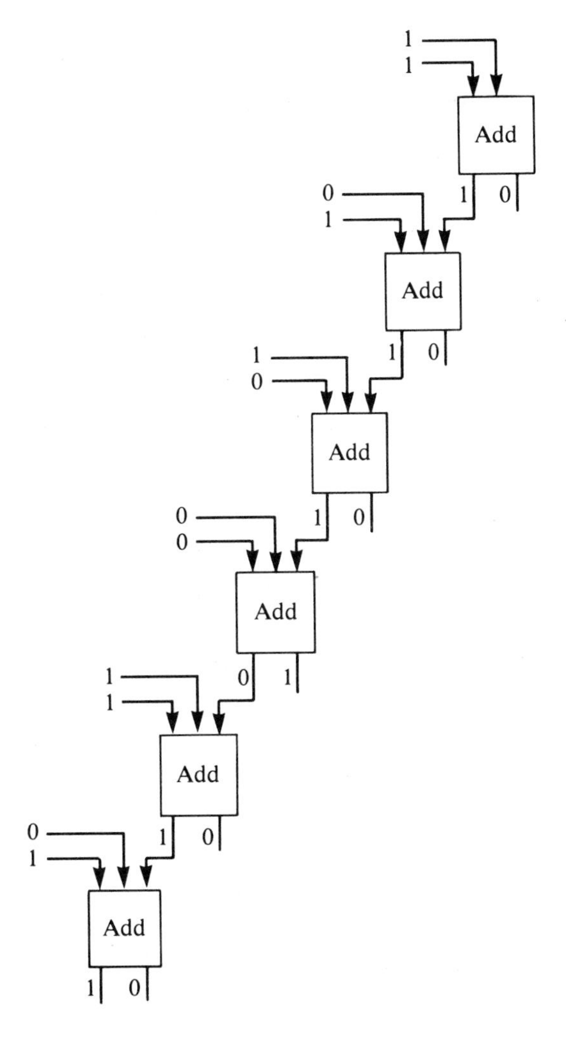

Figure 7.3 Three-input adder used as a two-input adder

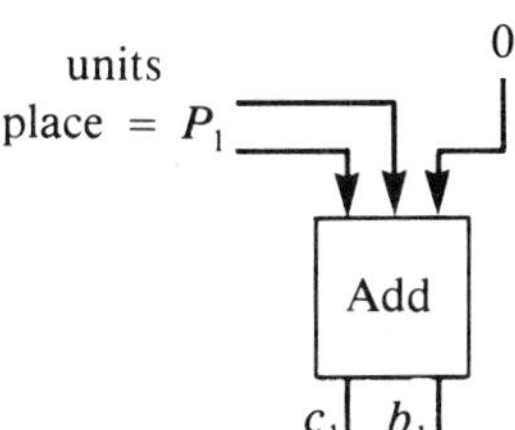

the place values. The carry outputs of Figure 7.1 will have to be used as successive inputs to a single module. Some delay and timing mechanism will be required to ensure that the carry output is accepted by the module

Table 7.1 i/o function for a three-input adder

Input bit values			Output bit values	
First summand	Second summand	Carry	Next carry	Place value for sum
0	0	0	0	0
0	0	1	0	1
0	1	0	0	1
0	1	1	1	0
1	0	0	0	1
1	0	1	1	0
1	1	0	1	0
1	1	1	1	1

at the same time as the next set of bits in the two summands. The module will then yield the bits of the sum one at a time, units bit first. Such a sequential network is indicated very schematically in Figure 7.4.

The Delay box of Figure 7.4 must store the carry output from the adder. So the Delay box is really a memory. Since the only information to be stored is whether the carry is 0 or 1, one bit of memory suffices.

The external behavior of Figure 7.4, along with the (internal) value of the memory, may be described by a simple but typical finite-state machine. Before the formal definition of a finite-state machine is given, let us review the essential aspects of Figure 7.4 from the finite-state machine point of view; we totally neglect the timing devices that must ensure that the adder receives its inputs at the proper times. The Delay box in Figure 7.4 contains a memory, which is either 0 or 1 according to whether the previous carry is 0 or 1. The adder is a combinatorial network that accepts three binary inputs and produces two binary outputs; two of these inputs

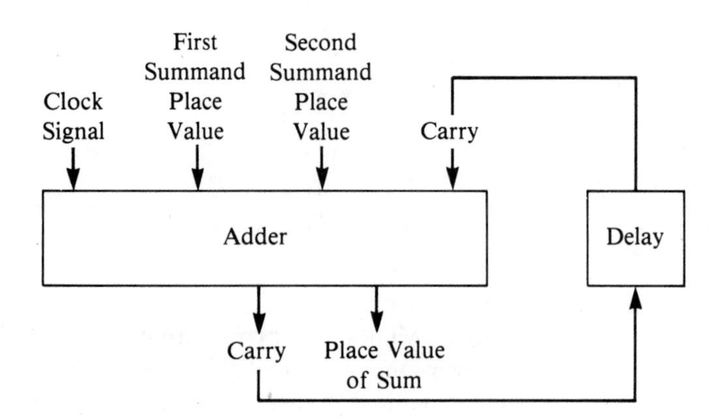

Figure 7.4 A sequential network version of Figure 7.1

are external, the remaining input is the contents of the memory. Table 7.1 gives the explicit relationship between the inputs and the outputs for the adder. One output from the adder is the desired place value of the sum; this output is seen externally. The other output of the adder is used internally to give the next value of the memory in the Delay box.

Example 7.2 We shall use Figure 7.4 to perform the addition in (7.1). As in Figure 7.3, the initial value for the memory in the Delay box must be set to 0. The place values of the summands are accepted successively, starting with the units places. The adder then produces the places of the sum, units place first. In order to get the highest bit value in the sum, which is underlined in (7.1), high-order 0's must be appended to the summands. This converts (7.1) to (7.2). With high-order 0's, the last carry will be 0; this carry is ignored.

$$\begin{array}{lccccccccc} \text{Carry:} & - & 1 & 1 & 0 & 1 & 1 & 1 & - \\ \text{0010101:} & & 0 & 0 & 1 & 0 & 1 & 0 & 1 \\ \text{0110011:} & & 0 & 1 & 1 & 0 & 0 & 1 & 1 \\ \hline \text{Sum:} & & 1 & 0 & 0 & 1 & 0 & 0 & 0 \end{array} \tag{7.2}$$

In Figure 7.5, we illustrate the status of the various inputs and outputs in Figure 7.4 during the first few time units of the addition in (7.2). In Figure 7.5, the number in the Delay box is the value of the memory. △

In Figure 7.5, selecting the initial value for the memory corresponds to programming an ordinary computer. An initial memory value of 0 gives the correct sum; an initial memory value of 1 gives an incorrect sum.

Think of the possible values of the memory as the states of the machine. A combinatorial network corresponds to a function. Then, very formally, we have Definition 7.1.

Definition 7.1 A **finite-state machine** (also called a **finite automaton**) consists of the following:

(i) S, a finite set of **states**.
(ii) I, a finite set of **inputs**.
(iii) ν, a function from $S \times I$ to S. ν is the **next-state function**.
(iv) Y, a finite set of **outputs**.
(v) β, a function from $S \times I$ to Y. β is the **output function**. ○

Often, we shall simplify things by not having a separate output set Y and output function β. In such cases, it is assumed that the user knows the state of the machine after each input. So the output of the machine is

Figure 7.5

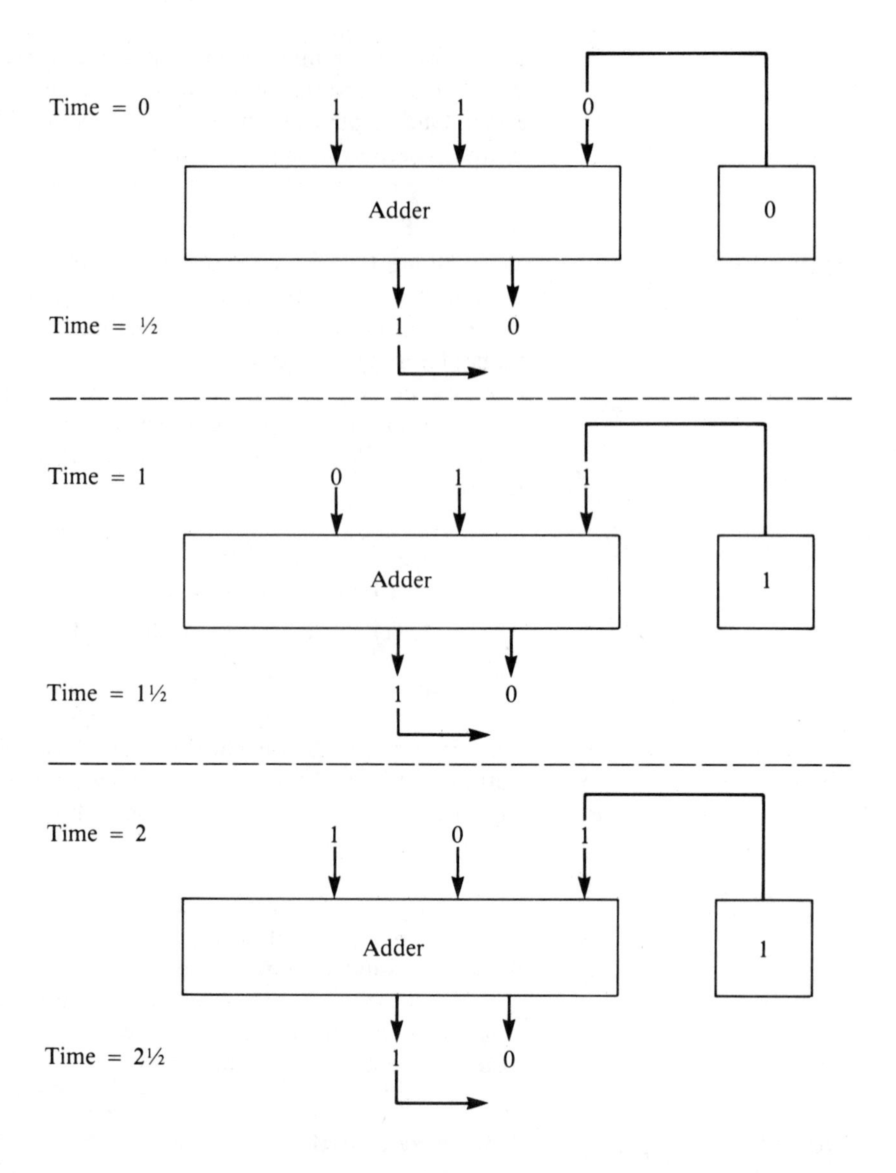

simply its state. Such machines are called **semiautomata**, in contrast to the full automata of Definition 7.1. Formally, we have Definition 7.2.

Definition 7.2

A **finite semiautomaton** consists of (i), (ii), and (iii) from Definition 7.1.

Every semiautomaton may be considered as a finite-state machine via

(iv) Y is given by $Y = S$.

(v) β is given by, for (s,i) in $S \times I$, $\beta(s,i) = \nu(s,i)$. ○

We shall frequently use the term **machine** to mean either a finite-state machine or a finite semiautomaton.

Definitions 7.1 and 7.2 are not as formidable as they appear. They say that a machine has a finite memory, called S, and accepts a finite set of inputs, called I. Upon accepting an input, the machine changes the contents of its memory. The new contents of the memory depend solely on the input and the old contents of the memory, as expressed by the function ν. This is all that a finite semiautomaton does. A finite-state machine, in addition, produces an output upon receiving an input. This output depends solely on the input and the (old) contents of the memory, as expressed by the function β. As drawn in Figure 7.6, one often thinks of a finite-state machine as accepting a sequence, or **string**, of inputs from an input tape. Upon accepting each input, the machine writes an output on an output tape, producing an output string.

Example 7.3

Let us now see how the machine of Figure 7.4 fits into the scheme of Definition 7.1. S, the set of states, is given by $\{0,1\}$, the possible carries. I, the set of inputs, is given by $I=\{(0,0), (0,1), (1,0), (1,1)\}$. That is, each element of I consists of bit values for the two summands. ν, the next-state function, is the value of the next carry (or state) in terms of the current input and the current carry (or state). So ν is given by the "Next carry" column of Table 7.1. Y, the set of outputs, is given by $Y=\{0,1\}$. Y is the place value of the sum. β, the output function, expresses the place value of the sum in terms of the current input and the current carry. Then β is given by the "Place value for sum" column of Table 7.1.

Figure 7.6 A finite-state machine

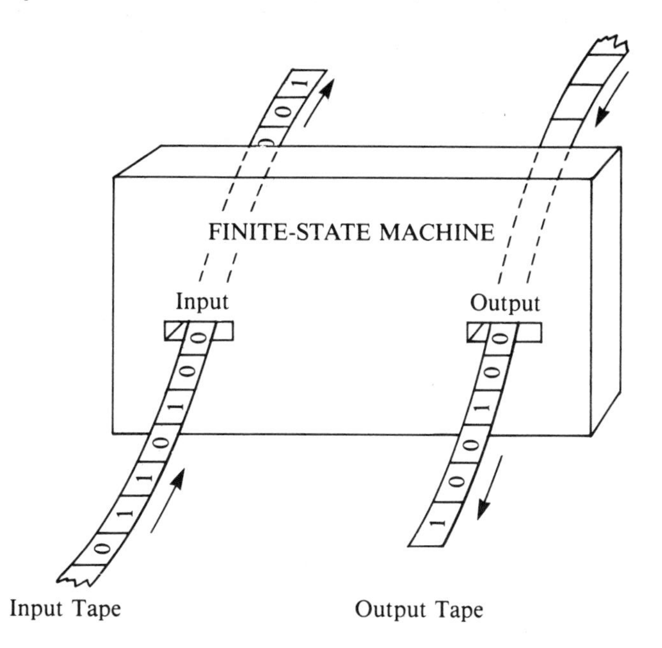

Typically, in describing a finite machine, v would be rewritten in the form of Table 7.2 and β would be rewritten in the form of Table 7.3. Unlike Table 7.1, Tables 7.2 and 7.3 clearly express v and β as functions of the *product* $S \times I$; the rows of Tables 7.2 and 7.3 are labeled by the elements of S and the columns are labeled by the elements of I. Each entry is then labeled by a state s and an input i. As required by Definition 7.1(iii), the (s,i)-entry in Table 7.2 is $v(s,i)$. As required by Definition 7.1(v), the (s,i)-entry in Table 7.3 is $\beta(s,i)$. $v(s,i)$ and $\beta(s,i)$ are easily read off from Table 7.1. Together, Tables 7.2 and 7.3 are called the **state table** of the machine.

For a finite-state machine, the tables for v and for β will often be written in a combined form. Thus, Tables 7.2 and 7.3 are condensed to Table 7.4. △

Table 7.2 Next-state function v for Table 7.1

Current state	Input (0,0)	(0,1)	(1,0)	(1,1)
0	0	0	0	1
1	0	1	1	1

Table 7.3 Output function β for Table 7.1

Current state	Input (0,0)	(0,1)	(1,0)	(1,1)
0	0	1	1	0
1	1	0	0	1

Table 7.4 The finite-state machine for Table 7.1

	Next-state function				Output function			
	Input				Input			
Current state	(0,0)	(0,1)	(1,0)	(1,1)	(0,0)	(0,1)	(1,0)	(1,1)
0	0	0	0	1	0	1	1	0
1	0	1	1	1	1	0	0	1

Example 7.4

We now describe a finite semiautomaton, as in Definition 7.2. This machine will tell if an input string of bits has an even or an odd number of 1's. We shall call this machine M a **binary counter**. Sometimes M is called a **parity check machine**. M has two states, EVEN and ODD; that is, $S = \{\text{EVEN, ODD}\}$. $I = \{0,1\}$. After accepting a string of 0's and 1's, the binary counter should be in state EVEN if there were an even number of 1's and in state ODD if there were an odd number of 1's. Before there is any input, there are an even number, zero, of 1's. So we must start M in the EVEN state. What should the next-state function be in order for M to always remain in the correct state? Accepting a 0 preserves the parity of the number of 1's. So M should remain in its current state when accepting a 0. Accepting a 1 changes the parity of the number of 1's. So accepting a 1 should change the state of the machine. In all, we get the next-state table of Table 7.5.

Table 7.5 Next-state function for a binary counter

Current state	Input 0	Input 1
EVEN	EVEN	ODD
ODD	ODD	EVEN

Let us observe how Table 7.5 works for the input string 1010010. This string has an odd number, three, of 1's. Strings are accepted from left to right. So the initial input is 1. Here is the effect of the successive inputs on the binary counter:

Input:	–	1	0	1	0	0	1	0
State:	EVEN	ODD	ODD	EVEN	EVEN	EVEN	ODD	ODD

(7.3)

Indeed the final state is the ODD state. Observe in (7.3) that also the machine's state gives the parity of the number of 1's for all intermediate input strings. For example, the input 101 puts the machine into the EVEN state, corresponding to there being an even number of 1's in the string 101.

What happens if we start the binary counter in the ODD state? (7.4) gives the states for the input string 0011.

Input:	–	0	0	1	1
State:	ODD	ODD	ODD	EVEN	ODD

(7.4)

In (7.4), the final state is ODD, which is incorrect for the input string 0011. △

Example 7.5

We describe a finite-state machine that produces its previous input. Such a machine is called a **flip-flop**. Flip-flops are frequently used as memory devices.

Let I, the set of inputs, be just $I = \{0, 1\}$. We shall need two states: A, corresponding to storing 0, and B, corresponding to storing 1. Table 7.6 gives the needed state table.

Table 7.6 A flip-flop

Current state	Next state function Input 0	1	Output function Input 0	1
A	A	B	0	0
B	A	B	1	1

Let us see what happens to the flip-flop of Table 7.6 under the input string 11001110. We shall not interpret the initial output. We arbitrarily start the flip-flop in state A.

$$\begin{array}{llllllllll} \text{Input:} & - & 1 & 1 & 0 & 0 & 1 & 1 & 1 & 0 \\ \text{State:} & A & B & B & A & A & B & B & B & A \\ \text{Output:} & - & 0 & 1 & 1 & 0 & 0 & 1 & 1 & 1 \end{array} \tag{7.5}$$

Indeed, except for the disregarded initial output bit, the output string is the same as the input string. Since the output is, by construction, one time unit behind the input, some new input would be needed to yield the last input bit in (7.5) as output. △

In Definitions 7.1 and 7.2, we explicitly list the states S, the inputs I, and the outputs Y. But the important parts of a machine are the next-state function ν and (if the machine is a full finite-state machine) the output function β. The functions ν and β will usually be given by state tables such as Tables 7.2–7.6 above. The sets S and I are given by the row-labels and column-labels of the tables. The set Y may essentially be given by the set of *entries* in the output table. For example, in Table 7.6, $Y=\{0,1\}$.

Exercises 7.1

1. Write out a table that gives the input/output relationship for a combinatorial network that accepts a digit d from 0 through 9 and that produces the digit 9-d.
2. Write out a table that gives the input/output relationship for a combinatorial network that multiplies two 2-bit binary numbers. The network should produce a 4-bit binary output. Space saver: Just fill in the table:

	00	01	10	11
00				
01				
10				
11				

3. Continue Figure 7.5 through Time $= 4\frac{1}{2}$.
4. As in Figure 7.7, replace the initial parity check module in Figure 6.11(ii) by two parity check modules and one initial input of 0.
   a. As in Figure 7.4, draw a sequential network version of the new switching circuit for Figure 6.11(ii).
   b. Give the state table for the corresponding finite semiautomaton.
5. Give the next-state function for a finite semiautomaton with input set $I = \{0,1,2\}$, state set $S = \{\text{EVEN, ODD}\}$ and such that, after receiving an input string of 0's, 1's, and 2's, the machine is in state EVEN or ODD according to whether the number of 0's is even or odd. Which is the starting state?
6. Give the next-state function for a finite semiautomaton with input set $I = \{0,1\}$, state set $S = \{s_0, s_1, s_2\}$ and such that, after receiving an input string, the machine is in the state determined as follows: Let n be the number of 1's in the input string. Let r be the remainder of n after division by 3. The machine is in state s_0, s_1, or s_2 according to whether r equals 0, 1, or 2. Which is the starting state?
7. Here is a variation on the flip-flop of Example 7.5: Give the next-state function for a finite semiautomaton with states A and B, inputs e, 0, and 1, and such that the input e preserves the current state, the input 0 sends the machine to state A, and the input 1 sends the machine to state B.
8. Here is another variation on the flip-flop: Give next-state and output functions for a finite-state machine that accepts 0's and 1's as inputs and that produces as output the opposite of the previous input.
9. a. Describe a finite-state machine with $I = \{0,1\}$ and such that the output equals the input.
   b. How many states are needed for this machine?

Figure 7.7

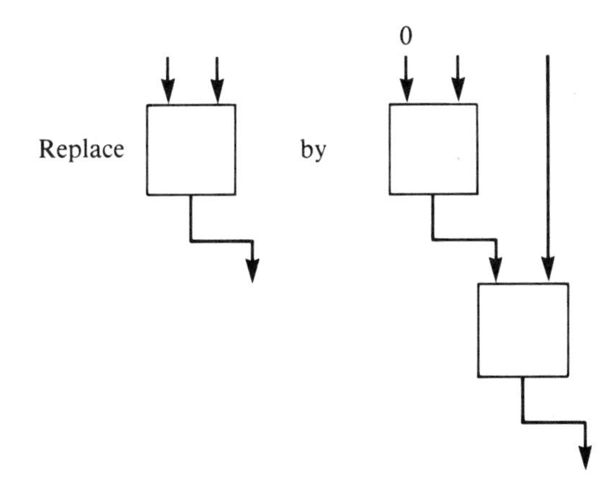

c. Can the i/o relationship of part (a) be achieved by a combinatorial network?

10. Explain why the i/o relationship for strings, as determined by the "Output Function" half of Table 7.4, cannot be achieved by a combinatorial network.

7.2 State Diagrams

A machine is completely determined by its state table. It is often clearer, however, to present the information in the state table in the form of a labeled, directed multigraph called the **state diagram** of the machine. The state diagram contains all of the information in the state table and so also completely determines the machine. We shall also sometimes call the state diagram the **graph** of the machine (even though, strictly speaking, it is a multigraph).

Given a machine M, we construct its state diagram as follows. The vertices of the graph correspond to the states. For each state s and input i, there is a directed edge from s to $\nu(s,i)$; this edge is labeled by i to show the input. In the case of a full finite-state machine, this edge receives the additional label $\beta(s,i)$, to indicate the output. Observe that each input i in I yields edges starting at *each* of the vertices (states) of the diagram.

Example 7.6

We construct the state diagram for the binary counter of Example 7.4. There are two vertices to the graph, EVEN and ODD. The input 0 directs a vertex to itself. The input 1 directs a vertex to the other vertex. Figure 7.8 gives the state diagram. △

Example 7.7

Let us give the state diagram for the binary adder of Example 7.3. The binary adder has two states, 0 and 1. So its graph will have two vertices, labeled 0 and 1. Since the binary adder is a finite-state machine, each edge is labeled by both an input and an output. There are four inputs, so each vertex is the beginning of four edges. Table 7.4 then yields Figure 7.9, the state diagram of the binary adder. △

Example 7.8

The flip-flop of Example 7.5 has the state diagram that is given in Figure 7.10. △

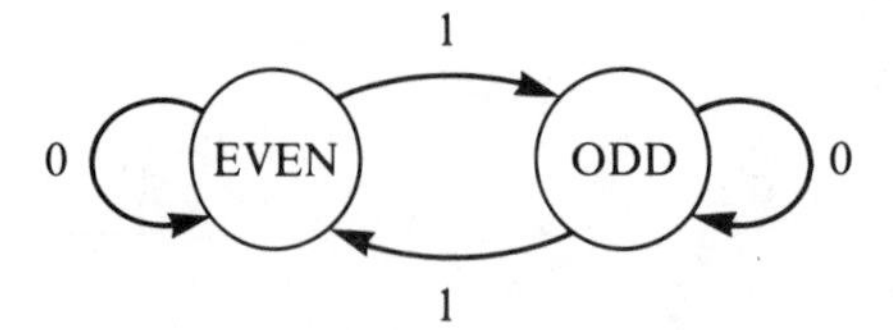

Figure 7.8 State diagram for a binary counter

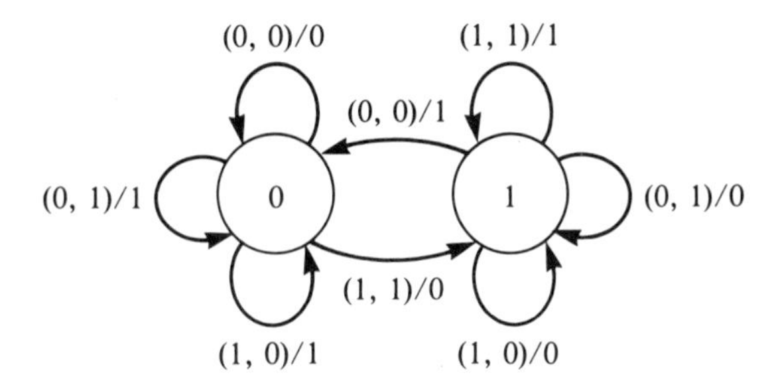

Figure 7.9 State diagram for the binary adder

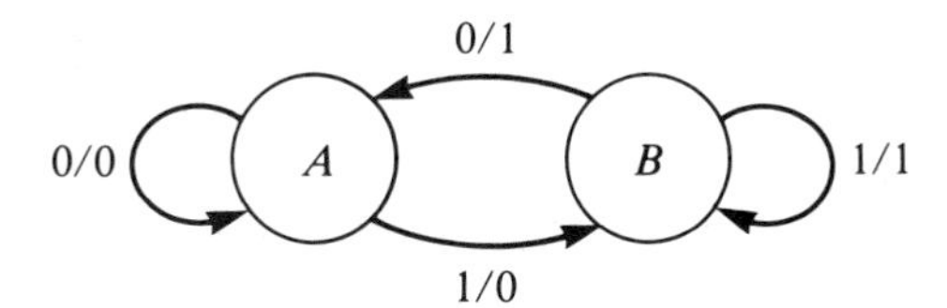

Figure 7.10 State diagram for a flip-flop

Example 7.9

We now describe a machine that multiplies binary numbers by three. The output will also be in binary. We shall first describe the machine by its state diagram. Then we shall give its state table.

In binary, we write three as 11. So to multiply by three, we must add the current input to the previous input. For example, thirteen times three equals thirty-nine is computed, in binary, as

$$\begin{array}{rrrrrrl} & & 1 & 1 & 0 & 1 & \\ & & & \times & 1 & 1 & \\ \hline & & 1 & 1 & 0 & 1 & \leftarrow \text{Current input} \\ & 1 & 1 & 0 & 1 & & \leftarrow \text{Previous input} \\ \hline 1 & 0 & 0 & 1 & 1 & 1 & \end{array} \tag{7.6}$$

We build a machine that "remembers" the previous input and also the value of the carry in the sum. So each state of the machine is a pair of bits, where the first bit is the previous input and the second bit is the value of the carry. This yields the machine of Figure 7.11.

(0,0) is the correct starting state for the machine of Figure 7.11. Let us check that the machine correctly multiplies thirteen by three, as in (7.6) above. The lower-order bits for thirteen are accepted first. So the sequence of inputs is 1, 0, 1, 1,

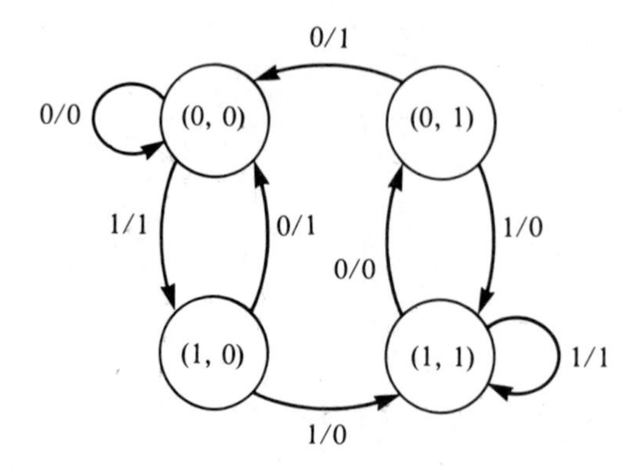

Figure 7.11 A machine to multiply by three

Current state	Input	Output	Next state
(0,0)	1	1	(1,0)
(1,0)	0	1	(0,0)
(0,0)	1	1	(1,0)
(1,0)	1	0	(1,1)

(7.7)

In order to complete the calculation, we must append two 0's to the input string. This amounts to writing thirteen with two high-order 0's: 001101. (7.7) then continues as follows:

Current state	Input	Output	Next state
(1,1)	0	0	(0,1)
(0,1)	0	1	(0,0)

In reverse order, the outputs are 100111. This is the binary representation for thirty-nine, as needed.

Table 7.7 gives the next-state and output functions for the machine of Figure 7.11. △

Example 7.10

We now describe a machine with input set $I = \{a,b,c\}$. After accepting an input string, the machine should tell whether or not the string terminated

Table 7.7 State table for Figure 7.11

Current state	Next-state function Input 0	1	Output function Input 0	1
(0,0)	(0,0)	(1,0)	0	1
(0,1)	(0,0)	(1,1)	1	0
(1,0)	(0,0)	(1,1)	1	0
(1,1)	(0,1)	(1,1)	0	1

with *aba*. Thus the output set Y will be $Y = \{\text{YES, NO}\}$. For example, the input string *cabacaba* should produce a (final) output of YES. The input string *accabba* should produce a (final) output of NO. This type of machine, for more general input sets of course, is often simulated in compilers and text editors.

Figure 7.12 gives the desired machine. In Figure 7.12 we have simplified the representation of the state diagram by combining edges that join the same vertices and that have the same output. The machine of Figure 7.12, started in state 0, works as follows: State 0 indicates no progress towards the string *aba*. State 1 indicates achievement of the *a* towards *aba*. State 2 means the string *ab* towards *aba*. State 3 means that the input string terminates in *aba*. From state 0, only an input of *a* will move the machine to state 1; other inputs mean no progress towards *aba* and so retain the machine in state 0. From state 1, only an input of *b* represents progress towards *aba*, moving the machine to state 2. An input of *a* retains state 1, while an input of *c* means that the string must start all over again towards *aba*. The remaining cases of states 2 and 3 are treated similarly.

(7.8) illustrates how the machine of Figure 7.12 handles the input string *abcababa*.

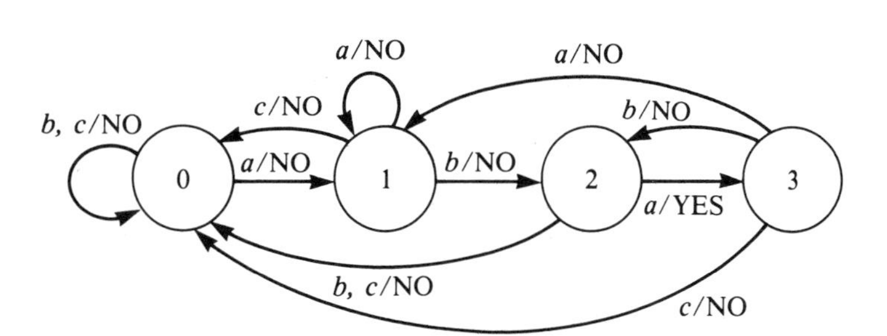

Figure 7.12 A machine to recognize strings ending in *aba*

Current state	Input	Output	Next state
0	a	NO	1
1	b	NO	2
2	c	NO	0
0	a	NO	1
1	b	NO	2
2	a	YES	3
3	b	NO	2
2	a	YES	3

(7.8)

We observe that the intermediate output was YES after the input string *abcaba*. This is correct, since *abcaba* does end with *aba*.

The next-state and output functions for the machine of Figure 7.12 are given in Table 7.8. △

Table 7.8 Next-state and output functions for Figure 7.12

Current state	Next-state function Input			Output function Input		
	a	b	c	a	b	c
0	1	0	0	NO	NO	NO
1	1	2	0	NO	NO	NO
2	3	0	0	YES	NO	NO
3	1	2	0	NO	NO	NO

Exercises 7.2

1. Draw a state diagram for each of the following finite-state machines.

a.

Current state	Next-state function Input		Output function Input	
	0	1	0	1
A	B	C	a	a
B	B	B	a	b
C	C	A	b	a

b.

Current state	Next-state function Input 0	1	2	Output function Input 0	1	2
A	A	B	C	a	a	b
B	A	C	B	b	b	b
C	A	A	A	b	a	b

2. Draw a state diagram for each of the following finite semiautomata.

a.

Current state	Next-state function Input 0	1
A	A	B
B	C	A
C	D	C
D	B	C

b.

Current state	Next-state function Input 0	1
A	B	C
B	D	E
C	A	B
D	D	D
E	E	A

c.

Current state	Next-state function Input 0	1	2
A	A	B	C
B	A	D	C
C	A	C	C
D	A	A	C

d.

Current state	Next-state function Input 0	1	2
A	C	B	D
B	B	C	A
C	C	A	B
D	D	E	B
E	E	D	A

3. For each of the following state diagrams, write out the corresponding next-state functions and output functions.

a.

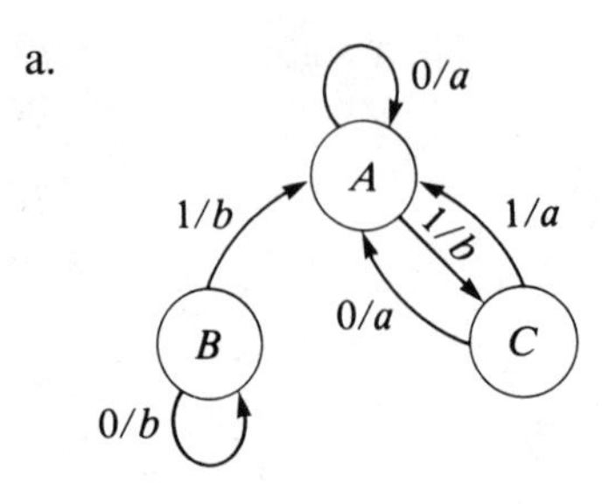

b.

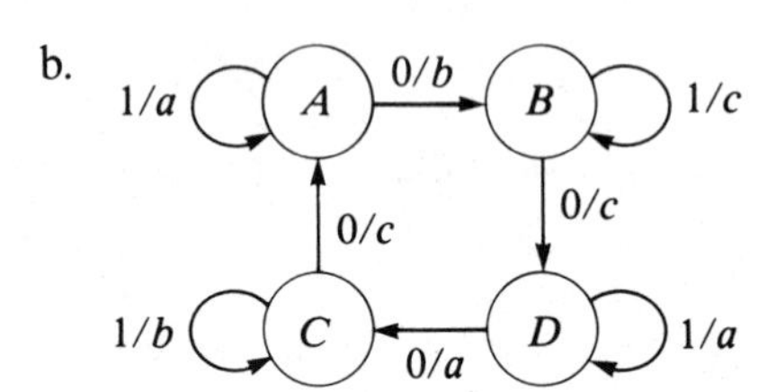

4. For each of the following state diagrams, write out the corresponding next-state functions.

a.

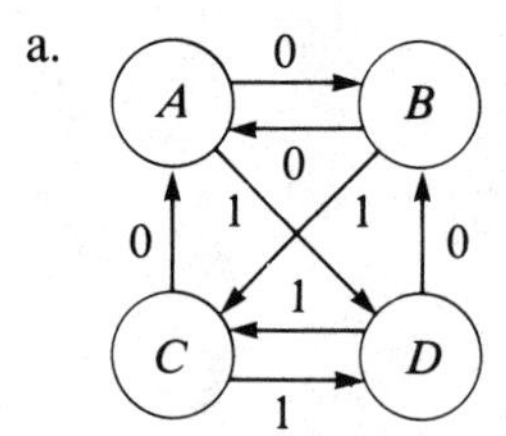

b.

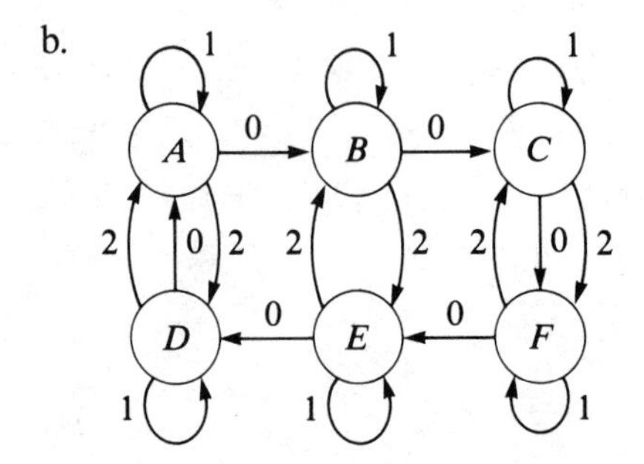

5. Consider a finite-state machine M that accepts strings of 0's and 1's and yields the remainder for the number of 1's in the string after division by four. M has four states: A, B, C, D; two inputs: 0, 1; and four outputs: 0, 1, 2, 3.

a. Write out the state table for such an M.
b. Draw the state diagram for M.
c. Which is the correct starting state for M?
d. Which finite semiautomaton M' could essentially perform the same calculation as does M?

6. Draw the state diagram of a finite-state machine M that has an input set $I = \{a,b,c\}$ and that recognizes input strings that begin with a and that also end with c. Give the correct starting state.
7. Construct a table similar to (7.7) that shows how the machine of Figure 7.11 multiplies six by three. Be sure to append any needed high-order 0's.
8. What calculation does the machine of Figure 7.11 perform when it starts in state (1,0)? In state (1,1)?
9. Draw the state diagram for a finite semiautomaton M with states: EQUAL, FIRST, and SECOND. The input set I is $I = \{(0,0), (1,0), (0,1), (1,1)\}$. Think of each input string as a pair of binary numbers, units places first. After accepting the last input, M should be in state EQUAL if the two numbers are equal, in state FIRST if the first number if larger, and in state SECOND if the second number is larger. Which is the starting state?

7.3 Limitations of Finite Machines

In the previous sections, we worked many examples of finite-state machines. For ease of understanding, these were machines with rather few states, which performed rather simple calculations. Machines with many states, such as real digital computers, can certainly perform very complex calculations. But we shall see in this section that *finite* machines cannot do all reasonable computations, such as, for example, the multiplication of arbitrarily large numbers. Not surprisingly, infinite machines can do all computations.

Definition 7.3

Let M be a finite-state machine. Start M in some state, call it s. Let $i_1 i_2 i_3 \ldots i_k$ be some input string for M. Let o_k be the final output produced by M after accepting $i_1 i_2 i_3 \ldots i_k$. The function β_s, which maps $i_1 i_2 i_3 \ldots i_k$ to o_k, is a **behavior**. We write $\beta_s(i_1 i_2 \ldots i_k) = o_k$. ○

Recall the output function $\beta : S \times I \to Y$ of Definition 7.1(v). If s is a state and i is an (single) input, then $\beta_s(i) = \beta(s,i)$.

Example 7.11

Let M be the machine of Figure 7.12. Then β_0 is YES or NO according to whether the input string does or does not terminate with *aba*. It is easy to check that β_1 is YES for those input strings that terminate with *aba* and also for the input string *ba*. △

Example 7.12

Let M be the binary adder of Figure 7.9. Then $\beta_0(i_1 i_2 \dots i_k)$ gives the kth place of the binary sum of the two numbers represented by $i_1 i_2 \dots i_k$. To get the complete binary sum, we look at

$$\beta_0(i_1),\quad \beta_0(i_1 i_2),\quad \dots,\quad \beta_0(i_1 i_2 \dots i_k),\quad \beta_0(i_1 i_2 \dots i_k(0,0))$$

We shall usually not be so formal and simply say that β_0 essentially gives the sum of the binary numbers that are the input string. Then β_1 essentially gives 1 plus the sum of the two binary numbers. △

Recall that we may think of the output of a semiautomaton as its (final) state. So Definition 7.3 also applies to finite semiautomata.

Example 7.13

Let M be the binary counter of Figure 7.9. Then β_{EVEN} is EVEN or ODD according to whether the number of 1's in the input string is even or odd. △

Example 7.14

What must a machine look like that can multiply, units place first, any two binary numbers? Here we have specified a behavior of the machine.

Consider the calculation $2^{10} \cdot 2^{10} = 2^{20}$, which we wish the machine to perform. 2^{10} is written with eleven bits. So, initially the machine must accept eleven pairs of bits, units places first. So far, the machine must produce eleven 0's as output. To complete the correct output, the machine must produce nine more 0's and then a 1 as output. To get an output from the machine, we must give it an input. This is no problem: we just give the machine ten high-order 0's. So the multiplication should look like

$$\begin{array}{r} 000\ 000\ 000\ 010\ 000\ 000\ 000 \\ \times\ \ 000\ 000\ 000\ 010\ 000\ 000\ 000 \\ \hline 100\ 000\ 000\ 000\ 000\ 000\ 000 \end{array} \tag{7.9}$$

While receiving the ten high-order 0's, the machine must "remember" to produce first nine 0's and then a 1.

More generally, in multiplying $2^n \cdot 2^n = 2^{2n}$, we shall have to input n high-order 0's. A machine that multiplies will have to "remember" the answer during this time. But n can be arbitrarily large. So the machine must be capable of remembering an arbitrarily large amount of information. Informally at least, this should not be possible with only a finite number of states. So finite machines cannot multiply arbitrary pairs of binary numbers. △

We shall now give an argument about the limitations of finite machines that is both more rigorous and more general than the argument of Example 7.14.

Theorem 7.1

Let the finite semiautomaton M have n states. Suppose that an input string terminates in n identical inputs. Then the last state of the machine M duplicates a state that the machine attained before one of these last n identical inputs.

Example 7.15

Before proving Theorem 7.1, we shall illustrate its statement. Let M be the machine given by the next-state function of Table 7.9. M has five states. Start M in state C and let the input string be 011111. Then M has successive states as follows:

$$\begin{array}{llllllll} \text{Inputs:} & & 0 & 1 & 1 & 1 & 1 & 1 \\ \text{States:} & C & B & \underline{C} & D & A & B & \underline{C} \end{array} \tag{7.10}$$

The final state C is underlined in (7.10). Also underlined in (7.10) is the previous occurrence of state C, as specified by Theorem 7.1. Observe that the initial state C, since it did not occur before one of the five final inputs of 1, is not a candidate in Theorem 7.1 for the duplication of the final state. △

Proof of Theorem 7.1

Let i denote each of the last n identical inputs. Let s_0 be the state of M before the first of the last n inputs. Let s_1 be the next state. Let s_n be the state of M after the nth input of i; see (7.11).

$$\begin{array}{lllllllllll} \text{Inputs:} & & i & i & i \ldots i & i & i \ldots i & i & i \ldots i \\ \text{States:} & s_0 & s_1 & s_2 & \cdots\ \underline{s_p} & s_{p+1} & \cdots\ \underline{s_q} & s_{q+1} & \cdots\ s_n \end{array} \tag{7.11}$$

Table 7.9 A state machine

Current state	Next-state function Input 0	1
A	C	B
B	C	C
C	B	D
D	E	A
E	E	E

Since M is given to have only n states, there must be some duplication among the $n+1$ states $s_0, s_1, s_2, \ldots, s_n$ of (7.11). As underlined in (7.11), suppose that s_p and s_q are duplicate states. We may take $q > p$. To show Theorem 7.1, we must show that q can be chosen to equal n.

The next state of a machine is given by the next-state function, which depends only on the current state and the current input. Look at (7.11). When M is in state s_p, the next input is i. Also, when M is in state s_q, the next input is i. By choice, s_p and s_q are the same state. So the next states are also the same. That is, s_{p+1} and s_{q+1} are the same state. Repeating the argument, we see that s_{p+2} and s_{q+2} are similarly the same state. We also see that $n-q$ repetitions of the argument show that s_{p+n-q} is the same as s_n. ◇

Corollary 7.2

Let M be a finite-state machine with n states. Then M cannot multiply 2^{n+1} by 2^{n+1}.

Proof of Corollary 7.2

As in (7.9), in order to allow for all $2n+3$ output bits, we must append $n+1$ high-order 0's (or some other symbol) to the initial input string of $(2^{n+1}, 2^{n+1})$. The needed output for these $n+1$ high-order 0's is first n 0's and then a 1. Look at the first n high-order 0's. Apply Theorem 7.1 to the finite semiautomaton given by the next-state function for M. Then M's state after the nth high-order 0 duplicates a state achieved before one of these first n high-order 0's; call this state s'. Since *all* of the first n high-order 0's result in an output of 0, $\beta(s',(0,0)) = 0$. But now let us look at the output for the last, $(n+1)$st, high-order 0. The state of the machine is s'. The input is (0,0). We have just seen that $\beta(s',(0,0)) = 0$. But in order to give the correct product, the output must be 1. So M fails to do the multiplication. ◇

Corollary 7.3

No finite-state machine can recognize all strings of 0's and 1's that have an equal number of 0's and 1's.

Intuitive Proof of Corollary 7.3

Any machine M that tries to recognize the indicated strings would have to keep track of the difference between the number of 0's and the number of 1's in an input string. Since this difference may be arbitrarily large, no finite machine suffices. ◇

Proof of Corollary 7.3

Suppose that a machine M has n states. Then we shall show that M cannot recognize the input string 00...0011...11, where there are $n+1$ 0's and $n+1$ 1's. Until receiving the very last 1, the machine must produce NO as its output, since there are more 0's than 1's in the input string. Before accepting the last, $(n+1)$st 1, there are n inputs of 1. By Theorem 7.1, the state of the machine before accepting the last 1 duplicates a state of the machine before accepting one of the first n 1's. The output in this case was NO. So also the output for the last 1 must be NO. Thus M fails to recognize the input string of $n+1$ 0's and $n+1$ 1's. ◇

Definitions 7.1 and 7.3 may easily be modified so as to allow an infinite number of states. Then we have Theorem 7.4.

Theorem 7.4

Any behavior may be realized by a possibly infinite-state machine. ◇

We shall not formally prove Theorem 7.4. Instead, in the next example, we shall give a construction for a particular behavior that may be readily modified so as to apply to any behavior.

Example 7.16

We construct a machine M that recognizes all strings of 0's and 1's that have an equal number of 0's and 1's. By Corollary 7.3, we shall need an infinite machine. As we shall see in the next section, our constructed machine will not be as efficient as possible. Rather, it will illustrate the general technique.

The input set is $I=\{0,1\}$. The output set is $Y=\{\text{YES, NO}\}$. The (infinite) state set S consists of all finite strings in 0 and 1 and also the state **e**, which may be thought as the empty string. **e** will be the starting state. Figure 7.13 gives the state diagram for the semiautomaton part of the machine. Observe in Figure 7.13 that an input simply moves the semiautomaton to the state given by appending the input to the current state. Formally, $\nu(i_1 i_2 \dots i_k, i) = i_1 i_2 \dots i_k i$.

In Figure 7.13, different input strings always lead to different states. So we are free to specify any output that we desire for any input string. To get our specified behavior, we just give outputs as in Figure 7.14. To save space in Figure 7.14, we use N for NO and Y for YES. △

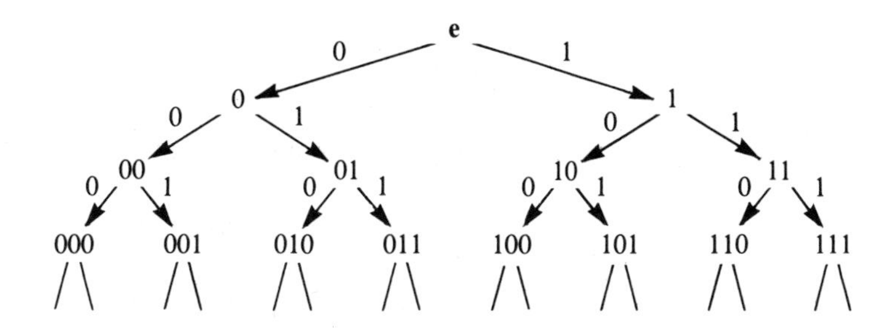

Figure 7.13 State diagram for an infinite semi-automaton

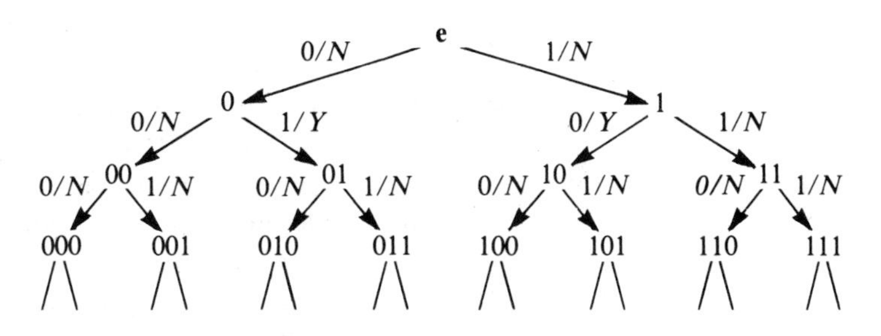

Figure 7.14 State diagram for an infinite-state machine

Exercises 7.3

1. Consider the finite-state machine given by the following state table.

Current state	Next-state function, Input 0	Next-state function, Input 1	Output function, Input 0	Output function, Input 1
A	B	C	b	c
B	A	C	a	a
C	B	A	b	a

a. Compute $\beta_A(0)$, $\beta_A(1)$, $\beta_A(00)$, $\beta_A(01)$, $\beta_A(10)$, and $\beta_A(11)$.
b. Compute $\beta_B(0)$, $\beta_B(1)$, $\beta_B(00)$, $\beta_B(01)$, $\beta_B(10)$, and $\beta_B(11)$.

2. Describe the behaviors β_2 and β_3 for the machine of Figure 7.12.
3. Describe $\beta_{(0,1)}$, $\beta_{(1,0)}$, and $\beta_{(1,1)}$ for the machine of Figure 7.11.
4. Consider a physical machine with a memory of $128\ \mathrm{K} = 128 \times 2^{10}$ words. Each word consists of 16 bits.
   a. Considering the memory alone, how many states are there for the machine?
   b. How serious is the limitation of Corollary 7.2?
5. a. Construct a finite-state machine that multiplies an arbitrary binary number by four. The number is to be accepted units place first.
   b. What is another interpretation for the behavior of the machine of part (a)?
6. Construct a finite-state machine that multiplies an arbitrary binary number by five.
7. a. Without fully constructing a machine, indicate roughly why for any given n there exists a finite-state machine M such that M multiplies binary numbers by n.
   b. Why does the result of part (a) not contradict Corollary 7.2?
8. A **palindrome** is a string that reads the same from right to left as from left to right. For example, neglecting capitalization, the following palindrome is traditionally attributed to Napoleon: "Able was I ere I saw Elba." More prosaically, *abba* and *aabaa* are palindromes, while *aabb* is not a palindrome. Show that no finite-state machine with input set $I = \{a,b\}$ can recognize all input strings that are palindromes.
9. Show that no machine, not even an infinite one, can accept two binary numbers, high-order bits first, and produce the high-order bits of the sum before the low-order bits of the summands are accepted.

   Hint: Are the high-order bits of the sum determined by the high-order bits of the summands?
10. A machine accepts two binary numbers, high-order bits first, followed by sufficiently many symbols for blanks to allow for the sum as output, low-order bit first. Show that no finite-state machine can exhibit this behavior.
11. Suppose that a finite-state machine accepts an infinite input string, all of the same input. Explain why the output string is eventually periodic.
12. Continue Figure 7.14 through all states that are given with four bits.
13. Give outputs for Figure 7.13 that start the behavior: $\beta_{\mathbf{e}}$ is YES for inputs strings that are prime numbers (units bit first) and $\beta_{\mathbf{e}}$ is NO otherwise.

7.4 State Reduction

From the user's viewpoint, the most important aspect of a machine is the output strings that it can produce from input strings, that is, its behaviors for the various starting states. It is therefore natural to ask: Given a finite-state machine M, how can we find, if possible, a second finite-state machine M' such that M' has fewer states than has M, but such that M' still exhibits the same behaviors as does M? In this section we give an algorithm to find the M' as above with the fewest possible states; this M' is called M_R, the **reduced machine** for M. The algorithm generalizes so as to yield an M_R also for an infinite machine M. In the previous section, we saw how to construct an infinite machine M with any specified behavior. This behavior may be realized by a finite machine if and only if M_R, for the infinite M, is finite. For both finite and infinite machines, M_R also serves as a normal form.

Example 7.17

Recall the machine M of Example 7.9, which multiplies binary numbers by three. In (7.12) we rewrite the multiplication in (7.6) to include the carries. The purpose of the memory (or states) in M is to store the first and third lines in the sum that is between the braces in (7.12), that is, to store the carry and the previous input. But the output depends only on the *sum* of the carry and the previous input, and not on their separate values.

$$
\begin{array}{rcccccc}
 & 0 & 0 & 1 & 1 & 0 & 1 \\
 & & & \times & & 1 & 1 \\
\hline
\text{Carry} & (1 & 1 & 0 & 0 & 0 & -) \\
 & 0 & 0 & 1 & 1 & 0 & 1 \\
 & 0 & 1 & 1 & 0 & 1 & \\
\hline
 & 1 & 0 & 0 & 1 & 1 & 1
\end{array}
\tag{7.12}
$$

This suggests that we may simplify the machine M by storing just the sum of the two bit entries in each state. Recall that M has the states (0,0), (1,0), (0,1), (1,1). The sums are respectively 0, 1, 1, 2. So M' should have the three states 0, 1, 2. Figure 7.15 (below and on p. 326) gives the state diagram and the state table for M'. The correct starting state for M' is state 0.

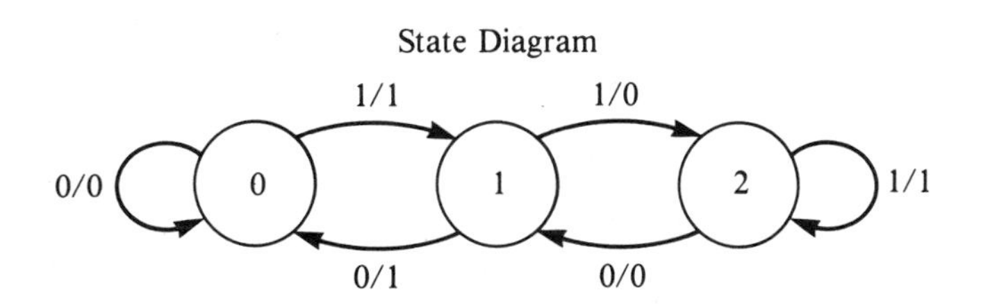

Figure 7.15 A machine M' to multiply by three

Figure 7.15 *Continued*

Current state	Next-state function Input 0	Next-state function Input 1	Output function Input 0	Output function Input 1
0	0	1	0	1
1	0	2	1	0
2	1	2	0	1

Let us check M' by doing the multiplication (7.12). The units place is accepted first. So the input string is 101100:

Current state	Input	Output	Next state
0	1	1	1
1	0	1	0
0	1	1	1
1	1	0	2
2	0	0	1
1	0	1	0

△

In Example 7.17, we may think of each state in M as corresponding to the state in M' that is its sum. That is, (0,0) corresponds to 0. (0,1) and (1,0) both correspond to 1. (1,1) corresponds to 2. So (0,1) and (1,0) were combined to give the new machine M', which performed the function of the old machine M. This process of combining states is called **state reduction**. But how might we do this in general?

Definition 7.4 Let s and s' be two states of a finite state machine M. s is **state-equivalent** to s' if $\beta_s = \beta_{s'}$. ○

Definition 7.4 does give an equivalence relation in the sense of Chapter 3, Section 3.1. We shall sometimes shorten "state-equivalent" to "equivalent."

Example 7.18 Table 7.10 reproduces Table 7.7, which describes the machine M of Examples 7.9 and 7.17. Let us see which states of M are equivalent in the sense of Definition 7.4.

Table 7.10 Next-state and output functions for M

Current state	Next-state function Input 0	Next-state function Input 1	Output function Input 0	Output function Input 1
(0,0)	(0,0)	(1,0)	0	1
(0,1)	(0,0)	(1,1)	1	0
(1,0)	(0,0)	(1,1)	1	0
(1,1)	(0,1)	(1,1)	0	1

From the output function table, we see immediately that equal inputs (both 0 or both 1) to the states (0,1) and (1,0) yield equal outputs (1 and 0 respectively). Moreover, an input of 0 gives a next-state of (0,0) regardless of whether the machine M is in state (0,1) or (1,0). Also, an input of 1 gives a next-state of (1,1) regardless of whether M is in state (0,1) or (1,0). So all input strings will yield the same output starting from either (0,1) or from (1,0). So (0,1) and (1,0) are state-equivalent as in Definition 7.4.

We claim that no other distinct states in Table 7.10 besides (0,1) and (1,0) are equivalent. To show that two states are not equivalent, we must give input strings for which their behaviors differ. Thus, directly from the output function table of Table 7.10, we see that an input of 0 (or an input of 1) gives different outputs from the starting states (0,0) and (1,1) than from the starting states (0,1) and (1,0). So neither state (0,0) nor state (1,1) can be equivalent to state (0,1) or to state (1,0). So the interesting question is whether or not state (0,0) is equivalent to state (1,1). But $\beta_{(0,0)}(00)=0$; that is, an input string of 00, yields a final output of 0 from state (0,0), while $\beta_{(1,1)}(00)=1$. So (0,0) and (1,1) are inequivalent states. △

Theorem 7.5

Let M be a finite-state machine as in Definition 7.1. For s a state of M, let $[s]$ denote the state-equivalence class of s. Let M_R, the **reduced machine** for M, be given as follows:

(i) The states S_R for M_R are the equivalence classes $[s]$ of the states S of M.
(ii) The inputs I_R for M_R are the same as the inputs I for M.
(iii) The next-state function ν_R for M_R is given by $\nu_R([s],i)=[\nu(s,i)]$, that is, the equivalence class of $\nu(s,i)$.
(iv) The outputs Y_R for M_R are the same as the outputs Y for M.
(v) The output function β_R for M_R is given by $\beta_R([s],i)=\beta(s,i)$.

Then M_R is a well-defined finite-state machine. Moreover, for all states s

for M, the behavior of M starting from s equals the behavior of M_R starting at $[s]$.

Example 7.19

Before proving Theorem 7.5, we illustrate the construction of M_R. We continue with M of Examples 7.9, 7.17, and 7.18. From Example 7.18, there are three equivalence classes as follows:

$$\begin{aligned}
&[(0,0)] = \{(0,0)\} \\
&[(0,1)] = [(1,0)] = \{(0,1),(1,0)\} \\
&[(1,1)] = \{(1,1)\}
\end{aligned} \tag{7.13}$$

So M_R has the three states in (7.13). To find the next-state function and output function tables for M_R, list together the equivalent states in the next-state and output function tables for M; this is done in Table 7.11.

Table 7.11 State reduction for Table 7.10

Current state	Next-state function Input 0	Next-state function Input 1	Output function Input 0	Output function Input 1
(0,0)	(0,0)	(1,0)	0	1
(0,1)	(0,0)	(1,1)	1	0
(1,0)	(0,0)	(1,1)	1	0
(1,1)	(0,1)	(1,1)	0	1

Now rename Table 7.11 by mapping each state of M into its equivalence class from (7.13). Namely,

$$\begin{aligned}
&(0,0) \to [(0,0)] \\
&(0,1) \to [(0,1)] \qquad (1,0) \to [(0,1)] \\
&(1,1) \to [(1,1)]
\end{aligned}$$

This gives Table 7.12. Observe that all identically labeled entries in Table 7.12 are the same. Eliminating duplicate entries in Table 7.12 gives Table 7.13, the description of M_R.

Observe that renaming the states of M_R via

$$[(0,0)] \to 0 \qquad [(0,1)] \to 1 \qquad [(1,1)] \to 2$$

converts Table 7.13 into the table in Figure 7.15 on p. 326. △

Table 7.12 Renaming of Table 7.11

Current state	Next-state function Input 0	1	Output function Input 0	1
[(0,0)]	[(0,0)]	[(0,1)]	0	1
[(0,1)]	[(0,0)]	[(1,1)]	1	0
[(0,1)]	[(0,0)]	[(1,1)]	1	0
[(1,1)]	[(0,1)]	[(1,1)]	0	1

Table 7.13 M_R for Table 7.10

Current state	Next-state function Input 0	1	Output function Input 0	1
[(0,0)]	[(0,0)]	[(0,1)]	0	1
[(0,1)]	[(0,0)]	[(1,1)]	1	0
[(1,1)]	[(0,1)]	[(1,1)]	0	1

Proof of Theorem 7.5

To show that M_R is well-defined, we must show that (iii) and (v) give the same definition regardless of which element s or s' we choose in the equivalence class $[s]$. So suppose that s is state-equivalent to s', as in Definition 7.4.

For (iii), we need to show that $\nu(s,i)$ is equivalent to $\nu(s',i)$. So we let $i_1 i_2 \ldots i_k$ be an input string for M. The state $\nu(s,i)$ is the next-state from s for an input of i. So the output from $\nu(s,i)$ via $i_1 i_2 \ldots i_k$ is the same as the output from s via $ii_1 i_2 \ldots i_k$. Similarly, output from $\nu(s',i)$ via $i_1 i_2 \ldots i_k$ is the same as output from s' via $ii_1 i_2 \ldots i_k$. But, since s and s' are state-equivalent,

$$\beta_s(ii_1 i_2 \ldots i_k) = \beta_{s'}(ii_1 i_2 \ldots i_k)$$

Hence also $\nu(s,i)$ and $\nu(s',i)$ are state-equivalent.

For (v), we need to show that $\beta(s,i) = \beta(s',i)$. Recall that $\beta(s,i) = \beta_s(i)$ and $\beta(s',i) = \beta_{s'}(i)$. $\beta_s(i) = \beta_{s'}(i)$ since s and s' are state-equivalent.

We now show that for s a state of M, $\beta_s = \beta_{R,[s]}$. We start M at state s, start M_R at state $[s]$, and consider the input string $i_1 i_2 \ldots i_k$. We let $s_1, s_2, \ldots, s_{k-1}, s_k$ be the successive states for M. By Theorem 7.5(iii), the successive states for M_R are $[s_1], [s_2], \ldots, [s_{k-1}], [s_k]$. By the definition of a behavior, $\beta_s(i_1 i_2 \ldots i_k) = \beta(s_{k-1}, i_k)$. Also, $\beta_{R,[s]}(i_1 i_2 \ldots i_k) = \beta_R([s_{k-1}], i_k)$. But $\beta_R([s_{k-1}], i_k) = \beta(s_{k-1}, i_k)$ by Theorem 7.5(v). So M and M_R have the same behaviors. ◇

We now give a practical procedure to determine M_R for a finite-state machine M. Proposition 7.7, which follows later, ensures that this procedure is a finite algorithm.

Definition 7.5

The **length** k of an input string $i_1 i_2 \ldots i_{k-1} i_k$ is the number of inputs in the string.

Let s and s' be states in the finite-state machine M. The states s and s' are ***k*-equivalent**, written $s \sim_k s'$, if β_s and $\beta_{s'}$ are equal for input strings of length at most k. ○

Example 7.20

Let us consider the machine M given in Table 7.14. M has been chosen to illustrate the general procedure of state reduction. Otherwise, there is no simple interpretation for the i/o relationships given by M.

Which states in M are 1-equivalent? From Definition 7.5, $s \sim_1 s'$ means that $\beta(s,i) = \beta(s',i)$ for all (single) inputs i. In terms of output function tables, $s \sim_1 s'$ thus means that the s-row equals the s'-row. So the 1-equivalence classes are given in (7.14).

Output row	*1-equivalence class*		
$x \quad x$	$\{A,C,D,E\}$	$=[A]_1$	
$x \quad y$	$\{B\}$	$=[B]_1$	**(7.14)**
$y \quad x$	$\{F,G\}$	$=[F]_1$	

Table 7.14 The finite-state machine M

Current state	Next-state function Input 0	Next-state function Input 1	Output function Input 0	Output function Input 1
A	F	A	x	x
B	C	D	x	y
C	G	C	x	x
D	G	E	x	x
E	F	B	x	x
F	F	B	y	x
G	G	B	y	x

Let us examine some possible 2-equivalences. D and B are not 2-equivalent since, from (7.14), D and B are not even 1-equivalent. D and E are not 2-equivalent, since $\beta_D(11) = x \neq \beta_E(11) = y$. Are D and C

2-equivalent? From (7.14), β_D and β_C agree on input strings of length 1. A straightforward check verifies that $\beta_D(00)=y=\beta_C(00)$, $\beta_D(01)=x=\beta_C(01)$, $\beta_D(10)=x=\beta_C(10)$, $\beta_D(11)=x=\beta_C(11)$. So $D\sim_2 C$. △

The proof of the following Proposition is left to the exercises.

Proposition 7.6

Let M be a finite-state machine. Let s and s' be states in M. Let k be an integer at least equal to 2. Then $s\sim_k s'$ if and only if

(i) $s\sim_{k-1}s'$, and
(ii) For all inputs i for M, $\nu(s,i)\sim_{k-1}\nu(s',i)$. □

Example 7.21

We use Proposition 7.6 to determine the k-equivalence classes for the M of Example 7.20 (and Table 7.14). We first find the 2-equivalence classes. From Proposition 7.6, all 2-equivalence classes may be found by partitioning the 1-equivalence classes (Proposition 7.6(i)) under the equivalence relation given by Proposition 7.6(ii). The 1-equivalence classes are given in (7.14). Take, for instance, $[A]_1=\{A,C,D,E\}$. The 1-equivalence classes of the next-states starting from in $[A]_1$ are given in (7.15). For example, $\nu(C,0)=G$ and $[\nu(C,0)]_1=[G]_1=[F]_1$.

	Next-state 0	Next-state 1		1-equivalence class 0	1-equivalence class 1
A	F	A	A	$[F]_1$	$[A]_1$
C	G	C	C	$[F]_1$	$[A]_1$
D	G	E	D	$[F]_1$	$[A]_1$
E	F	B	E	$[F]_1$	$[B]_1$

(7.15)

Then, from (7.15), A, C, and D are all 2-equivalent, since they are all 1-equivalent and equal inputs take them to 1-equivalent states. But A and E are not 2-equivalent, since the input 1 takes them to 1-inequivalent states. In all, Proposition 7.6 partitions $[A]_1$ into the 2-equivalence classes

$$\{A,C,D\}=[A]_2 \quad \text{and} \quad \{E\}=[E]_2 \qquad \textbf{(7.16)}$$

No further partition of the singleton $[B]_1$ is possible. So $[B]_1=[B]_2=\{B\}$.

We partition $[F]_1$ in a manner similar to that used in (7.15) as follows:

	Next-state 0	Next-state 1		1-equivalence class 0	1-equivalence class 1
F	F	B	F	$[F]_1$	$[B]_1$
G	G	B	G	$[F]_1$	$[B]_1$

So $F \sim_2 G$. In all, recalling (7.16), we have the following 2-equivalence classes:

$$\{A,C,D\} = [A]_2 \qquad \{E\} = [E]_2 \qquad \{B\} = [B]_2 \qquad \{F,G\} = [F]_2 \tag{7.17}$$

We now find the 3-equivalence classes. This computation is as above; we partition the 2-equivalence classes in (7.17), showing the calculation for $[A]_2 = \{A,C,D\}$:

	Next-state 0	Next-state 1		2-equivalence class 0	2-equivalence class 1
A	F	A	A	$[F]_2$	$[A]_2$
C	G	C	C	$[F]_2$	$[A]_2$
D	G	E	D	$[F]_2$	$[E]_2$

$$\{A,C\} = [A]_3, \{D\} = [D]_3$$

In all, we get the 3-equivalence classes of (7.18) as follows:

$$\begin{array}{lll} \{A,C\} = [A]_3 & \{D\} = [D]_3 & \{E\} = [E]_3 \\ \{B\} = [B]_3 & \{F,G\} = [F]_3 & \end{array} \tag{7.18}$$

An easy computation shows that all k-equivalence classes for $k \geq 4$ coincide with the 3-equivalence classes of (7.18). So (7.18) also gives the state-equivalence classes. These equivalence classes are then the states of M_R. The computation of the next-state and output functions for M_R is given in Table 7.15. △

Proposition 7.7

Let M be a finite-state machine. Suppose that the integer m is such that the m-equivalence classes coincide with the $(m+1)$-equivalence classes. Then m-equivalence is the same as state-equivalence.

Suppose that M has n states. Then $(n-1)$-equivalence is the same as state-equivalence.

Table 7.15 Reduced machine computation for Table 7.14

$\{A,C\}=[A]$ $\{D\}=[D]$ $\{E\}=[E]$ $\{B\}=[B]$ $\{F,G\}=[F]$

	M					Equivalence classes			
	Next-state function		Output function			Next-state function		Output function	
Current state	Input 0	Input 1	Input 0	Input 1	Current state	Input 0	Input 1	Input 0	Input 1
A	F	A	x	x	$[A]$	$[F]$	$[A]$	x	x
C	G	C	x	x	$[A]$	$[F]$	$[A]$	x	x
D	G	E	x	x	$[D]$	$[F]$	$[E]$	x	x
E	F	B	x	x	$[E]$	$[F]$	$[B]$	x	x
B	C	D	x	y	$[B]$	$[A]$	$[D]$	x	y
F	F	B	y	x	$[F]$	$[F]$	$[B]$	y	x
G	G	B	y	x	$[F]$	$[F]$	$[B]$	y	x

M_R

	Next-state function		Output function	
Current state	Input 0	Input 1	Input 0	Input 1
$[A]$	$[F]$	$[A]$	x	x
$[D]$	$[F]$	$[E]$	x	x
$[E]$	$[F]$	$[B]$	x	x
$[B]$	$[A]$	$[D]$	x	y
$[F]$	$[F]$	$[B]$	y	x

Proof of Proposition 7.7 Let s and s' be states of M. By Proposition 7.6, $s \sim_{m+2} s'$, if and only if

(i) $s \sim_{m+1} s'$, and
(ii) For all inputs i for M, $\nu(s,i) \sim_{m+1} \nu(s',i)$.

But $(m+1)$-equivalence is given to be the same as m-equivalence. So (i) and (ii) above may be replaced by (i)′ and (ii)′ below.

(i)′ $s \sim_m s'$, and
(ii)′ For all inputs i for M, $\nu(s,i) \sim_m \nu(s',i)$.

By Proposition 7.6, (i)′ and (ii)′ are the conditions for $(m+1)$-equivalence. So $(m+2)$-equivalence is the same as $(m+1)$-equivalence, which is given to be the same as m-equivalence.

Repeating the argument of the previous paragraph shows that also $(m+3)$-equivalence, $(m+4)$-equivalence, ... all coincide with m-equivalence. Since state-equivalence in Definition 7.4 means k-equivalence for all k, we have shown the first part of Proposition 7.7.

Now suppose that M has n states. We may compute the k-equivalence classes by partitioning the $(k-1)$-equivalence classes. We stop at m when the partition for $(m+1)$ is the same as the partition for m. So each needed partition must increase the number of equivalence classes. With n states, there can be at most n equivalence classes in any partition. So m may be at most $n-1$. Since m-equivalence coincides with state-equivalence and $m \leq n-1$, $(n-1)$-equivalence also coincides with state equivalence. □

Example 7.22

Theorem 7.5 says that M and M_R have the same behaviors. Let us illustrate this for Table 7.15. We start M in state G. Let 101001 be the input string. $[G]=[F]$ is the corresponding starting state for M_R. Here is what happens:

M				M_R			
Current state	Input	Output	Next state	Current state	Input	Output	Next state
G	1	x	B	$[F]$	1	x	$[B]$
B	0	x	C	$[B]$	0	x	$[A]$
C	1	x	C	$[A]$	1	x	$[A]$
C	0	x	G	$[A]$	0	x	$[F]$
G	0	y	G	$[F]$	0	y	$[F]$
G	1	x	B	$[F]$	1	x	$[B]$

Observe that indeed M_R produces the same output string as does M. △

Example 7.23

In Examples 7.20 and 7.21, we saw that states A and D were 2-equivalent, but not 3-equivalent. How may we find an input string of length 3 that distinguishes between β_A and β_D? The first input should take A and D to 2-inequivalent states; the second input should then take A and D to 1-inequivalent states. The 1-inequivalent states then have different outputs for a suitable input. The input string 111 suffices. Indeed $\beta_A(111)=x$ while $\beta_D(111)=y$. △

Example 7.24

Using Propositions 7.6 and 7.7, we compute M_R for the machine of Figure 7.12. Recall that, starting in state 0, this machine produces the output YES for input strings that end in *aba*. Its state table is given in Table 7.8, which is reproduced as Table 7.16.

Table 7.16 State table for Figure 7.12

Current state	Next-state function Input			Output function Input		
	a	*b*	*c*	*a*	*b*	*c*
0	1	0	0	NO	NO	NO
1	1	2	0	NO	NO	NO
2	3	0	0	YES	NO	NO
3	1	2	0	NO	NO	NO

1-equivalence classes correspond to different output rows:

Output row			*1-equivalence class*
NO	NO	NO	$\{0,1,3\}=[0]_1$
YES	NO	NO	$\{2\}=[2]_1$

We partition $[0]_1$, using Proposition 7.6, as follows.

	Next-state				1-equivalence class		
	a	*b*	*c*		*a*	*b*	*c*
0	1	0	0	0	$[0]_1$	$[0]_1$	$[0]_1$
1	1	2	0	1	$[0]_1$	$[2]_1$	$[0]_1$
3	1	2	0	3	$[0]_1$	$[2]_1$	$[0]_1$

So the 2-equivalence classes are

$$\{0\}=[0]_2 \qquad \{1,3\}=[1]_2 \qquad \{2\}=[2]_2 \tag{7.19}$$

Figure 7.16 Reduced machine to recognize strings ending in *aba*

Current state	Next-state function Input *a*	*b*	*c*	Output function Input *a*	*b*	*c*
[0]	[1]	[0]	[0]	NO	NO	NO
[1]	[1]	[2]	[0]	NO	NO	NO
[2]	[1]	[0]	[0]	YES	NO	NO

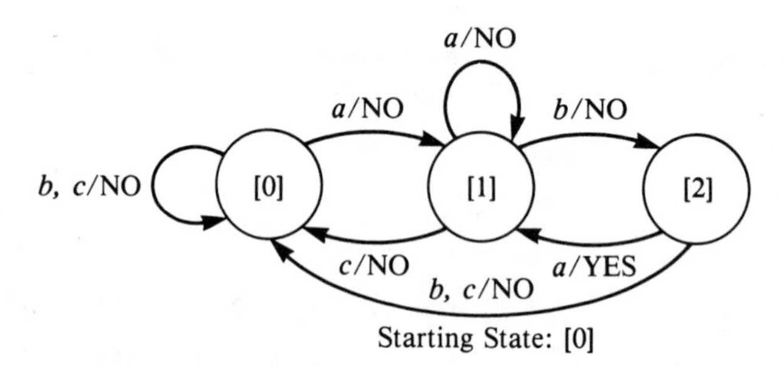

3-equivalence is the same as 2-equivalence. Hence by Proposition 7.7, 2-equivalence coincides with state-equivalence. Using (7.19), we get M_R as in Figure 7.16. In order to produce an output of YES for all input strings that end in *aba*, M_R must be started in state [0]. Observe that while the machine of Figure 7.12 had a more intuitive construction than has the machine of Figure 7.16, the latter machine has fewer states. △

Example 7.25

With a minimum of prose, we compute M_R for the M of Table 7.17.

Table 7.17 Machine M

Current state	Next-state function Input 0	1	Output function Input 0	1
A	*B*	*C*	*y*	*y*
B	*E*	*A*	*x*	*y*
C	*E*	*G*	*x*	*y*
D	*C*	*C*	*y*	*y*
E	*C*	*A*	*y*	*y*
F	*B*	*D*	*y*	*y*
G	*B*	*B*	*y*	*y*

Output row	*1-equivalence class*
$y \quad y$	$\{A,D,E,F,G\} = [A]_1$
$x \quad y$	$\{B,C\} = [B]_1$

Partition of 1-Equivalence Classes

		Next-state		1-equivalence class	
		0	1	0	1
	A	B	C	$[B]_1$	$[B]_1$
	D	C	C	$[B]_1$	$[B]_1$
$[A]_1$:	E	C	A	$[B]_1$	$[A]_1$
	F	B	D	$[B]_1$	$[A]_1$
	G	B	B	$[B]_1$	$[B]_1$

		Next-state		1-equivalence class	
		0	1	0	1
$[B]_1$:	B	E	A	$[A]_1$	$[A]_1$
	C	E	G	$[A]_1$	$[A]_1$

2-equivalence classes

$\{A,D,G\} = [A]_2 \qquad \{E,F\} = [E]_2 \qquad \{B,C\} = [B]_2$

Partition of 2-Equivalence Classes

		Next-state		2-equivalence class	
		0	1	0	1
	A	B	C	$[B]_2$	$[B]_2$
$[A]_2$:	D	C	C	$[B]_2$	$[B]_2$
	G	B	B	$[B]_2$	$[B]_2$

		Next-state 0	Next-state 1	2-equivalence class 0	2-equivalence class 1
$[E]_2$:	E	C	A	$[B]_2$	$[A]_2$
	F	B	D	$[B]_2$	$[A]_2$

		Next-state 0	Next-state 1	2-equivalence class 0	2-equivalence class 1
$[B]_2$:	B	E	A	$[E]_2$	$[A]_2$
	C	E	G	$[E]_2$	$[A]_2$

3-equivalence classes

$\{A,D,G\}=[A]_3 \qquad \{E,F\}=[E]_3 \qquad \{B,C\}=[B]_2$

The 2-equivalence classes coincide with the 3-equivalence classes. So we stop. The reduced machine M_R is given in Table 7.18. △

Table 7.18 M_R for M of Table 7.17

Current state	Next-state function Input 0	Next-state function Input 1	Output function Input 0	Output function Input 1
$[A]$	$[B]$	$[B]$	y	y
$[E]$	$[B]$	$[A]$	y	y
$[B]$	$[E]$	$[A]$	x	y

Theorem 7.8

Let M_R be the reduced machine for the finite-state machine M. Suppose that M_R has the same behavior starting in state $[s]$ as starting in state $[t]$. Then $[s]=[t]$. In particular, of all machines that exhibit the same behaviors as does M, M_R has the fewest states.

Proof of Theorem 7.8

It is given that $\beta_{R,[s]}=\beta_{R,[t]}$. By Theorem 7.5, $\beta_{R,[s]}=\beta_s$ and $\beta_{R,[t]}=\beta_t$. So $\beta_s=\beta_t$. By Theorem 7.5(i), $[s]$ and $[t]$ are the same state in M_R.

Suppose that a machine M' exhibits the same behaviors as does M. We consider states v and w in M'. If $\beta'_v \neq \beta'_w$, then $v \neq w$. So the number of states in M' is at least equal to the number of different behaviors for M. By

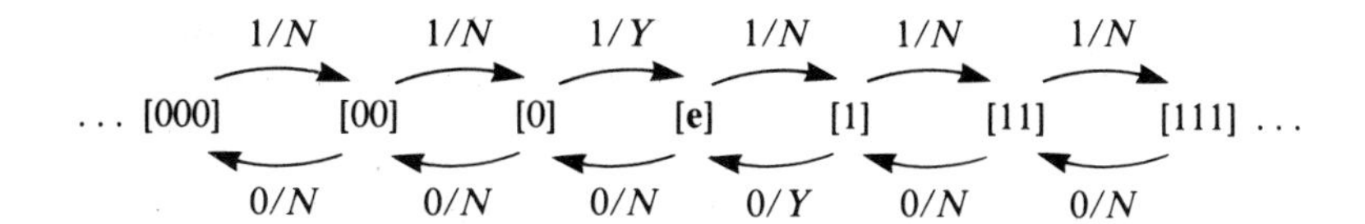

Figure 7.17 M_R for M of Figure 7.14

Theorem 7.5 and the result of the previous paragraph, the number of different behaviors for M equals the number of states for M_R. ◇

Example 7.26

We give an example of an infinite reduced machine. Let us consider M of Example 7.16. Figure 7.14 describes its (infinite) state diagram. It is not too hard to show that two states of M are state-equivalent if and only if they have the same difference between the number of 1's and the number of 0's in the strings representing the states. Then M_R has the states

$$\ldots, \quad [000], \quad [00], \quad [0], \quad [\mathbf{e}], \quad [1], \quad [11], \quad [111], \quad \ldots$$

Figure 7.17 gives the state diagram for M_R. Since M_R has an infinite number of states, we see that no finite machine can exhibit the behaviors of M. △

Theorem 7.5(i) and Theorem 7.8 say that the behaviors of a machine M correspond to the states of M_R. The external appearance of a machine is given by its behaviors. So *two finite-state machines M and M' have the same external behavior if and only if they have essentially the same (isomorphic) reduced machines M_R and M_R'.* This statement is analogous to Chapter 5, Theorem 5.11 about equivalent Boolean polynomials.

Exercises 7.4

1. For each of the following finite-state machines, find the state-equivalence classes and give the state table for the corresponding reduced machine.

a.

Current state	Next-state function Input 0	Next-state function Input 1	Output function Input 0	Output function Input 1
A	C	B	x	x
B	A	B	y	x
C	A	C	x	x

b.

Current state	Next-state function Input 0	1	Output function Input 0	1
A	B	A	y	y
B	C	A	x	x
C	D	D	x	x
D	B	D	y	y

c.

Current state	Next-state function Input 0	1	Output function Input 0	1
A	E	D	x	x
B	B	F	x	x
C	E	B	x	x
D	B	F	x	x
E	D	A	x	y
F	E	B	x	y

d.

Current state	Next-state function Input 0	1	2	Output function Input 0	1	2
A	C	F	D	x	x	y
B	A	B	C	x	x	x
C	D	E	F	x	x	x
D	C	G	A	x	x	y
E	A	F	B	y	y	y
F	A	G	B	y	y	y
G	D	G	B	y	y	y

2. Each machine M in Exercise 1 starts in state C and accepts the input string 101101. For each part of Exercise 1,

   (i) Compute the output string.

(ii) What is the corresponding starting state for M_R?
(iii) Compute the output string for M_R using the corresponding starting state from part (ii) and the same input string, 101101.

3. In Exercise 1(c), E and F are 2-inequivalent. Find an input string of length 2 that explicitly shows this inequivalence.
4. Show that state-equivalence and k-equivalence are equivalence relations.
5. Prove Proposition 7.6.
6. a. Partition the machine of Table 7.14 into 2-equivalence classes.
   b. Explain why this partition cannot be used to construct another machine.
7. Consider M of Example 7.16. Prove, as asserted in Example 7.26, that two states of M are state-equivalent if and only if they have the same difference between the number of 1's and the number of 0's in the strings that represent the states.
8. Say that two inputs to a finite-state machine are equivalent if they have the same columns in the machine's next-state and output tables. Explain how to "reduce" the number of inputs to a machine.

7.5 Simulation and Homomorphism

One common use of a digital computer is to simulate some other digital computer. So there is the corresponding mathematical question of when, or how, one finite machine M, in the sense of Definitions 7.1 and 7.2, can simulate another finite machine M'. Certainly M and its reduced machine M_R of the previous section simulate each other. But a more flexible theory than that of state reduction is desirable. Corresponding to different assumptions about the allowed electrical connections between physical machines, there are several approaches to the mathematical theory of simulation. In this section, we discuss simulation via submachines and via homomorphisms. Some alternative approaches are indicated in the exercises.

A general definition for simulation will be given in Definition 7.8, which follows later. But we certainly want machine M to simulate machine M' if every behavior of M' is also a behavior of M. This will certainly happen if M' is a submachine of M. Formally, we have Definition 7.6.

Definition 7.6

Let M be a finite-state machine, with S, I, ν, Y, β as in Definition 7.1(i)–(v). A machine M_1, with $S_1, I_1, \nu_1, Y_1, \beta_1$ as in Definition 7.1(i)–(v), is a **submachine** of M if

(i) S_1, I_1, Y_1 are subsets of S, I, Y respectively, and
(ii) For (s,i) in $S_1 \times I_1, \nu_1(s,i) = \nu(s,i)$ and $\beta_1(s,i) = \beta(s,i)$. ○

Definition 7.7

Let M be a finite semiautomaton, with S, I, ν as in Definition 7.2(i)–(iii). A semiautomaton M_1, with S_1, I_1, ν_1 as in Definition 7.2(i)–(iii), is a **subsemiautomaton** of M if

(a) S_1 and I_1 are subsets of S and I respectively, and

(b) For (s,i) in $S_1 \times I_1, \nu_1(s,i) = \nu(s,i)$. ○

We observe that if the semiautomata M and M_1 of Definition 7.7 are considered to be full finite-state machines, as in Definition 7.2(iv)–(v), then M_1 is a subsemiautomaton of M if and only if M_1 is a submachine of M in the sense of Definition 7.6. So we shall often use the term submachine, rather than subsemiautomaton, when discussing semiautomata.

Submachines are very much like subgroups. For finite machines, to check that subsets S_1 and I_1 determine a submachine, look in the next-state table for M and check that the entries for states in S_1 and inputs in I_1 are also in S_1 (rather than just in S). This is analogous to checking that a subset of a finite group is closed under composition and is therefore a subgroup. The state table for M_1 is then a subtable of the state table for M. In the case of a full finite-state machine, we may take Y_1 to be the set of entries in the output table for M_1.

Examples 7.27

Consider the machine M given in Figure 7.18. Then, as underlined in the state table for M, $S_1 = \{A,C\}$ and $I_1 = \{0,2\}$ determine a submachine M_1 of M. The state table and machine diagram for M_1 are given in Figure 7.19. From the output function table for M_1, $Y_1 = \{x,y,z\}$. △

In Figure 7.18 we consider $S_2 = \{A,C\}$ and $I_2 = \{0,1,2\}$. Then S_2 and I_2 do *not* determine a submachine M_2 of M: As circled in Figure 7.18, $\nu(A,1) = B$ and $\nu(C,1) = D$. B and D are not elements of S_2. △

Example 7.28

Table 7.19 gives a semiautomaton M and a subsemiautomaton M_1. △

A machine M simulates a submachine M_1 in the obvious, trivial way: To simulate the behavior of machine M_1 in starting state s, we just start machine M in state s. Since M_1 is a submachine of M, s *is* a state of M.

In discussing simulation, it is excessively restrictive to require that M and M' use exactly the same inputs and outputs. Physically, we shall allow the inputs and outputs to be influenced by combinatorial networks. Figure 7.20 then gives a schematic picture of the environment in which we envision that M in starting state s simulates M' in starting state s'. M' accepts an input string $\mathbf{i}' = i'_1 i'_2 \ldots i'_k$ and writes the output string $\mathbf{o}' = o'_1 o'_2 \ldots o'_k$. With the aid of combinatorial networks, M must do the same thing. So during the jth time interval, the input i'_j is accepted by a combinatorial network, call it h_i. The combinatorial network h_i converts the input i'_j to an input i_j that is acceptable to M. The input i_j is accepted by

Figure 7.18 A finite-state machine M

Current state	Next-state function Input 0	①	2	Output function Input 0	1	2
$\underline{A}$	$\underline{A}$	Ⓑ	$\underline{C}$	$\underline{x}$	x	$\underline{y}$
B	B	C	D	y	z	z
$\underline{C}$	$\underline{C}$	Ⓓ	$\underline{A}$	$\underline{z}$	y	$\underline{x}$
D	D	A	B	z	z	z

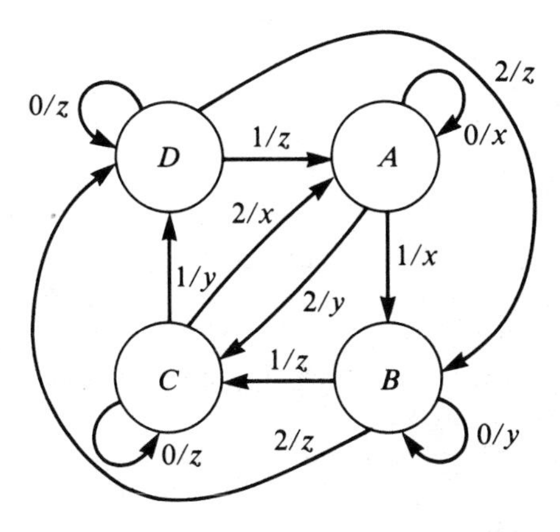

Figure 7.19 A submachine M_1 of M of Figure 7.18

Current state	Next-state function Input 0	2	Output function Input 0	2
A	A	C	x	y
C	C	A	z	x

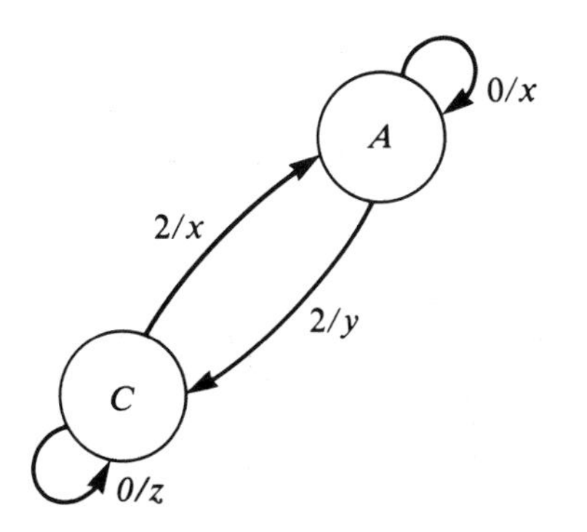

Table 7.19 Semiautomaton M and subsemiautomaton M_1

M

States A, B, C, D, E, F, G

Inputs $0, 1$

Current state	Next-state function, Input 0	Next-state function, Input 1
$\underline{A}$	$\underline{A}$	$\underline{D}$
$\underline{B}$	$\underline{G}$	$\underline{D}$
C	C	B
$\underline{D}$	$\underline{B}$	$\underline{E}$
$\underline{E}$	$\underline{G}$	$\underline{B}$
F	D	F
$\underline{G}$	$\underline{A}$	$\underline{D}$

M_1

States A, B, D, E, G

Inputs $0, 1$

Current state	Next-state function, Input 0	Next-state function, Input 1
A	A	D
B	G	D
D	B	E
E	G	B
G	A	D

M, which produces the output o_j. Then another combinatorial network, call it h_o, converts the output o_j from M to the desired output o'_j. In order for simulation to occur, the output string $\mathbf{o}'$ from h_o must coincide with the output string $\mathbf{o}'$ from M'. Equivalently, each o'_j from h_o must coincide with the output o'_j from M'.

The mathematical equivalent of a black-box combinatorial network such as h_i or h_o in Figure 7.20 is a map (or a function). The map describes the i/o relationship of the network. The top part of Figure 7.20 is described mathematically by $\beta'_{s'}$, the behavior of M' in starting state s'. The bottom part of Figure 7.20 is described mathematically by the composition of h_o, β_s, and h_i. Simulation requires that $\beta'_{s'} = h_o \circ \beta_s \circ h_i$. Formally, we have Definition 7.8.

Definition 7.8 Let M and M' be finite-state machines. Let h_i and h_o be maps as follows:

(i) $h_i : I' \to I$, where I and I' are the input sets for M and M' respectively.

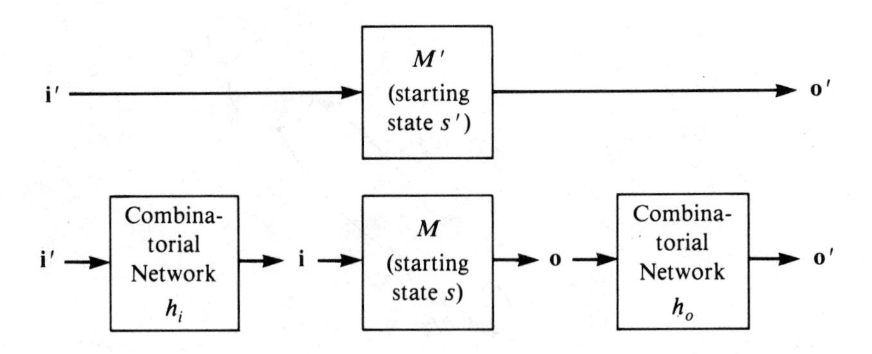

Figure 7.20 Machine M simulates machine M'

(ii) $h_o: Y_1 \to Y'$, where Y' is the output set for M' and Y_1 is a subset of the output set Y for M.

For a string $\mathbf{i}' = i'_1 i'_2 \ldots i'_k$ of inputs to M', let

$$h_i(\mathbf{i}') = h_i(i'_1)h_o(i'_2)\ldots h_o(i'_k)$$

denote the corresponding input string for M. Then M in starting state s **simulates** M' in starting states s' via the maps h_i and h_o if, for all input strings $\mathbf{i}'$ for M',

$$\beta'_{s'}(\mathbf{i}') = h_o(\beta_s(h_i(\mathbf{i}'))). \qquad \bigcirc$$

Example 7.29

Let M and M' be as in Table 7.20. Then with h_i and h_o as indicated in Table 7.20, starting M in state B simulates starting M' in state X. We shall completely verify the simulation later, in Example 7.31. For now, we just have M' accept the input string 453345. As in Table 7.21, M' and M produce the same output strings via h_i and h_o. $\triangle$

Table 7.20 Machine M simulates machine M'

M

Current state	Next-state function, Input 0	1	2	Output function, Input 0	1	2
A	E	F	B	d	a	a
B	D	C	A	a	b	b
C	D	B	D	c	b	c
D	E	B	E	d	a	d
E	C	D	F	c	b	a
F	A	C	F	a	b	b

M'

Current state	Next-state function, Input 3	4	5	Output function, Input 3	4	5
X	Z	X	X	x	y	y
Y	X	Z	Z	x	y	y
Z	Y	X	X	z	x	x

$h_i: 3 \to 0,\ 4 \to 1,\ 5 \to 1 \qquad h_o: a \to x,\ b \to y,\ c \to x,\ d \to z$

If M' starts in state X, start M in state B.

Example 7.30

Table 7.22 is another example of machine simulation, this time for finite semiautomata. Recall our convention that the "output" of a finite semiautomaton is simply its state. Using Table 7.22, we start M' in state X and input the string 343554. Then the successive next-states for M', that is, the output string for M', is

$$XXXZZY \qquad \textbf{(7.20)}$$

Table 7.21 Input string 453345 for Table 7.20

M'				M				
Current state	Input i'	Output	Next state	Current state	$h_i(i')$	Output o	$h_o(o)$	Next state
X	4	y	X	B	1	b	y	C
X	5	y	X	C	1	b	y	B
X	3	x	Z	B	0	a	x	D
Z	3	z	Y	D	0	d	z	E
Y	4	y	Z	E	1	b	y	D
Z	5	x	X	D	1	a	x	B

Let us now look at the simulation by M. The function h_i changes the input string 343554 for M' into the input string 000220 for M. We start M in state A. Then the successive next-states for M are

$$EAEGFB \tag{7.21}$$

h_o changes (7.21) into (7.20), as desired.

Table 7.22 Machine M simulates machine M'

M: Next-state function

Current state	Input 0	1	2
A	E	G	G
B	A	H	B
C	D	D	F
D	C	E	F
E	A	A	G
F	B	B	G
G	B	D	F
H	B	C	F

M': Next-state function

Current state	Input 3	4	5
X	X	X	Z
Y	X	X	Y
Z	Y	Y	Z

$h_i: 3 \to 0, \quad 4 \to 0, \quad 5 \to 2$

$h_o: A \to X, \quad B \to Y, \quad E \to X, \quad F \to Z, \quad G \to Z$

If M' starts in state X, start M in state A.

We shall give a verification of the simulation for all input strings in Example 7.32, which follows later. △

We now wish to find a condition that will ensure simulation in the sense of Definition 7.8. We shall formalize this condition, the homomorphism condition, only for finite semiautomata. The homomorphism condition for full finite-state machines is similar, but more complicated.

Suppose that machine M starting in state s simulates machine M' starting in state s'. Let $i'_1 i'_2 \ldots i'_k$ be an input string for M'. Let $s'_1, s'_2, \ldots, s'_k$ be the successive states for M'. Let $h_i(i'_1)h_i(i'_2)\ldots h_i(i'_k)$ be the corresponding input string for M. Let $s_1, s_2, \ldots, s_k$ be the successive states for M. Then, as in Exercise 9 of this section, for any j, $1 \le j \le k$, starting M in state s_j simulates starting M' in state s'_j, using the same h_i and h_o. Including s', the states s'_j that can appear in this manner are called the states that are **accessible** from s'. As in Exercise 8 of this section, the accessible states (from s') and the full set of inputs for M' determine a submachine of M'. So simulation for just one state s' of M' necessitates simulation of a full submachine of M'. Following the usual terminology, however, we shall define, in Definition 7.9 below, a homomorphism from M onto M' in such a manner that the existence of such a homorphism implies that M may simulate M' in *any* starting state.

Example 7.31

We shall completely verify the simulation of Example 7.29. As we have seen, using the input string 453345 in Table 7.21, all states of M' are accessible from state X. As seen from the corresponding next-states in Table 7.21, the map h of (7.22) tells which states of M can be used to simulate states of M'.

$$h: B \to X, \quad C \to X, \quad D \to Z, \quad E \to Y \tag{7.22}$$

In (7.22), only the states $S_1 = \{B, C, D, E\}$ of M appear. In Table 7.20, only the inputs $I_1 = \{0, 1\}$ of M appear in the map h_i. This correctly suggests that S_1 and I_1 determine a submachine M_1 of M. Moreover, as in Table 7.23, the maps h_i and h_o of Table 7.20 and the map h of (7.22) rename the next-state and output tables for M_1 as the corresponding tables for M'. In Table 7.20, input 1 for M appears as the image of both input 4 and input 5 for M'. So in the renaming in Table 7.23, the 1-column for M_1 is replaced by both a 4-column and a 5-column. As formally proven in Theorem 7.9 below for finite semiautomata, this renaming establishes that we have a simulation. △

Example 7.32

We completely verify the simulation of Example 7.30. As in Example 7.31, successive states of M may be used to simulate successive states of M'.

Table 7.23 Renaming from M_1 to M' of Table 7.20

	M_1					Renaming via h_i, h_o, h					
	Next-state function		Output function			Next-state function			Output function		
Current state	Input 0	1	Input 0	1	Current state	Input 3	4	5	Input 3	4	5
B	D	C	a	b	X	Z	X	X	x	y	y
C	D	B	c	b	X	Z	X	X	x	y	y
D	E	B	d	a	Z	Y	X	X	z	x	x
E	C	D	c	b	Y	X	Z	Z	x	y	y

Then (7.20) and (7.21) suggest the map h of (7.23) from the states of a submachine M_1 of M to the states of M'.

$$h: A \to X, \quad B \to Y, \quad E \to X, \quad F \to Z, \quad G \to Z \tag{7.23}$$

Observe that the map h of (7.23) coincides with the map h_o of Table 7.22. Table 7.24 checks that $S_1 = \{A,B,E,F,G\}$ does give a submachine M_1 of M, with input set $I_1 = \{0,2\}$, and also checks that h_i and h_o do provide a renaming of M_1 into M'. As will be shown formally in Theorem 7.9 below, this does establish the correctness of the simulation. △

Table 7.24 Renaming from M_1 to M' of Table 7.22

	M_1			Renaming via h_i and h_o		
	Next-state function			Next-state function		
Current state	Input 0	2	Current state	Input 3	4	5
A	E	G	X	X	X	Z
E	A	G	X	X	X	Z
B	A	B	Y	X	X	Y
F	B	G	Z	Y	Y	Z
G	B	F	Z	Y	Y	Z

The formal definition of homomorphism for finite semiautomata will now be given. Table 7.24 is a typical homomorphism verification.

Definition 7.9

Let M and M' be finite semiautomata. Let S, I, v and S', I', v' be the state sets, input sets, and next-state functions for M and M' respectively. A **homomorphism** from M onto M' is a pair of maps

$$h_i : I' \to I \quad \text{and}$$
$$h : S_1 \to S'$$

where S_1 is a subset of S and h is onto, such that, letting I_1 denote the image of h_i,

(i) S_1 and I_1 determine a submachine M_1 of M, and

(ii) $h[v(s,h_i(i'))] = v'(h(s),i')$

for all s in S_1 and all i' in I'. ○

Definition 7.9 is really a condition on the submachine M_1 of M, rather than a condition on all of M. The definition was made in this manner in order to allow M (rather than just M_1) to simulate M'. Observe that the map h of Definition 7.9 is required to be onto. This will allow simulation of M' from any starting state. Condition (i) of Definition 7.9 is needed to ensure that the map $h[(v(s,h_i(i'))]$ in Definition 7.9(ii) is defined. As in Example 7.32, Definition 7.9(ii) is precisely the needed condition to ensure that h_i and h rename the next-state table for M_1 as (all of) the next-state table for M'. Indeed, look at the (s,i_1) entry in the next-state table for M_1. Since M_1 is a submachine of M, the value of the entry is $v(s,i_1)$. If $i_1 = h_i(i')$, one of the corresponding entries in the next-state table for M' is the $(h(s),i')$ entry, and $v'(h(s),i')$ is the value of this entry. $v(s,i_1)$ is renamed to $h[v(s,i_1)]$. So correct renaming requires that $h[v(s,i_1)] = v'(h(s),i')$. Since $i_1 = h_i(i')$, this is just Definition 7.9(ii).

Example 7.33

Table 7.25 (p. 350) gives and verifies a homomorphism from the finite semiautomaton M onto the finite semiautomaton M'. In verifying the homomorphism via renaming of the next-state table for M_1, it is convenient to rearrange the states S_1 of M_1 so that states with the same image in S' are adjacent. △

Theorem 7.9 below says that simulation and homomorphism are almost the same for finite semiautomata.

Theorem 7.9

Let the finite semiautomaton M in starting state s simulate the finite semiautomaton M' in starting state s', as in Definition 7.8. Let I_1, a subset of I, denote the image of the map h_i. Let S_1 denote the states of M that are accessible from s via inputs in I_1. Let M_1 denote the submachine of M determined by S_1 and I_1. Let M'_1 denote the submachine of M' determined

Table 7.25
Homomorphism and verification

M — Next-state function

Current state	Input 0	1	2
A	G	H	A
B	D	B	D
C	G	E	A
D	E	G	D
E	F	E	E
F	C	F	H
G	B	D	A
H	A	B	C

M' — Next-state function

Current state	Input 3	4	5
X	Y	X	X
Y	X	Y	Y

$h_i: 3 \to 0, \quad 4 \to 1, \quad 5 \to 1$

$h: B \to X, \quad C \to X, \quad D \to Y, \quad E \to X, \quad F \to Y, \quad G \to Y$

$S_1 = \{B, C, D, E, F, G\}$ Partition of $S_1: B, C, E | D, F, G$

Homomorphism Verification

M_1 — Next-state function

Current state	Input 0	1
B	D	B
C	G	E
E	F	E
D	E	G
F	C	F
G	B	D

Renaming — Next-state function

Current state	Input 3	4	5
X	Y	X	X
X	Y	X	X
X	Y	X	X
Y	X	Y	Y
Y	X	Y	Y
Y	X	Y	Y

M' — Next-state function

Current state	Input 3	4	5
X	Y	X	X
Y	X	Y	Y

by all states S'_1 that are accessible from s' via inputs in all of I'. Let h denote the restriction to S_1 of the map h_o (with $Y = S$) of Definition 7.8(ii). Then $h_i: I' \to I$ and $h: S_1 \to S'_1$ give a homomorphism from M onto M'_1.

Conversely, let $h_i: I' \to I$ and $h: S_1 \to S$ give a homomorphism from the finite semiautomaton M onto the finite semiautomaton M'. Then for s in S_1, starting M in state s simulates starting M' in state $s' = h(s)$.

Example 7.34

Before proving Theorem 7.9, we shall illustrate the terms that are used in its statement. Let M and M' be as in Table 7.26. Let h_i and h also be as in Table 7.26. Then as we shall see, starting M in state D simulates (via h_i and h) starting M' in state p. Let us identify all the objects named in the first part of Theorem 7.9. I_1, the image of h_i, is given by $I_1 = \{2,1\}$. It is easy to check that the states that are accessible from D via inputs in I_1 form $S_1 = \{A,B,C,D,E,F,H\}$, as in Table 7.26. The submachine M_1 is given in Table 7.26. The states for M_1 have been partitioned according to their images under h, for the homomorphism verification. It is easy to check that $S'_1 = \{p,q,r,s\}$ gives the states of M' that are accessible from p. The submachine M'_1 of M' is as indicated. No restriction of h in Table 7.26 to a smaller set is needed. Finally, Table 7.26 verifies the homomorphism from M (via M_1) onto M'_1. As we have observed in previous examples, and as we will prove in the proof of the second part of Theorem 7.9, this homomorphism verification shows that simulation takes place. △

Proof of Theorem 7.9

We first verify the homomorphism from M onto M'_1. We need to show first that h is onto. But if s'_k is accessible from s' via the input string $i'_1 i'_2 \ldots i'_k$, then the simulation condition assures that $s'_k = h(s_k)$, with s_k accessible from s via the input string $h_i(i'_1)h_i(i'_2)\ldots h_i(i'_k)$. The verification that S_1 and I_1 determine a submachine is left to the exercises. Let s_k and s'_k be as before. We need to verify Definition 7.9(ii), that for any input i'_{k+1} in I',

$$h[v(s_k, h_i(i'_{k+1}))] = v'(s'_k, i'_{k+1}) \qquad \textbf{(7.24)}$$

Continuing with the obvious subscript notation,

$$v(s_k, h_i(i'_{k+1})) = s_{k+1} \quad \text{and} \quad v'(s'_k, i'_{k+1}) = s'_{k+1}$$

Then (7.24) holds because of the given simulation.

We now suppose that we have a homomorphism. Let $i'_1 i'_2 \ldots i'_k$ be an input string for M'. Starting from state s', the successive states for M' are

$$s', v'(s', i'_1) = s'_1, v'(s'_1, i'_2) = s'_2, \ldots, v'(s'_{k-1}, i'_k) = s'_k$$

Let $h_i(i'_1)h_i(i'_2)\ldots h_i(i'_k) = i_1 i_2 \ldots i_k$ be the corresponding input string for M. Starting from state s, the successive states for M are

$$s, v(s, i_1) = s_1, v(s_1, i_2) = s_2, \ldots, v(s_{k-1}, i_k) = s_k$$

We are given that $h(s) = s'$. Then Definition 7.9(ii) implies that

$$h(s_1)=h[v(s,i_1)]=h[v(s,h_i(i'_1))]=v'(h(s),i'_1)$$
$$=v'(s',i'_1)=s'_1$$

Similarly, $h(s_2)=s'_2,\ldots,h(s_k)=s'_k$. So we do have a simulation. ◇

Table 7.26 Simulation and homomorphism

M

Current state	Next-state function Input 0	1	2
A	B	C	F
B	D	C	H
C	I	A	E
D	A	E	F
E	G	A	C
F	F	D	B
G	A	B	C
H	I	B	D
I	G	H	I

M'

Current state	Next-state function Input 0	1
p	r	q
q	q	s
r	p	p
s	r	q
t	r	s

$h_i: 0\rightarrow 2,\quad 1\rightarrow 1$

$h: A\rightarrow s,\quad B\rightarrow p,\quad C\rightarrow q,\quad D\rightarrow p,\quad E\rightarrow q,\quad F\rightarrow r,\quad H\rightarrow r$

Homomorphism Verification

$S_1=\{A,B,C,D,E,F,H\} \qquad I_1=\{2,1\} \qquad S'_1=\{p,q,r,s\}$

M$_1$

Current state	Next-state function Input 2	1
B	H	C
D	F	E
C	E	A
E	C	A
F	B	D
H	D	B
A	F	C

Renaming

Current state	Next-state function Input 0	1
p	r	q
p	r	q
q	q	s
q	q	s
r	p	p
r	p	p
s	r	q

M'$_1$

Current state	Next-state function Input 0	1
p	r	q
q	q	s
r	p	p
s	r	q

Exercises 7.5

1. For each of the following machines M, tell whether or not the given subsets S_1 and I_1 determine a submachine M_1. If M_1 does exist, write out its next-state table. Also, if M_1 is a finite-state machine, give its output table.

a.

Current state	Next-state function Input 0	1
A	B	A
B	A	B
C	C	A

$S_1 = \{A, B\}$ $I_1 = \{0, 1\}$

b.

Current state	Next-state function Input 1	2	3	Output function Input 1	2	3
A	E	C	C	a	b	a
B	C	A	B	b	a	a
C	B	A	B	b	b	b
D	A	D	E	a	a	a
E	C	E	D	b	b	b

$S_1 = \{A, C, D, E\}$ $I_1 = \{2, 3\}$

c.

Current state	Next-state function Input 1	2	3
A	B	A	C
B	C	B	F
C	D	F	D
D	F	F	F
E	A	C	F
F	B	A	D

$S_1 = \{B, C, D, F\}$ $I_1 = \{2, 3\}$

d.

Current state	Next-state function Input 1	2	3	Output function Input 1	2	3
A	C	E	F	b	b	c
B	D	F	A	a	a	b
C	C	A	B	c	c	c
D	D	B	A	a	b	c
E	C	A	B	c	b	a
F	D	B	E	a	a	a

$S_1 = \{A, B, E, F\}$ $I_1 = \{2, 3\}$

2. In Table 7.20, machine M in starting state B simulates machine M' in starting state X. Choose an appropriate starting state for M and verify directly, as in Table 7.21, that M may also simulate M' in starting state Y with input string 345335.

3. We are given the following machines M and M' with maps h_i and h_o. For the input string 343333 for M', verify that starting M in state B simulates starting M' in state Z.

M

Current state	Next-state function Input 0	1	Output function Input 0	1
A	F	D	a	b
B	D	A	b	b
C	F	B	c	b
D	B	C	b	b
E	E	B	b	c
F	A	B	a	a

M'

Current state	Next-state function Input 3	4	Output function Input 3	4
X	Y	Z	x	y
Y	X	Z	x	x
Z	Z	X	y	y

$h_i: 3 \to 0,\ 4 \to 1 \qquad h_o: a \to x,\ b \to y,\ c \to x$

4. a. Verify that the following maps h_i and h give a machine homomorphism.
   b. Give an explicit calculation, as in Table 7.21, of M simulating M' in starting state X with input string 53345.

M

Current state	Next-state function Input 1	2
A	F	A
B	E	F
C	D	F
D	D	B
E	B	C
F	D	C

M'

Current state	Next-state function Input 3	4	5
X	X	X	Z
Y	Y	Y	X
Z	Y	Y	Z

$h_i: 3 \to 1,\ 4 \to 1,\ 5 \to 2$

$h: B \to X,\ C \to Z,\ D \to Y,\ E \to X,\ F \to Z$

5. a. Verify that the following maps h_i and h give a machine homomorphism.

b. Give an explicit calculation, as in Table 7.21, of M simulating M' in starting state Z with input string 65556.

M — Next-state function

Current state	Input 0	1	2
A	H	D	B
B	G	D	F
C	F	G	H
D	C	A	G
E	D	A	B
F	F	D	A
G	E	C	H
H	B	A	D

M′ — Next-state function

Current state	Input 5	6
W	Z	X
X	X	Z
Y	W	Y
Z	Y	X

$h_i: 5 \to 2, \quad 6 \to 1$

$h: A \to X, \quad B \to X, \quad C \to Y, \quad D \to Z, \quad F \to X, \quad G \to Y, \quad H \to W$

6. a. Explain why the machine M of Figure 7.21 (p. 356) may be considered a mod 4 counter.
   b. Give a homomorphism from M of Figure 7.21 onto the binary counter of Figure 7.8.
7. Rewrite Definition 7.8 to give a formal definition for simulation using finite semiautomata.
8. Let I_1 be a set of inputs for a machine M. Let s be a state for M. Let S_1 be the set of all states of M that are accessible from s via inputs in I_1. Explain why S_1 and I_1 determine a submachine of M.
9. Suppose that the maps h_i and h_o allow machine M in starting state A to simulate machine M' in starting state X.
   a. Suppose that some input string to M' will move M' from initial state X to final state Y. Explain why M can simulate M' in starting state Y.
   b. Give an example of machines M and M', with starting states A and X as above, but such that M' has a starting state Z for which M cannot simulate M'.
10. a. Expand upon Definition 7.9 to give a definition for homomorphism between finite-state machines.

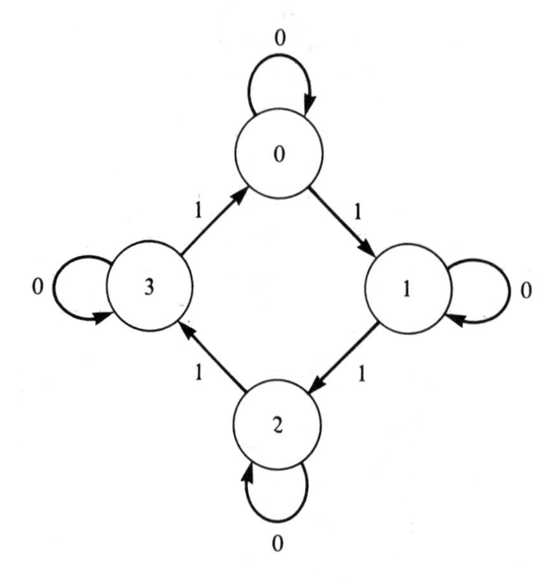

Figure 7.21 A mod 4 counter M

b. State, but do not prove, the corresponding theorem to Theorem 7.9 for finite-state machines.

11. Figure 7.22 is a schematic picture of a **cascade** composition of two machines M_1 and M_2.
    a. If M_1 has n_1 states, and M_2 has n_2 states, how many states does the cascade composition have?
    b. Explain how special cases of the cascade composition may be thought of as parallel or as series composition.
12. Let M be a finite semiautomaton such that for each input i, the i-column of the next-state table for M is a permutation of the outside column of states.
    a. Show that for any submachine M_1 of M with input i, the i-column for M_1 is also a permutation of the outside column of states for M_1.
    b. Let $h_i: I' \to I_1$ be part of a machine homomorphism such that $h_i(i') = i$, for some input i' for M'. Show that the i'-column for M' is also a permutation of the outside column of states for M'.
    c. Suppose that all columns of the next-state table for M are permutations of the outside column. How does this restrict the types of machines that M can simulate?

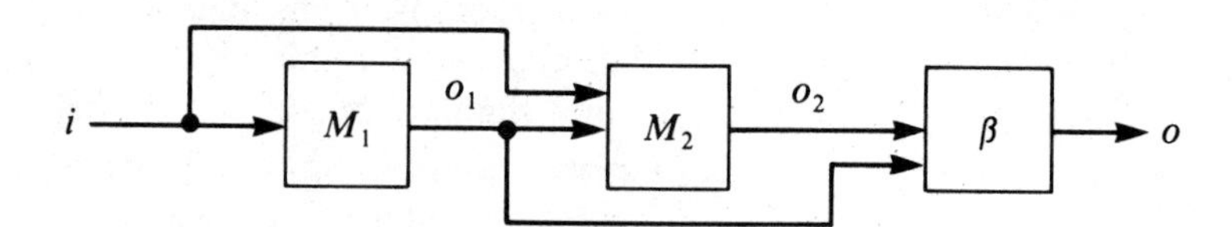

Figure 7.22 Cascade composition

13. Using Exercise 12, explain why machine M can simulate neither machine M' nor machine M''.

M

Next-state function

Current state	Input 0	1	2
A	B	D	E
B	C	E	F
C	D	A	D
D	E	B	C
E	F	C	A
F	A	F	B

M'

Next-state function

Current state	Input 3	4
P	P	Q
Q	R	Q
R	Q	Q
S	S	S

M''

Next-state function

Current state	Input 5	6
X	Z	Y
Y	X	Z
Z	X	X

7.6 Monoids, Semigroups, and Machines

Groups have been used extensively in this text. In this section the related notions of monoids and semigroups are introduced. We shall see that each semiautomaton has a monoid naturally associated with it. As we shall demonstrate in the last section of the next chapter, monoids may replace machines in some applications.

Monoids and semigroups are defined by deleting conditions in Definition 2.3 for a group. For a monoid, condition (iii), for inverses, is omitted. For a semigroup, both condition (iii) and condition (ii), for the identity, are omitted. Formally,

Definition 7.10

A **monoid** $(G,\circ)$ is a set $G=\{a,b,c,d,\ldots\}$ with a law of composition $\circ$ that satisfies the following axioms:

Table 7.27 A semigroup $(G,\circ)$

$\circ$	a	b
a	a	a
b	b	b

Table 7.28 A monoid $(H,\circ)$

$\circ$	e	a	b
e	e	a	b
a	a	a	a
b	b	b	b

(o) (Closure) For any two elements a,b of G, $a\circ b$ is also an element of G.

(i) (Associativity) For any three elements a,b,c of G,

$$(a\circ b)\circ c = a\circ(b\circ c)$$

(ii) (Identity) There is a special element e of G, called the **identity**, such that for any element a of G,

$$e\circ a = a \qquad a\circ e = a$$

A **semigroup** $(G,\circ)$ is a set $G=\{a,b,c,\ldots\}$ with a law of composition $\circ$ that satisfies axioms (o) and (i) just given. ○

Every group is both a monoid and a semigroup. So we certainly have many examples of monoids and semigroups. Here are some examples that distinguish between groups, monoids, and semigroups.

Examples 7.35

We let $G=\{0,1,2,3,\ldots\}$ and let $+$ denote the usual addition. Then $(G,+)$ is monoid but not a group. Indeed, 0 serves as the identity, but inverses are lacking in general. △

Let $P=\{1,2,3,\ldots\}$. Then $(P,+)$ is a semigroup, but is not a monoid. Namely, P has no identity (since we removed it from G). △

Examples 7.36

Let $\cdot$ denote the usual multiplication for integers. Let G be as in Example 7.35. Then $(G,\cdot)$ is a monoid, but not a group. The integer 1 serves as the identity. $(P,\cdot)$ with P as in Example 7.35 is also a monoid but not a group. Let $H=\{2,3,4,5,\ldots\}$. Then $(H,\cdot)$ is a semigroup but not a monoid. △

Recall $(\mathbb{Z}_6,\cdot)$ of Example 2.19. Then $(\mathbb{Z}_6,\cdot)$ is a monoid. In general, $(\mathbb{Z}_n,\cdot)$ is a monoid but not a group. △

Example 7.37

Let $(G,\circ)$ have the law of composition as given in Table 7.27. It is easy to check that $\circ$ is associative and so that $(G,\circ)$ is a semigroup. $(G,\circ)$ is not a monoid. By adding an identity element e to G, we may form the monoid $(H,\circ)$ of Table 7.28. △

Example 7.38

Let $X=\{A,B\}$ be a set with two elements. Recall from Chapter 2, Section 2.6, that $(S_2,\circ)$ is the *group* of all permutations of X. The reason for looking at just permutations, rather than at all self-maps, is to get inverses, and thus a group. △

Call a general self-map of a set X to itself a **transformation** of X. Recall the law of composition $\circ$ for transformations, as given in Chapter 2, Definition 2.1. To follow the usual conventions for finite-state machines later, we introduce another law of composition, $\diamond$, for transformations. Let f be a transformation of the set X. When we use $\diamond$, we will find it convenient to write the function evaluation as $(x)f$, rather than as $f(x)$.

Definition 7.11

Let f and g be transformations of the set X. The **right-composition** of f and g, denoted by $f \diamond g$, is the transformation of X given by

$$(x)(f \diamond g) = ((x)f)g \qquad \bigcirc$$

Observe that $f \diamond g$ could also be defined simply by $f \diamond g = g \circ f$. When we use the term *right-composition* for $\diamond$, we use the term **left-composition** for $\circ$. As for $\circ$, $\diamond$ is an associative law of composition and id_X is an identity.

Example 7.39

Let T_2 denote the set of all transformations of $X = \{A, B\}$. Then $(T_2, \diamond)$ is a monoid. The four elements of T_2 are named and listed as follows, using the same notation for transformations as for permutations.

$$e = \begin{pmatrix} A & B \\ A & B \end{pmatrix} \quad a = \begin{pmatrix} A & B \\ A & A \end{pmatrix} \quad b = \begin{pmatrix} A & B \\ B & B \end{pmatrix} \quad c = \begin{pmatrix} A & B \\ B & A \end{pmatrix}$$

Table 7.29 gives the composition table for $(T_2, \diamond)$. △

Table 7.29 Law of composition for $(T_2, \diamond)$

$\diamond$	e	a	b	c
e	e	a	b	c
a	a	a	b	b
b	b	a	b	a
c	c	a	b	e

$(T_2, \diamond)$ of Example 7.39 generalizes readily to $(T_n, \diamond)$, the monoid of all transformations on a set of n letters. Under a general transformation, each of the n letters has n possible images. The choices of the images are independent. So there are n^n elements in T_n.

Example 7.40

Let I be a set. We are thinking of I as the input set for a machine. Let I^+ denote the set of input strings to the machine using the elements of I. For example, with $I = \{0, 1\}$, typical elements of I^+ are

1, 010, 111011, 000010

We now give a law of composition $\circ$, **concatenation**, which makes $(I^+, \circ)$ a semigroup. Recall that strings are accepted from left to right. We let typical elements of I be denoted by $i_1, i_2, i_3, \ldots$. We let $\mathbf{a} = i_1 i_2 \ldots i_k$ and $\mathbf{b} = i_{k+1} i_{k+2} \ldots i_j$ be elements of I^+. Then we define $\mathbf{a} \circ \mathbf{b}$, usually written simply as **ab**, as

$$\mathbf{ab} = i_1 i_2 \ldots i_k i_{k+1} i_{k+2} \ldots i_j$$

That is, **ab** means first accept the input **a** and then accept the input **b**. For example,

$$\mathbf{a}=00011, \quad \mathbf{b}=0101, \quad \mathbf{ab}=000110101$$

$$\mathbf{a}=111001, \quad \mathbf{b}=1, \quad \mathbf{ab}=1110011$$

Concatenation is easily seen to be associative. So $(I^+,\circ)$ is a semigroup.

$(I^+,\circ)$ is not a monoid since there is no identity. To get a monoid, we shall add an identity element, denoted by **e**, as was done in Example 7.37. We may interpret **e** as the empty string, representing no inputs at all. For any string **a**, **ea** = **a** and **ae** = **a**. Recall that the empty string **e** has already been useful in Theorem 7.4. $I^+ \cup \{\mathbf{e}\}$ is denoted by I^*. Then $(I^*,\circ)$ is a monoid. I^* is sometimes called the set of all **words over the alphabet** I.

△

Many of the properties of groups carry over to monoids. Some of the group properties also are true for semigroups. We shall discuss this further in the exercises. But, in particular, we have the notion of a submonoid and a subsemigroup.

Definition 7.12

Let $(G,\circ)$ be a monoid. Let S be a subset of G. Then $(S,\circ)$ is a **submonoid** of $(G,\circ)$ if $\circ$ is a law of composition on S that makes $(S,\circ)$ into a monoid with the same identity as in $(G,\circ)$.

Let us suppose that $(G,\circ)$ is only given to be a semigroup. Then $(S,\circ)$ is a **subsemigroup** if $\circ$ is a law of composition on S that makes $(S,\circ)$ a semigroup. ○

To say that $\circ$ is a law of composition on S is only to say that S is closed under composition. Then, since composition is associative in G, it will automatically be associative in S. So we may reformulate Definition 7.12 as the following Proposition.

Proposition 7.10

Let $(G,\circ)$ be a monoid. Let S be a subset of G. Then $(S,\circ)$ is a submonoid of $(G,\circ)$ if and only if S is closed under the composition $\circ$, and e, the identity in G, is also an element of S.

Suppose that $(G,\circ)$ is only given to be a semigroup. Then $(S,\circ)$ is a subsemigroup if and only if S is closed under the composition $\circ$. □

Example 7.41

Let us suppose that $(G,\circ)$ is a finite *group*. We let S be a subset of G. Recall that by Theorem 2.13, $(S,\circ)$ is a subgroup if and only if S is closed under

Table 7.30 $(\{a,b\},\diamond)$ from Table 7.29

$\diamond$	a	b
a	a	b
b	a	b

composition. Then e is automatically included in S. However, for a monoid $(G,\circ)$, we must assume the inclusion of e in S in order to conclude that $(S,\circ)$ is a submonoid. For example. look at $(T_2,\diamond)$ of Table 7.29. Let $S=\{a,b\}$. Then $\diamond$ gives the composition on S of Table 7.30. But $(S,\circ)$ is not a submonoid of $(T_2,\diamond)$ since e is not an element of S. Of course, $(S,\diamond)$ is a subsemigroup of the semigroup $(T_2,\diamond)$. △

Example 7.42

BEWARE. For the monoid $(S,\circ)$ to be considered a submonoid of the monoid $(G,\circ)$, the identity element in S must also be the identity element in G. That is, it is possible for the subset S of G to be closed under composition and have an identity element e_S for $(S,\circ)$ such that e_S is not the identity element for $(G,\circ)$. Table 7.31 gives such an example. Moreover, the law of composition in Table 7.31 is associative. △

Table 7.31 $G=\{e_G,e_S,a\}$, $S=\{e_S,a\}$

$\circ$	e_G	e_S	a
e_G	e_G	e_S	a
e_S	e_S	e_S	a
a	a	a	e_S

Just as we talked about permutation groups in Definition 2.11, we may also talk about transformation monoids (and transformation semigroups). A **transformation monoid** is a submonoid of $(T_n,\diamond)$, that is, a set of transformations on the same n letters that is closed under composition and that includes the identity transformation.

Example 7.43

Here are the elements of a transformation monoid. Table 7.32 gives its composition table.

$$e=\begin{pmatrix} A & B & C \\ A & B & C \end{pmatrix} \quad a=\begin{pmatrix} A & B & C \\ B & C & A \end{pmatrix} \quad b=\begin{pmatrix} A & B & C \\ C & A & B \end{pmatrix}$$

$$c=\begin{pmatrix} A & B & C \\ A & A & A \end{pmatrix} \quad d=\begin{pmatrix} A & B & C \\ B & B & B \end{pmatrix} \quad f=\begin{pmatrix} A & B & C \\ C & C & C \end{pmatrix}$$

△

Table 7.32 A monoid

$\diamond$	e	a	b	c	d	f
e	e	a	b	c	d	f
a	a	b	e	c	d	f
b	b	e	a	c	d	f
c	c	d	f	c	d	f
d	d	f	c	c	d	f
f	f	c	d	c	d	f

Example 7.44

Here is another transformation monoid. Its composition table is given in Table 7.33.

$$e=\begin{pmatrix} A & B & C & D \\ A & B & C & D \end{pmatrix} \quad a=\begin{pmatrix} A & B & C & D \\ B & A & D & C \end{pmatrix} \quad b=\begin{pmatrix} A & B & C & D \\ A & A & C & D \end{pmatrix}$$

$$c=\begin{pmatrix} A & B & C & D \\ B & B & C & D \end{pmatrix} \quad d=\begin{pmatrix} A & B & C & D \\ A & A & D & C \end{pmatrix} \quad f=\begin{pmatrix} A & B & C & D \\ B & B & D & C \end{pmatrix}$$

△

Table 7.33 A monoid

◇	e	a	b	c	d	f
e	e	a	b	c	d	f
a	a	e	d	f	b	c
b	b	f	b	c	d	f
c	c	d	b	c	d	f
d	d	c	d	f	b	c
f	f	b	d	f	b	c

Let S be a set of transformations on the same set of n letters. We let $\langle S\rangle$, or more formally $(\langle S\rangle, \diamond)$, denote the submonoid of T_n **generated** by S. $\langle S\rangle$ should then be the smallest submonoid of T_n that contains the set S. So to compute $\langle S\rangle$, we adjoin to S, if necessary, e, the identity transformation, and also as many transformations as are needed to make the larger set closed under composition.

Example 7.45 We compute $\langle S\rangle$ for

$$S=\left\{\begin{pmatrix} A & B & C & D \\ A & C & D & B \end{pmatrix}, \begin{pmatrix} A & B & C & D \\ B & B & B & B \end{pmatrix}\right\}$$

Let

$$a=\begin{pmatrix} A & B & C & D \\ A & C & D & B \end{pmatrix} \quad b=\begin{pmatrix} A & B & C & D \\ B & B & B & B \end{pmatrix} \quad e=\begin{pmatrix} A & B & C & D \\ A & B & C & D \end{pmatrix}$$

Then we have the partial composition table

◇	e	a	b
e	e	a	b
a	a	c	b
b	b	d	b

with $c=\begin{pmatrix} A & B & C & D \\ A & D & B & C \end{pmatrix}$ and $d=\begin{pmatrix} A & B & C & D \\ C & C & C & C \end{pmatrix}$. The next partial composition table uses e, a, b, c, and d

$\diamond$	e	a	b	c	d
e	e	a	b	c	d
a	a	c	b	e	d
b	b	d	b	f	d
c	c	e	b	a	d
d	d	f	b	b	d

with $f=\begin{pmatrix} A & B & C & D \\ D & D & D & D \end{pmatrix}$. The next composition table uses e, a, b, c, d, f:

$\diamond$	e	a	b	c	d	f
e	e	a	b	c	d	f
a	a	c	b	e	d	f
b	b	d	b	f	d	f
c	c	e	b	a	d	f
d	d	f	b	b	d	f
f	f	b	b	d	d	f

This last composition table shows that $\{e,a,b,c,d,f\}$ is closed under the composition $\diamond$. Hence $S=\{e,a,b,c,d,f\}$. $\triangle$

Proposition 7.11 gives a more efficient way to compute $\langle S\rangle$ from S.

Proposition 7.11

Let S be a set of transformations on n letters. Then $\langle S\rangle$ may be found by adjoining to S

(i) The identity transformation e, if necessary, and
(ii) S_i for $i=1,2,3,\ldots$ until $S_i=\varnothing$.

S_i is defined by $S_0=S$. For $i\geq 1$, S_i equals the set of all new transformations that appear as compositions of elements of S_{i-1} and elements of S.

Example 7.46

Before proving Proposition 7.11, we illustrate its statement by computing $\langle S\rangle$ for

$$S=\left\{\begin{pmatrix} A & B & C & D \\ A & A & C & C \end{pmatrix}, \begin{pmatrix} A & B & C & D \\ A & B & B & D \end{pmatrix}\right\}$$

The new transformations are underlined as they appear.

	$\diamond$	S: $\begin{pmatrix} A & B & C & D \\ A & A & C & C \end{pmatrix}$	S: $\begin{pmatrix} A & B & C & D \\ A & B & B & D \end{pmatrix}$
$S=S_0$	$\begin{pmatrix} A & B & C & D \\ A & A & C & C \end{pmatrix}$	$\begin{pmatrix} A & B & C & D \\ A & A & C & C \end{pmatrix}$	$\begin{pmatrix} A & B & C & D \\ \underline{A} & \underline{A} & \underline{B} & \underline{B} \end{pmatrix}$
	$\begin{pmatrix} A & B & C & D \\ A & B & B & D \end{pmatrix}$	$\begin{pmatrix} A & B & C & D \\ \underline{A} & \underline{A} & \underline{A} & \underline{C} \end{pmatrix}$	$\begin{pmatrix} A & B & C & D \\ A & B & B & D \end{pmatrix}$
S_1	$\begin{pmatrix} A & B & C & D \\ A & A & B & B \end{pmatrix}$	$\begin{pmatrix} A & B & C & D \\ \underline{A} & \underline{A} & \underline{A} & \underline{A} \end{pmatrix}$	$\begin{pmatrix} A & B & C & D \\ A & A & B & B \end{pmatrix}$
	$\begin{pmatrix} A & B & C & D \\ A & A & A & C \end{pmatrix}$	$\begin{pmatrix} A & B & C & D \\ A & A & A & C \end{pmatrix}$	$\begin{pmatrix} A & B & C & D \\ \underline{A} & \underline{A} & \underline{A} & \underline{B} \end{pmatrix}$
S_2	$\begin{pmatrix} A & B & C & D \\ A & A & A & A \end{pmatrix}$	$\begin{pmatrix} A & B & C & D \\ A & A & A & A \end{pmatrix}$	$\begin{pmatrix} A & B & C & D \\ A & A & A & A \end{pmatrix}$
	$\begin{pmatrix} A & B & C & D \\ A & A & A & B \end{pmatrix}$	$\begin{pmatrix} A & B & C & D \\ A & A & A & A \end{pmatrix}$	$\begin{pmatrix} A & B & C & D \\ A & A & A & B \end{pmatrix}$

There are no more new transformations, so the computation is complete.

$$\langle S\rangle = \left\{ \begin{pmatrix} A & B & C & D \\ A & B & C & D \end{pmatrix}, \begin{pmatrix} A & B & C & D \\ A & A & C & C \end{pmatrix}, \begin{pmatrix} A & B & C & D \\ A & B & B & D \end{pmatrix}, \begin{pmatrix} A & B & C & D \\ A & A & B & B \end{pmatrix}, \begin{pmatrix} A & B & C & D \\ A & A & A & C \end{pmatrix}, \begin{pmatrix} A & B & C & D \\ A & A & A & A \end{pmatrix}, \begin{pmatrix} A & B & C & D \\ A & A & A & B \end{pmatrix} \right\}$$

△

Proof of Proposition 7.11

Let us first observe that $\langle S\rangle$ must consist of e and all compositions of the form

$$f_1 \diamond f_2 \diamond f_3 \diamond \ldots \diamond f_k \tag{7.25}$$

with each f_i an element of S. Indeed, since $\langle S\rangle$ is a submonoid of T_n and so is closed under composition, $\langle S\rangle$ must contain all transformations as in (7.25). Conversely, the compositions of e and elements of the form (7.25) are again e and elements of the form (7.25). So $\langle S\rangle$ is as claimed.

So we must show that all compositions as in (7.25) appear among the S_i. Let $g_1 = f_1 \diamond f_2$. Then g_1 is in either $S = S_0$ or in S_1. Let $g_2 = g_1 \diamond f_3$. Then g_2 is in either S_0, S_1, or S_2. Observe that

$$g_2 = g_1 \diamond f_3 = f_1 \diamond f_2 \diamond f_3 \tag{7.26}$$

Continuing, we let $g_i = g_{i-1} \diamond f_{i+1}$. Then, if g_{i-1} is in S_j, g_i must be in $S_0, S_1, \ldots, S_j$, or S_{j+1}. Continuing (7.26), we see that g_{k-1} equals the transformation of (7.25).

Since T_n has only a finite number of elements, eventually $S_i = \varnothing$ and the computation is complete. □

Example 7.47

We redo Example 7.45 using the technique of Proposition 7.11. We retain the notation of Example 7.45 for the various transformations.

		a	b
$S = S_0$	a	$\underline{c}$	b
	b	$\underline{d}$	b
S_1	c	$\underline{e}$	b
	d	$\underline{f}$	b
S_2	e	a	b
	f	b	b

There are no new transformations, so the computation is complete. $S = \{e, a, b, c, d, f\}$. If we wished, we could have omitted e from S_2. △

Just as there are group homomorphisms, there are also monoid and semigroup homomorphisms. The definitions are all quite similar, except that for monoid homomorphisms, we must assume that the identity is mapped to the identity. We shall give a formal definition only for monoids.

Definition 7.13

Let $f: G \to H$ be a map between the monoids $(G, \circ)$ and $(H, *)$. Let e_G and e_H be the identities in G and H respectively. Then f is a **homomorphism** if

(i) $f(a \circ b) = f(a) * f(b)$ for all a, b in G, and also

(ii) $f(e_G) = f(e_H)$.

A homomorphism is **onto** if every element h of H is in the image of f; that is, $f(g) = h$ for some g in G. A homomorphism f is an **isomorphism** if f is also a one-to-one correspondence. ○

Just as group homomorphisms renamed composition tables, a monoid homomorphism $f: G \to H$ will rename the composition table for G as the composition table for a submonoid of H. In doing the renaming, it is convenient first to partition G into those subsets that have the same image under f.

Example 7.48

We let $(G,\circ)$ and $(H,*)$ be the monoids of Table 7.34 and let $f:G\to H$ be given by

$$f:e\to x,\quad a\to x,\quad b\to x,\quad c\to y,\quad d\to x,\quad f\to y$$

Then, as verified in Table 7.34, f is a monoid homomorphism.

For group homomorphisms, it is true that all subsets in the partition have the same number of elements. Observe that this need not be so for monoid homomorphisms. △

Table 7.34 A monoid homomorphism

G

∘	e	a	b	c	d	f
e	e	a	b	c	d	f
a	a	e	b	c	d	f
b	b	d	b	c	d	f
c	c	f	c	c	f	f
d	d	b	b	c	d	f
f	f	c	c	c	f	f

H

*	x	y
x	x	y
y	y	y

Partition of $G: eabd \mid cf$

Homomorphism Verification

G

∘	e	a	b	d	c	f
e	e	a	b	d	c	f
a	a	e	b	d	c	f
b	b	d	b	d	c	f
d	d	b	b	d	c	f
c	c	f	c	f	c	f
f	f	c	c	f	c	f

*	x	x	x	x	y	y
x	x	x	x	x	y	y
x	x	x	x	x	y	y
x	x	x	x	x	y	y
x	x	x	x	x	y	y
y	y	y	y	y	y	y
y	y	y	y	y	y	y

H

*	x	y
x	x	y
y	y	y

Example 7.49

Table 7.35 gives a map $f:G\to H$ between monoids that satisfies Definition 7.13(i), but does not satisfy Definition 7.13(ii). So f is not a *monoid* homomorphism. Note that f *is* a *semigroup* homomorphism. △

Table 7.35 Definition 7.13(i) but not Definition 7.13(ii)

G

∘	e	a
e	e	a
a	a	a

H

*	x	y
x	x	y
y	y	y

$f:e\to y \quad a\to y$

Observe that the map f of Example 7.49 was not onto. The following facts about monoids are demonstrated in the exercises. The identity in a monoid is unique. For a map f between monoids satisfying Definition 7.13(i), $f(e_G)$ is an identity for all elements of H that are in the image of f. So if f is an onto map that satisfies Definition 7.13(i), then f necessarily satisfies Definition 7.13(ii) and so is a monoid homomorphism.

Definition 7.14

Let M be a finite semiautomaton with state set S and input set I. The **monoid of M**, denoted by $(G(M), \diamond)$ or simply $G(M)$, is the monoid of transformations of S that is generated by the transformations of S given by the inputs in the set I, that is, by the transformations of S given by the columns of the next-state table for M. ○

Let i be an input for the machine M of Definition 7.14. We let f_i denote the transformation of S associated to i. That is, $(s)f_i = \nu(s,i)$. Let j be a second input to M. Then $f_i \diamond f_j$ means to first apply f_i and then apply f_j. Looking at a state s in S, we see that f_i first takes s to its next state under the input i. Then f_j takes this state to *its* next state under the input j. So the effect of $f_i \diamond f_j$ is to move s to another state via the input string ij.

For an input string $i_1 i_2 \ldots i_k$ for M, we let $f_{i_1 i_2 \ldots i_k}$ denote the transformation on S resulting from successive inputs of $i_1, i_2, \ldots i_k$. Then

$$f_i \diamond f_j = f_{ij}$$

In general, if a and b are input strings,

$$f_{\mathbf{a}} \diamond f_{\mathbf{b}} = f_{\mathbf{ab}} \tag{7.27}$$

Table 7.36 A finite semiautomaton M

Current state	Next-state function Input 0	1
x	y	y
y	z	y
z	z	y

where **ab** is the concatenation of the strings **a** and **b**. Recall that **e** denotes the empty string. Then we let $f_{\mathbf{e}}$ denote the identity transformation *on* S; that is, receiving no input, the machine M retains its current state. Then $G(M)$ of Definition 7.14 may also be thought of as all transformations of S that occur as the result of input *strings*, and not merely single inputs.

It is important to observe that often we shall have $f_{\mathbf{a}} = f_{\mathbf{b}}$ with **a** and **b** different input strings. Indeed, since S is a finite set, there can only be a finite number of transformations in $G(M)$. But since the input strings may be arbitrarily long, there are an infinite number of input strings.

Example 7.50

We use Proposition 7.11 to compute $G(M)$ for M of Table 7.36. Since the current states are listed in a column in a next-state table, it is convenient to represent transformations using columns, rather than rows. Thus,

$$f_0 = \begin{pmatrix} x & y \\ y & z \\ z & z \end{pmatrix} \quad f_1 = \begin{pmatrix} x & y \\ y & y \\ z & y \end{pmatrix} \quad f_{\mathbf{e}} = \begin{pmatrix} x & x \\ y & y \\ z & z \end{pmatrix}$$

Table 7.37 Composition table for $(G(M), \diamond)$

$\diamond$	f_e	f_0	f_1	f_{00}
f_e	f_e	f_0	f_1	f_{00}
f_0	f_0	f_{00}	f_1	f_{00}
f_1	f_1	f_{00}	f_1	f_{00}
f_{00}	f_{00}	f_{00}	f_1	f_{00}

$$S = S_0 \begin{array}{c|cc} \diamond & f_0 & f_1 \\ \hline f_0 & f_{00} & f_1 \\ f_1 & f_{00} & f_1 \\ \hline S_1 \; f_{00} & f_{00} & f_1 \end{array} \tag{7.28}$$

where $f_{00} = f_{10} = \begin{pmatrix} x & z \\ y & z \\ z & z \end{pmatrix}$. Then $G(M) = \{f_e, f_0, f_1, f_{00}\}$.

Using (7.28) as follows, or by direct computation, we can compute Table 7.37, the composition table for $(G(M), \diamond)$.

$$\begin{aligned} f_1 \diamond f_{00} &= f_1 \diamond (f_0 \diamond f_0), && \text{from (7.28)} \\ &= (f_1 \diamond f_0) \diamond f_0, && \text{by associativity} \\ &= f_{00} \diamond f_0, && \text{from (7.28)} \\ &= f_{00}, && \text{from (7.28)} \end{aligned}$$

△

Example 7.51

Using (7.27) and (7.28), we compute $f_{\mathbf{a}}$ for M of Table 7.36 and various input strings $\mathbf{a}$.

$$\begin{aligned} f_{110} &= f_1 \diamond f_1 \diamond f_0, && \text{by (7.27)} \\ &= (f_1 \diamond f_1) \diamond f_0, && \text{by associativity} \\ &= f_1 \diamond f_0, && \text{by (7.28)} \\ &= f_{00}, && \text{by (7.28)} \end{aligned}$$

$$f_{110} = f_{00} = \begin{pmatrix} x & z \\ y & z \\ z & z \end{pmatrix}, \text{ listed in (7.28)}$$

$$\begin{aligned} f_{1010} &= (f_1 \diamond f_0) \diamond f_1 \diamond f_0 = f_{00} \diamond f_1 \diamond f_0 \\ &= (f_{00} \diamond f_1) \diamond f_0 = f_1 \diamond f_0 = f_{00} \end{aligned}$$

△

Table 7.38 A finite semiautomaton M

Current state	Next-state function, Input 0	Input 1
x	y	y
y	z	y
z	x	y

Example 7.52

We compute $G(M)$ for M of Table 7.38.

$$f_0 = \begin{pmatrix} x & y \\ y & z \\ z & x \end{pmatrix} \quad f_1 = \begin{pmatrix} x & y \\ y & y \\ z & y \end{pmatrix} \quad f_e = \begin{pmatrix} x & x \\ y & y \\ z & z \end{pmatrix}$$

	$\diamond$	f_0	f_1
$S=S_0$	f_0	f_{00}	f_1
	f_1	f_{10}	f_1
S_1	f_{00}	f_e	f_1
	f_{10}	f_{100}	f_1
S_2	f_{100}	f_1	f_1

$$f_{00}=\begin{pmatrix} x & z \\ y & x \\ z & y \end{pmatrix} \qquad f_{10}=\begin{pmatrix} x & z \\ y & z \\ z & z \end{pmatrix}$$

$$f_{100}=\begin{pmatrix} x & x \\ y & x \\ z & x \end{pmatrix}$$

Then $G(M)=\{f_e,f_0,f_1,f_{00},f_{10},f_{100}\}$.

A compact way to write out the elements of $G(M)$ as transformations is

Current state	f_e	f_0	f_1	f_{00}	f_{10}	f_{100}
x	x	y	y	z	z	x
y	y	z	y	x	z	x
z	z	x	y	y	z	x

△

Proposition 7.12

Let M be a finite semiautomaton with input set I. Let $F:I^*\rightarrow G(M)$ be given by $F(\mathbf{a})=f_{\mathbf{a}}$. Then F is an onto monoid homomorphism from $(I^*,\circ)$ to $(G(M),\diamond)$.

Proof of Proposition 7.12

$G(M)$ is precisely all transformations of the form $f_{\mathbf{a}}$, with $\mathbf{a}$ an input string. So F is certainly an onto map. We must verify the two conditions of Definition 7.13.

For Definition 7.13(i), let $\mathbf{a}$ and $\mathbf{b}$ be input strings, that is, elements of I^*. We must compare $F(\mathbf{ab})$ with $F(\mathbf{a})\diamond F(\mathbf{b})$. $F(\mathbf{ab})=f_{\mathbf{ab}}$, while $F(\mathbf{a})\diamond F(\mathbf{b})=f_{\mathbf{a}}\diamond f_{\mathbf{b}}$. However, $f_{\mathbf{ab}}=f_{\mathbf{a}}\diamond f_{\mathbf{b}}$ is just (7.27). So Definition 7.28(i) is satisfied.

The empty string $\mathbf{e}$ is the identity element in I^*. $F(\mathbf{e})=f_e$ is the identity transformation. □

Exercises 7.6

1. Verify that the following laws of composition are not associative. Are these sets monoids?

a.

$\circ$	a	b	c
a	a	b	c
b	b	a	b
c	c	b	a

b.

$\circ$	a	b	c	d
a	b	a	c	a
b	c	c	c	b
c	b	a	d	c
d	a	b	c	d

2. Verify that the following map f from $(\mathbb{Z}_6, \cdot)$ to $(\mathbb{Z}_2, \cdot)$ is a monoid homomorphism.

$$f: 0 \to 0, \quad 1 \to 1, \quad 2 \to 0, \quad 3 \to 1, \quad 4 \to 0, \quad 5 \to 1$$

3. Verify that the following map $f: G \to H$ is a monoid homomorphism. G and H are the following monoids.

$$f: e \to E, \quad a \to A, \quad b \to A$$

G

	e	a	b
e	e	a	b
a	a	a	a
b	b	b	b

H

	E	A
E	E	A
A	A	A

4. Compute $\langle S \rangle$ for each of the following sets S of transformations.

a. $\begin{pmatrix} a & b \\ b & a \end{pmatrix}, \begin{pmatrix} a & b \\ b & b \end{pmatrix}$ b. $\begin{pmatrix} A & B & C \\ B & A & C \end{pmatrix}, \begin{pmatrix} A & B & C \\ B & B & B \end{pmatrix}$

c. $\begin{pmatrix} a & b & c \\ b & c & c \end{pmatrix}, \begin{pmatrix} a & b & c \\ a & a & b \end{pmatrix}$

5. For the following machine, compute the transformations on states given by the given input strings.

Current state	Next-state function, Input 0	1	2
w	w	x	y
x	x	x	z
y	y	x	z
z	z	y	x

a. 02 b. 1120 c. 11200

6. Compute the monoid of each of the following finite semiautomata. You need not give the composition table.

a.

Current state	Next-state function Input 0	1
x	z	x
y	x	y
z	y	z

b.

Current state	Next-state function Input 0	1	2
x	z	x	y
y	x	x	y
z	y	x	y

c.

Current state	Next-state function Input 0	1	2
w	w	x	w
x	x	x	w
y	y	y	z
z	z	y	z

d.

Current state	Next-state function Input 0	1	2
w	x	w	z
x	y	w	z
y	w	w	z
z	z	w	z

7. Assuming associativity, explain why $(\mathbb{Z}_n, \cdot)$ is a monoid for all positive integers n. Why is $(\mathbb{Z}_n, \cdot)$ not a group for $n \geq 2$?
8. a. Show that the monoids $(\mathbb{Z}_2, +)$ and $(\mathbb{Z}_2, \cdot)$ are not isomorphic.
   b. Let $(G, \circ)$ be a monoid with two elements. Show that $(G, \circ)$ is isomorphic either to $(\mathbb{Z}_2, +)$ or to $(\mathbb{Z}_2, \cdot)$.
9. Show that the operation of concatenation, from Example 7.40, is associative.
10. Show that $(I^+, \circ)$ from Example 7.40 has no identity.
    Hint: Show that concatenation adds the lengths of the strings.
11. Let $(G, \circ)$ be a monoid. Show that the identity in G is unique.
12. Let S_i be defined as in Proposition 7.11. Explain why e is contained in one of the sets $S_0, S_1, S_2, \ldots, S_i$ if and only if some element of $S = S_0$ is a permutation.
13. Show that $\langle S \rangle$ may also be computed by Proposition 7.11 changed to have S_i, $i \geq 2$, defined as the set of all new transformations that appear as compositions of elements of S and elements of S_{i-1}.
14. Define homomorphism for semigroups.
15. a. Define transformation semigroups.
    b. Modify Proposition 7.11 so as to compute the transformation semigroup generated by S.

16. Let $f: G \to H$ be a map between monoids $(G, \circ)$ and $(H, *)$ such that $f(a \circ b) = f(a) * f(b)$. Let I denote the image of the map f. Show that $(I, *)$ is a monoid with $f(e_G)$ as the identity.
17. Let $f: G \to H$ be an onto map between the monoids $(G, \circ)$ and $(H, *)$ such that $f(a \circ b) = f(a) * f(b)$. Let e_G and e_H denote the identities in G and in H respectively. Show that $f(e_G) = e_H$.

    Hint: Use Exercises 11 and 16.
18. Let $I = \{a, b\}$. Let $(G, \circ)$ be any monoid. Let $f: I \to G$ be any map. Show that there is a unique monoid homomorphism $f^*: I^* \to G$ such that $f^*(a) = f(a)$ and $f^*(b) = f(b)$.
19. Let S be a set of permutations on n letters. Explain why the set $\langle S \rangle$ computed as a subset of S_n using $\circ$ as composition is the same as $\langle S \rangle$ computed as subset of T_n using $\diamond$ as composition.

8 Formal Languages

The mathematical formalization of grammar has been inspired by natural languages such as English and French, and by high-level computer languages such as FORTRAN, ALGOL, and Pascal. Historically, parts of Noam Chomsky's seminal work on natural languages were seen to apply to ALGOL.

This chapter begins with a simplified version of Chomsky's phrase-structure grammar for English. We then see that this type of grammar is similar to Backus-Naur form for ALGOL. The second section formalizes the grammars of the first section as context-free grammars. The corresponding languages are called context-free languages. The third section is devoted to the simple, but important, class of context-free languages called *regular languages*. Regular languages are precisely those languages that can be recognized by finite-state machines. In the final section of this chapter, we use monoid homomorphisms to give a purely algebraic description of regular languages.

8.1 Examples

First, a variation of Chomsky's phrase-structure grammar for English is given. Then we describe ALGOL numbers using Backus-Naur form. The reader may wish to learn elsewhere about Chomsky's more sophisticated transformational grammar.

Example 8.1

Consider the sentence *John and Mary solved many hard problems.* Words in English can be divided into parts of speech. In the above sentence, there are nouns: *John, Mary, problems*; a verb: *solved*; adjectives: *many, hard*; and a conjunction: *and.* The structure of the sentence, that is, how the words are connected, may be described by using some of rules (i)–(vii), which follow. In these rules, → means "may be replaced by one of the following." The abbreviations in (i)–(vii) are

S = sentence

NP = noun phrase

VP = verb phrase

N = noun

A = adjective

C = conjunction

V = verb

(i) S → NP VP
(ii) NP → {NP C NP, A NP, N}
(iii) VP → V NP
(iv) N → {*John, Mary, problems, men, women, fruit, ...*}
(v) C → {*and, or, ...*}
(vi) A → {*many, hard, old, ...*}
(vii) V → {*solved, eat, saw, see, ...*}

Table 8.1 shows how to use rules (i)–(vii) to give the structure of the sentence *John and Mary solved many hard problems*. Such a sequence of applications of grammatical rules, starting from *S*, is a **derivation**. △

Table 8.1 A derivation

Rule(s)	Derived string
	S
S → NP VP	NP VP
NP → NP C NP	NP C NP VP
NP → N NP → N	N C N VP
C → *and*	N *and* N VP
N → *John* N → *Mary*	*John and Mary* VP
VP → V NP	*John and Mary* V NP
V → *solved*	*John and Mary solved* NP
NP → A NP	*John and Mary solved* A NP
NP → A NP	*John and Mary solved* A A NP
NP → N	*John and Mary solved* A A N
A → *many* A → *hard*	*John and Mary solved many hard* N
N → *problems*	*John and Mary solved many hard problems*

Table 8.1 is unnecessarily complicated for showing the derivation. So it is customary and convenient to eliminate the duplications and to form a *derivation tree*, as in Figure 8.1. The derivation tree starts at the top with S, the initial derived string in Table 8.1. Each use of a rule in the derivation

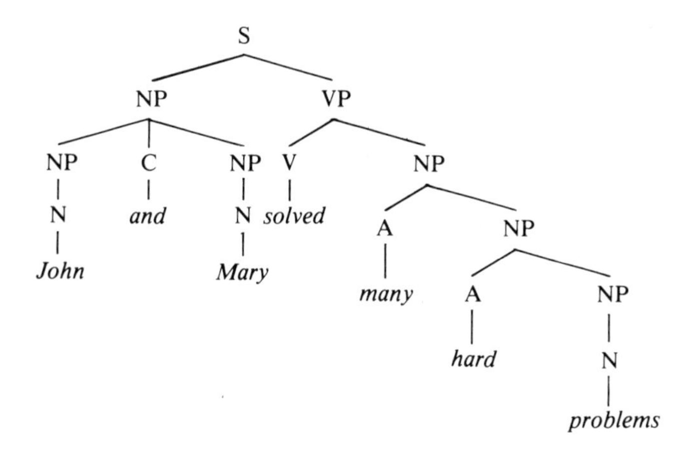

Figure 8.1 Derivation tree for Table 8.1

yields new edges and new vertices as follows: The rule says to replace an old symbol by a chosen set of new symbols. The old symbol is already a vertex of the tree. Add the new symbols to the tree as vertices. Add edges to the tree connecting the old symbol to the new symbols. In a drawing of the derivation tree, the new symbols are placed below the old symbol.

The original sentence *John and Mary solved many hard problems* may be recovered from Figure 8.1 by reading the English words in their order from the "outside" of the tree. More formally, both postorder of Definition 4.13 and preorder of Definition 4.14 yield the (same) correct order on the English words. So what information has been lost in going from the derivation of Table 8.1 to the derivation tree of Figure 8.1? Table 8.1 lists the exact order in which the rules are applied. Figure 8.1 only says that the use of some rules must precede the use of other rules. But this loss of information is desirable, since the lost information is really unrelated to the structure of the sentence.

Example 8.2

Table 8.2 gives another derivation, besides that of Table 8.1, for *John and Mary solved many hard problems.* We could easily check that Table 8.2 also has Figure 8.1 as its derivation tree. △

We could, of course, have introduced different rules in Example 8.1 and obtained a shorter derivation. However, in addition to *John and Mary solved many hard problems*, the rules of Example 8.1 will generate many other sentences that are typical of English. So we accept the long derivation of Example 8.1.

Needless to say, rules (i)–(vii) of Example 8.1 are woefully inadequate to describe English. Most grammatically correct sentences require additional rules. Also, the rules of Example 8.1 yield grammatically correct nonsense sentences such as *Old problems saw fruit.* Finally, these rules are

Table 8.2 A derivation

Rule(s)	Derived string
	S
S→NP VP	NP VP
VP→V NP	NP V NP
V→*solved*	NP *solved* NP
NP→A NP	NP *solved* A NP
NP→A NP	NP *solved* A A NP
NP→N	NP *solved* A A N
A→*many* A→*hard*	NP *solved many hard* N
N→*problems*	NP *solved many hard problems*
NP→NP C NP	NP C NP *solved many hard problems*
NP→N NP→N	N C N *solved many hard problems*
N→*John* N→*Mary*	*John* C *Mary solved many hard problems*
C→*and*	*John and Mary solved many hard problems*

in error in that they do not require, for example, in (i) that NP and VP both be singular or plural.

One major advantage of a set of rules such as (i)–(vii) of Example 8.1, or of more traditional grammars also, is that they often resolve ambiguities in meaning. As suggested above, it is a difference in derivation trees (and not in derivations) that distinguishes meanings.

Example 8.3

Consider the sentence

Old men and women eat fruit. **(8.1)**

Two common interpretations of (8.1) are:

(1) Old men and old women eat fruit, but nothing is said about young women; that is, *old* modifies both *men* and *women.*
(2) Old men and all women eat fruit; that is, *old* modifies *men* but does not modify *women.*

The different derivation trees for (1) and (2) are given in Figure 8.2 and Figure 8.3 respectively. △

Parts of many computer programming languages are described in Backus-Naur form (BNF). In BNF, the symbol | means "or", ⟨...⟩ means an element of the given set, and ::= means "is defined to be."

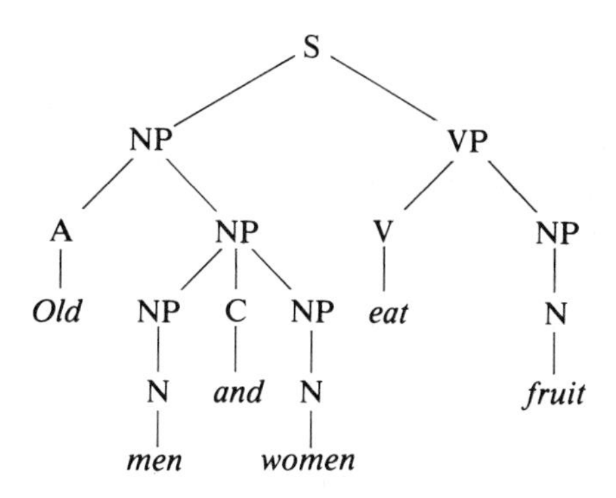

Figure 8.2 Derivation tree for (1)

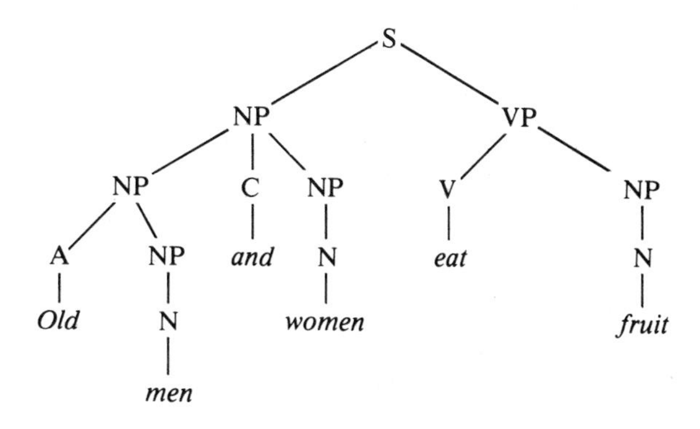

Figure 8.3 Derivation tree for (2)

Example 8.4

Neglecting exponential parts, numbers in ALGOL are defined in BNF as follows:

(i) ⟨digit⟩ ::= 0|1|2|3|4|5|6|7|8|9
(ii) ⟨unsigned integer⟩ ::= ⟨digit⟩|⟨unsigned integer⟩ ⟨digit⟩
(iii) ⟨decimal number⟩ ::= ⟨unsigned integer⟩|. ⟨unsigned integer⟩|
⟨unsigned integer⟩. ⟨unsigned integer⟩
(iv) ⟨number⟩ ::= ⟨decimal number⟩|+⟨decimal number⟩|
−⟨decimal number⟩

We shall use the following abbreviations:

D = digit

UI = unsigned integer

DN = decimal number

Nu = number

Then, following the notation of Example 8.1, rules (i)–(iv) may be rewritten as

(i) D→{0,1,2,3,4,5,6,7,8,9}
(ii) UI→{D, UI D}
(iii) DN→{UI, .UI, UI.UI}
(iv) Nu→{DN, +DN, −DN}

The numbers 7, −315, and 2.713 then have derivation trees as in Figures 8.4, 8.5, and 8.6 respectively. △

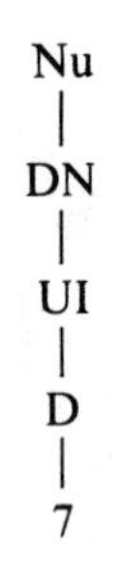

Figure 8.4 Derivation tree for 7

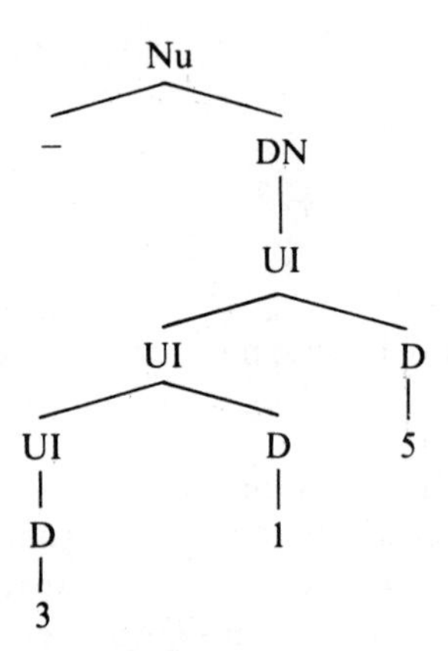

Figure 8.5 Derivation tree for −315

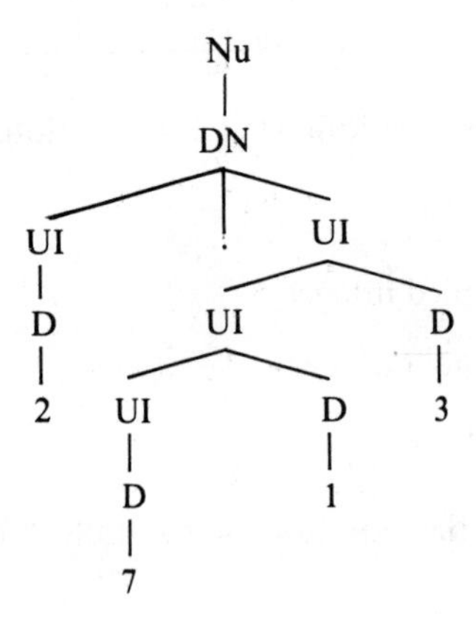

Figure 8.6 Derivation tree for 2.713

Exercises 8.1

1. Write out a derivation, as in Table 8.1, for each of the following sentences. Use the rules of Example 8.1.
   a. *John saw Mary.*
   b. *Peaches and pears are fruits.*
   c. *John eats raw meat.*

2. Write out a second, different derivation for each of the sentences in Exercise 1.

3. Give derivation trees for each of the sentences in Exercise 1.

4. Write derivation trees for each of the following sentences. Use the rules of Example 8.1.
   a. *Three old men threw four bowling balls.*
   b. *John and Mary climbed six tall hills and two huge mountains.*

5. Using the rules of Example 8.4, give derivation trees for the following ALGOL numbers
   a. 29 b. -7.91 c. $+.124$ d. -21.90

6. For each of the following ambiguous sentences, give two distinct derivation trees.
   a. *Bill likes red apples and wine.*
   b. *Four boys and girls visited Jane.*

7. *The*, *a*, and *an* are called **articles**. Observe that successive articles never occur in English. Let NP′ denote a noun phrase that does not begin with an article.
   a. Modify the rules of Example 8.1 so as to include the use of articles.
   b. Give derivation trees for the sentences

      (i) *The handsome young man kissed the beautiful woman.*
      (ii) *John and the old dog walked home.*

8. In ALGOL, an **identifier** is a letter followed by zero or more digits and letters.
   a. Write rules, as in Example 8.4, that describe all identifiers.
   b. Give derivation trees for the following identifiers

      L, LABEL, AOK, A123

9. Write out the rules that are used in each of the following derivation trees.

a.

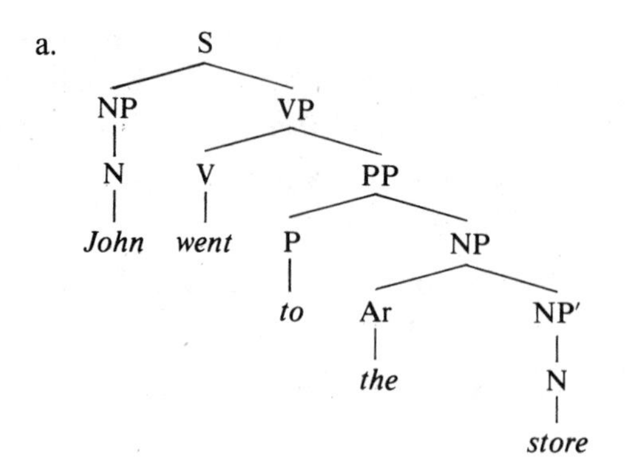

b.

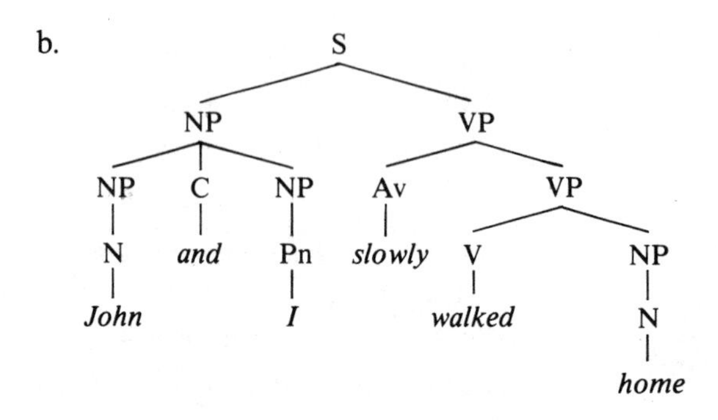

10. Instead of using the ALGOL term "number," Pascal uses the term *constant*. Neglecting exponential parts, Pascal constants are described in BNF via

 (i) ⟨digit⟩ ::= 0|1|2|3|4|5|6|7|8|9
 (ii) ⟨unsigned integer⟩ ::= ⟨digit⟩|⟨digit⟩ ⟨unsigned integer⟩
 (iii) ⟨unsigned number⟩ ::= ⟨unsigned integer⟩|
 ⟨unsigned integer⟩.⟨unsigned integer⟩
 (iv) ⟨sign⟩ ::= +|−
 (v) ⟨constant⟩ ::= ⟨unsigned number⟩|⟨sign⟩ ⟨unsigned number⟩

 a. Using your own abbreviations, give the derivation trees for each of the Pascal constants

 7, −315, 2.713

 b. Explain why .37 is a valid ALGOL number, but is not a valid Pascal constant.

8.2 Context-Free Languages

We now formalize some of the ideas introduced in the previous section. Context-free grammars and languages will be defined and illustrated. Context-sensitive grammars are also mentioned briefly.

Let V be a set. Recall from Example 7.40 that V^* denotes all strings of elements of V. The empty string **e** is included in V^*.

Example 8.5

Let $V = \{man, eats, food\}$. Here are some typical elements of V^*:

man eats food, *food eats man*, *food*, *food food man*, *e*,

man man eats

These strings are simply sequences of some English words. Only some of the strings make sense. △

Example 8.6

Let V consist of those symbols that are needed to write all ALGOL numbers; that is $V = \{0,1,2,3,4,5,6,7,8,9,.,+,-\}$. Some elements of V^* are:

$$90.003, \quad -556, \quad +67-9..-09, \quad ..+-987.07-, \quad .00078$$

Only some of these strings are valid ALGOL numbers. △

Example 8.7

At the machine level, computers tend to work with bits. So a common V is $V = \{0,1\}$. The following notation will be convenient: 0^n denotes a string of n 0's. Thus $0^3 = 000$, $0^4 = 0000$. Similarly, 1^n denotes a string of n 1's. These symbols may be combined. Here are some elements of V^*:

$$0^3 1^4 0^2 1 = 0001111001 \qquad 1^3 1^2 0^4 10 = 11111000010$$

$$0^5 1^5 0^5 = 000001111100000 \qquad 1^0 = \mathbf{e}$$

△

Think of V as providing the words for a language. Think of V^* as all possible, including nonsense, sentences. Then

Definition 8.1

Let V be a set. A **language** L is a subset of V^*. L may be $\varnothing$, the empty subset. ○

Example 8.8

Let $V = \{0,1\}$. Here are some examples of languages, in formal set notation, using this V.

V^*, that is, all strings $\mathbf{v}$

$\{\mathbf{v} \in V^* \mid \mathbf{v}$ has an even number of 1's$\}$

$\{\mathbf{v} \in V^* \mid \mathbf{v}$ is a string of 0's followed by a string of 1's$\}$

$\{\mathbf{v} \in V^* \mid \mathbf{v} = 0^i 1^j 0^i$, for i and j nonnegative integers$\}$ △

Definition 8.2

A **grammar** G is a set of rules for constructing a language. The constructed language, called the **language generated by the grammar**, is denoted by $L(G)$. ○

The rules of Example 8.1 and Example 8.4 are thus grammars in the sense of Definition 8.2. For Example 8.4, the language generated by the grammar is the set of ALGOL numbers.

Example 8.9

The same language may be described by more than one grammar. Thus consider the language of all ALGOL numbers. Example 8.4 gives one grammar for this language. Rules (iii) and (iv) of Example 8.4 may be replaced by the more complicated rule (iii′) as follows:

$$\text{(iii}'\text{)}\quad \text{Nu} \rightarrow \{\text{UI},\ \ .\text{UI},\ \ \text{UI.UI},\ \ +\text{UI},\ \ +.\text{UI},\ \ +\text{UI.UI},\ \ -\text{UI},\ \ -.\text{UI},\ \ -\text{UI.UI}\}$$

Then rules (i), (ii), and (iii′) also give a grammar that generates all ALGOL numbers. △

The rules of Example 8.1, Example 8.4, and Example 8.9 all give context-free grammars, defined formally in Definition 8.3. Each replacement choice in a rule will now be called a **production**.

Definition 8.3

A **context-free grammar** G consists of the following:

(i) N, a finite set of **nonterminals**.

(ii) s, a special element of N called the **starting symbol**.

(iii) T, a finite set of **terminals**. N and T must have no elements in common.

(iv) P, a finite set of **productions**. Each production is of the form $a \rightarrow \mathbf{b}$ with a in N and $\mathbf{b}$ in $(N \cup T)*$. In particular, $\mathbf{b}$ may be the empty string $\mathbf{e}$. ○

Definition 8.4

Let G be a context-free grammar, as in Definition 8.3. $L(G)$, the language **generated** by G, is the subset of T^* whose elements appear in the following construction: The starting symbol s is the initial **derived** string in $(N \cup T)^*$. If $s \rightarrow \mathbf{b}$ is a production, then s may be replaced by $\mathbf{b}$ to form a new derived string in $(N \cup T)^*$. In general, given a derived string $\mathbf{v}$ in $(N \cup T)^*$ such that $\mathbf{v}$ contains the nonterminal a, if $a \rightarrow \mathbf{c}$ is a production, then a may be replaced by $\mathbf{c}$ in $\mathbf{v}$ to form a new derived string in $(N \cup T)^*$. $L(g)$ consists of those derived strings that are in fact elements of T^*. ○

Definition 8.5

Let $\mathbf{v}$ be generated by the context-free grammar G; that is, $\mathbf{v}$ is in $L(G)$. A sequence

$$s = \mathbf{v}_0, \quad b = \mathbf{v}_1, \quad \mathbf{v}_2, \ldots, \mathbf{v}_{k-1}, \quad \mathbf{v}_k = \mathbf{v}$$

of derived strings as in Definition 8.4 that demonstrate that **v** is indeed in $L(G)$ is a **derivation** of **v**. ○

Given a derivation as in Definition 8.5, we may construct a derivation tree as in Section 8.1. Since none of our theorems will involve derivation trees, we shall omit a formal definition.

Example 8.10

We describe a context-free grammar G such that $L(G)$ consists of all strings of 0's followed by a single 1.

(i) and (ii) $N=\{s\}$
(iii) $T=\{0,1\}$
(iv) There are two productions:

$$s \to 0s \qquad s \to 1$$

It turns out that derivations (and hence also derivation trees) are unique for this G. Table 8.3 gives the derivation of 00001. Figure 8.7 gives the derivation tree.

Table 8.3 Derivation for 00001

Production	Derived string
	s
$s \to 0s$	$0s$
$s \to 0s$	$00s$
$s \to 0s$	$000s$
$s \to 0s$	$0000s$
$s \to 1$	00001

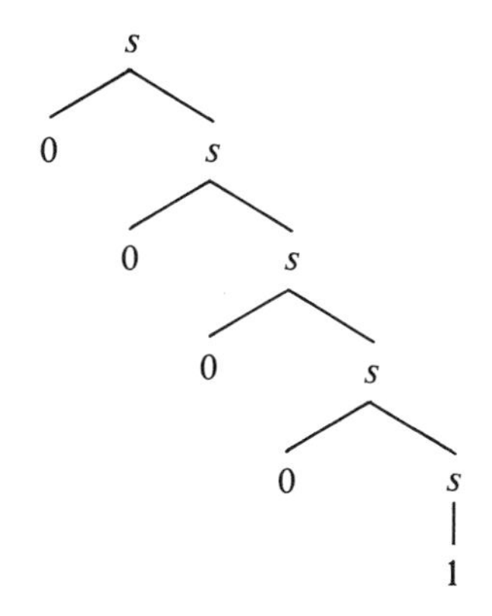

Figure 8.7 Derivation tree for Table 8.3

To see that $L(G)$ is as claimed, we may argue as follows: A derivation stops when the derived string consists only of terminals. In (iv), production $s \to 0s$ retains the number of nonterminals while production $s \to 1$ decreases the number of nonterminals by 1. A derivation starts with s, one nonterminal. So a derivation requires an initial sequence of the productions $s \to 0s$, yielding derived strings of 0's followed by s, and finally the production $s \to 1$, yielding the derived string of 0's followed by 1. △

Example 8.11

$L(G)$ will be $\{0,1\}^* - \{\mathbf{e}\}$, that is, all nonempty strings of 0's and 1's. G will be context-free.

(i) and (ii) $N = \{s\}$
(iii) $T = \{0,1\}$
(iv) There are four productions,

$$s \to 0s \qquad s \to 1s \qquad s \to 0 \qquad s \to 1$$

To see that $L(G)$ is as claimed, first observe that the productions $s \to 0$ and $s \to 1$ yield the two possible strings of length 1. The productions $s \to 0s$ and $s \to 1s$ combine to yield as derived strings all possible nonempty sequences of 0's and 1's that are followed by an s. Replacing this last s with a 0 or a 1 via $s \to 0$ or $s \to 1$, respectively, gives all strings of length at least two as derived strings. △

Example 8.12

$L(G)$ will be $\{0,1\}^*$. G will be context-free.

(i) and (ii) $N = \{s\}$
(iii) $T = \{0,1\}$
(iv) There are three productions

$$s \to \mathbf{e} \qquad s \to 0s \qquad s \to 1s$$

where $\mathbf{e}$ is the empty string. Table 8.4 gives the derivation for 1011. Observe in Table 8.4 that the final production $s \to \mathbf{e}$ just deletes s from the

Table 8.4 Derivation of 1011

Production	Derived string
	s
$s \to 1s$	$1s$
$s \to 0s$	$10s$
$s \to 1s$	$101s$
$s \to 1s$	$1011s$
$s \to \mathbf{e}$	1011

old derived string. The complete verification that $L(G)=T^*$ is left as an exercise. △

Example 8.13

We give a context-free grammar G such that $L(G)$ is all nonempty strings of 0's and 1's with an even number of 1's.

(i) and (ii) $N=\{s,t\}$
(iii) $T=\{0,1\}$
(iv) There are six productions:

$$s\to 0 \qquad s\to 0s \qquad s\to 1t \qquad t\to 1 \qquad t\to 0t \qquad t\to 1s$$

Table 8.5 gives the derivation of 1001110, but why is $L(G)$ completely as claimed? The productions in (iv) either retain or decrease the number of nonterminals in a derived string. So a derivation has an initial multiple use of the productions $s\to 0s$, $s\to 1t$, $t\to 0t$, and $t\to 1s$. These derived strings consist of, as in Table 8.5, 0's and 1's followed by either s or t. The final production in a derivation is either $s\to 0$ or $t\to 1$. Think of s as denoting an even number of 1's and t as denoting an odd number of 1's. The initial derived string, s, has (correctly) an even number, zero, of 1's. The productions $s\to 0s$, $s\to 1t$, $t\to 0t$, $t\to 1s$ add a 0 or a 1 to the derived string and appropriately choose s or t at the end. The final production of $s\to 0$ or $t\to 1$ appropriately retains or changes the parity of the number of 1's. △

Table 8.5 Derivation of 1001110

Production	Derived string
	s
$s\to 1t$	$1t$
$t\to 0t$	$10t$
$t\to 0t$	$100t$
$t\to 1s$	$1001s$
$s\to 1t$	$10011t$
$t\to 1s$	$100111s$
$s\to 0$	1001110

Example 8.14

$L(G)$ will consist of all nonempty palindromes in 0 and 1, that is, all strings in 0 and 1 that are the same written backwards. For example, 101 is a palindrome, while 1010 is not. G will be context-free.

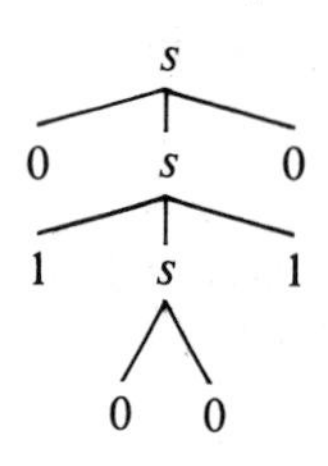

Figure 8.8 Derivation tree for 010010

(i) and (ii) $N=\{s\}$
(iii) $T=\{0,1\}$
(iv) There are six productions:

$$s \to 0s0 \qquad s \to 1s1 \qquad s \to 0 \qquad s \to 1 \qquad s \to 00 \qquad s \to 11$$

Figure 8.8 gives the derivation tree for 010010.

The productions $s \to 0s0$ and $s \to 1s1$ yield derived strings in $(N \cup T)^*$ that are palindromes with an s in the middle. The productions $s \to 0$, $s \to 1$, $s \to 00$, and $s \to 11$ convert these palindromes in $(N \cup T)^*$ to palindromes in T^*. So $L(G)$ consists only of palindromes.

Why does $L(G)$ consist of *all* palindromes in T^*? Consider a palindrome $\mathbf{v}$ of length k. For $k=1,2$, $\mathbf{v}$ is in $L(G)$ via $s \to 0$, $s \to 1$, $s \to 00$, or $s \to 11$. For $k \geq 3$, either $\mathbf{v}=0\mathbf{w}0$ or $v=1\mathbf{w}1$ with $\mathbf{w}$ a palindrome of length $(k-2)$ in T^*. The argument for the two cases are entirely similar, so let us take $\mathbf{v}=0\mathbf{w}0$. If the derivation

$$s=\mathbf{w}_0, \quad \mathbf{w}_1, \quad \mathbf{w}_2, \ldots, \mathbf{w}_{j-1}, \quad \mathbf{w}_j=\mathbf{w}$$

shows that $\mathbf{w}$ is in $L(G)$, then the derivation

$$s=\mathbf{v}_0, \quad 0s0=0\mathbf{w}_0 0=\mathbf{v}_1, \quad 0\mathbf{w}_1 0=\mathbf{v}_2, \quad \ldots, \quad 0\mathbf{w}_{j-1}0=\mathbf{v}_j,$$
$$0\mathbf{w}_j 0=0\mathbf{w}0=\mathbf{v}_{j+1}=\mathbf{v}$$

shows that $\mathbf{v}$ is in $L(G)$. But $\mathbf{w}$ is a palindrome of shorter length than $\mathbf{v}$. Repeating the argument on $\mathbf{w}$ as often as necessary, we see that $\mathbf{v}$ being in $L(G)$ eventually depends on a palindrome of length 1 or 2 being in $L(G)$; but this is true. △

Example 8.15

$L(G)$ will consist of all nonempty strings of 0's and 1's with an equal number of 0's and 1's. G is context-free:

(i) and (ii) $N=\{s\}$
(iii) $T=\{0,1\}$
(iv) There are five productions:

$$s \to 0s1 \qquad s \to 1s0 \qquad s \to ss \qquad s \to 01 \qquad s \to 10$$

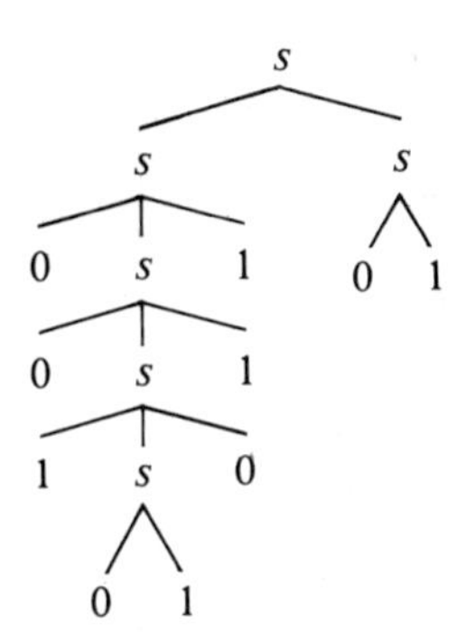

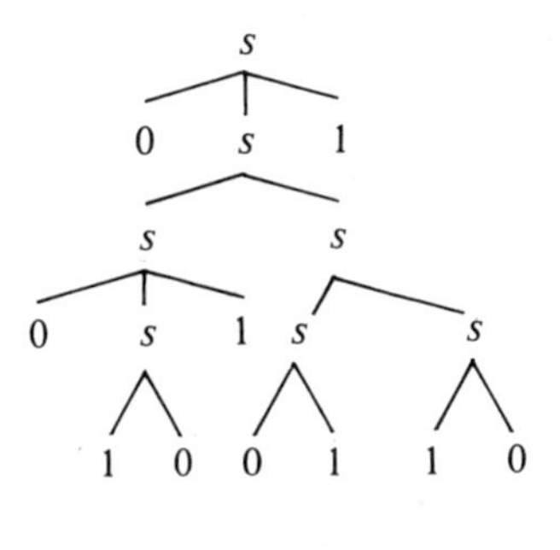

Figure 8.9 Two derivation trees for 0010101101

It should be clear that the productions in (iv) yield only derived strings with an equal number of 0's and 1's. That they yield *all* such strings is not so clear, but it is true; the proof is left as an exercise. With this grammar, derivation trees are not always unique: Figure 8.9 gives two distinct derivation trees for 0010101101. △

Definition 8.6

A language L is **context-free** if there is a context-free grammar G such that $L = L(G)$; that is, L is generated by some context-free grammar. ○

The languages in Examples 8.10–8.15 are, by definition, context free. With difficulty, it may be shown that

$$L = \{\mathbf{v} \in \{0,1\}^* \mid \mathbf{v} = 0^n 1^n 0^n \text{ with } n \text{ a positive integer}\} \tag{8.2}$$

is not context free. In general, it may be extremely difficult to determine if a given language is context free. Also, given two context-free grammars, it can be extremely difficult to determine if they generate the same language.

We close this section with a few words about context-sensitive grammars. A **context-sensitive** grammar is of the form in Definition 8.3 except that productions are of the form

$$\mathbf{p}a\mathbf{q} \to \mathbf{pbq}, \quad \text{with } a \in N, \quad \mathbf{p},\mathbf{q} \in N^*, \quad \mathbf{b} \in (N \cup T)^* - \{\mathbf{e}\} \tag{8.3}$$

(8.3) says that the nonterminal a may be replaced by the nonempty string $\mathbf{b}$ in the context of strings $\mathbf{p}$ and $\mathbf{q}$. L of (8.2) can in fact be generated by a context-sensitive grammar. "Context-sensitive" is more general than "context-free" in the sense that the following will explain. Let L be a context-free language. Then there is a grammar G that is both context free and context sensitive such that $L(G)$ is all of L except possibly for $\mathbf{e}$.

Exercises 8.2

1. For Example 8.4, list explicitly N, s, T, and P of Definition 8.3.
2. Below are productions for "grammars" with $N=\{s,t,u\}$ and $T=\{0,1\}$. Tell which of the grammars are context-free and which are not.
   a. $s\to 01s \quad s\to 0t1 \quad t\to u \quad u\to s0$
   b. $s\to st \quad st\to 010 \quad u\to 01t$
   c. $s\to 01 \quad 0\to 1u \quad u\to 01t$
   d. $s\to 0s \quad s\to 1s \quad s\to t$
   e. $s\to 0s \quad s\to 1t \quad t\to \mathbf{e}$
3. a. As defined in Example 8.4, is 37. an ALGOL number? Why?
   b. What additional rule(s) would be needed to make 37. an ALGOL number?
4. Draw the derivation tree for the derivation of Table 8.4.
   Hint: One of the vertices is **e**.
5. For each of the following languages, give a context-free language that generates it.
   a. $\{\mathbf{v}\in\{0,1\}^* \mid \mathbf{v}$ is all 0's or $\mathbf{v}$ is all 1's, $\mathbf{v}\neq\mathbf{e}\}$
   b. $\{\mathbf{v}\in\{0,1\}^* \mid \mathbf{v}$ has every 0 followed by a 1, $\mathbf{v}\neq\mathbf{e}\}$
   c. $\{\mathbf{v}\in\{0,1\}^* \mid \mathbf{v}$ has length less than 3$\}$
   d. $\{\mathbf{v}\in\{0,1\}^* \mid \mathbf{v}$ has length at least 2$\}$
   e. $\{\mathbf{v}\in\{0,1\}^* \mid \mathbf{v}=0^i1^j0^i$ with i and j positive integers$\}$
6. Give a description, as in Example 8.8 and Exercise 5, for each of the languages generated by the following grammars. All of the grammars are context free with $N=\{s,t,u\}$ and $T=\{0,1\}$. The productions are as indicated.
   a. $s\to 0t \quad t\to 1s \quad s\to 0$
   b. $s\to t1t \quad t\to 0t \quad t\to 0$
   c. $s\to 0t \quad t\to 0t \quad s\to 1t \quad t\to \mathbf{e}$
7. Show as follows that $L(G)$ is as claimed in Example 8.15. Let $\mathbf{v}$ be a string with an equal number of 0's and 1's. Work backwards to get a derivation for $\mathbf{v}$.
   a. Suppose that $\mathbf{v}$ begins with 0 and ends with 1 (or begins with 1 and ends with 0). Then there is a string $\mathbf{w}$, with an equal number of 0's and 1's, such that $\mathbf{v}=0\mathbf{w}1$. As in Example 8.14, if $\mathbf{w}$ is in $L(G)$, then also $\mathbf{v}$ is in $L(G)$.
   b. If $\mathbf{v}$ begins and ends with a 0 (or with a 1), then $\mathbf{v}$ is the concatenation of two shorter strings, each of which has an equal number of 0's and 1's.
   Hint: From left to right, look successively at the number of 0's minus the number of 1's.
8. Explain why a context-free grammar G is also context sensitive if and only if G has no production of the form $a\to\mathbf{e}$.

9. a. Explain how to make a derivation tree into an ordered tree in the sense of Definition 4.12.
   b. Explain why we can recover the generated string $\mathbf{v}=t_1t_2\ldots t_n$ from the tree structure as follows: the t_i are the vertices with no successors, given in either preorder or postorder.
10. Let $T=\{x,y,z,O,I,\vee,\wedge,',(,)\}$. Let $L=\{\mathbf{v}\in T^*|\mathbf{v}$ is a Boolean polynomial in $x,y,z\}$. Show that L is a context-free language.

8.3 Regular Languages

In the previous section many examples of context-free languages were defined and given. In this section, we study the simple, but important, class of context-free languages called **regular languages**. Sometimes regular languages are called **regular sets**. In this section we shall see that regular languages are precisely those languages that can be recognized by finite-state machines. So regular languages are additionally called **finite-state languages**. Machine recognition is of great help in studying regular languages; we show that some context-free languages are not regular languages. In the exercises an algorithm is given to determine whether or not two regular languages are the same.

Definition 8.7

A **regular grammar** is a context-free grammar such that each production is of the form (i) or of the form (ii) as follows:
(i) $a\rightarrow rb$, with a and b nonterminals and r a terminal.
(ii) $a\rightarrow\mathbf{e}$, with a a nonterminal and $\mathbf{e}$ the empty string. ○

A more general definition of a regular grammar is given in the exercises. However, both definitions yield the same regular languages, as in Definition 8.8, which follows.

Definition 8.8

A language L is a **regular language** if $L=L(G)$ for some regular grammar G. ○

Examples 8.16

The grammar of Example 8.12 is a regular grammar. So $\{0,1\}^*$ is a regular language. △

Recall G of Example 8.10. $N=\{s\}$. $T=\{0,1\}$. There are two productions:

$$s\rightarrow 0s \qquad s\rightarrow 1 \tag{8.4}$$

Then G is not a regular grammar since $s\rightarrow 1$ of (8.4) is not of the proper form.

However, $L(G)$ *is* a regular language. Namely, let G' be the regular grammar with $N' = \{s,t\}$, $T' = T = \{0,1\}$ and productions

$$s \to 0s \qquad s \to 1t \qquad t \to \mathbf{e}$$

Then $L(G) = L(G')$ because any use of the production $s \to 1$ in a derivation for $\mathbf{v}$ in $L(G)$ may be replaced by the successive use of the productions $s \to 1t$ and $t \to \mathbf{e}$ to give a derivation for $\mathbf{v}$ in $L(G')$. For example, the derivation in Table 8.3 for 00001 in $L(G)$ becomes the derivation in Table 8.6 for 00001 in $L(G')$. △

Table 8.6 Derivation for 00001

Production	Derived string
	s
$s \to 0s$	$0s$
$s \to 0s$	$00s$
$s \to 0s$	$000s$
$s \to 0s$	$0000s$
$s \to 1t$	$00001t$
$t \to \mathbf{e}$	00001

Example 8.17

G of Example 8.15 is not a regular grammar since none of its productions

$$s \to 0s1 \qquad s \to 1s0 \qquad s \to ss \qquad s \to 01 \qquad s \to 10$$

are of form (i) or (ii) in Definition 8.7. We shall see in Corollary 8.4 that $L(G)$ is not a regular language. △

Proposition 8.1

Let G be a regular grammar. Let v in $L(G)$ have the derivation

$$s = \mathbf{v}_0, \mathbf{v}_1, \mathbf{v}_2, \ldots, \mathbf{v}_{k-1}, \mathbf{v}_k = \mathbf{v}$$

Then the production used to go from $\mathbf{v}_{i-1}$ to $\mathbf{v}_i$ is of the form of Definition 8.7(i) for $i = 1,2,\ldots,k-1$ and of the form of Definition 8.7(ii) for $i = k$. For $i = 1,2,\ldots,k-1$, $\mathbf{v}_i$ consists of a string of terminals followed by a single nonterminal.

Example 8.18

Before proving Proposition 8.1, we shall illustrate its statement. Let G be the regular grammar given by

$$N = \{s,t\} \qquad T = \{0,1\}$$

G has the five productions:

$$s \to 0s \qquad s \to 1t \qquad t \to 0t \qquad t \to 1s \qquad s \to \mathbf{e}$$

The following table gives the derivation of the string 00101 in $L(G)$:

Production	Derived string
	s
$s \to 0s$	$0s$
$s \to 0s$	$00s$
$s \to 1t$	$001t$
$t \to 0t$	$0010t$
$t \to 1s$	$00101s$
$s \to \mathbf{e}$	00101

△

Proof of Proposition 8.1

Look at the number of nonterminals in each $\mathbf{v}_i$. The initial $\mathbf{v}_0 = s$ has one nonterminal. Each production of the form Definition 8.7(i) preserves the number of nonterminals. Each production of the form of Definition 8.7(ii) decreases the number of nonterminals by one. The derivation stops when it reaches a derived string consisting solely of terminals. So the number of nonterminals decreases by one precisely in the derivation step from $\mathbf{v}_{k-1}$ to $\mathbf{v}_k = \mathbf{v}$. □

We now turn to machine recognition of languages. Recall that we allow the empty string $\mathbf{e}$ as an element of a language. We must slightly modify our machines of Chapter 7 so as to get an output for the empty input string $\mathbf{e}$.

Definition 8.9

Let M be a finite semiautomaton, with input set I, as in Definition 7.2. Suppose that the states of M are partitioned into YES states and NO states. Start M in state s_0. M **recognizes** a language L contained in I^* if M reaches a YES state for each input string in L and M reaches a NO state for each input string that is not in L. In particular, M reaches the state s_0 for the empty input string $\mathbf{e}$. ○

Example 8.19

The machine of Figure 8.10 has the states s_0 and s_1. The YES state is s_0 and is double circled in Figure 8.10. The NO state is s_1 and has just a single circle. We can easily see that M of Figure 8.10 recognizes precisely those strings with an even number of 1's. Indeed, the input 1 changes M's state, while the input 0 preserves M's state. So, starting at s_0, to get back to s_0 we

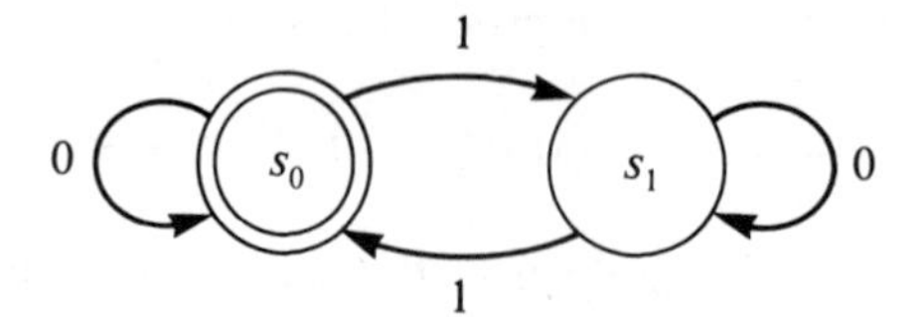

Figure 8.10 A machine M to recognize strings with an even number of 1's

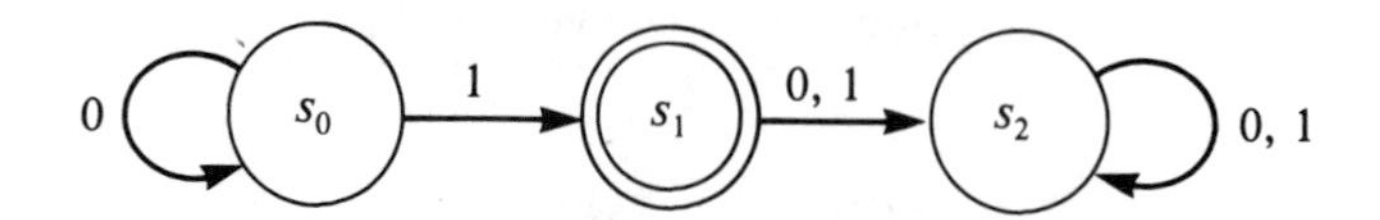

Figure 8.11 A machine M

must leave, return, leave, return, ..., leave, return. This requires an even number of 1's. The 0's are irrelevant. △

Example 8.20

As in Figure 8.10, the machine M of Figure 8.11 has its YES state s_1 double circled. The other, single-circled states are NO states. Then M of Figure 8.11 recognizes those strings that consist of an initial string of all 0's, followed by a single 1. Indeed, starting at s_0 in Figure 8.11, we stay at s_0 as long as the input is 0. Then we go to the YES state s_1 upon receiving a 1. Any additional input sends us to the NO state s_2, where we must remain. △

Theorem 8.2

Let L be the language recognized by the finite machine M, in the sense of Definition 8.9. Then L is a regular language.

Proof of Theorem 8.2

We must exhibit a regular grammar G that generates the language L.

The set N of nonterminals for G is the set S of states for M. The starting symbol s for G is the starting state s_0 for M. The set T of terminals for G is the set I of inputs for M. The productions P for G are given as follows:

(i) Let s_j be a current state for M and let i be an input for M. Let $s_k = \nu(s_j, i)$ be the next state for M. Then G has the production

$$s_j \rightarrow i s_k$$

(ii) Suppose that s_j is a YES state for M. Then G has the production

$$s_j \rightarrow \mathbf{e}$$

G is a regular grammar, since (i) and (ii) preceding are in the form of (i) and (ii) of Definition 8.7.

To see that indeed $L=L(G)$, we must show two things: that every string recognized by M is generated by G and that every string generated by G is recognized by M.

Let $i_1 i_2 i_3 \ldots i_n$ be an input string that is recognized by M. Then the string takes M from its initial state s_0 to some YES state, call it s_n. This state change is given by repeated applications of the next-state function ν, that is, s_0 goes to $s_1=\nu(s_0,i_1)$ and s_1 goes to $s_2=\nu(s_1,i_2)$ and so on until s_{n-1} goes to $s_n=\nu(s_{n-1},i_n)$. The corresponding productions from (i) are

$$s_0 \to i_1 s_1, \quad s_1 \to i_2 s_2, \quad \ldots, \quad s_{n-1} \to i_n s_n \tag{8.5}$$

The productions in (8.5) give

$$i_1 i_2 \ldots i_n s_n \tag{8.6}$$

as a derived string. Since s_n is a YES state, G also has the production $s_n \to \mathbf{e}$ from (ii). Applying this production to (8.6) gives $i_1 i_2 \ldots i_n$ as a derived string.

Now we reconsider the string $i_1 i_2 \ldots i_n$ and suppose that it can be generated by the regular grammar G. We need to show that the string puts M into a YES state. By Proposition 8.1, any derivation for $i_1 i_2 \ldots i_n$ uses productions as follows: $s_1, s_2, \ldots, s_n$ are suitable nonterminals.

$$\begin{aligned} s_0 &\to i_1 s_1 \\ s_1 &\to i_2 s_2 \\ &\cdots \\ s_{n-1} &\to i_n s_n \\ s_n &\to \mathbf{e} \end{aligned} \tag{8.7}$$

However, the first n productions in (8.7) correspond to next-state maps $\nu(s_j,i_{j+1})=s_{j+1}$. So, from starting state s_0, the input string $i_1 i_2 \ldots i_n$ moves M to state s_n. The last derivation in (8.7) says that s_n is a YES state. ◇

Example 8.21

We give an example for the construction in the proof of Theorem 8.2. Figure 8.12 on p. 394 gives the state diagram for the machine M that recognizes all strings of 0's and 1's that contain at least one 1. As usual, the YES state s_1 is double circled. Figure 8.12 also includes a next-state table for the machine M. Appended to the next-state table on p. 394 is a table for YES and NO states.

$N=\{s_0,s_1\}$ with s_0 as the starting symbol

$T=\{0,1\}$

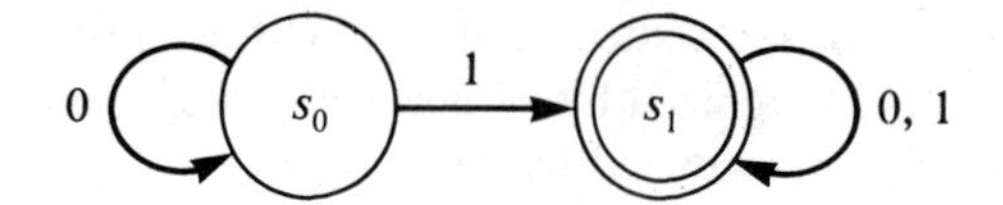

Figure 8.12 A machine M that recognizes strings containing 1

Current state	Next-state function Input 0	1	State type
s_0	s_0	s_1	NO
s_1	s_1	s_1	YES

Each state and input yields a production as in (i) of the proof of Theorem 8.2.

$$s_0 \to 0s_0 \qquad s_0 \to 1s_1 \qquad s_1 \to 0s_1 \qquad s_1 \to 1s_1 \tag{8.8}$$

Each YES state yields a production as in (ii) of the proof of Theorem 8.2 as follows:

$$s_1 \to \mathbf{e} \tag{8.9}$$

Then (8.8) and (8.9) give the productions of the grammar G.

We can easily see directly that $L(G)$ is the set of strings with at least one 1. In fact, virtually the same argument shows that $L(G)$ and the language recognized by M are as claimed. △

Example 8.22

Figure 8.13 gives the state diagram for a machine M that recognizes all strings that begin with 1. Let us give the corresponding grammar G from the proof of Theorem 8.2.

$$N = \{s_0, s_1, s_2\} \qquad s_0 \text{ is the starting symbol}$$
$$T = \{0, 1\}$$

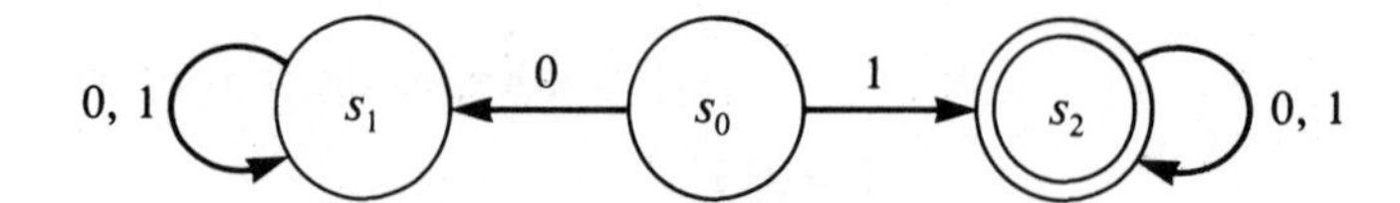

Figure 8.13 A machine M to recognize strings beginning with 1

Three states and two inputs yield $3 \times 2 = 6$ productions of type (i) as follows:

$$s_0 \to 0s_1 \qquad s_0 \to 1s_2 \qquad s_1 \to 0s_1 \qquad s_1 \to 1s_1$$
$$s_2 \to 0s_2 \qquad s_2 \to 1s_2 \tag{8.10}$$

The single YES state yields one production of the form (ii):

$$s_2 \to \mathbf{e} \tag{8.11}$$

Let us consider a derivation using the productions in (8.10) and (8.11). The last production must be (8.11). We observe that the production $s_0 \to 0s_1$ in (8.10) can never lead to a derived string containing s_2 since (8.10) requires that s_1 be replaced by only $0s_1$ or $1s_1$. So the production $s_0 \to 0s_1$ never occurs in a derivation. In fact, the grammar G' with

$N' = \{s_0, s_2\}$ $\quad s_0$ is the starting symbol

$T' = \{0,1\}$ **(8.12)**

G' has the productions

$$s_0 \to 1s_2 \qquad s_2 \to 0s_2 \qquad s_2 \to 1s_2 \qquad s_2 \to \mathbf{e}$$

satisfies $L(G) = L(G')$. So the grammar given in the proof of Theorem 8.2 is not always the most economical regular grammar for generating L. △

Theorem 8.3 states the converse to Theorem 8.2.

Theorem 8.3 Let G be a regular grammar. Then there is a finite semiautomaton M, with starting state s_0 and a partition of the states into YES and NO states, such that M recognizes $L(G)$.

Before proving Theorem 8.3, we shall illustrate the difficulties of its proof and give and illustrate the construction of M.

Examples 8.23 A first attempt to prove Theorem 8.3 might be to reverse the construction of the proof of Theorem 8.2. Let us see what goes wrong.

Let us consider the grammar G' of (8.12) and try to let the states of M be the nonterminals N' of G'. We must give the next-state function. The productions $s_2 \to 0s_2$ and $s_2 \to 1s_2$ tell us that $\nu(s_2,0) = s_2$ and $\nu(s_2,1) = s_2$. We also know from $s_0 \to 1s_2$ that $\nu(s_0,1) = s_2$. However, we do not know $\nu(s_0,0)$ because G' has no production of the form $s_0 \to 0b$, with b a nonterminal. △

Here is a more serious complication. Consider a grammar G with productions

$$s \to 0t \qquad s \to 0u \qquad t \to \mathbf{e}$$

We might like the states of M to be the nonterminals s,t,u. But the production $s \to 0t$ should say that $\nu(s,0)=t$, while the production $s \to 0u$ gives the contradictory next-state value $\nu(s,0)=u$. △

Construction of M for Theorem 8.3

We recall from Definitions 8.3 and 8.7 that G consists of

(i) N, a set of nonterminals
(ii) s, a starting symbol in N
(iii) T, a set of terminals
(iv) Productions of the form

(iv.i) $a \to rb$, a,b in N and r in T
(iv.ii) $a \to \mathbf{e}$, a in N

To specify the semiautomaton M, we must give Definition 7.1(i)–(iii):

(8.13)(i) The state set for M is $\mathscr{P}(N)$, the set of all subsets of N.

(8.13)(ii) The input set for M is T.

(8.13)(iii) The next-state function $\nu:\mathscr{P}(N)\times T \to \mathscr{P}(N)$ for M is given by, for A in $\mathscr{P}(N)$; that is, $A \subset N$, and i in T,

$$\nu(A,i)=\{b \in N \mid \text{there exists a production in } G \text{ of the form } a \to ib, \text{ with } a \in A\}.$$

Theorem 8.3 also requires a starting state s_0 for M and a partition of the states as follows:

(8.13)(iv) $s_0=\{s\}$

(8.13)(v) A in $\mathscr{P}(N)$ is a YES state for M if (and only if) there is some nonterminal a in A such that G has the production $a \to \mathbf{e}$. ○

Before showing that this construction works, we shall give some more examples.

Example 8.24

Consider G given by

$$N=\{s,t\} \qquad T=\{0,1\}$$

G has the productions

$$s \to 1t \qquad t \to 0t \qquad t \to 1t \qquad t \to \mathbf{e}$$

Then G is the same as G' in (8.12), except that s_0, s_2 have been changed to s,t in order to avoid subscripts. Then $L(G)$ is all strings that begin with 1.

Let us describe M as constructed above for Theorem 8.3. N has the following four subsets, which are the states of M:

$$\varnothing, \quad \{s\}, \quad \{t\}, \quad \{s,t\} \qquad \textbf{(8.14)}\text{(i)}$$

The input set for M is

$$T = \{0,1\} \qquad \textbf{(8.14)}\text{(ii)}$$

(8.14)(iii) We must compute the next-state function for M; $v(\{s,t\}, 1)$ is computed as follows: We look for productions in G of the form $a \to 1b$ with a an element of $\{s,t\}$. There are two such productions: $s \to 1t$ and $t \to 1t$. The set of values taken by b is just $\{t\}$. So

$$v(\{s,t\},1) = \{t\}$$

Similarly, $v(\{s\},0)$ is computed as follows: We look at productions of the form $a \to 0b$ with a an element of $\{s\}$. The only element of $\{s\}$ is s, and there are no productions of the form $s \to 0b$. So

$$v(\{s\},0) = \varnothing$$

What about $v(\varnothing,0)$? We look for productions of the form $a \to 0b$ with a an element of $\varnothing$. But $\varnothing$, by definition, has no elements. So there can be no such productions. So

$$v(\varnothing,0) = \varnothing$$

All of the other next-state values for M are computed similarly, yielding the next-state table in Table 8.7.

$$s_0 = \{s\}, \qquad \text{as in (8.14)(i)} \qquad \textbf{(8.14)}\text{(iv)}$$

(8.14)(v) Only the production $t \to \mathbf{e}$ for G is of the form of Definition 8.7(ii). The nonterminal t is an element of $\{t\}$ and $\{s,t\}$ in (8.14)(i). So, as indicated in Table 8.7 on p. 398, these are the YES states for M.

Figure 8.14 gives the machine graph for M. We can easily see directly from Figure 8.14 that M recognizes all strings that begin with 1. Observe, however, that state $\{s,t\}$ is not accessible from the starting state $\{s\}$. So

Table 8.7 Machine M for Example 8.24

Current state	Next-state function, Input 0	Next-state function, Input 1	State type
$\varnothing$	$\varnothing$	$\varnothing$	NO
$\{s\}$	$\varnothing$	$\{t\}$	NO
$\{t\}$	$\{t\}$	$\{t\}$	YES
$\{s,t\}$	$\{t\}$	$\{t\}$	YES

deleting the vertex $\{s,t\}$ and the edges that start at $\{s,t\}$ from Figure 8.14 gives a simpler machine (in fact, the machine of Figure 8.13) that recognizes the same language. △

Example 8.25

Here is another example for the construction of Theorem 8.3. G is given by

$N=\{s,t,u\}$ s is the starting symbol

$T=\{0,1\}$

G has the productions:

$s\to 0t$ $s\to 0u$ $s\to 1u$ $t\to 1u$

$u\to 0u$ $u\to 1s$ $u\to 1u$ $u\to \mathbf{e}$

The states of M are the eight subsets of N:

$\varnothing$ $\{s\}$ $\{t\}$ $\{u\}$

$\{s,t\}$ $\{s,u\}$ $\{t,u\}$ $\{s,t,u\}$

Let us compute $v(\{s\},0)$. We look for productions of the form $a\to 0b$ with a an element of $\{s\}$; a must be s. There are two such productions, $s\to 0t$ and $s\to 0u$. So

$$v(\{s\},0)=\{t,u\}$$

Figure 8.14 Machine graph for Table 8.7

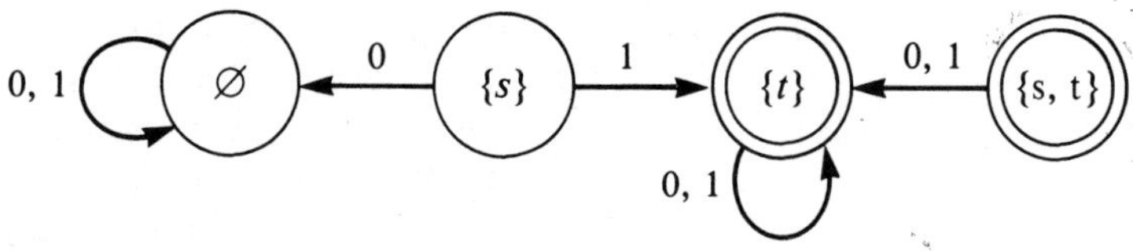

We compute $\nu(\{s,t\},1)$. The relevant productions are $s \to 1u$ and $t \to 1u$. So

$$\nu(\{s,t\},1) = \{u\}$$

Figure 8.15 includes a complete next-state function table for M.

$\{s\}$ is the starting state for M.

Only the production $u \to \mathbf{e}$ for G is of the form of Definition 8.7(ii). So the YES states for M are those states that have u as an element, which are as follows:

$\{u\}$ $\{s,u\}$ $\{t,u\}$ $\{s,t,u\}$ are the YES states.

Figure 8.15 M for Example 8.25

Current state	Next-state function Input 0	1	State type
$\varnothing$	$\varnothing$	$\varnothing$	NO
$\{s\}$	$\{t,u\}$	$\{u\}$	NO
$\{t\}$	$\varnothing$	$\{u\}$	NO
$\{u\}$	$\{u\}$	$\{s,u\}$	YES
$\{s,t\}$	$\{t,u\}$	$\{u\}$	NO
$\{s,u\}$	$\{t,u\}$	$\{s,u\}$	YES
$\{t,u\}$	$\{u\}$	$\{s,u\}$	YES
$\{s,t,u\}$	$\{t,u\}$	$\{s,u\}$	YES

State diagram

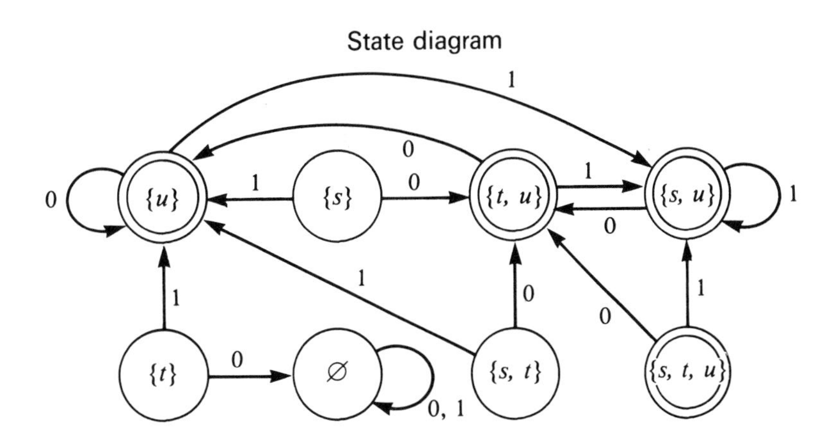

Figure 8.15 gives a complete description of M, including a state diagram. It is clear from the state diagram that $L(G)$ consists of all nonempty strings of 0's and 1's. It is harder to see this directly from the definition of G. △

Proof of Theorem 8.3

We let $i_1 i_2 \ldots i_n$ be a string of terminals that is in $L(G)$. Then, by Proposition 8.1, there is a sequence of productions of the form

$$\begin{array}{lll} s \to i_1 b_1 & b_1 \to i_2 b_2 & b_2 \to i_3 b_3 \ldots \\ b_{n-1} \to i_n b_n & b_n \to \mathbf{e} & \end{array} \tag{8.15}$$

that gives a derivation for $i_1 i_2 \ldots i_n$. In the machine M we start at state $\{s\}$. The production $s \to i_1 b_1$ of (8.15) ensures that $v(\{s\}, i_1)$, call it B_1, contains b_1. The production $b_1 \to i_2 b_2$ of (8.15) ensures that $v(B_1, i_2)$, call it B_2, contains b_2. This continues until the production $b_{n-1} \to i_n b_n$ ensures that $v(B_{n-1}, i_n)$, call it B_n, contains b_n. Thus the input string $i_1 i_2 \ldots i_n$ moves M from starting state $\{s\}$ to state B_n, which contains b_n. The production $b_n \to \mathbf{e}$ of (8.15) says that B_n is a YES state. So the machine M correctly recognizes the string $i_1 i_2 \ldots i_n$ in $L(G)$.

Now suppose that $i_1 i_2 \ldots i_n$ moves M from starting state $\{s\}$ to the YES state B_n; that is,

$$\begin{array}{lll} v(\{s\}, i_1) = B_1 & v(B_1, i_2) = B_2 & v(B_2, i_3) = B_3 \ldots \\ v(B_{n-1}, i_n) = B_n & \text{and} & B_n \text{ is a YES state} \end{array} \tag{8.16}$$

We must give a derivation of $i_1 i_2 \ldots i_n$ using the grammar G. Since B_n is a YES state, there is a nonterminal, call it b_n, in B_n such that G has the production

$$b_n \to \mathbf{e} \tag{8.17}$$

Since $v(B_{n-1}, i_n) = B_n$ in (8.16), there is a nonterminal, call it b_{n-1}, in B_{n-1} and a production in G

$$b_{n-1} \to i_n b_n \tag{8.18}$$

Since $v(B_{n-2}, i_{n-1}) = B_{n-1}$ in (8.16), there is a nonterminal, call it b_{n-2}, in B_{n-2} and a production in G

$$b_{n-2} \to i_{n-1} b_{n-1} \tag{8.19}$$

(8.18) and (8.19) continue until we reach a production

$$s \to i_1 b_1 \tag{8.20}$$

with b_1 in B_1. Then the productions in (8.20) through (8.17) give the desired derivation of $i_1 i_2 \ldots i_n$. ◇

Corollary 8.4

The context-free language

$$L = \{\mathbf{v} \in \{0,1\}^* \mid \mathbf{v} \neq \mathbf{e} \text{ and } \mathbf{v} \text{ has an equal number of 0's and 1's}\}$$

is not a regular language.

Proof of Corollary 8.4

We saw in Example 8.15 that L is context free.

It is easy to replace a finite semiautomaton M with YES and NO states by a finite-state machine M', with YES and NO as outputs, such that M and M' recognize the same nonempty input strings. Then Corollary 7.3 implies that no finite M' can recognize L. Thus no finite M can recognize L. By Theorem 8.3, L is not a regular language. ◇

Chapter 7, Section 7.3 may also be used to show that many other languages are not regular. For example, the palindromes of Example 8.14 form a nonregular language by Chapter 7, Section 7.3, Exercise 8.

Exercises 8.3

1. For each of the following grammars, $N = \{s,t,u\}$ and $T = \{0,1\}$. The productions follow. Which grammars are regular, in the sense of Definition 8.7?
   a. $s \to 0s$ $\quad s \to 1t$ $\quad t \to 1u$ $\quad t \to \mathbf{e}$
   b. $s \to st$ $\quad s \to \mathbf{e}$ $\quad t \to 1$
   c. $s \to 0u$ $\quad u \to 0s$ $\quad u \to \mathbf{e}$
   d. $s \to s0$ $\quad s \to 0s$ $\quad s \to \mathbf{e}$
2. Consider the regular grammar G with $N = \{s,t\}$, $T = \{0,1\}$ and productions

$$s \to 1s \qquad s \to 0t \qquad t \to 1s \qquad s \to \mathbf{e} \qquad t \to \mathbf{e}$$

   a. Give derivations for each of the following strings.
      (i) 0110 (ii) 1101 (iii) 101011
   b. Explain why $L(G)$ consists of all strings of 0's and 1's with no consecutive 0's.
3. Let $T = \{0,1\}$. Construct a regular grammar G such that
   a. $L(G) = \{\mathbf{v} \in T^* \mid \mathbf{v}$ starts with a 0 and terminates with a 1$\}$
   b. $L(G) = \{\mathbf{v} \in T^* \mid \mathbf{v}$ contains the substring 01$\}$
   c. $L(G) = \{\mathbf{v} \in T^* \mid \mathbf{v}$ does not contain the substring 01$\}$
4. Explain why the machine in Figure 8.16 recognizes all strings of 0's and 1's.

Figure 8.16

5. Explain why the machine in Figure 8.17 recognizes all strings of 0's and 1's such that 3 divides the number of 1's in the string.

Figure 8.17

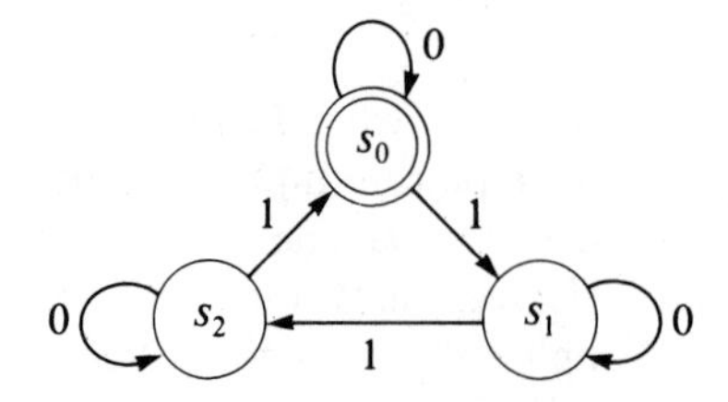

6. Explain why the machine in Figure 8.18 recognizes precisely the strings 0 and 01.

Figure 8.18

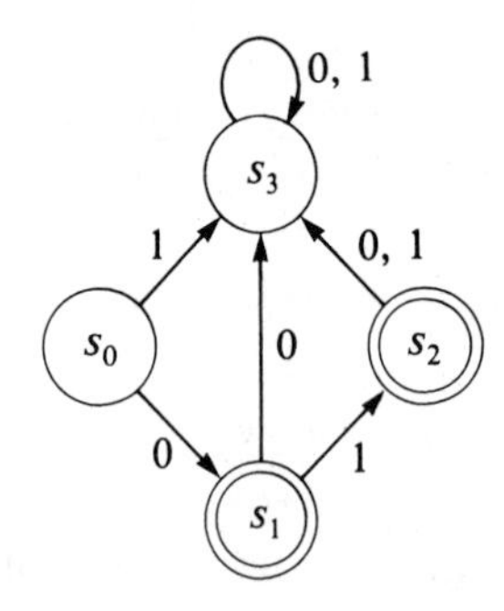

7. a. Explain why the machine in Figure 8.19 recognizes the language $L = \varnothing$.

Figure 8.19

b. Explain why the machine in Figure 8.20 recognizes the language $L = \{\mathbf{e}\}$.

Figure 8.20

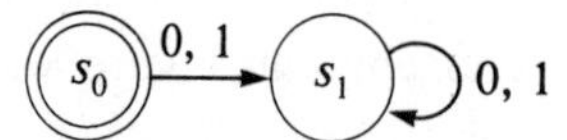

8. Using the proof of Theorem 8.2, construct regular grammars that generate the languages recognized by each of the following machines.

a.

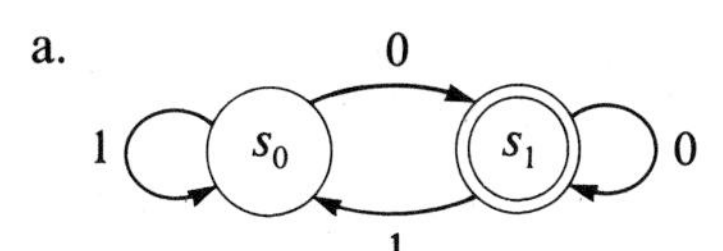

b.

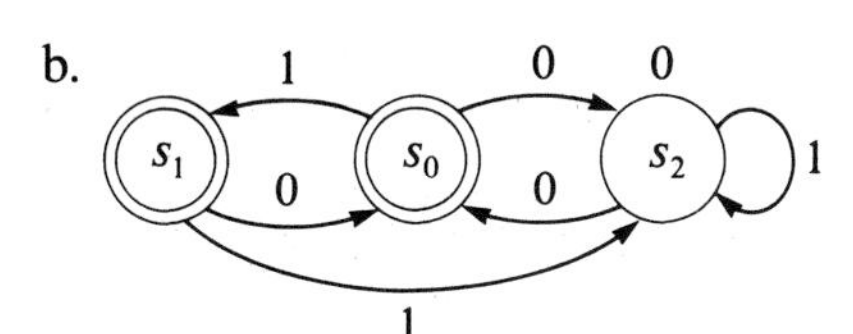

c.

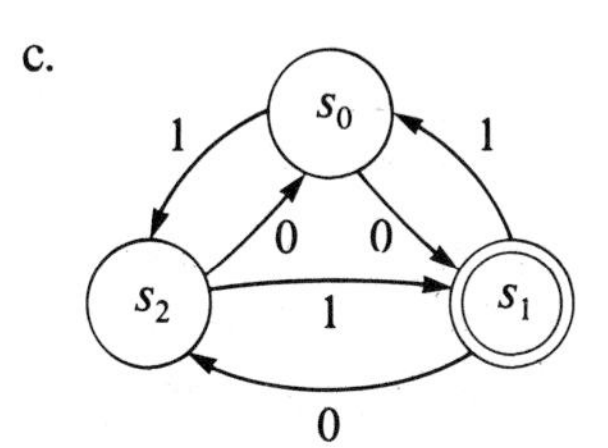

9. For each of the following regular grammars, use Theorem 8.3 to construct a machine M that recognizes the language generated by the grammar. Give both the state table and the machine diagram for M. Also, see if any states may be deleted from M to produce a simpler machine M' that recognizes the same language. For each grammar, $T=\{0,1\}$ and N is the appropriate subset of $\{s,t,u\}$. Here are the productions.

a. $s\to 0t$ $\quad s\to 0s$ $\quad s\to 1t$ $\quad t\to 0t$ $\quad t\to \mathbf{e}$

b. $s\to 1t$ $\quad t\to 0s$ $\quad t\to 0t$ $\quad t\to 1t$ $\quad s\to \mathbf{e}$

c. $s\to 0s$ $\quad s\to 1t$ $\quad t\to 1s$ $\quad t\to 0u$ $\quad u\to \mathbf{e}$

10. Another common definition for regular grammars requires them to be context-free grammars with productions allowed to be of the form in Definition 8.7 (i) or (ii) or *also* of the form

(iii) $a\to r$, with a a nonterminal and r a terminal

Let G be a grammar of the above type. Show that there is a regular grammar G', in the sense of Definition 8.7, such that $L(G')=L(G)$.

Hint: Replace the production $a \to r$ by the productions $a \to rq$ and $q \to \mathbf{e}$, with q a new nonterminal.

11. Let G be a regular grammar. Let M be the machine given in the construction of M for Theorem 8.3. Explain why $\varnothing$ is a NO state. Explain why, for all inputs i, $\nu(\varnothing,i) = \varnothing$.
12. In the construction of M for Theorem 8.3,
    a. Show that $\nu(A \cup B,i) = \nu(A,i) \cup \nu(B,i)$.
    b. Explain how Exercise 11 and part (a) of this exercise allow the computation of the next-state function for M solely from the knowledge of $\nu(\{a\},i)$ for all nonterminals a and all inputs i.
13. a. Show that

$$L = \{\mathbf{v} \in \{0,1\}^* \mid \mathbf{v} = 0^n 1^m \text{ with } n \text{ and } m \text{ positive integers}\}$$

    is a regular language.

    b. Show that

$$L = \{\mathbf{v} \in \{0,1\}^* \mid \mathbf{v} = 0^n 1^n \text{ with } n \text{ a positive integer}\}$$

    is a context-free, but not a regular language.

14. Show that the language of all Boolean polynomials in x, y, z, as in Section 8.2, Exercise 10, is not a regular language.

    Hint: Consider Boolean polynomials that end with long strings of)))...))).

15. Draw the state diagrams for full finite-state machines, with output sets {YES, NO}, which recognize the same nonempty strings as the finite semiautomata of

    a. Figure 8.10 b. Figure 8.11

16. Let T be a finite set. Let L be a regular language such that $L \subset T^*$. Show that $T^* - L$ is also a regular language.
17. A context-free grammar G is **ambiguous** if, as in Figure 8.9, a string $\mathbf{v}$ in $L(G)$ has two different derivation trees. Suppose that L is a regular language. Show that there is an unambiguous regular grammar G such that $L = L(G)$.

    Hint: Apply Theorem 8.3 and Theorem 8.2.

18. Let M be a finite semiautomaton, with starting state s_0 and a partition of its states into YES and NO states.
    a. Let M_a be the submachine of M whose states S_a are all states that are accessible from s_0 via arbitrary input strings. (See Chapter 7, Section 7.5, Exercise 8.) Explain why M and M_a recognize the same input strings.
    b. Explain how the state reduction process of Chapter 7, Section 7.4

may be applied to M_a so as to produce the unique smallest machine $M_{a,R}$ that recognizes the same input strings as does M.

c. Let G_1 and G_2 be regular grammars. Describe a finite algorithm to determine whether or not $L(G_1)=L(G_2)$.

8.4 An Algebraic Characterization of Regular Languages

At the end of the previous chapter, monoids and machine monoids were introduced. In the previous section, we saw that machines are closely related to regular languages. In this section, we see how this relationship may be expressed purely in terms of monoids.

Definition 8.10

Let $F:X \to Z$ be a map between the sets X and Z. Let Y be a subset of Z. $F^{-1}(Y)$, **the inverse image of Y under the map F**, consists of all x in X such that $F(x)$ is in Y. ○

Example 8.26

Let $X=\{1,2,3,4,5\}$ and $Z=\{a,b,c\}$. Let $F:X \to Z$ be given by

$$1 \to a \qquad 2 \to c \qquad 3 \to b \qquad 4 \to a \qquad 5 \to b$$

Let $Y=\{a,c\}$. Then $F^{-1}(Y)=\{1,2,4\}$. Also, $F^{-1}(\{b,c\})=\{2,3,5\}$. △

Theorem 8.5

Let M be a finite semiautomaton with a partition of states into YES and NO states and a starting state s_0. Let L be the (regular) language that is recognized by M. Let I be the input set of M and let $G(M)$ be the monoid of M. Let

$$F:I^* \to G(M)$$

be the onto monoid homomorphism of Proposition 7.12. Let $Y=\{f_a \in G(M) \mid (s_0)f_a \text{ is a YES state of } M\}$. Then

$$L=F^{-1}(Y)$$

Example 8.27

Before proving Theorem 8.5, we shall illustrate its statement. Let M be as in Figure 8.13. Then L consists of all strings of 0's and 1's that begin with 1. Table 8.8 gives the next-state function and lists the state types for M.

A straightforward computation gives $G(M)=\{f_e,f_0,f_1\}$ as the monoid of M. Table 8.9 gives the composition table for $(G(M),\diamond)$. From

Table 8.8 M of Figure 8.13

Current state	Next-state function Input 0	1	State type
s_0	s_1	s_2	NO
s_1	s_1	s_1	NO
s_2	s_2	s_2	YES

Table 8.9, we see that, for **a** in $\{0,1\}^*$, F is given by

$$F(\mathbf{a}) = \begin{cases} f_e & \text{if } \mathbf{a} = \mathbf{e} \\ f_0 & \text{if } \mathbf{a} \text{ begins with a } 0 \\ f_1 & \text{if } \mathbf{a} \text{ begins with a } 1 \end{cases} \qquad \mathbf{(8.21)}$$

Table 8.9 Composition table for $G(M)$

$\diamond$	f_e	f_0	f_1
f_e	f_e	f_0	f_1
f_0	f_0	f_0	f_0
f_1	f_1	f_1	f_1

$(s_0)f_e = s_0$, a NO state

$(s_0)f_0 = s_1$, a NO state

$(s_0)f_1 = s_2$, a YES state

So $Y = \{f_1\}$. From (8.21), we see immediately that $L = F^{-1}(Y)$. △

Proof of Theorem 8.5

Since M recognizes L, L consists of those strings **a** in I^* such that M is moved by **a** from s_0 to a YES state. That is, $(s_0)f_{\mathbf{a}}$ is a YES state. Since $F(\mathbf{a}) = f_{\mathbf{a}}$, L is just $F^{-1}(Y)$. ◇

We are aiming for the converse to the algebraic part of Theorem 8.5; this will be Theorem 8.7. First we need some preliminaries.

Definition 8.11

Let $(G,\circ)$ be a monoid. Let I be a subset of G. Then $\langle I \rangle$, or more formally $(\langle I \rangle,\circ)$, is the smallest submonoid of $(G,\circ)$ that contains I. $\langle I \rangle$ is called the submonoid of G **generated** by I. ○

In Proposition 7.11, we have already considered $\langle I \rangle$ for $(G,\circ) = (T_n, \diamond)$. The ideas and the construction of Proposition 7.11 carry over to Definition 8.11 for any *finite* monoid $(G,\circ)$.

Example 8.28

Let $(G,\circ)$ be the monoid with a composition table such as the one in Table 8.10. Let $I = \{a,b\}$. Then, with I replacing S in the notation of Proposition 7.11 and Example 7.46, $\langle I \rangle$ is computed as follows. Compositions come from Table 8.10.

Table 8.10 A monoid $(G,\circ)$

$\circ$	e	a	b	c	d	f
e	e	a	b	c	d	f
a	a	e	b	c	d	f
b	b	d	b	c	d	f
c	c	f	c	c	f	f
d	d	b	b	c	d	f
f	f	c	c	c	f	f

	$\circ$	I: a	b
$I=I_0$	a	$\underline{e}$	b
	b	$\underline{d}$	b
I_1	e	a	b
	d	b	b

The computation is complete and $\langle I\rangle=\{e,a,b,d\}$. △

Proposition 8.6

Let $(G,\circ)$ be a finite monoid. Let I be a subset of G such that $\langle I\rangle=G$. Let $M(G,I)$ be the finite-state machine given as follows:

The state set S equals G.

The input set I equals I.

The next-state function v is given by, for g in G and i in I, $v(g,i)=g\circ i$, where $\circ$ is composition in $(G,\circ)$. Let $(\bar{G},\diamond)$ be the monoid of $M(G,I)$. Let e be the identity in G. Let $h:\bar{G}\to G$ be given by, for $\mathbf{a}$ in I^*,

$$h(f_{\mathbf{a}})=(e)f_{\mathbf{a}}$$

Write $\mathbf{a}=i_1i_2\ldots i_n$. Then also

$$h(f_{\mathbf{a}})=i_1\circ i_2\circ\cdots\circ i_n \tag{8.22}$$

where $\circ$ is composition in $(G,\circ)$.

h is an isomorphism of monoids. Let g be an element of G. Then $h^{-1}(g)$ is the transformation on G given by

$$(x)h^{-1}(g)=x\circ g$$

Table 8.11 $M(G,I)$ for G from Table 8.10

	Next-state function, Input: a	c	d
e	a	c	d
a	e	c	d
b	d	c	d
c	f	c	f
d	b	c	d
f	c	c	f

Example 8.29

Before proving Proposition 8.6, we shall illustrate its statement. Let $(G,\circ)$ be given as in Table 8.10. Let $I=\{a,c,d\}$. It is easy to check that $\langle I\rangle=G$. Table 8.11 gives the next-state function table for $M(G,I)$. We observe that the columns in Table 8.11 are just the corresponding columns in Table 8.10.

We compute that $\bar{G}=\{f_e,f_a,f_c,f_d,f_{cd},f_{da}\}$. Table 8.12 lists the transformations in $\bar{G}$. The reordering of $\bar{G}$ in Table 8.12 was chosen so that the entries in Table 8.12 agree with those in Table 8.10. The map $h:\bar{G}\to G$ of

Proposition 8.6 is given by the e-row of Table 8.12:

$$f_e \to e \quad f_a \to a \quad f_{da} \to b \quad f_c \to c \quad f_d \to d \quad f_{cd} \to f$$

Table 8.13 gives the composition table for $(\bar{G}, \diamond)$. It is easy to see that h is indeed an isomorphism. △

Table 8.12 Elements of $\bar{G}$ for Table 8.11

States	f_e	f_a	f_{da}	f_c	f_d	f_{cd}
e	e	a	b	c	d	f
a	a	e	b	c	d	f
b	b	d	b	c	d	f
c	c	f	c	c	f	f
d	d	b	b	c	d	f
f	f	c	c	c	f	f

Table 8.13 Composition table for $(\bar{G}, \diamond)$

$\diamond$	f_e	f_a	f_{da}	f_c	f_d	f_{cd}
f_e	f_e	f_a	f_{da}	f_c	f_d	f_{cd}
f_a	f_a	f_e	f_{da}	f_c	f_d	f_{cd}
f_{da}	f_{da}	f_e	f_{da}	f_c	f_d	f_{cd}
f_c	f_c	f_{cd}	f_c	f_c	f_{cd}	f_{cd}
f_d	f_d	f_{da}	f_{da}	f_c	f_d	f_{cd}
f_{cd}	f_{cd}	f_c	f_c	f_c	f_{cd}	f_{cd}

Proof of Proposition 8.6

With $\mathbf{a} = i_1 i_2 \ldots i_n$, we first show (8.22): $h(f_{\mathbf{a}}) = i_1 \circ i_2 \circ \cdots \circ i_n$. Recall that $h(f_{\mathbf{a}})$ is defined to be $(e)\, f_{\mathbf{a}}$, that is, the final state for $M(G,I)$ from initial state e via the input $i_1 i_2 \ldots i_n$. The input i_1 takes $M(G,I)$ to $v(e,i_1) = e \circ i_1 = i_1$. The input i_2 takes $M(G,I)$ to $v(i_1,i_2) = i_1 \circ i_2$. The input i_3 takes $M(G,I)$ to $v(i_1 \circ i_2, i_3) = i_1 \circ i_2 \circ i_3$. Eventually, $i_1 i_2 \ldots i_n$ does take $M(G,I)$ to $i_1 \circ i_2 \circ \cdots \circ i_n$, as needed.

We let $\mathbf{a} = i_1 i_2 \ldots i_n$ and $\mathbf{b} = j_1 j_2 \ldots j_m$ be elements of I^*. Then $f_{\mathbf{a}} \diamond f_{\mathbf{b}} = f_{\mathbf{ab}}$ by (7.27). So

$$h(f_{\mathbf{a}} \diamond f_{\mathbf{b}}) = h(f_{\mathbf{ab}}) = i_1 \circ i_2 \circ \cdots \circ i_n \circ j_1 \circ j_2 \circ \cdots \circ j_m$$

by (8.22). Also,

$$h(f_{\mathbf{a}}) \circ h(f_{\mathbf{b}}) = (i_1 \circ i_2 \circ \cdots \circ i_n) \circ (j_1 \circ j_2 \circ \cdots \circ j_m)$$

by (8.22). Since also $h(f_e) = (e) f_e = e$, h is a homomorphism.

We need to show that h is a one-to-one correspondence. Let **a** and **b** be as above. From $v(g,i)=g \circ i$, we see that

$$(x)f_{\mathbf{a}}=x \circ i_1 \circ i_2 \circ \cdots \circ i_n \quad \textbf{(8.23)}$$

If $h(f_{\mathbf{a}})=h(f_{\mathbf{b}})$, by (8.22), $i_1 \circ i_2 \circ \cdots \circ i_n = j_1 \circ j_2 \circ \cdots \circ j_m$. So by (8.23), $f_{\mathbf{a}}=f_{\mathbf{b}}$. So h is a one-to-one map. Since $\langle I \rangle = G$, h is onto by (8.22).

To see that h^{-1} is as claimed, we write $g=i_1 \circ i_2 \circ \cdots \circ i_n$, and apply (8.22) and (8.23). □

Theorem 8.7

Let V be a finite set. Let $(G,\circ)$ be a finite monoid with Y a subset of G. Let

$$F: V^* \to G$$

be an onto monoid homomorphism. Let $L=F^{-1}(Y)$. Let M_F be the finite semiautomaton given as follows:

The state set S equals G.

The input set equals V.

The next-state function v_F is given by, for g in G and v in V, $v_F(g,v)=g \circ F(v)$, where $\circ$ is composition in $(G,\circ)$. Let e, the identity in G, be the starting state for M_F. Let the set of YES states for M_F be given as Y. Then L is the language recognized by M_F.

Example 8.30

Before proving Theorem 8.7, we shall illustrate its statement. We let the monoid $(G,\circ)$ be given by Table 8.14. We let $Y=\{x,y\}$, let $V=\{0,1,2,3\}$, and let $F: V \to G$ be given by

$$0 \to x \qquad 1 \to x \qquad 2 \to y \qquad 3 \to z$$

Then F extends to map $F: V^* \to G$, for all of V^*, via

$$\text{for } \mathbf{v}=i_1 i_2 \dots i_k, \quad F(\mathbf{v})=F(i_1) \circ F(i_2) \circ \cdots \circ F(i_k) \quad \textbf{(8.24)}$$

From Table 8.14, we see that for $\mathbf{v}$ in V^*,

$$F(\mathbf{v}) = \begin{cases} z & \text{if } \mathbf{v} \text{ contains 3} \\ y & \text{if } \mathbf{v} \text{ contains 2 but not 3} \\ x & \text{if } \mathbf{v} \text{ contains only 0's and 1's, and } \mathbf{v} \text{ has odd length} \\ e & \text{if } \mathbf{v} \text{ contains only 0's and 1's, and } \mathbf{v} \text{ has even length} \end{cases}$$

Then $F^{-1}(Y)=\{\mathbf{v} \in V^* \mid \mathbf{v}$ contains 2 but not 3, or $\mathbf{v}$ contains only 0's and 1's, and $\mathbf{v}$ has odd length$\}$

Table 8.14 A monoid $(G,\circ)$

$\circ$	e	x	y	z
e	e	x	y	z
x	x	e	y	z
y	y	y	y	z
z	z	z	z	z

Table 8.15 gives the next-state function table for M_F and also lists the YES and NO states. From Table 8.15, we see that, starting in state e, M_F indeed recognizes L. △

Table 8.15 Machine M_F

Current state	Next-state function Input 0	1	2	3	State type
e	x	x	y	z	NO
x	e	e	y	z	YES
y	y	y	y	z	YES
z	z	z	z	z	NO

Proof of Theorem 8.7

Let $I=F(V)$. By (8.24), since $F(V^*)$ is given to be G, $\langle I\rangle=G$. Let $M(G,I)$ be defined as in Proposition 8.6. Then M_F and $M(G,I)$ both have G as their state sets. We recall that $(\bar{G},\diamond)$ denotes the monoid of $M(G,I)$. Let $(G(M_F),\diamond)$ denote the monoid of M_F. Since $\nu_F(g,v)=g\circ F(v)$ and $\nu(g,i)=g\circ i$, for v in V, f_v in $G(M_F)$ equals $f_{F(v)}$ in $\bar{G}$. By Proposition 8.6, $f_{F(v)}$, in turn, corresponds to $F(v)$ in G. This shows that $G(M_F)$ is isomorphic to G (by Proposition 8.6) and that the map F of Theorem 8.7 is the same (via this isomorphism) as the map F of Proposition 7.12. Then M_F recognizes L by Theorem 8.5. ◇

Putting together Theorem 8.2, Theorem 8.3, Theorem 8.5, and Theorem 8.7, we have our desired algebraic characterization of regular languages:

Theorem 8.8

Let V be a finite set. Let L be a subset of V^*. Then L is a regular language if and only if there is a finite monoid G, a subset Y of G, and an onto monoid homomorphism

$$F: V^* \to G$$

such that $L=F^{-1}(Y)$. ◇

Example 8.31

Let L be all strings of 0's and 1's with an even number of 1's. Let us construct $F: V^* \to G$ and Y. L is recognized by the machine M of Figure 8.10. An easy computation shows that $(G(M),\diamond)$ is given as in Table 8.16.

Table 8.16 Machine monoid for Figure 8.10

$\diamond$	f_e	f_1
f_e	f_e	f_1
f_1	f_1	f_e

Let $V=\{0,1\}$. Then the map $F: V^* \to G(M)$ of Proposition 7.12 is given by, for $\mathbf{v}$ in V^*,

$$F(\mathbf{v}) = \begin{cases} f_e & \text{for } \mathbf{v} \text{ with an even number of 1's} \\ f_1 & \text{for } \mathbf{v} \text{ with an odd number of 1's} \end{cases}$$

Then let $G=G(M)$ and $Y=\{f_e\}$. △

Example 8.32

Let G be as in Table 8.17. Let $V=\{0,1\}$. Let $F: V \to G$ be given by $F(0)=b$ and $F(1)=i$. Then F extends to a monoid homomorphism, also called F, $F: V^* \to G$ given by, for $\mathbf{v}$ in V^*,

$$F(\mathbf{v}) = \begin{cases} i & \text{if } \mathbf{v} \text{ is all 1's or if } \mathbf{v}=\mathbf{e} \\ a & \text{if } \mathbf{v} \text{ has at least one 0, and the number of 0's leaves a remainder of 0 upon division by 3} \\ b & \text{if the number of 0's in } \mathbf{v} \text{ leaves a remainder of 1 upon division by 3} \\ c & \text{if the number of 0's in } \mathbf{v} \text{ leaves a remainder of 2 upon division by 3} \end{cases}$$

Let $Y=\{i,b\}$. Let $L=F^{-1}(Y)$. We first give directly a regular grammar G that generates L:

$N=\{i,a,b,c\}$, with i the starting symbol

$T=\{0,1\}$

P has the productions:

$i \to \mathbf{e}$ $\quad i \to 1i$ $\quad$ (for $F^{-1}(i)$)

$$\left.\begin{array}{llll} i \to 1a & i \to 0b & a \to 1a & a \to 0b \\ b \to 1b & b \to 0c & c \to 1c & c \to 0a \\ b \to \mathbf{e} & & & \end{array}\right\} \text{(for } F^{-1}(b)) \tag{8.25}$$

The construction of Theorems 8.7 and 8.2 has one less production than has (8.25). Namely, from the $1=i$-column and the $0=b$-column of Table 8.17, we see that the $i \to 1a$ production of (8.25) may be deleted. This can, of course, also be seen directly. △

Table 8.17 A monoid $(G,\circ)$

$\circ$	i	a	b	c
i	i	a	b	c
a	a	a	b	c
b	b	b	c	a
c	c	c	a	b

Exercises 8.4

1. Consider the monoid $(G,\circ)$ with the following composition table:

$\circ$	i	a	b	c	d
i	i	a	b	c	d
a	a	a	c	c	a
b	b	a	d	c	b
c	c	a	a	c	c
d	d	a	b	c	d

   Compute $\langle I \rangle$ for each of the following subsets I of G.
   a. $\{a,b\}$ b. $\{b,c\}$ c. $\{c,d\}$ d. $\{b\}$
2. For each I in Exercise 1 for which $\langle I \rangle = G$, write out the next-state function table for $M(G,I)$ of Proposition 8.6 and compute $(\bar{G},\diamond)$ directly.
3. Interpret the meaning of the nonterminals a,b,c in (8.25).
4. Let M be the finite semiautomaton given by the next-state function table of Table 8.18.

Table 8.18 A machine M

Current state	Next-state function Input 0	1
A	A	B
B	A	A

   a. Draw the state diagram for M.
   b. Compute the composition table for $(G(M),\diamond)$.

   Let $F:\{0,1\}^* \to G(M)$ be the onto monoid homomorphism of Proposition 7.12.

   c. Verify that $F^{-1}(f_e)$ equals all strings with no 0's and even number of 1's.
   d. Show that $F^{-1}(f_0)$ equals all strings with at least one 0 that take M from state A back to state A.

   Hint: Apply Theorem 8.5.
5. Let $V=\{0,1\}$. Let $(G,\circ)$ be the monoid of Exercise 1. Let $F:V^* \to G$ be determined by $F(0)=a$, $F(1)=b$.
   a. Compute $F(011)$, $F(1110)$, $F(00001)$
   b. Verify that $F:V^* \to G$ is onto.
   c. Using Theorems 8.7 and 8.2, construct a regular grammar G that generates $F^{-1}(c)$.
6. For each I in Exercise 1 for which $\langle I \rangle \neq G$, write out the next-state function table for an $M(G,I)$ defined in a manner similar to that of Proposition 8.6. Let $(\bar{G},\diamond)$ again denote the monoid of $M(G,I)$. Compute $\bar{G}$ and explain why it cannot be isomorphic to G.
7. Let V be a finite set. Let $F:V^* \to G$ be a homomorphism of monoids that is not given to be onto. Suppose that G is finite and that L is a subset of G. Explain why $F^{-1}(Y)$ is a regular language.

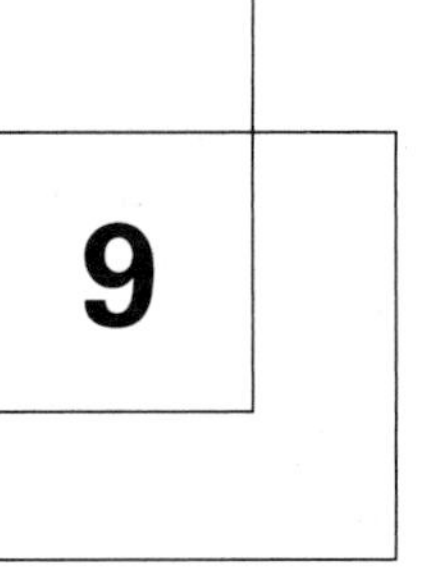

9 Rings and Fields

Rings and fields are generalizations of the integers and of the real numbers, respectively. They differ from groups by having two binary compositions, rather than just one. In this chapter only the most important examples and properties of rings and fields are given. This leaves room for the detailed discussion of three applications.

This chapter begins with the Euclidean algorithm, which is an efficient method for computing the greatest common divisor of two integers. We use the Euclidean algorithm to solve some equations in modular number systems. In Section 9.5, the analog of the Euclidean algorithm is introduced for some polynomial rings.

Rings are formally defined in the second section. The modular number system with base n is easily seen to be a ring. Polynomials with coefficients in a given ring are shown to form another ring under the usual rules for polynomial addition and multiplication.

Fourier series and their discrete version, discrete Fourier transforms, have many important mathematical and scientific applications. The fast Fourier transform algorithm, which is described in the third section, uses polynomial division to give a very rapid computation of the discrete Fourier transform. In the fourth section, the fast Fourier transform plays an essential role in a simplified version of the Schönhage-Strassen algorithm for ordinary integer multiplication. The Schönhage-Strassen algorithm is asymptotically the fastest known way to multiply two integers.

Fields, especially finite fields, are discussed in the fifth section. Finite fields may be constructed from polynomial rings in a manner analogous to the construction of the modular number systems. The last section uses finite fields to describe Bose-Chaudhuri-Hocquenghem (BCH) codes. These are group codes with error-detecting and error-correcting capabilities far greater than the capabilities of the codes examined in Chapter 1.

9.1 The Euclidean Algorithm

The set $\mathbb{Z}$ of all integers, with its two binary operations of addition and multiplication, is the prototype of all rings. In this section the Euclidean algorithm, an important way to compute the greatest common divisor of two integers, is described. In particular, we will use the Euclidean algorithm to solve some equations in the modular number systems introduced in Chapter 2. Solving these equations answers a question from Chapter 6, Section 6.5 about the Chinese Remainder Theorem.

Let a and b be integers. It is convenient, but not really necessary, to think of a and b as positive. Recall that a **divides** b, written $a|b$, if $\frac{b}{a}$ is an integer. If a divides b, a is a **divisor** of b and b is a **multiple** of a. For example, the positive divisors of 18 are

1, 2, 3, 6, 9, 18

The positive divisors of 25 are

1, 5, 25

For our purposes, it suffices to find the divisors of a number by trial-and-error, but there are, of course, much more efficient means.

With a and b integers, an integer c is a **common divisor** of a and b if c is a divisor of both a and b. Observe that 1 divides all integers, so that 1 is always a common divisor for a and b. The **greatest common divisor** of a and b, denoted by $\gcd(a,b)$, is the largest of the common divisors of a and b.

Examples 9.1

We will compute $\gcd(9,12)$ by listing the positive divisors of 9 and 12 as follows:

$$\begin{array}{ll} \text{Positive divisors of 9:} & \underline{1}, \underline{3}, 9 \\ \text{Positive divisors of 12:} & \underline{1}, 2, \underline{3}, 4, 6, 12 \end{array} \tag{9.1}$$

The common divisors in (9.1), 1 and 3, are underlined. The integer 3 is the greatest common divisor. △

We compute $\gcd(36,84)$ by the same technique:

$$\begin{array}{ll} \text{Positive divisors of 36:} & \underline{1}, \underline{2}, \underline{3}, \underline{4}, \underline{6}, 9, \underline{12}, 18, 36 \\ \text{Positive divisors of 84:} & \underline{1}, \underline{2}, \underline{3}, \underline{4}, \underline{6}, 7, \underline{12}, 14, 21, 28, 42, 84 \end{array} \tag{9.2}$$

The greatest common divisor in (9.2) is 12. △

Observe in (9.1) and especially in (9.2) that not only is the greatest common divisor larger than all of the other common divisors, but also the greatest common divisor is a *multiple* of all of the other common divisors. Thus in (9.2), the common divisors 1, 2, 3, 4, and 6 all divide 12. In (9.1), the common divisor 1 divides 3. One way to see this in general is via the Euclidean algorithm, as follows.

Theorem 9.1

(The Euclidean Algorithm) Let a and b be positive integers. Take $a \geq b$. Let r_1 be the remainder for a divided by b. If $r_1 \neq 0$, let r_2 be the remainder for b divided by r_1. If $r_2 \neq 0$, let r_3 be the remainder for r_1 divided by r_2. In general, letting $a = r_{-1}$ and $b = r_0$, for $r_{i-1} \neq 0$, r_i is the remainder for r_{i-2} divided by r_{i-1}. Let g be the last nonzero remainder r_j. Then every common divisor of a and b divides g. Hence $g = \gcd(a,b)$.

Before illustrating and proving Theorem 9.1, we need some notation for division and remainders. If b divides q times into a with a remainder of r, then we may write

$$a = q \cdot b + r, \qquad 0 \leq r < b \tag{9.3}$$

It is easily shown, as in Exercises 9.1, that q and r are uniquely determined by a and b in (9.3).

Examples 9.2

Consider 17 divided by 5. The integer 5 divides 3 times into 17 with a remainder of 2.

$$17 = 3 \cdot 5 + 2$$ △

Consider 24 divided by 6. The integer 6 divides exactly 4 times into 24; that is, the remainder is 0.

$$24 = 4 \cdot 6 + 0$$ △

It is very easy to check that

$$108 = 7 \cdot 14 + 10 \tag{9.4}$$

Since $0 \leq 10 < 14$, (9.4) implies that 14 divides 7 times into 108, with a remainder of 10. △

Example 9.3

We shall illustrate the algorithm of Theorem 9.1 with $a = 36$ and $b = 14$. First we divide 36 by 14.

$$36 = 2 \cdot 14 + 8$$

The remainder is 8. So we divide 14 by 8:

$$14 = 1 \cdot 8 + 6$$

The remainder is 6. So we divide 8 by 6:

$$8 = 1 \cdot 6 + \underline{2} \tag{9.5}$$

The remainder is 2. So we divide 6 by 2.

$$6 = 3 \cdot 2 + 0$$

The remainder is 0, so we have completed the computation. The last nonzero remainder, 2, appeared in (9.5). So, by Theorem 9.1, gcd(36,14) = 2. This can, of course, be checked directly, as in Examples 9.1. △

Example 9.4 With a minimum of prose, we give the algorithm of Theorem 9.1 for $a = 90$ and $b = 66$. Then we illustrate the proof of Theorem 9.1.

$$90 = 1 \cdot 66 + 24 \qquad \textbf{(9.6)}$$

$$66 = 2 \cdot 24 + 18 \qquad \textbf{(9.7)}$$

$$24 = 1 \cdot 18 + \underline{6} \qquad \textbf{(9.8)}$$

$$18 = 3 \cdot 6 + 0 \qquad \textbf{(9.9)}$$

The computation is complete: 6 = gcd(90,66).

Using (9.6)–(9.9), let us verify that 6 is indeed a common divisor of 90 and 66. From (9.9), 6|18. In (9.8), 6|6, since every integer divides itself, and 6|18, from (9.9). So

$$\frac{24}{6} = 1 \cdot \frac{18}{6} + \frac{6}{6}$$

is an integer. Thus 6|24. We now know that 6 divides 24 and 18, on the right side of (9.7). So 6|66. Similarly, using (9.6), 6|90.

Now we consider 3, a common divisor of 90 and 66. From (9.6),

$$24 = 90 - 1 \cdot 66$$

Since 3|90 and 3|66, also 3|24. From (9.7),

$$18 = 66 - 2 \cdot 24$$

Since 3|66 and 3|24, also 3|18. Finally, from (9.8), 3|6. △

Proof of Theorem 9.1 The remainders, r_i, are given as follows:

$$a = q_1 b + r_1 \qquad \textbf{(9.10)}_1$$

$$b = q_2 r_1 + r_2 \qquad \textbf{(9.10)}_2$$

$$r_1 = q_3 r_2 + r_3 \qquad \textbf{(9.10)}_3$$

$$r_2 = q_4 r_3 + r_4 \qquad \textbf{(9.10)}_4$$

$$\cdots$$

$$r_{i-2} = q_i r_{i-1} + r_i \qquad \textbf{(9.10)}_i$$

$$\cdots$$

$$r_{j-2} = q_j r_{j-1} + r_j \qquad \textbf{(9.10)}_j$$

$$r_{j-1} = q_{j+1} r_j + 0 \qquad \textbf{(9.10)}_{j+1}$$

Since $r_1 > r_2 > r_3 > \cdots$ and all of these remainders are nonnegative integers, eventually a remainder of 0 must be reached, as in $(9.10)_{j+1}$.

g is given to be r_j. Let us see that g is a common divisor for a and b. From $(9.10)_{j+1}$, $g|r_{j-1}$. Since $g = r_j$ and $g|r_{j-1}$, from $(9.10)_j$, $g|r_{j-2}$. In general in $(9.10)_i$, we know that $g|r_i$ and $g|r_{i-1}$. From $(9.10)_i$, we conclude that also $g|r_{i-2}$. Eventually, we see that $g|r_0$ with $r_0 = b$ and $g|r_{-1}$, with $r_{-1} = a$. So g is a common divisor.

Let c be a common divisor for a and b. Let us show that $c|g$. Then also $c \leq g$, so g will be shown to be the *greatest* common divisor. We solve $(9.10)_1$ for r_1:

$$r_1 = a - q_1 b \qquad \textbf{(9.11)}_1$$

Since c divides a and b, from $(9.11)_1$, also $c|r_1$. We solve $(9.10)_2$ for r_2:

$$r_2 = b - q_2 r_1 \qquad \textbf{(9.11)}_2$$

$c|b$, as given, and $c|r_1$, as shown. From $(9.11)_2$, $c|r_2$. In general, we solve $(9.10)_i$ for r_i as follows:

$$r_i = r_{i-2} - q_i r_{i-1} \qquad \textbf{(9.11)}_i$$

In $(9.11)_i$, we know that $c|r_{i-2}$ and $c|r_{i-1}$; we conclude that $c|r_i$. Eventually, we reach $(9.10)_j$ and

$$r_j = r_{j-2} - q_j r_{j-1} \qquad \textbf{(9.11)}_j$$

From $(9.11)_j$, we conclude that $c|r_j$. Since $g = r_j$, the proof is complete. ◇

The equations (9.11) from the proof of the Euclidean algorithm will yield the following important result.

Theorem 9.2 Let a and b be positive integers. Let $g = \gcd(a,b)$. Then there exist integers λ and μ such that

$$\lambda a + \mu b = g$$

Example 9.5 Using (9.6)–(9.8) of Example 9.4, we shall illustrate the proof below of Theorem 9.2.

gcd(90,66) = 6. We wish to express 6 in terms of 90 and 66. From (9.8),

$$6 = 24 - 1 \cdot 18 \tag{9.12}$$

From (9.7),

$$18 = 66 - 2 \cdot 24$$

When we substitute this expression for 18 into (9.12), we obtain

$$\begin{aligned} 6 &= 24 - 1(66 - 2 \cdot 24) \\ &= 3 \cdot 24 - 1 \cdot 66 \end{aligned} \tag{9.13}$$

From (9.6),

$$24 = 90 - 1 \cdot 66$$

When we substitute this expression for 24 into (9.13), we obtain

$$\begin{aligned} 6 &= 3(90 - 1 \cdot 66) - 1 \cdot 66 \\ &= 3 \cdot 90 - 4 \cdot 66 \end{aligned}$$

In the notation of Theorem 9.2, $\lambda = 3$ and $\mu = -4$. △

Proof of Theorem 9.2 We apply Theorem 9.1 to compute g in terms of a and b. Then g is given as r_j in $(9.11)_j$. $(9.11)_{j-1}$ is

$$r_{j-1} = r_{j-3} - q_{j-1} r_{j-2}$$

Substituting this expression for r_{j-1} into $(9.11)_j$ gives

$$\begin{aligned} r_j &= r_{j-2} - q_j(r_{j-3} - q_{j-1} r_{j-2}) \\ &= -q_j r_{j-3} + (1 + q_j q_{j-1}) r_{j-2} \end{aligned} \tag{9.14}$$

(9.14) expresses r_j in terms of r_{j-3} and r_{j-2}, using *integer* coefficients. $(9.11)_{j-2}$ expresses r_{j-2} in terms of r_{j-3} and r_{j-4}, also using integer coefficients. So, substituting for r_{j-2} in (9.14) expresses r_j in terms of r_{j-3} and r_{j-4}. Continuing in this fashion, we eventually use $(9.11)_1$ to complete the expression of r_j in terms of a and b, using some integer coefficients λ and μ. ◇

Suppose that a and b are integers. An expression $\lambda a + \mu b$, with λ and μ also integers, as in Theorem 9.2 and its proof, is called an **integral combination** of a and b.

Example 9.6 Let $g = \gcd(293, 121)$. We compute g and also express g as an integral combination of 293 and 121. We first find g using the Euclidean algorithm as follows:

$$\begin{aligned} 293 &= 2 \cdot 121 + 51 \\ 121 &= 2 \cdot 51 + 19 \\ 51 &= 2 \cdot 19 + 13 \\ 19 &= 1 \cdot 13 + 6 \\ 13 &= 2 \cdot 6 + \underline{1} \\ 6 &= 6 \cdot 1 + 0 \end{aligned} \tag{9.15}$$

The computation is complete and $\gcd(293, 121) = 1$.

We express 1 as an integral combination of 292 and 121 by using the equations in (9.15) in reverse order:

$$\begin{aligned} 1 &= 13 - 2 \cdot 6 \\ &= 13 - 2(19 - 1 \cdot 13) = -2 \cdot 19 + 3 \cdot 13 \\ &= -2 \cdot 19 + 3(51 - 2 \cdot 19) = 3 \cdot 51 - 8 \cdot 19 \\ &= 3 \cdot 51 - 8(121 - 2 \cdot 51) = -8 \cdot 121 + 19 \cdot 51 \\ &= -8 \cdot 121 + 19(293 - 2 \cdot 121) = 19 \cdot 293 - 46 \cdot 121 \end{aligned}$$

△

We take n to be a positive integer and let a and b be arbitrary integers. Recall that $a \equiv b \pmod{n}$ if $n|(a - b)$. Let us formalize two facts that we have used implicitly earlier in this text. In Section 9.5 we shall need the corresponding statements for polynomials.

Proposition 9.3 Let n be a positive integer. Let a, b, c, d be integers such that

$$a \equiv b \quad \text{and} \quad c \equiv d \pmod{n}$$

Then

$$a + c \equiv b + d \quad \text{and} \quad a \cdot c \equiv b \cdot d \pmod{n}$$

Example 9.7 Before proving Proposition 9.3, we shall illustrate its statement. Take $n = 7$, $a = 9$, $b = 16$, $c = -2$, and $d = 12$. Then

$$9 \equiv 16 \quad \text{and} \quad -2 \equiv 12 \pmod 7 \tag{9.16}$$

Adding corresponding sides in (9.16) gives $9+(-2)=7$ and $16+12=28$. Indeed,

$$7 \equiv 28 \pmod 7$$

Multiplying corresponding sides in (9.16) gives $9\cdot(-2)=-18$ and $16\cdot 12=192$. An easy computation shows that indeed

$$-18 \equiv 192 \pmod 7$$

△

Proof of Proposition 9.3 Let

$$\frac{a-b}{n}=p \quad \text{and} \quad \frac{c-d}{n}=q$$

p and q are given to be integers.

We consider the equation $a+c \equiv b+d \pmod n$.

$$\begin{aligned}\frac{(a+c)-(b+d)}{n} &= \frac{(a-b)+(c-d)}{n}\\ &= \frac{a-b}{n}+\frac{c-d}{n}\\ &= p+q, \qquad \text{an integer}\end{aligned}$$

So, as desired, $a+c \equiv b+d \pmod n$ is true.

Now we consider the equation $a\cdot c \equiv b\cdot d \pmod n$.

$$\begin{aligned}\frac{a\cdot c-b\cdot d}{n} &= \frac{a\cdot c-b\cdot c+b\cdot c-b\cdot d}{n}\\ &= \frac{(a-b)c+b(c-d)}{n}\\ &= \frac{a-b}{n}c+b\frac{c-d}{n}\\ &= p\cdot c+b\cdot q, \qquad \text{an integer}\end{aligned}$$

□

Let n be a positive integer. Recall $\mathbb{Z}_n=\{0,1,2,\ldots,n-1\}$, the modular number system with base n, of Chapter 2, Section 2.3. Elements of $\mathbb{Z}_n$ are added and multiplied by first adding and multiplying them as ordinary integers, and then keeping the remainder after division by n. Temporarily denote addition and multiplication for $\mathbb{Z}_n$ by $+_n$ and $\cdot_n$, respectively, leaving $+$ and $\cdot$ to denote the usual addition and multiplication for integers. Then, for a,b in $\mathbb{Z}_n$, $+_n$ and $\cdot_n$ may be given by

$$\begin{aligned} a +_n b &\equiv a + b \pmod{n} \\ a \cdot_n b &\equiv a \cdot b \pmod{n} \end{aligned} \tag{9.17}$$

Example 9.8

Let us consider $(\mathbb{Z}_6, +_6, \cdot_6)$ and illustrate (9.17) with $n = 6$. Take $a = 4$ and $b = 5$.

$$4 +_6 5 = 3, \quad 4 + 5 = 9, \quad \text{and} \quad 3 \equiv 9 \pmod{6}$$

$$4 \cdot_6 5 = 2, \quad 4 \cdot 5 = 20, \quad \text{and} \quad 2 \equiv 20 \pmod{6}$$

△

Proposition 9.3 and (9.17) imply that we can perform any computation in $\mathbb{Z}_n$ by first computing in $\mathbb{Z}$ and then keeping the remainder after division by n.

Example 9.9

We shall compute $3 \cdot_8 (4 +_8 6) \cdot_8 (1 +_8 5)$ in two different ways. Computing in $\mathbb{Z}_8$,

$$3 \cdot_8 (4 +_8 6) \cdot_8 (1 +_8 5) = 3 \cdot_8 2 \cdot_8 6 = 6 \cdot_8 6 = 4$$

Computing in $\mathbb{Z}$,

$$3(4 + 6)(1 + 5) = 3 \cdot 10 \cdot 6 = 180$$

$$180 \equiv 4 \pmod{8}$$

So $3 \cdot_8 (4 +_8 6) \cdot_8 (1 +_8 5) = 4$.

△

Theorem 9.4

Let a be an element in the modular number system $\mathbb{Z}_n$. Let $\cdot$ denote multiplication in $\mathbb{Z}_n$. Then the equation

$$a \cdot x = 1 \tag{9.18}$$

has a solution in $\mathbb{Z}_n$ if and only if $\gcd(a,n) = 1$.

Example 9.10

Before proving part of Theorem 9.4, we shall illustrate its statement. We consider $n = 10$. With $0 \le a < 10$, $\gcd(a,10) = 1$ only for $a = 1,3,7,9$. In $\mathbb{Z}_{10}$,

$$1 \cdot 1 = 1 \qquad 3 \cdot 7 = 1 \qquad 7 \cdot 3 = 1 \qquad 9 \cdot 9 = 1$$

So (9.18) has a solution for these values of a.

The other elements of $\mathbb{Z}_{10}$ are 0, 2, 4, 5, 6, 8.

$$\gcd(0,10)=10 \qquad \gcd(2,10)=2 \qquad \gcd(4,10)=2$$
$$\gcd(5,10)=5 \qquad \gcd(6,10)=2 \qquad \gcd(8,10)=2$$

A case-by-case check shows that (9.18) has no solution for these values of a.

△

Partial Proof of Theorem 9.4

We shall only show that $\gcd(a,n)=1$ implies that (9.18) has a solution. The proof that $\gcd(a,n)>1$ implies that (9.18) has no solution is left to the exercises.

Assume that $\gcd(a,n)=1$. Let $\cdot$ and $+$ now denote operations in $\mathbb{Z}$. Proposition 9.3 and (9.17) imply that solving (9.18) in $\mathbb{Z}_n$ is equivalent to finding an integer x such that

$$a\cdot x\equiv 1 \pmod{n} \tag{9.19}$$

By Theorem 9.2, there exist integers λ and μ such that

$$\lambda a+\mu n=1$$

Then

$$\lambda a\equiv 1 \pmod{n}$$

The desired solution to (9.19) is $x=\lambda$. ◇

Examples 9.11

$\gcd(25,108)=1$. In $\mathbb{Z}_{108}$, let us solve the equation

$$25\cdot x=1 \tag{9.20}$$

First we apply the Euclidean algorithm:

$$108=4\cdot 25+8$$
$$25=3\cdot 8+\underline{1}$$
$$8=8\cdot 1+0 \qquad \text{Stop}$$

We find λ and μ of Theorem 9.2:

$$\begin{aligned}1&=25-3\cdot 8\\&=25-3(108-4\cdot 25)\\&=13\cdot 25-3\cdot 108\end{aligned}$$

We observe that

$$1 \equiv 13 \cdot 25 \pmod{108}$$

$x = 13$ in (9.20). △

$\gcd(5,108) = 1$. Let us solve

$$5 \cdot x = 1 \tag{9.21}$$

in $\mathbb{Z}_{108}$.

$$\begin{aligned}
108 &= 21 \cdot 5 + 3 \\
5 &= 1 \cdot 3 + 2 \\
3 &= 1 \cdot 2 + \underline{1} \\
2 &= 2 \cdot 1 + 0 \qquad \text{Stop} \\
1 &= 3 - 1 \cdot 2 \\
&= 3 - 1 \cdot (5 - 1 \cdot 3) = 2 \cdot 3 - 5 \\
&= 2 \cdot (108 - 21 \cdot 5) - 5 = 2 \cdot 108 - 43 \cdot 5 \\
1 &\equiv -43 \cdot 5 \pmod{108}
\end{aligned}$$

Since $-43 \equiv 65 \pmod{108}$, $x = 65$ in (9.21). △

Recall the map f of Theorem 6.9, the Chinese Remainder Theorem. The proof of Theorem 9.4 completes the computation of f^{-1}, as follows.

Example 9.12

Recall $f : \mathbb{Z}_{300} \to \mathbb{Z}_4 \times \mathbb{Z}_3 \times \mathbb{Z}_{25}$ of Example 6.33. We may describe f as follows: Take x in $\mathbb{Z}_{300}$, $0 \le x < 300$. $f(x) = (x_1, x_2, x_3)$ with x_1 in $\mathbb{Z}_4$, x_2 in $\mathbb{Z}_3$, x_3 in $\mathbb{Z}_{25}$; that is, $0 \le x_1 < 4$, $0 \le x_2 < 3$, $0 \le x_3 < 25$, and, most importantly,

$$\begin{aligned}
x &\equiv x_1 \pmod{4} \\
x &\equiv x_2 \pmod{3} \\
x &\equiv x_3 \pmod{25}
\end{aligned} \tag{9.22}$$

In Example 6.33, we saw how to compute f^{-1} from a knowledge of $f^{-1}(1,0,0)$, $f^{-1}(0,1,0)$, and $f^{-1}(0,0,1)$. Finding $f^{-1}(1,0,0)$ involves solving the simultaneous equations (9.22) with $x_1 = 1$, $x_2 = 0$, $x_3 = 0$.

$$x \equiv 1 \pmod 4$$
$$x \equiv 0 \pmod 3 \tag{9.23}$$
$$x \equiv 0 \pmod{25}$$

From the last two equations in (9.23), we see that x is a multiple of both 3 and 25. Since 3 and 25 are powers of different primes, x is also a multiple of $3 \cdot 25 = 75$. We write $x = 75y$. Then the first equation in (9.23) becomes

$$75y \equiv 1 \pmod 4 \tag{9.24}$$

By Proposition 9.3, since $75 \equiv 3 \pmod 4$, (9.24) is equivalent to the equation

$$3y \equiv 1 \pmod 4 \tag{9.25}$$

Trial-and-error easily gives $y = 3$ as a solution to (9.25). As in Example 6.33, $x = 75 \cdot 3 = 225$.

Now let us look at $f^{-1}(0,0,1)$. (9.22) becomes

$$x \equiv 0 \pmod 4$$
$$x \equiv 0 \pmod 3 \tag{9.26}$$
$$x \equiv 1 \pmod{25}$$

From the first two equations in (9.26), we see that x is a multiple of 4 and of 3, and hence also of 12. If we write $x = 12y$, the third equation in (9.26) becomes

$$12y \equiv 1 \pmod{25} \tag{9.27}$$

In contrast to (9.25), a trial-and-error solution of (9.27) may not be so easy. Observe, however, that $\gcd(12,25) = 1$. So we may solve (9.27) using the method of the proof of Theorem 9.4:

$$25 = 2 \cdot 12 + \underline{1} \tag{9.28}$$
$$12 = 12 \cdot 1 + 0$$

From (9.28),

$$-2 \cdot 12 + 25 = 1$$

$y \equiv -2 \pmod{25}$ in (9.27). We require, of course, that $0 \leq 12y < 300$, or

$0 \leq y < 25$. Since $-2 \equiv 23 \pmod{25}$, we take $y = 23$ in (9.27). $x = 12y = 276$, as in Example 6.33.

The computation of $f^{-1}(0,1,0)$ is left to the exercises. △

Exercises 9.1

1. a. List all positive divisors of 30 and of 42.
   b. List all common positive divisors of 30 and 42. Find the greatest common divisor.
   c. Show that the greatest common divisor of 30 and 42 is a multiple of all common positive divisors of 30 and 42.
2. Using the Euclidean algorithm, compute
   a. gcd(42,30) b. gcd(90,39) c. gcd(143,153)
3. For each (a,b) in Exercise 2, express $\gcd(a,b)$ as an integral combination of a and b.
4. Compute
   a. in $\mathbb{Z}_7$, $(3+5)(6+4)+6$ b. in $\mathbb{Z}_6$, $(2^4 \cdot 3^2) + (2^4 \cdot 5)$
5. Solve the following for x.
   a. In $\mathbb{Z}_{24}$, $11x = 1$. b. In $\mathbb{Z}_{77}$, $41x = 1$.
6. Let f be as in Example 9.12. Find $f^{-1}(0,1,0)$.
7. Let $f: \mathbb{Z}_{90} \to \mathbb{Z}_2 \times \mathbb{Z}_9 \times \mathbb{Z}_5$ be the Chinese Remainder map. Find
   a. $f^{-1}(1,0,0)$ b. $f^{-1}(0,1,0)$ c. $f^{-1}(0,0,1)$
8. Let b be a positive integer and let a be an arbitrary integer. Suppose that $a = q_1 b + r_1$ and $a = q_2 b + r_2$ for integers q_1, r_1, q_2, r_2 such that $0 \leq r_1 \leq r_2 < b$. Show that $r_1 = r_2$ and $q_1 = q_2$.
   Hint: $(q_1 - q_2)b = r_2 - r_1$. So $b|(r_2 - r_1)$. However, $0 \leq r_2 - r_1 < b$.
9. With the notation of Theorem 9.4, suppose that $g = \gcd(a,n) > 1$. Let $k = n/g$. Then $0 < k < n$. Show that $k \cdot a = 0$ in $\mathbb{Z}_n$. Show that (9.18) cannot hold.
10. Let p be a prime number and let a be an arbitrary positive integer. Show that either $p|a$ or $\gcd(p,a) = 1$.
11. Let a,b,c be positive integers such that $c|ab$ and $\gcd(c,a) = 1$. Show that $c|b$.
    Hint: For suitable λ and μ, $\lambda a + \mu c = 1$. Then $\lambda ab + \mu cb = b$.
12. Let a,b,p be positive integers with p prime. Using Exercises 10 and 11, show that if $p|ab$, then either $p|a$ or $p|b$.
13. Using Exercise 12, show that the factorization of an integer $n \geq 2$ into prime factors is unique, except for the order of multiplication.

9.2 Rings; Polynomial Rings

In this section, we give a formal definition for a ring. We observe that each modular number system with base n is a ring, under modular addition and multiplication. A few basic properties are proven for all rings. We see that the set of polynomials with coefficients in a given ring is again a ring, under the usual polynomial addition and multiplication. Finally, we examine the division algorithm for such polynomial rings.

Examples 9.13

We assume knowledge of the usual laws of addition and multiplication for $\mathbb{R}$, the set of all real numbers. Here are some easy computations:

$$3+(-3)=0 \qquad 2\cdot\frac{1}{2}=1 \qquad 2\cdot 2=4$$

Recall that the sum and the product of two real numbers is again a real number and that $(\mathbb{R},+)$ is in fact a commutative group. △

Let us consider the usual operations of addition and multiplication on $\mathbb{Z}$, the set of all integers. Then the sum and the product of two integers is again an integer. Also, $(\mathbb{Z},+)$ is a commutative group. △

Example 9.14

Let $i=\sqrt{-1}$. Recall that we may manipulate i as we would a real number, subject to the rule $i^2=-1$. Recall that a complex number c is an expression of the form $a+bi$, with a and b real numbers. Complex numbers are added and multiplied in the obvious way. For example,

$$(2+i)+\left(-\frac{3}{2}-2i\right)=\left(2-\frac{3}{2}\right)+(i-2i)=\frac{1}{2}-i$$

$$\begin{aligned}(2+i)\cdot(3-i)&=2(3-i)+i(3-i)\\&=6-2i+3i-i^2\\&=6-2i+3i-(-1)\\&=7+i\end{aligned}$$

$$\begin{aligned}\left(\frac{\sqrt{2}}{2}+\frac{\sqrt{2}}{2}i\right)^2&=\left(\frac{\sqrt{2}}{2}\right)^2+2\left(\frac{\sqrt{2}}{2}\right)\left(\frac{\sqrt{2}}{2}i\right)+\left(\frac{\sqrt{2}}{2}i\right)^2\\&=\frac{2}{4}+2\cdot\frac{2}{4}\cdot i+\frac{2}{4}i^2\\&=\frac{1}{2}+i-\frac{1}{2}\\&=i\end{aligned}$$

In particular, the sum and the product of two complex numbers is again a complex number.

If $c=a+bi$, then $-c=-a-bi$ satisfies $c+(-c)=0+0i$. As is customary, we consider a complex number of the form $a+0i$ to be the real number a. Then $c+(-c)=0$. Let $\mathbb{C}$ be the set of all complex numbers. Then $(\mathbb{C},+)$ is a commutative group. △

Examples 9.15

We consider polynomials in the variable x with real coefficients. Polynomials are added and multiplied in the usual way:

$\left(2x^2 - 4x + \frac{4}{5}\right) + (\sqrt{3}x - 2)$ is computed via

$$\begin{array}{rrr} & 2x^2 & -4x + \frac{4}{5} \\ + & & \sqrt{3}x - 2 \\ \hline & 2x^2 + (-4+\sqrt{3})x - \frac{6}{5} & \end{array}$$

$\left(x^2 + \frac{2}{3}x - \frac{1}{2}\right) \cdot \left(2x^2 - \frac{3}{2}x + 6\right)$ is computed via

$$\begin{array}{rrrrr} & & x^2 + & \frac{2}{3}x - & \frac{1}{2} \\ & \times & 2x^2 - & \frac{3}{2}x + & 6 \\ \hline & & 6x^2 + & 4x - & 3 \\ & -\frac{3}{2}x^3 - & x^2 + & \frac{3}{4}x & \\ 2x^4 + & \frac{4}{3}x^3 - & x^2 & & \\ \hline 2x^4 - & \frac{1}{6}x^3 + & 4x^2 + & \frac{19}{4}x - & 3 \end{array}$$

△

We observe that if two polynomials have integer coefficients, then also their sum and product have integer coefficients:

$$\begin{array}{rr} & 3x^3 - 2x^2 + x - 3 \\ + & x^3 + 9x^2 \quad + 7 \\ \hline & 4x^3 + 7x^2 + x + 4 \end{array}$$

$$\begin{array}{rrrrr} & & -7x^2 + & 4x - & 3 \\ & \times & 2x^2 - & x + & 2 \\ \hline & & -14x^2 + & 8x - & 6 \\ & 7x^3 - & 4x^2 + & 3x & \\ -14x^4 + & 8x^3 - & 6x^2 & & \\ \hline -14x^4 + & 15x^3 - & 24x^2 + & 11x - & 6 \end{array}$$

△

In Examples 9.13–9.15, we discussed addition and multiplication for real numbers, for integers, for complex numbers, and for polynomials. In each example, addition and multiplication satisfy similar laws. As formally defined in Definition 9.1, which follows, the operations of addition and multiplication make each of the preceding sets into **rings**.

Definition 9.1

A **ring** $(R, +, \cdot)$ is a set R with two laws of composition, $+$ and $\cdot$, usually called **addition** and **multiplication** respectively, such that

(i) $(R, +)$ is a commutative group. The identity for $(R, +)$, called the **zero**, is denoted by 0.

(ii) (*Associativity*) For any three elements a,b,c of R,

$$(a \cdot b) \cdot c = a \cdot (b \cdot c)$$

(iii) (*Identity*) There is an identity, called the **unit** and denoted by 1, for $(R, \cdot)$ such that $1 \neq 0$. In particular, for any element a of R,

$$1 \cdot a = a \qquad a \cdot 1 = a$$

(iv) (*Commutativity*) For any two elements a,b of R,

$$a \cdot b = b \cdot a$$

(v) (*Distributivity*) For any three elements a,b,c of R,

$$a \cdot (b + c) = a \cdot b + a \cdot c$$

○

Definition 9.1 may also be rephrased more succinctly as: A **ring** is a set that is a commutative group under addition, a commutative monoid under multiplication, and such that multiplication distributes over addition. As is usual for commutative groups, the additive inverse of an element b in a ring is denoted by $-b$. In a ring, as in any commutative group, **subtraction** $-$ is defined as

$$a - b = a + (-b)$$

As is common in algebra, we shall often omit the symbol $\cdot$ when denoting multiplication. Frequently, we shall call the ring $(R, +, \cdot)$ simply R.

Proposition 9.5

The modular number system $(\mathbb{Z}_n, +_n, \cdot_n)$ is a ring. □

We shall not prove Proposition 9.5; it follows easily from Proposition 9.3 and (9.17).

Example 9.16

Consider $(\mathbb{Z}_7, +_7, \cdot_7)$. Let us verify Definition 9.1(v) with $a=3, b=5, c=2$.

$$3\cdot_7(5+_7 2)=3\cdot_7 0=0$$
$$3\cdot_7 5+_7 3\cdot_7 2=1+_7 6=0$$

△

Many of the important properties of the integers are true in any ring. Let us use Definition 9.1 to prove some of these.

Proposition 9.6

Let a be an element of the ring $(R, +, \cdot)$. Then

$$0\cdot a=a$$

Proof of Proposition 9.6

$0+0=0,$	by the definition of 0
$0\cdot a+0\cdot a=0\cdot a,$	by multiplication by a
$0\cdot a+0\cdot a-0\cdot a=0\cdot a-0\cdot a,$	by subtraction of $0\cdot a$
$0\cdot a+0=0,$	$0\cdot a-0\cdot a=0$
$0\cdot a=0,$	by the definition of 0 □

Proposition 9.7

Let a be an element of the ring $(R, +, \cdot)$. Then

$$(-1)\cdot a=-a$$

Example 9.17

Before proving Proposition 9.7, we shall discuss and illustrate its statement, which is not as trivial as it seems. The additive inverse of the multiplicative identity 1 is -1. The left side in Proposition 9.7 is given by a multiplication. The right side is given as an additive inverse.

We consider $\mathbb{Z}_6$ with addition and multiplication denoted, as usual, by $+$ and $\cdot$. Since $1+5=0$ in $\mathbb{Z}_6$, $-1=5$. Take $a=4$ in Proposition 9.7.

$$(-1)\cdot 4=5\cdot 4=2$$

Since $2+4=0$ in $\mathbb{Z}_6$, $2=-4$, as required by Proposition 9.7. △

Proof of Proposition 9.7

$(-1)\cdot a+a=(-1)\cdot a+1\cdot a,$	by Definition 9.1(iii)
$=(-1+1)\cdot a,$	by Definition 9.1(iv) and (v)
$=0\cdot a,$	by the definition of -1
$=0,$	by Proposition 9.6 □

Proposition 9.8

Let a and b be elements of the ring $(R, +, \cdot)$. Then

$$(-a)\cdot(-b)=a\cdot b$$

Example 9.18

Before proving Proposition 9.8, we illustrate its statement. Take $R=\mathbb{Z}_7$, $a=3$, and $b=5$.

$$-3=4 \qquad -5=2$$
$$(-3)\cdot(-5)=4\cdot 2=1$$
$$3\cdot 5=1$$

△

Proof of Proposition 9.8

By Proposition 9.7 and commutativity, $(-a)\cdot(-b)=(-1)\cdot a\cdot(-1)\cdot b=(-1)\cdot(-1)\cdot a\cdot b$. So it suffices to show that $(-1)\cdot(-1)=1$.

$1+(-1)=0,$ by the definition of -1

$(-1)\cdot 1+(-1)\cdot(-1)=0,$ by multiplication by -1, Proposition 9.6

$-1+(-1)\cdot(-1)=0,$ by the definition of 1

$(-1)\cdot(-1)=1,$ by adding 1 and simplifying □

Given any ring R, we may form $R[x]$, the set of polynomials in the variable x using coefficients from R. Polynomials in $R[x]$ may be added and multiplied in the usual manner, as in Examples 9.15. As will be proved in the exercises, these binary compositions of addition and multiplication make $R[x]$ into a ring, which is also denoted by $R[x]$.

Examples 9.19

Let us compute some operations in $\mathbb{Z}_6[x]$.

$$\begin{array}{r} 3x^3+2x^2+3x \\ +\ \ 5x^3+\ x^2+3x+4 \\ \hline 2x^3+3x^2+0x+4 \end{array} = 2x^3+3x^2+4$$

△

$$(4x^2+2x+3)-(4x^2+x+4)=(4x^2+2x+3)+(2x^2+5x+2)=$$

$$\begin{array}{r} 4x^2+2x+3 \\ +\ \ 2x^2+5x+2 \\ \hline 0x^2+x+5 \end{array} = x+5$$

△

$$\begin{array}{r} 2x^2+5x+2 \\ \times \qquad 2x+4 \\ \hline 2x^2+2x+2 \\ 4x^3+4x^2+4x \quad \\ \hline 4x^3+0x^2+0x+2 \end{array} = 4x^3+2$$

△

$$\begin{array}{r} 2x^2+3x+1 \\ \times \qquad 3x+5 \\ \hline 4x^2+3x+5 \\ 0x^3+3x^2+3x \quad \\ \hline 0x^3+1x^2+0x+5 \end{array} = x^2+5$$

△

Definition 9.2

Let R be a ring. Let $p(x) \neq 0$ be a polynomial in $R[x]$. Write

$$p(x) = a_n x^n + a_{n-1} x^{n-1} + \cdots + a_1 x + a_0, \qquad a_n \neq 0$$

Then n is the **degree** of $p(x)$. We write $\deg(p(x)) = n$. a_n is the **leading coefficient** of $p(x)$.

The polynomial 0 is considered to have degree $-\infty$ and leading coefficient 0. ○

Formal computations with the symbol $-\infty$ are discussed in the exercises. The definitions of degree and leading coefficient for the polynomial 0 lead to correct special cases for the theorems that will follow.

Example 9.20

We give the degrees and leading coefficients for some polynomials in $\mathbb{Z}[x]$:

	Polynomial	Degree	Leading coefficient
	$2x^3+3x^2-4x+2$	3	2
	$-x^5+7x^4-9x^2+7x+4$	5	-1
	17	0	17
	$(2x^2+3x-4)+(-2x^2+x-2)=$		
	$0x^2+4x-6=$		
	$4x-6$	1	4
(9.29)	$(x^3+1)\cdot(x^3-1)=x^6-1$	6	1

△

Now we consider some degrees and leading coefficients in $\mathbb{Z}_6[x]$ (as shown in the tabulation overleaf).

Observe the contrast between (9.29) and (9.30) with respect to the behavior of the degrees. In (9.29), the degree of the product equals the sum of the degrees of the factors. In (9.30), since $2 \cdot 3 = 0$ in $\mathbb{Z}_6$, the degree of the product is *less than* the sum of the degrees of the factors. This phenomenon

	Polynomial	Degree	Leading coefficient
	$4x^2+5x$	2	4
	$(2x^3+x^2+2)+(3x^3+4x+5)=$		
	$5x^3+x^2+4x+1$	3	5
	$(2x+2)\cdot(3x+1)=$		
(9.30)	$2\cdot 3x^2+(2\cdot 1+2\cdot 3)x+2\cdot 1=$		
	$0x^2+2x+2=$		
	$2x+2$	1	2

△

in $\mathbb{Z}_6[x]$ is awkward. However, as described in Definition 9.3, it can often be avoided.

Definition 9.3

An element a of the ring R is **invertible** if there is an element b in R such that

$$a\cdot b=1$$

b is called the **multiplicative inverse** of a and is denoted by a^{-1}. ○

In any ring, the unit 1 is invertible, with $1^{-1}=1$. Namely, $1\cdot 1=1$ by Definition 9.1(iii). In $\mathbb{Z}$, the ring of integers, only 1 and -1 are invertible. In $\mathbb{R}$, the ring of all real numbers, all nonzero elements are invertible. Theorem 9.4 may be reworded to say that the element a in $\mathbb{Z}_n$ is invertible if and only if $\gcd(a,n)=1$. Proposition 9.6 and the $1\neq 0$ condition of Definition 9.1 imply that the zero of a ring is never invertible.

Example 9.21

Let us see that every nonzero complex number $c=a+bi$ is invertible. Since $c\neq 0+0i$, $a\neq 0$ and/or $b\neq 0$. So $a^2+b^2>0$. In particular, division by the real number a^2+b^2 is possible.

$$\begin{aligned}\frac{1}{c}&=\frac{1}{a+bi}\\&=\frac{a-bi}{(a+bi)(a-bi)}\\&=\frac{a-bi}{a^2-i^2b^2}\\&=\frac{a-bi}{a^2+b^2}\\&=\frac{a}{a^2+b^2}+\frac{-b}{a^2+b^2}i\end{aligned} \tag{9.31}$$

So $\frac{1}{c}$ is again a complex number. For example, using (9.31),

$$\frac{1}{1+2i} = \frac{1}{1^2+2^2} + \frac{-2}{1^2+2^2}i = \frac{1}{5} - \frac{2}{5}i$$

Indeed, $\left(\frac{1}{5} - \frac{2}{5}i\right)(1+2i) = \frac{1}{5} + \frac{2}{5}i - \frac{2}{5}i - \frac{4}{5}i^2 = \frac{1}{5} - \left(-\frac{4}{5}\right) = 1$ △

Proposition 9.9 Let a and b be elements of a ring and such that a is invertible and $b \neq 0$. Then $a \cdot b \neq 0$.

Example 9.22 Before proving Proposition 9.9, we shall illustrate its statement. Consider the element 2 in the ring $\mathbb{Z}_5$. Since $2 \cdot 3 = 1$ in $\mathbb{Z}_5$, 2 is invertible with $2^{-1} = 3$. The nonzero elements of $\mathbb{Z}_5$ are 1,2,3,4. The products

$$2 \cdot 1 = 2 \qquad 2 \cdot 2 = 4 \qquad 2 \cdot 3 = 1 \qquad 2 \cdot 4 = 3$$

are all nonzero. △

Proof of Proposition 9.9

$$a^{-1} \cdot (a \cdot b) = (a^{-1} \cdot a) \cdot b = 1 \cdot b = b \neq 0$$

By Proposition 9.6 and commutativity, $a \cdot b \neq 0$. □

Proposition 9.10 Let $p(x) \neq 0$ and $q(x)$ be polynomials in the ring $R[x]$. Suppose that the leading coefficient of $p(x)$ is invertible. Then

$$\deg(p(x)q(x)) = \deg(p(x)) + \deg(q(x))$$ □

Proposition 9.10 follows immediately from Proposition 9.9; a formal proof is left to the exercises. The reader should also construct examples for Proposition 9.10.

Consider a polynomial ring $R[x]$. Just as a nonzero integer b may be divided into another integer a, yielding (9.3), so may any polynomial $p(x)$ in $R[x]$, with invertible leading coefficient, be divided into another polynomial $d(x)$ in $R[x]$. We wish to describe this division process and to establish the analog of (9.3). A polynomial $p(x)$ with leading coefficient 1 is said to be **monic**. Recall that 1 is always invertible in a ring.

Example 9.23 Consider the ring $\mathbb{Z}[x]$, of polynomials with integer coefficients. Let us divide the monic polynomial $x^2 + 2x + 4$ into the polynomial $2x^3 + 3x - 7$. We use the usual algorithm:

$$
\begin{array}{r@{}l}
 & \phantom{2x^3+0x^2+{}}2x-4 \\
x^2+2x+4 \,\big)\!\! & \overline{2x^3+0x^2+3x-7} \\
 & \underline{2x^3+4x^2+8x\phantom{{}-7}} \\
 & -4x^2-5x-7 \\
 & \underline{-4x^2-8x-16} \\
 & \phantom{2x^3-4x^2-{}}3x+9
\end{array}
$$

$3x+9$ is the remainder. It is easy to check that

$$2x^3+3x-7=(2x-4)(x^2+2x+4)+(3x+9) \qquad \triangle$$

Example 9.24

In $\mathbb{Z}[x]$, we attempt to divide the polynomial $3x+2$ into the polynomial $6x^2+2x+1$:

$$
\begin{array}{r@{}l}
 & \phantom{6x^2+{}}2x-\frac{2}{3} \\
3x+2 \,\big)\!\! & \overline{6x^2+2x+1} \\
 & \underline{6x^2+4x\phantom{{}+1}} \\
 & -2x+1
\end{array}
\tag{9.32}
$$

But since $-\frac{2}{3}$ is not an integer, the term $-\frac{2}{3}$ in (9.32) is not allowed in the ring $\mathbb{Z}[x]$. So the division cannot be done. $\triangle$

In general, dividing a polynomial with leading coefficient a into another polynomial requires finding c/a for various ring elements c. If a is invertible, with $a^{-1}=b$, we may think of c/a as

$$\frac{c}{a}=c\cdot a^{-1}=cb \tag{9.33}$$

We may clear fractions in (9.33); $\frac{c}{a}\cdot a$ should equal c. Indeed, $(cb)a=c(ba)=c(ab)=c\cdot 1=c$.

Example 9.25

In $\mathbb{Z}_{10}$, $3\cdot 7=1$, so $3^{-1}=7$. Computing in $\mathbb{Z}_{10}$:

$$\frac{4}{3}=4\cdot 3^{-1}=4\cdot 7=8 \quad \text{and} \quad 3\cdot 8=4$$

$$\frac{5}{3}=5\cdot 3^{-1}=5\cdot 7=5 \quad \text{and} \quad 3\cdot 5=5 \qquad \triangle$$

Example 9.26

Let us consider the ring $\mathbb{Z}_8[x]$. Since $3 \cdot 3 = 1$ in $\mathbb{Z}_8$, 3 is invertible in $\mathbb{Z}_8$ with $3^{-1} = 3$. We shall divide the polynomial $3x - 6$ into the polynomial $2x^2 + x - 3$. Since subtraction is the addition of the additive inverse, $3x - 6 = 3x + 2$ and $2x^2 + x - 3 = 2x^2 + x + 5$. The division starts as follows:

$$\begin{array}{r} \frac{2}{3}x \\ 3x+2 \overline{\big) 2x^2 + x + 5} \end{array} \tag{9.34}$$

Since $3^{-1} = 3$ in $\mathbb{Z}_8$, $\frac{2}{3} = 2 \cdot 3 = 6$ in $\mathbb{Z}_8$. (9.34) continues as

$$\begin{array}{r} 6x \\ 3x+2 \overline{\big) 2x^2 + x + 5} \\ \underline{2x^2 + 4x} \end{array} \tag{9.35}$$

The subtraction $(2x^2 + x + 5) - (2x^2 + 4x)$ in (9.35) is computed in $\mathbb{Z}_8[x]$ as

$$\begin{aligned} (2x^2 + x + 5) - (2x^2 + 4x) &= (2x^2 + x + 5) + (6x^2 + 4x) \\ &= 0x^2 + 5x + 5 \\ &= 5x + 5 \end{aligned}$$

Here is the complete division:

$$\begin{array}{r} 6x + 7 \\ 3x+2 \overline{\big) 2x^2 + x + 5} \\ \underline{2x^2 + 4x} \\ 5x + 5 \\ \underline{5x + 6} \\ 7 \end{array}$$

It is easy to check that $2x^2 + x + 5 = (6x + 7)(3x + 2) + 7$ in $\mathbb{Z}_8[x]$. △

Theorem 9.11

Let R be a ring. Let $p(x)$ be an element of $R[x]$ with an invertible leading coefficient. Let $d(x)$ be an arbitrary element of $R[x]$. Then there exist unique elements $q(x)$ and $r(x)$ in $R[x]$ such that

$$d(x) = q(x)p(x) + r(x)$$

with $\deg(r(x)) < \deg(p(x))$.

Proof of Theorem 9.11

The division algorithm, as illustrated in Examples 9.23 and 9.26, constructs one such $q(x)$ and $r(x)$. We shall not formally verify that the division algorithm works. We shall, however, prove that $q(x)$ and $r(x)$ are unique. Suppose that $q_1(x)$, $r_1(x)$, $q_2(x)$, and $r_2(x)$ are polynomials in $R[x]$ that satisfy

$$d(x)=q_1(x)p(x)+r_1(x) \tag{9.36}$$

$$d(x)=q_2(x)p(x)+r_2(x) \tag{9.37}$$

and the degrees of $r_1(x)$ and of $r_2(x)$ are less than the degree of $p(x)$. We need to show that $q_1(x)=q_2(x)$ and that $r_1(x)=r_2(x)$.

Equating the right sides of (9.36) and (9.37), we have

$$q_1(x)p(x)+r_1(x)=q_2(x)p(x)+r_2(x)$$

$$r_1(x)-r_2(x)=(q_2(x)-q_1(x))p(x) \tag{9.38}$$

The degree of the left side of (9.38) is less than the degree of $p(x)$, so this is also true of the right side of (9.38). Since the leading coefficient of $p(x)$ is invertible, by Proposition 9.10, $q_1(x)-q_2(x)=0$. That is, $q_1(x)=q_2(x)$. Also, from (9.38), since $q_1(x)-q_2(x)=0$, $r_1(x)-r_2(x)=0$. That is, $r_1(x)=r_2(x)$. ◇

Just as polynomials with real coefficients may be thought of as yielding functions of a real variable, so may elements of $R[x]$, for any ring R, be thought of as yielding functions of the elements of R. However, while real polynomials are determined by their function values, this is not true for arbitrary coefficient rings.

Example 9.27

We compute the function values for some polynomials in $\mathbb{Z}_3[x]$. Let $p(x)=x^2+1$. Then

$$p(0)=0\cdot 0+1=1$$

$$p(1)=1\cdot 1+1=2$$

$$p(2)=2\cdot 2+1=1+1=2$$

Now consider $q(x)=x^3+2x$:

$$q(0)=0\cdot 0\cdot 0+2\cdot 0=0$$

$$q(1)=1\cdot 1\cdot 1+2\cdot 1=1+2=0$$

$$q(2)=2\cdot 2\cdot 2+2\cdot 2=2+1=0$$

Observe that the polynomial $q(x)=x^3+2x$ has the same function values as the polynomial $r(x)=0$. But x^3+2x and 0 are different polynomials, since they have different coefficients. △

The following easy theorem, sometimes called the Remainder Theorem, will be crucial in the next section. Division by a monic polynomial is always possible. If the monic polynomial has degree 1, then by Theorem 9.11, the remainder either is 0 or else has degree 0. In both cases, the remainder lies in the coefficient ring.

Theorem 9.12 Let a be an element of the ring R. Let $p(x)$ be an element of $R[x]$. Write

$$p(x)=q(x)\cdot(x-a)+r \qquad \textbf{(9.39)}$$

with r in R. Then $p(a)=r$.

Example 9.28 Before proving Theorem 9.12, we illustrate its statement. Take $R=\mathbb{Z}_3$, $a=2$, and $p(x)=x^2+1$. As computed in Example 9.27, $p(2)=2$. In Theorem 9.12, $x-a=x-2=x+1$. Let us divide $x+1$ into x^2+1:

$$\begin{array}{r} x+2 \\ x+1 \overline{) x^2+0x+1} \\ \underline{x^2+\ x} \\ 2x+1 \\ \underline{2x+2} \\ 2 \end{array}$$

Indeed, the remainder is 2. △

Proof of Theorem 9.12 Let $x=a$ in (9.39):

$$p(a)=q(a)\cdot(a-a)+r$$

But $a-a=0$ and $q(a)\cdot 0=0$ by Proposition 9.6. Hence $p(a)=r$. ◇

Exercises 9.2

1. Perform the indicated calculations in $\mathbb{Z}_6[x]$.
   a. $(2x^2+x+1)+(x^2+5x+4)$
   b. $(2x^2+x+1)+(4x^2+x+2)$
   c. $(2x+3)\cdot(4x+2)$
   d. $(4x+3)\cdot(3x+1)$

2. With $p(x)$ and $d(x)$ as indicated in $\mathbb{Z}[x]$, use the division algorithm to find $q(x)$ and $r(x)$ of Theorem 9.11.
   a. $d(x)=2x^3+x^2-9 \quad p(x)=x^2+3x$
   b. $d(x)=4x^3+3x^2-2x+1 \quad p(x)=x^3-2x^2+7$
3. With $p(x)$ and $d(x)$ as indicated in $\mathbb{Z}_2[x]$, use the division algorithm to find $q(x)$ and $r(x)$ of Theorem 9.11.
   a. $d(x)=x^3+x^2+1 \quad p(x)=x^2+x+1$
   b. $d(x)=x^4+x^2+x \quad p(x)=x^2+1$
4. With $p(x)$ and $d(x)$ as indicated in $\mathbb{Z}_7[x]$, use the division algorithm to find $q(x)$ and $r(x)$ of Theorem 9.11.
   a. $d(x)=2x^2+3x+4 \quad p(x)=3x+5$
   b. $d(x)=4x^3+2x^2+4x \quad p(x)=4x^2+3x$
5. Computing in $\mathbb{Z}_2$, find $p(0)$ and $p(1)$.
   a. $p(x)=x^4+x^2+x+1$ b. $p(x)=x^5+x^4+x^3+x$
6. Computing in $\mathbb{Z}_6$, find $p(1)$, $p(2)$ and $p(4)$.
   a. $p(x)=x^2+4x+1$ b. $p(x)=2x^2+4$
7. Prove Proposition 9.5.
8. Let R be a ring. Show that $R[x]$ is also a ring.
9. a. Let n be an integer. Informally justify the notations

$$-\infty+n=-\infty \qquad \max(-\infty,n)=n$$

   b. Restate and prove Proposition 9.10 in the case that $q(x)=0$.
   c. Show that $\deg(p(x)+q(x))\leq\max(\deg(p(x)),\deg(q(x)))$ for any two polynomials $p(x)$, $q(x)$ in a ring $R[x]$.
10. Prove Proposition 9.10 in the case $q(x)\neq 0$.
11. Show that, in any ring R, $(-1)^{-1}=-1$.
12. With a in the ring R, show that $(x-a)|p(x)$ in $R[x]$ if and only if $p(a)=0$.

9.3 The Fast Fourier Transform

Fourier series are a very important tool for studying periodic functions of a real variable. For functions, such as data points, that are defined for only a finite number of values, the discrete Fourier transform is appropriate. In a suitable sense, the discrete Fourier transform approximates a Fourier series. After these ideas are illustrated at the beginning of this section, the fast Fourier transform, which is a very efficient algorithm for computing the discrete Fourier transform, is described. Most of the examples in this section will be about real-valued or complex-valued functions. However, in order to be able to describe the Schönhage-Strassen algorithm in the next section, we study the discrete Fourier transform for more general ring-valued functions.

Consider a function $y=f(x)$, as in Calculus, which is defined and continuous on the interval $[0,2\pi]$. Without causing any serious difficulties, we could allow $f(x)$ to have simple types of discontinuities.

The **Fourier coefficients** for $f(x)$ are defined by

$$a_0=\frac{1}{2\pi}\int_0^{2\pi} f(x)dx$$

$$\text{for } m\geq 1, \quad a_m=\frac{1}{\pi}\int_0^{2\pi} f(x)\cos mx\,dx \tag{9.40}$$

$$b_m=\frac{1}{\pi}\int_0^{2\pi} f(x)\sin mx\,dx$$

The **Fourier series** for $f(x)$ is defined by

$$a_0+\sum_{m=1}^{\infty} a_m\cos mx+b_m\sin mx \tag{9.41}$$

Defining the coefficients as in (9.40) results in the series of (9.41) converging to $f(x)$ wherever $f(x)$ has a continuous derivative.

Example 9.29

We compute the Fourier series for the function $f(x)=x$, $0\leq x\leq 2\pi$. From (9.40),

$$a_0=\frac{1}{2\pi}\int_0^{2\pi} x\,dx=\frac{1}{2\pi}\frac{x^2}{2}\bigg|_0^{2\pi}=\frac{1}{2\pi}\cdot\frac{(2\pi)^2}{2}=\pi$$

b_m, $m\geq 1$, is computed via an integration by parts:

$$b_m=\frac{1}{\pi}\int_0^{2\pi} x\sin mx\,dx$$

We let

$$u=x \qquad dv=\sin mx\,dx$$

$$du=dx \qquad v=-\frac{\cos mx}{m}$$

$$b_m=\frac{1}{\pi}\left\{\frac{-x\cos mx}{m}\bigg|_0^{2\pi}+\int_0^{2\pi}\frac{\cos mx}{m}dx\right\}$$

An easy computation shows that $\int_0^{2\pi} \frac{\cos mx}{m} dx = 0$. So

$$b_m = \frac{1}{\pi} \cdot \frac{-2\pi \cos 2\pi m}{m} = \frac{-2}{m}$$

A similar calculation, which we leave to the exercises, shows that, for $m \geq 1$,

$$a_m = 0$$

From (9.41), $f(x) = x$ has the Fourier series

$$\pi - \sum_{m=1}^{\infty} \frac{2}{m} \sin mx$$ △

Let us consider the definite integral

$$\int_a^b g(x)\, dx \tag{9.42}$$

Recall from the Calculus, as in Figure 9.1, that the integral of (9.42) may be approximated numerically by dividing the interval of integration, $[a,b]$, into N equal pieces and then computing the sum of the areas of the indicated rectangles as follows:

$$\int_a^b g(x) dx \approx \frac{b-a}{N} \sum_{j=0}^{N-1} g(x_j), \qquad x_j = a + j\frac{b-a}{N} \tag{9.43}$$

Figure 9.1 Numerical integration

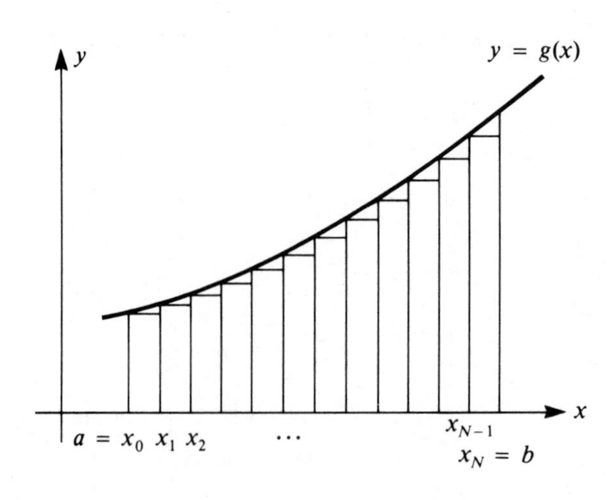

We apply (9.43) to (9.40) and make the obvious simplifications:

$$a_0 \approx \frac{1}{N}\sum_{j=0}^{N-1} f\left(\frac{2\pi j}{N}\right)$$

$$\text{for } m \geq 1, \qquad a_m \approx \frac{2}{N}\sum_{j=0}^{N-1} f\left(\frac{2\pi j}{N}\right)\cos\left(\frac{2\pi m j}{N}\right) \tag{9.44}$$

$$b_m \approx \frac{2}{N}\sum_{j=0}^{N-1} f\left(\frac{2\pi j}{N}\right)\sin\left(\frac{2\pi m j}{N}\right)$$

Example 9.30

We use (9.44) with $N = 100$ to approximate some of the Fourier coefficients for $f(x) = x$ of Example 9.29. We give our answers to three decimal places.

	Exact		Approximate	
m	a_m	b_m	a_m	b_m
0	$\pi = 3.141$		3.110	
1	0	$-\frac{2}{1} = -2.000$	-0.063	-1.999
2	0	$-\frac{2}{2} = -1.000$	-0.063	-0.999
3	0	$-\frac{2}{3} = -0.667$	-0.063	-0.665
4	0	$-\frac{2}{4} = -0.500$	-0.063	-0.497
5	0	$-\frac{2}{5} = -0.400$	-0.063	-0.397
6	0	$-\frac{2}{6} = -0.333$	-0.063	-0.329
7	0	$-\frac{2}{7} = -0.286$	-0.063	-0.281
8	0	$-\frac{2}{8} = -0.250$	-0.063	-0.245
9	0	$-\frac{2}{9} = -0.222$	-0.063	-0.216
10	0	$-\frac{2}{10} = -0.200$	-0.063	-0.193

△

Example 9.31

A typical use of Fourier coefficients is to extract periodic phenomena from nonperiodic data. Let's consider the 100 data points of Figure 9.2. These were formed by adding a sequence with period 9 to a quadratic function.

In Figure 9.2, we can see this periodic behavior superimposed on the overall trend. We apply the right sides of (9.44) to the $N = 100$ data points, giving approximate Fourier coefficients. For $0 \leq m \leq 50$, Figure 9.3 gives the plot for $\sqrt{a_m^2 + b_m^2}$, on a semilogarithmic scale. The reason for plotting $\sqrt{a_m^2 + b_m^2}$, rather than a_m and b_m, is that $a_m \cos mx + b_m \sin mx$, on the right side of (9.41), is just a phase-shifted sine wave of amplitude $\sqrt{a_m^2 + b_m^2}$. Observe the relatively high values in Figure 9.3 at $m = 11$, $m = 22$, $m = 34$, and $m = 44$. These correspond to multiples of the frequency of the periodic sequence; with 100 data points and period 9, the frequency is $100/9 = 11.1$. △

We now begin a reformulation of (9.44) using complex numbers. As in Figure 9.4, plot a complex number $c = a + bi$ using polar coordinates.

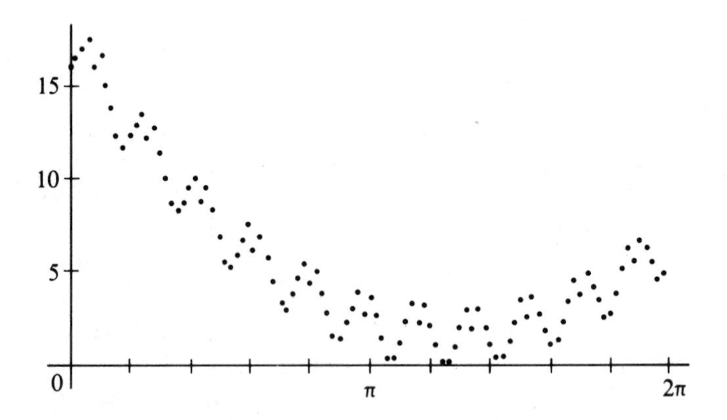

Figure 9.2 Data points

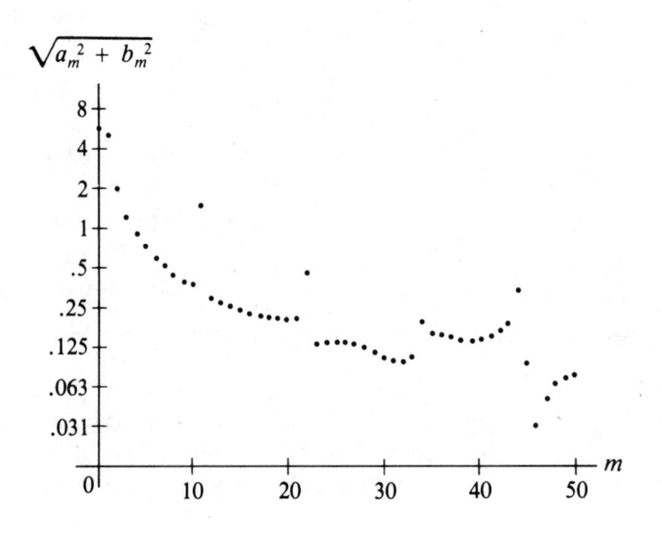

Figure 9.3 Fourier transform norms for Figure 9.2

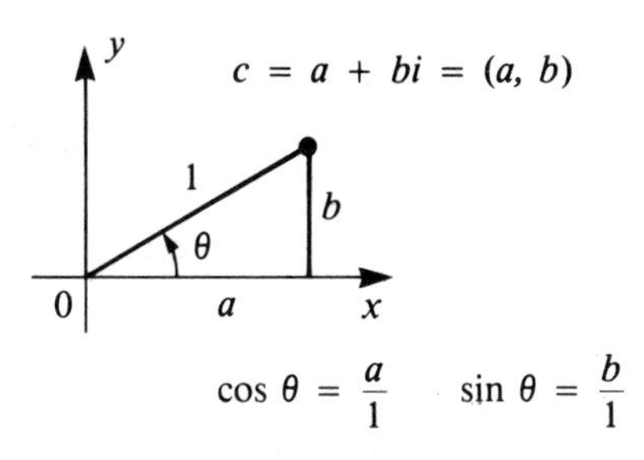

Figure 9.4 Polar coordinates for $c = a + bi$, $|c| = 1$

The **absolute value** of c, denoted by $|c|$, is the distance from c to 0; that is,

$$\text{for } c = a + bi, \quad |c| = \sqrt{a^2 + b^2}$$

We are primarily interested in having $|c| = 1$. Then, as in Figure 9.4, $a = \cos\theta$ and $b = \sin\theta$. We may write:

$$\text{for } |c| = 1, \quad c = \cos\theta + i\sin\theta$$

Let $d = \cos\varphi + i\sin\varphi$ be another complex number with $|d| = 1$. Then, recalling from trigonometry the addition formulas for sine and cosine,

$$\begin{aligned} c \cdot d &= (\cos\theta + i\sin\theta)(\cos\varphi + i\sin\varphi) \\ &= \cos\theta\cos\varphi - \sin\theta\sin\varphi + i(\cos\theta\sin\varphi + \sin\theta\sin\varphi) \\ &= \cos(\theta + \varphi) + i\sin(\theta + \varphi) \end{aligned} \tag{9.45}$$

In particular, let $d = c$ in (9.45).

$$c^2 = \cos 2\theta + i\sin 2\theta$$

Let $d = c^2$ in (9.45).

$$\begin{aligned} c^3 = c \cdot c^2 &= \cos(\theta + 2\theta) + i\sin(\theta + 2\theta) \\ &= \cos 3\theta + i\sin 3\theta \end{aligned}$$

In general,

$$\text{for } c = \cos\theta + i\sin\theta, \quad c^n = \cos n\theta + i\sin n\theta \tag{9.46}$$

Examples 9.32

Let $c = i$. Then

$$i = \cos\frac{\pi}{2} + i\sin\frac{\pi}{2}, \qquad \theta = \frac{\pi}{2}$$

$$i^2 = -1 = \cos \pi + i \sin \pi, \qquad 2\theta = \pi$$

$$i^3 = -i = \cos \frac{3\pi}{2} + i \sin \frac{3\pi}{2}, \qquad 3\theta = \frac{3\pi}{2}$$

$$i^4 = 1 = \cos 2\pi + i \sin 2\pi, \qquad 4\theta = 2\pi$$

Of course, we may also think of 1 as

$$1 = \cos 0 + i \sin 0$$

and so give 1 a polar angle of 0. But polar angles of 0 and 2π are the same geometrically in polar coordinates. △

$$c = -\frac{1}{2} + i\frac{\sqrt{3}}{2} = \cos \frac{2\pi}{3} + i \sin \frac{2\pi}{3}, \qquad \theta = \frac{2\pi}{3}$$

$$c^2 = -\frac{1}{2} - i\frac{\sqrt{3}}{2} = \cos \frac{4\pi}{3} + i \sin \frac{4\pi}{3}, \qquad 2\theta = \frac{4\pi}{3}$$

$$c^3 = 1 = \cos 2\pi + i \sin 2\pi, \qquad 3\theta = 2\pi$$

△

With N fixed, let

$$\omega = \cos \frac{2\pi}{N} + i \sin \frac{2\pi}{n} \tag{9.47}$$

From (9.46),

$$\omega^{mj} = \cos \frac{2\pi mj}{N} + i \sin \frac{2\pi mj}{N}$$

From (9.44), for $m \geq 1$,

$$\begin{aligned} a_m + ib_m &\approx \frac{2}{N}\left\{\sum_{j=0}^{N-1} f\left(\frac{2\pi mj}{N}\right)\left[\cos\left(\frac{2\pi mj}{N}\right) + i \sin\left(\frac{2\pi mj}{N}\right)\right]\right\} \\ &= \frac{2}{N}\left\{\sum_{j=0}^{N-1} f\left(\frac{2\pi mj}{N}\right)\omega^{mj}\right\} \end{aligned} \tag{9.48}$$

For applications in the next section, we shall need the analog of ω of (9.47) in other rings besides $\mathbb{C}$. Observe that $\omega^N = 1$. Any ring element α such that $\alpha^N = 1$ is called an ***N*th root of unity**. ω is special in that

$$\omega^m \neq 1 \quad \text{for } 0 < m < N \tag{9.49}$$

An Nth root of unity ω that satisfies (9.49) is said to be **primitive**. In $\mathbb{C}$, if α is any Nth root of unity and ω is any primitive Nth root of unity, then $\alpha = \omega^m$ for a unique m such that $0 \le m < N$. So in the ring $\mathbb{C}$, the choice of ω in Definition 9.4, which follows, controls only the ordering of the $F(\mathbf{f})_m$. Observe that the slightly unusual indexing in (9.50) makes (9.50) similar to (9.48).

Definition 9.4

Let R be a ring with a primitive Nth root of unity ω. Let Ω be the $N \times N$ matrix given by $\Omega_{i,j} = \omega^{i \cdot j}$, $0 \le i, j \le N-1$. Let $\mathbf{f} = (f_0, f_1, \ldots, f_{N-1})^t$ be any column N-tuple with entries in R. The **discrete Fourier transform**, $F(\mathbf{f})$, of $\mathbf{f}$ is the column N-tuple $\Omega\mathbf{f}$. Writing $F(\mathbf{f}) = (F(\mathbf{f})_0, F(\mathbf{f})_1, \ldots, F(\mathbf{f})_{N-1})^t$, we have

$$F(\mathbf{f})_m = \sum_{j=0}^{N-1} \Omega_{m,j} f_j = \sum_{j=0}^{N-1} f_j \omega^{mj} = \sum_{j=0}^{N-1} f_j (\omega^m)^j \tag{9.50}$$

○

Example 9.33

We compute a discrete Fourier transform using the ring of complex numbers and $N = 4$. By the first part of Examples 9.32, we may take $\omega = i$. Then

$$\Omega = \begin{pmatrix} i^0 & i^0 & i^0 & i^0 \\ i^0 & i^1 & i^2 & i^3 \\ i^0 & i^2 & i^4 & i^6 \\ i^0 & i^3 & i^6 & i^9 \end{pmatrix} = \begin{pmatrix} 1 & 1 & 1 & 1 \\ 1 & i & -1 & -i \\ 1 & -1 & 1 & -1 \\ 1 & -i & -1 & i \end{pmatrix}$$

Let $\mathbf{f} = (2, 1+i, 2i, 0)^t$. Then

$$F(\mathbf{f}) = \begin{pmatrix} 1 & 1 & 1 & 1 \\ 1 & i & -1 & -i \\ 1 & -1 & 1 & -1 \\ 1 & -i & -1 & i \end{pmatrix} \begin{pmatrix} 2 \\ 1+i \\ 2i \\ 0 \end{pmatrix}$$

$$= \begin{pmatrix} 1\cdot 2 + 1\cdot(1+i) + 1\cdot 2i + 1\cdot 0 \\ 1\cdot 2 + i\cdot(1+i) - 1\cdot 2i - i\cdot 0 \\ 1\cdot 2 - 1\cdot(1+i) + 1\cdot 2i - 1\cdot 0 \\ 1\cdot 2 - i\cdot(1+i) - 1\cdot 2i + i\cdot 0 \end{pmatrix} = \begin{pmatrix} 3+3i \\ 1-i \\ 1+i \\ 3-3i \end{pmatrix}$$

△

Example 9.34

Let us consider the ring $\mathbb{Z}_5$. Then 2 is a primitive 4th root of unity. Namely,

$$2^1 = 2 \qquad 2^2 = 4 \qquad 2^3 = 3 \qquad 2^4 = 1$$

$$\Omega = \begin{pmatrix} 2^0 & 2^0 & 2^0 & 2^0 \\ 2^0 & 2^1 & 2^2 & 2^3 \\ 2^0 & 2^2 & 2^4 & 2^6 \\ 2^0 & 2^3 & 2^6 & 2^9 \end{pmatrix} = \begin{pmatrix} 1 & 1 & 1 & 1 \\ 1 & 2 & 4 & 3 \\ 1 & 4 & 1 & 4 \\ 1 & 3 & 4 & 2 \end{pmatrix}$$

Let $\mathbf{f} = (1,0,3,3)^t$. Then, computing in $\mathbb{Z}_5$,

$$F(\mathbf{f}) = \begin{pmatrix} 1 & 1 & 1 & 1 \\ 1 & 2 & 4 & 3 \\ 1 & 4 & 1 & 4 \\ 1 & 3 & 4 & 2 \end{pmatrix} \begin{pmatrix} 1 \\ 0 \\ 3 \\ 3 \end{pmatrix} = \begin{pmatrix} 2 \\ 2 \\ 1 \\ 4 \end{pmatrix}$$

△

For approximating Fourier coefficients as in (9.48), the discrete Fourier transform of (9.50) gives the correct answer up to a factor of $2/N$, $m \geq 1$. $F(\mathbf{f})_0$ differs from a_0 by a factor of $1/N$. So the discrete Fourier transform contains all of the information available in the first N Fourier coefficients. As explained in the exercises, with N data points, only N Fourier coefficients are meaningful. So the discrete Fourier transform using a primitive Nth root of unity may be a good way to analyze N data points.

(9.50) leads immediately to the following formulation of the discrete Fourier transform in terms of the evaluation of polynomials. We shall omit a formal proof.

Proposition 9.13

Let $\mathbf{f} = (f_0, f_1, \ldots, f_{N-1})^t$ be a column N-tuple with entries in the ring R. Let $p(x)$ be the polynomial in $R[x]$ given by

$$p(x) = f_0 + f_1 x + f_2 x^2 + \cdots + f_{N-1} x^{N-1}$$

Suppose that R has a primitive Nth root of unity ω. Let $F(\mathbf{f})$ be the discrete Fourier transform of f. Then

$$F(\mathbf{f})_m = p(\omega^m)$$

□

Example 9.35

Take $R = \mathbb{C}$. Let $\mathbf{f} = (2, 1+i, 2i, 0)^t$, as in Example 9.33. We recompute $F(\mathbf{f})$ using Proposition 9.13.

$$p(x) = 2 + (1+i)x + 2ix^2$$

$\omega = i$.

$$F(\mathbf{f})_0 = p(i^0) = p(1) = 2 + (1+i) + 2i = 3 + 3i$$
$$F(\mathbf{f})_1 = p(i^1) = p(i) = 2 + (1+i)i + 2i(-1) = 1 - i$$
$$F(\mathbf{f})_2 = p(i^2) = p(-1) = 2 + (1+i)(-1) + 2i = 1 + i$$
$$F(\mathbf{f})_3 = p(i^3) = p(-i) = 2 + (1+i)(-i) + 2i(-1) = 3 - 3i$$

This agrees, of course, with $F(\mathbf{f})$ of Example 9.33. △

We now describe the fast Fourier transform algorithm for $N = 2^n$. By Proposition 9.13 and Theorem 9.12, $F(\mathbf{f})_m$ may be computed as the remainder of $p(x)$ after division by $x - \omega^m$. By itself, this computation of $F(\mathbf{f})_m$ is no more efficient than the use of (9.50). However, with $N = 2^n$, the fast Fourier transform algorithm computes all N remainders with $2N - 1$ very simple divisions. An analysis of the comparative speeds of the fast Fourier transform and of (9.50) will be done later. Variants of the fast Fourier transform algorithm, which we shall not present, are available for arbitrary N.

Let $N = 2^n$ and let ω be any Nth root of unity. As is true in (9.47), we require that $\omega^{N/2} = \omega^{2^{n-1}} = -1$. We wish to factor the polynomial $x^N - 1 = x^N - \omega^0$. Recall that, in any ring, $a^2 - b^2 = (a-b)(a+b)$. Also, since $\omega^{N/2} = -1$, for any exponent q, $+\omega^q = -\omega^{q+N/2}$. Consider $N = 4 = 2^2$: $\omega^0 = 1$, $\omega^2 = -1$.

$$\begin{aligned} x^4 - \omega^0 & \\ &= (x^2 - \omega^0)(x^2 + \omega^0) = (x^2 - \omega^0)(x^2 - \omega^2) \\ &= (x - \omega^0)(x + \omega^0)(x - \omega)(x + \omega) = (x - \omega^0)(x - \omega^2)(x - \omega)(x - \omega^3) \end{aligned}$$

As in Figure 9.5, where $N = 8$, it is sometimes convenient to arrange this factorization into a rooted tree. Each vertex is a polynomial of the form $x^s - \omega^t$. If s and t are both even, we may factor

$$\begin{aligned} x^s - \omega^t &= (x^{s/2} - \omega^{t/2})(x^{s/2} + \omega^{t/2}) \\ &= (x^{s/2} - \omega^{t/2})(x^{s/2} - \omega^{(t+N)/2}) \end{aligned}$$

Figure 9.5 Factoring $x^8 - \omega^0$

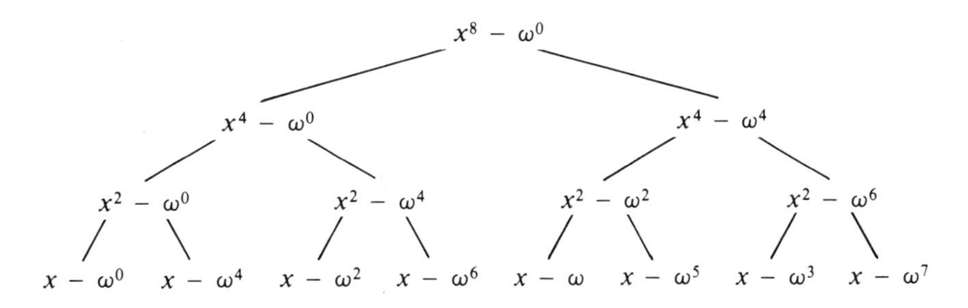

These last two factors become the vertices below $x^s - \omega^t$. Since $N = 2^n$, there are n levels of factorization. After the final factorization, as verified in the exercises, there are the linear factors $x - \omega^m$, $0 \leq m \leq N-1$, although not in this order. Of course, $\omega^0 = 1$.

Proposition 9.14 Let R be a ring. Suppose that

$$p(x) = a(x)b(x) \tag{9.51}$$

in $R[x]$, with $a(x)$ and $p(x)$ monic polynomials. Let $d(x)$ be a polynomial in $R[x]$. Divide $p(x)$ into $d(x)$:

$$d(x) = q(x)p(x) + r(x) \tag{9.52}$$

with $\deg(r(x)) < \deg(p(x))$. Divide $a(x)$ into $r(x)$:

$$r(x) = c(x)a(x) + s(x) \tag{9.53}$$

with $\deg(s(x)) < \deg(a(x))$. Then $s(x)$ also equals the remainder for $a(x)$ divided into $d(x)$.

Example 9.36 Before proving Proposition 9.14, we shall illustrate its statement. Take $R = \mathbb{Z}$.

$$x^4 - 4x^2 = (x^2 - 2x)(x^2 + 2x)$$

Proposition 9.14 implies that the remainder for division by $x^2 - 2x$ can be calculated by first dividing by $x^4 - 4x^2$ and then dividing the resulting remainder by $x^2 - 2x$.

We calculate the remainder for $x^5 - 9x^2 + 1$ divided by $x^2 - 2x$ using Proposition 9.14 as follows:

$$x^5 - 9x^2 + 1 = x(x^4 - 4x^2) + (4x^3 - 9x^2 + 1)$$

for a remainder of $4x^3 - 9x^2 + 1$.

$$4x^3 - 9x^2 + 1 = (4x - 1)(x^2 - 2x) + (-2x + 1)$$

for a desired remainder of $-2x + 1$.

A direct calculation gives

$$x^5 - 9x^2 + 1 = (x^3 + 2x^2 + 4x - 1)(x^2 - 2x) + (-2x + 1)$$

for a remainder of $-2x + 1$. This agrees, of course, with the previous calculation. △

Proof of Proposition 9.14

Substitute (9.53) into (9.52) and then apply (9.51) as follows:

$$\begin{aligned} d(x) &= q(x)p(x) + c(x)a(x) + s(x) \\ &= q(x)a(x)b(x) + c(x)a(x) + s(x) \\ &= [q(x)b(x) + c(x)]a(x) + s(x) \end{aligned}$$

Since the degree of $s(x)$ is less than the degree of $a(x)$ and since remainders are unique by Theorem 9.11, $s(x)$ does equal the remainder for $a(x)$ divided into $p(x)$. □

Putting all of the above remarks together yields the desired algorithm:

Theorem 9.15

(Fast Fourier Transform Algorithm) Let ω be a primitive Nth root of unity in the ring R, such that $N = 2^n$ and $\omega^{N/2} = -1$. Let $\mathbf{f} = (f_0, f_1, \ldots, f_{N-1})^t$ be a column N-tuple with entries in R. Then $F(\mathbf{f})$, the discrete Fourier transform of $\mathbf{f}$, may be computed as follows:

(i) Successively factor $x^N - \omega^0$ into factors of form $x^s - \omega^t$, as in Figure 9.5.
(ii) With $p(x) = f_0 + f_1 x + f_2 x^2 + \cdots + f_{N-1} x^{N-1}$, successively use Proposition 9.14 to compute the remainders for $p(x)$ divided by the $x^s - \omega^t$. $F(\mathbf{f})_m$ is given by the remainder after division by $x - \omega^m$. ◇

Example 9.37

Using the complex numbers $\mathbb{C}$ as the ring R, we take $\mathbf{f} = (2, 1+i, 2i, 0)^t$. This is the same $\mathbf{f}$ as in Examples 9.33 and 9.35. We illustrate the fast Fourier transform using $\omega = i$. Then $x^4 - 1 = x^4 - i^0$ factors as in Figure 9.6. In Figure 9.6, polynomials such as $x - (-i)$ are written as $x + i$, for a simpler notation.

$$p(x) = 2 + (1+i)x + 2ix^2 = 2ix^2 + (1+i)x + 2$$

We start computing remainders after division by the polynomials of Figure 9.6. The first polynomial, $x^4 - 1$, in Figure 9.6 has a greater degree than has $p(x)$. So the first remainder is $p(x)$. The next two divisions are by $x^2 - 1$ and by $x^2 + 1$.

Figure 9.6 Factorization of $x^4 - 1$

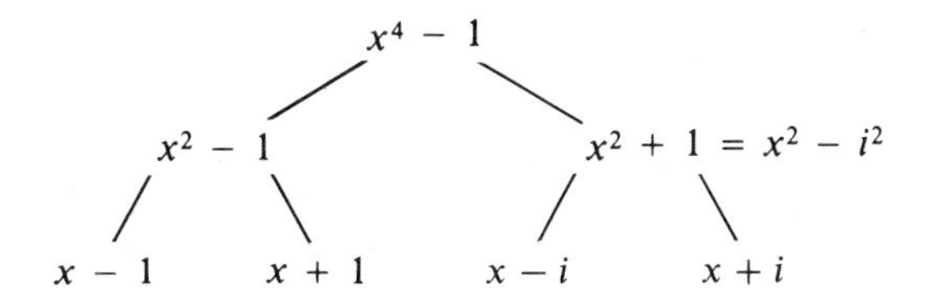

$$\begin{array}{r} 2i \\ x^2-1\overline{)2ix^2+(1+i)x+2} \\ \underline{2ix^2 \qquad\quad -2i} \\ (1+i)x+(2+2i) = \text{Remainder} \end{array}$$

$$\begin{array}{r} 2i \\ x^2+1\overline{)2ix^2+(1+i)x+2} \\ \underline{2ix^2 \qquad\quad +2i} \\ (1+i)x+(2-2i) = \text{Remainder} \end{array}$$

$(1+i)x+(2+2i)$ is divided by $x-1$ and $x+1$, leaving respective remainders of $3+3i$ and $1+i$. $(1+i)x+(2-2i)$ is divided by $x-i$ and $x+i$, leaving respective remainders of $1-i$ and $3-3i$. These remainders are given again in Figure 9.7.

Theorem 9.12 implies that the remainders in the last row of Figure 9.7, after division by $x-1$, $x+1$, $x-i$, $x+i$, correspond to $p(1)$, $p(-1)$, $p(i)$, $p(-i)$ respectively. So

$$F(\mathbf{f}) = (p(1), p(i), p(-1), p(-i))^t = (3+3i, 1-i, 1+i, 3-3i)^t$$

This agrees, of course, with the results of Examples 9.33 and 9.35. △

The divisions in Example 9.37 were especially easy because $p(x)$ had degree 2, rather than the largest possible degree of 3. Nonetheless, the divisions in the fast Fourier transform always divide $x^s-\omega^t$ into a polynomial of degree at most $2s-1$. Division in such cases may be done easily as follows.

Proposition 9.16 In the polynomial ring $R[x]$, let

$$p(x) = a_{2s-1}x^{2s-1} + a_{2s-2}x^{2s-2} + \cdots + a_1x + a_0$$

Divide $p(x)$ by the polynomial $x^s - c$. Then the remainder is $r(x) = a_{s-1}x^{s-1} + a_{s-2}x^{s-2} + \cdots + a_0 + c(a_{2s-1}x^{s-1} + a_{2s-2}x^{s-2} + \cdots + a_s)$

Figure 9.7 Remainders from Figure 9.6

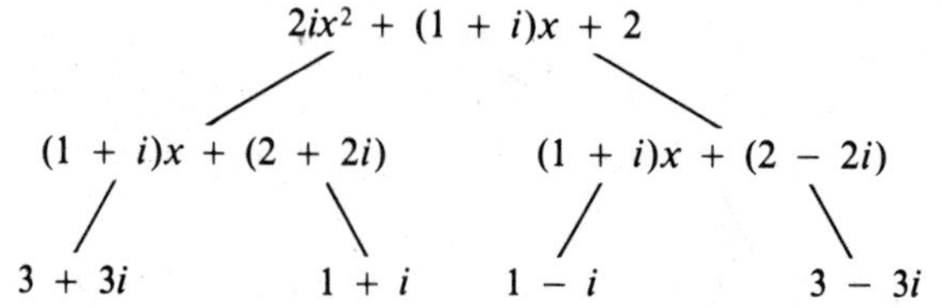

$$2ix^2 + (1+i)x + 2$$

$$(1+i)x + (2+2i) \qquad\qquad (1+i)x + (2-2i)$$

$$3+3i \qquad 1+i \qquad 1-i \qquad 3-3i$$

Proof of Proposition 9.16

We can check directly that

$$p(x)=(a_{2s-1}x^{s-1}+a_{2s-2}x^{s-2}+\cdots+a_s)(x^s-c)+r(x) \qquad \square$$

Example 9.38

Using $\mathbb{C}$, we compute $F(\mathbf{f})$ with $\mathbf{f}=(1,2,-i,2i,3,0,-2,i)^t$. $N=8=2^3$.

$$p(x)=ix^7-2x^6+3x^4+2ix^3-ix^2+2x+1$$

From (9.47), $\omega=\cos\frac{\pi}{4}+i\sin\frac{\pi}{4}=\frac{\sqrt{2}}{2}+i\frac{\sqrt{2}}{2}$. Then

$$\omega^0=1 \quad \omega^1=\frac{\sqrt{2}}{2}+i\frac{\sqrt{2}}{2} \quad \omega^2=i \quad \omega^3=-\frac{\sqrt{2}}{2}+i\frac{\sqrt{2}}{2}$$

$$\omega^4=-1 \quad \omega^5=-\frac{\sqrt{2}}{2}-i\frac{\sqrt{2}}{2} \quad \omega^6=-i \quad \omega^7=\frac{\sqrt{2}}{2}-i\frac{\sqrt{2}}{2}$$

The first division of $p(x)$ in the fast Fourier transform, by $x^8-\omega^0$ of Figure 9.5, leaves $p(x)$ as remainder. We use Proposition 9.16 to compute the remainder for $p(x)$ divided by $x^4-\omega^0=x^4-1$; $c=1$.

$$\begin{array}{rl} & 2ix^3 \quad -ix^2+2x+1 \\ + & ix^3 \quad -2x^2 \quad +3 \\ \hline & 3ix^3+(-2-i)x^2+2x+4 \end{array}$$

Similarly, we divide $p(x)$ by $x^4-(-1)$ for a remainder of

$$\begin{array}{rl} & 2ix^3 \quad -ix^2+2x+1 \\ -[& ix^3 \quad -2x^2 \quad +3\ ] \\ \hline & ix^3+(2-i)x^2+2x-2 \end{array}$$

Figure 9.8 lists all of the remainders needed to compute $F(\mathbf{f})$ via the fast Fourier transform algorithm. Reordering the last remainders gives

$$\begin{aligned} F(\mathbf{f})=\Bigg(&4+2i,-1+\frac{\sqrt{2}}{2}+i\left(2+\frac{\sqrt{2}}{2}\right),9+3i, \\ &-3-\frac{3\sqrt{2}}{2}+i\left(-2+\frac{3\sqrt{2}}{2}\right),-4i, \\ &-1-\frac{\sqrt{2}}{2}+i\left(2-\frac{\sqrt{2}}{2}\right),3-i,-3+\frac{3\sqrt{2}}{2}+i\left(-2-\frac{3\sqrt{2}}{2}\right)\Bigg)^t \end{aligned}$$

$\triangle$

Figure 9.8 Remainders from Figure 9.5

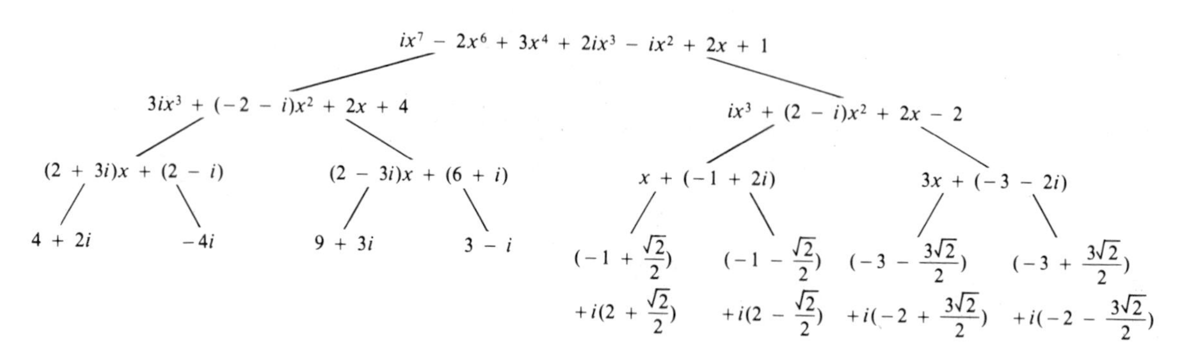

What are the comparative speeds, or time complexities, of computations of the discrete Fourier transform via (9.50) and via the fast Fourier transform? We shall not worry about the time needed to compute $\omega^0, \omega^1, \omega^2, \ldots, \omega^{N-1}$, since this time is small in comparison to the time needed for the other computations. We measure speed by the required number of computations. For each value of m, (9.50) requires N multiplications, namely the $f_j \cdot \omega^{mj}$, and $N-1$ additions, from $\sum$. Since m runs from 0 to $N-1$, in all, (9.50) requires N^2 multiplications and $N(N-1)$ additions.

Consider the fast Fourier transform, as in Figure 9.5, with $N = 2^n$. The first division, by $x^N - 1$, may be omitted in the computation. Thereafter, we consider divisions by polynomials of the form $x^{2^j} - c$, $j = n-1, n-2, \ldots, 0$. For each value of j, there are 2^{n-j} such divisions. By Proposition 9.16, each such division requires 2^j multiplications and 2^j additions for the computation of the remainder. So $2^{n-j} \cdot 2^j = 2^n$ multiplications and additions are required for each value of j. In all, the fast Fourier transform requires $n2^n = N \log_2 N$ multiplications and additions, a very considerable savings over (9.50).

Exercises 9.3

1. For each of the following complex numbers c, verify that $|c| = 1$ and write c in the form $c = \cos\theta + i\sin\theta$

   a. $-i$ b. $\dfrac{\sqrt{2}}{2} + i\dfrac{\sqrt{2}}{2}$ c. $-\dfrac{\sqrt{3}}{2} - i\dfrac{1}{2}$

2. Let $\omega = \cos\dfrac{2\pi}{6} + i\sin\dfrac{2\pi}{6} = \dfrac{1}{2} + i\dfrac{\sqrt{3}}{2}$. Verify directly that $\omega^6 = 1$.

3. Let $N = 4$ and $\omega = i$. Use Definition 9.4 to compute the discrete Fourier transform of each of the following 4-tuples of complex numbers.

   a. $(1,2,0,2)$ b. $(i, -1, 2i, 2)$

4. Consider the ring $\mathbb{Z}_5$. With $N=4$ and $\omega=2$, use Definition 9.4 to compute the discrete Fourier transform of each of the following 4-tuples of elements in $\mathbb{Z}_5$.
   a. $(1,3,0,2)$ b. $(4,1,3,3)$
5. In the ring $\mathbb{Z}[x]$, use Proposition 9.16 to compute the remainders for the following divisions.
   a. x^3+2x^2-x+3 divided by x^2-1
   b. x^3+2x^2-x+3 divided by x^2+1
   c. $2x^5+x^3-3x^2+3x+5$ divided by x^3-4
6. As in Figure 9.7, write the remainders for the divisions of the fast Fourier transform algorithm for the 4-tuples of Exercise 3.
7. Draw the analog of Figure 9.6 for the ring $\mathbb{Z}_5$, $N=4$, $\omega=2$.
8. As in Figure 9.7, write the remainders for the divisions of the fast Fourier transform algorithm for the 4-tuples of Exercise 4.
9. a. Verify that 3 is a primitive 6th root of unity in the ring $\mathbb{Z}_7$.
   b. With $N=6$ and $\omega=3$, write out the matrix Ω of Definition 9.4, for the ring $\mathbb{Z}_7$.
10. As stated in Example 9.29, verify that $a_m=0$ for $m\geq 1$ and $f(x)=x$.
11. In (9.44), for $m\geq 1$, explain why $a_{m+N}=a_m$ and $b_{m+N}=b_m$.
12. In (9.44), for $m\geq 1$, explain why $a_{N-m}=a_m$ and $b_{N-m}=-b_m$.
13. Let α be an Nth root of unity in the ring R. Show that, for every integer m, α^m is also an Nth root of unity in R.
14. Let $\mathbb{C}$ be the ring of complex numbers. Find the three 3rd roots of unity in $\mathbb{C}$ by solving the equation $x^3=1$. Compare your answers to the second part of Example 9.32.
15. Let $N=2^n$. Let m, $0\leq m<N$, have the binary representation $m_{n-1}m_{n-2}\ldots m_1m_0$. Factor $x^N-\omega^0$ as in Theorem 9.15(i). Show that, for $j=n,n-1,\ldots,2,1$, following $x^{2^j}-\omega^t$ by $x^{2^{j-1}}-\omega^{t/2}$ or $x^{2^{j-1}}-\omega^{(t+N)/2}$, according to whether $m_{n-j}=0$ or $m_{n-j}=1$, gives a sequence of factors for $x^N-\omega^0$ that terminates in $x-\omega^m$.
16. Explain why preorder, of Definition 4.14, is an efficient order in which to compute remainders by the divisors of the fast Fourier transform. *Hint:* Example 4.23.

9.4 Fast Multiplication

In the previous section, we described the fast Fourier transform algorithm. In this section, we prove the convolution theorem for the discrete Fourier transform. The fast Fourier transform then provides a rapid way to multiply polynomials. Ordinary integer multiplication may be reformulated using polynomial multiplication. This leads to a description of a simplified version of the Schönhage-Strassen algorithm for multiplication.

For very large numbers, with tens of thousands of bits, the fastest known method of multiplication is the Schönhage-Strassen algorithm.

Let R be a ring. Let us consider two polynomials in $R[x]$ of degree at most k:

$$\begin{aligned} p(x) &= f_k x^k + f_{k-1}x^{k-1} + \cdots + f_1 x + f_0 \\ q(x) &= g_k x^k + g_{k-1}x^{k-1} + \cdots + g_1 x + g_0 \end{aligned} \tag{9.54}$$

Then $p(x)q(x)$ is a polynomial in $R[x]$ of degree at most $2k$. We may write

$$p(x)q(x) = h_{2k}x^{2k} + h_{2k-1}x^{2k-1} + \cdots + h_1 x + h_0 \tag{9.55}$$

with

$$h_m = \sum_{i=0}^{k} f_{m-i}g_i \tag{9.56}$$

where $f_{m-i} = 0$ in case $m-i > k$ or $m-i < 0$.

Example 9.39

We illustrate (9.56), which is just ordinary multiplication of polynomials. Take $k=2$.

$$\begin{array}{rrrrr} & & f_2x^2 + & f_1x + & f_0 \\ & & g_2x^2 + & g_1x + & g_0 \\ \hline 0 & + \ 0 & + f_2g_0x^2 & + f_1g_0x & + f_0g_0 \\ 0 & + f_2g_1x^3 & + f_1g_1x^2 & + f_0g_1x + & 0 \\ f_2g_2x^4 & + f_1g_2x^3 & + f_0g_2x^2 + & 0 \ + & 0 \\ \hline \end{array} \tag{9.57}$$

The omitted sums in (9.57) are precisely (9.56) with $k=2$. △

Definition 9.5

Let $\mathbf{f} = (f_0, f_1, \ldots, f_k, 0, 0, \ldots, 0)^t$ and $\mathbf{g} = (g_0, g_1, \ldots, g_k, 0, 0, \ldots, 0)^t$ be column N-tuples with entries in a ring R such that $f_m = g_m = 0$ for $m \geq N/2$. The **convolution** of $\mathbf{f}$ and $\mathbf{g}$, denoted by $\mathbf{f} * \mathbf{g}$, is the column N-tuple $(h_0, h_1, \ldots, h_{N-1})^t$ with h_m given by (9.56). ○

As discussed before Definition 9.5, convolution is simply a way of doing polynomial multiplication without explicitly writing out the powers of the variable. The vectors **f** and **g** in Definition 9.5 are the coefficients of the polynomials that are multiplied.

Theorem 9.17

Let R be a ring with ω an Nth root of unity. Let $\mathbf{f}$ and $\mathbf{g}$ be as in Definition 9.5. Let $F(\mathbf{f})$, $F(\mathbf{g})$ and $F(\mathbf{f}*\mathbf{g})$ be the discrete Fourier transforms from Definition 9.4. Then

$$F(\mathbf{f}*\mathbf{g}) = (F(\mathbf{f})_0 \cdot F(\mathbf{g})_0, F(\mathbf{f})_1 \cdot F(\mathbf{g})_1, \ldots, F(\mathbf{f})_{N-1} \cdot F(\mathbf{g})_{N-1})^t$$

Proof of Theorem 9.17

As in (9.54), let $\mathbf{f}$ and $\mathbf{g}$ correspond to polynomials. Then $\mathbf{f}*\mathbf{g}$ corresponds to the polynomial $p(x)q(x)$ of (9.55). By Proposition 9.13, $F(\mathbf{f})_m$ may be found by evaluating $p(x)$ at $x=\omega^m$, with corresponding statements for $F(\mathbf{g})_m$ and $F(\mathbf{f}*\mathbf{g})_m$. But $p(x)q(x)$ evaluated at ω^m is just the product of $p(x)$ evaluated at ω^m and $q(x)$ evaluated at ω^m. ◇

Example 9.40

We illustrate the statement of Theorem 9.17. Let $R=\mathbb{Z}_5$. As in Example 9.34, 2 is a primitive 4th root of unity in $\mathbb{Z}_5$. Consider the polynomials

$$p(x) = 2x+3 = 3+2x$$

$$q(x) = 4x+1 = 1+4x$$

in $\mathbb{Z}_5[x]$. $p(x)$ and $q(x)$ then correspond to the respective 4-tuples $\mathbf{f}=(3,2,0,0)^t$ and $\mathbf{g}=(1,4,0,0)^t$.

$$\mathbf{f}*\mathbf{g} = (3\cdot 1, 2\cdot 1 + 3\cdot 4, 2\cdot 4, 0)^t = (3,4,3,0)^t$$

Of course, $h(x)=p(x)q(x)=3x^2+4x+3=3+4x+3x^2$. Computing as in Example 9.34,

$$F(\mathbf{f}*\mathbf{g}) = \begin{pmatrix} 1 & 1 & 1 & 1 \\ 1 & 2 & 4 & 3 \\ 1 & 4 & 1 & 4 \\ 1 & 3 & 4 & 2 \end{pmatrix} \begin{pmatrix} 3 \\ 4 \\ 3 \\ 0 \end{pmatrix} = \begin{pmatrix} 0 \\ 3 \\ 2 \\ 2 \end{pmatrix}$$

Similarly, $F(\mathbf{f})=(0,2,1,4)^t$ and $F(\mathbf{g})=(0,4,2,3)^t$. Indeed, in $\mathbb{Z}_5$,

$$0\cdot 0=0 \qquad 2\cdot 4=3 \qquad 1\cdot 2=2 \qquad 4\cdot 3=2$$ △

Let R be a ring with a primitive Nth root of unity ω. Let $\mathbf{f}$ be a column N-tuple with entries in R. Then $F(\mathbf{f})$ is also a column N-tuple with entries in R. Since both $\mathbf{f}$ and $F(\mathbf{f})$ have N entries, it is reasonable to expect that often $\mathbf{f}$ and $F(\mathbf{f})$ determine each other. This will happen if the matrix Ω of Definition 9.4 has an inverse matrix Ω^{-1}.

Theorem 9.18

Let n be a nonnegative integer. Let $M=2^{2^n}+1$ and $N=2^{n+1}$. Then $\omega=2$ is a primitive Nth root of unity in $\mathbb{Z}_M$ such that $\omega^{N/2}=-1$. N is invertible in $\mathbb{Z}_M$. Let Ω be the $N \times N$ matrix of Definition 9.4 given by $\Omega_{i,j} = \omega^{i \cdot j}$. Then Ω^{-1} is given by

$$\Omega^{-1}{}_{i,j} = N^{-1}\omega^{-i \cdot j}$$ ◇

A proof of Theorem 9.18 is outlined in the exercises. Theorem 9.18 also holds for much more general rings than $\mathbb{Z}_M$. For instance, we may take the ring $\mathbb{C}$ of complex numbers, N arbitrary, and ω as in (9.47).

Example 9.41

We illustrate the statement of Theorem 9.18 with $n=1$. $M = 2^{2^1} + 1 = 2^2 + 1 = 5$. $N = 2^2 = 4$. As in Example 9.34, 2 is a primitive 4th root on unity in $\mathbb{Z}_5$. Also, $2^{N/2} = 2^2 = 4 = -1$ in $\mathbb{Z}_5$. $4^{-1} = 4$ in $\mathbb{Z}_5$.

Ω is given in Example 9.34. We compute Ω^{-1}. Since $\omega^{-i \cdot j} = (\omega^{-1})^{i \cdot j}$, we need to know ω^{-1}. In $\mathbb{Z}_5$, $2^{-1} = 3$.

$$\Omega^{-1} = 4\begin{pmatrix} 3^0 & 3^0 & 3^0 & 3^0 \\ 3^0 & 3^1 & 3^2 & 3^3 \\ 3^0 & 3^2 & 3^4 & 3^6 \\ 3^0 & 3^3 & 3^6 & 3^9 \end{pmatrix} = 4\begin{pmatrix} 1 & 1 & 1 & 1 \\ 1 & 3 & 4 & 2 \\ 1 & 4 & 1 & 4 \\ 1 & 2 & 4 & 3 \end{pmatrix} = \begin{pmatrix} 4 & 4 & 4 & 4 \\ 4 & 2 & 1 & 3 \\ 4 & 1 & 4 & 1 \\ 4 & 3 & 1 & 2 \end{pmatrix}$$

We let I denote the 4×4 identity matrix. We can verify directly that indeed $\Omega \cdot \Omega^{-1} = \Omega^{-1} \cdot \Omega = I$. △

Let M, N, and $\omega = 2$ be as in Theorem 9.18. Let $\mathbf{g}$ be a column N-tuple with entries in $\mathbb{Z}_M$. We denote $\Omega^{-1}\mathbf{g}$ by $F^{-1}(\mathbf{g})$ and call $F^{-1}(\mathbf{g})$ the **inverse Fourier transform** of $\mathbf{g}$. Indeed, if $\mathbf{f}$ is a column N-tuple with entries in $\mathbb{Z}_M$,

$$F^{-1}(F(\mathbf{f})) = \Omega^{-1} \cdot \Omega \cdot \mathbf{f} = I \cdot \mathbf{f} = \mathbf{f} \qquad \textbf{(9.58)}$$

We wish to have an efficient computation method for finding $F^{-1}(\mathbf{g})$. Observe that multiplication by the matrix Ω^{-1} may be achieved by first multiplying by the matrix A with $A_{i,j} = \omega^{-i \cdot j}$ and then multiplying by the constant factor N^{-1}. Since $\omega^N = 1$, also $(\omega^{-1})^N = (\omega^N)^{-1} = 1^{-1} = 1$. So ω^{-1} is an Nth root of unity. Thus, multiplication by A is the discrete Fourier transform using the Nth root of unity ω^{-1}. As shown in the exercises of this section, $(\omega^{-1})^{N/2} = -1$. So the fast Fourier transform algorithm may be applied to multiply by A.

Let us consider polynomials $p(x)$ and $q(x)$ as in (9.54). The polynomials $p(x)$ and $q(x)$ have coefficients given by $\mathbf{f}$ and $\mathbf{g}$ respectively. The polynomial $p(x)q(x)$ has coefficients given by $\mathbf{h}$, with h_m from (9.56). Then

$$\begin{aligned} \mathbf{h} &= F^{-1}(F(\mathbf{h})), && \text{by (9.58)} \\ &= F^{-1}(F(\mathbf{f} * \mathbf{g})), && \text{by Definition 9.5} \end{aligned}$$

$F(\mathbf{f}*\mathbf{g})$ may be computed via Theorem 9.17 and $F^{-1}(F(\mathbf{f}*\mathbf{g}))$ may then be computed via Theorem 9.18. Via the fast Fourier transform algorithm, this method for multiplying $p(x)$ and $q(x)$ is much faster than the method for (9.56), for large $\deg(p(x))$ and $\deg(q(x))$.

Example 9.42

In $\mathbb{Z}_{17}[x]$, we shall multiply the polynomials $p(x)=2x^3+3x^2+3x+2$ and $q(x)=x^3+2x^2+3x+3$ using the technique of the previous paragraph.

$17=2^{2^n}+1$ with $n=2$, so Theorem 9.18 applies. $\omega=2$ is an 8th root of unity such that, in $\mathbb{Z}_{17}$,

$$2^1=2 \quad 2^2=4 \quad 2^3=8 \quad 2^4=16$$

$$2^5=15 \quad 2^6=13 \quad 2^7=9 \quad 2^8=1$$

Figure 9.5, as needed for the fast Fourier transform, becomes Figure 9.9. The polynomials $p(x)$ and $q(x)$ correspond to 8-tuples $\mathbf{f}$ and $\mathbf{g}$, but we need not write out $\mathbf{f}$ and $\mathbf{g}$ explicitly. $F(\mathbf{f})$ and $F(\mathbf{g})$ are computed via the fast Fourier transform algorithm in Figure 9.10.

From Figure 9.10 and Figure 9.5,

$$F(\mathbf{f})=(10,2,3,1,0,9,12,13)$$

$$F(\mathbf{g})=(9,8,9,4,1,14,10,3)$$

By Theorem 9.17,

$$F(\mathbf{f}*\mathbf{g})=(10\cdot 9,2\cdot 8,3\cdot 9,1\cdot 4,0\cdot 1,9\cdot 14,12\cdot 10,13\cdot 3)$$
$$=(5,16,10,4,0,7,1,5)$$

We now compute $F^{-1}F(\mathbf{f}*\mathbf{g})$ using Theorem 9.18. $2^{-1}=9$ in $\mathbb{Z}_{17}$. 9 is an 8th root of unity with

$$9^1=9 \quad 9^2=13 \quad 9^3=15 \quad 9^4=16$$

$$9^5=8 \quad 9^6=4 \quad 9^7=2 \quad 9^8=1$$

Figure 9.9 Factoring x^8-1 in $\mathbb{Z}_{17}[x]$

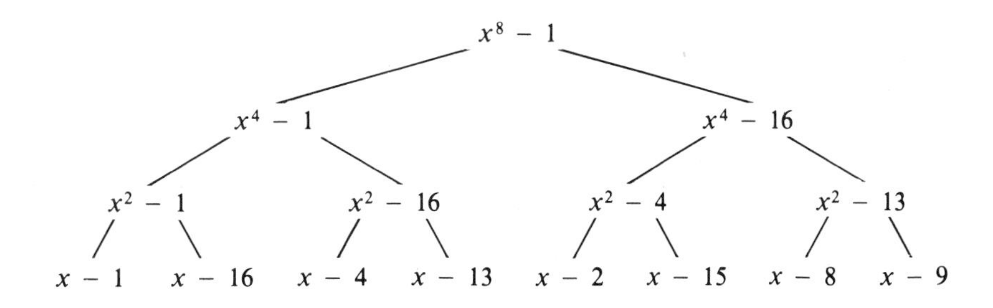

With $\omega=9$, Figure 9.5 becomes Figure 9.11. Figure 9.12 computes the Fourier transform of $F(\mathbf{f}*\mathbf{g})$ using $\omega=9$.

As specified in Figure 9.5, we rearrange the last row in Figure 9.12 to obtain

$$\begin{aligned} F^{-1}F(\mathbf{f}*\mathbf{g}) &= 8^{-1}(14,1,6,14,1,5,16,0) \\ &= 15(14,1,6,14,1,5,16,0) \\ &= (6,15,5,6,15,7,2,0) \end{aligned}$$

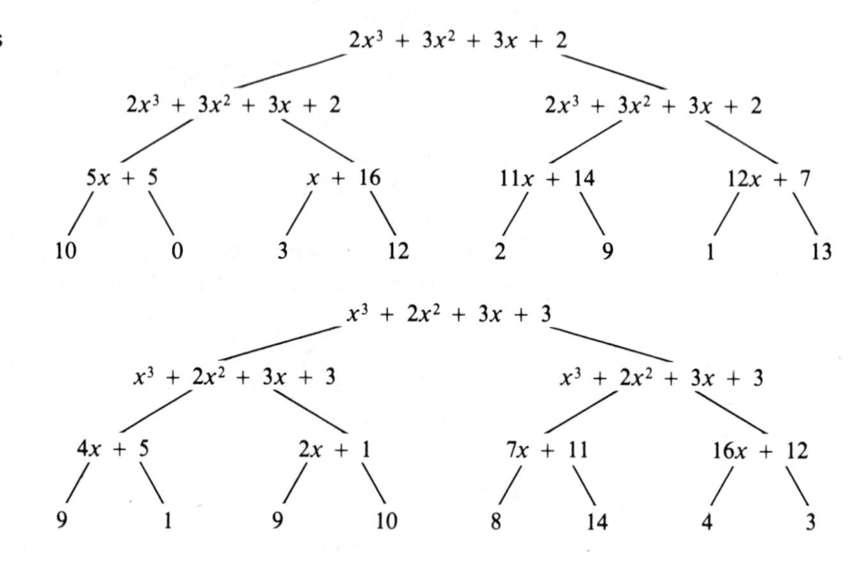

Figure 9.10 Remainders for fast Fourier transforms

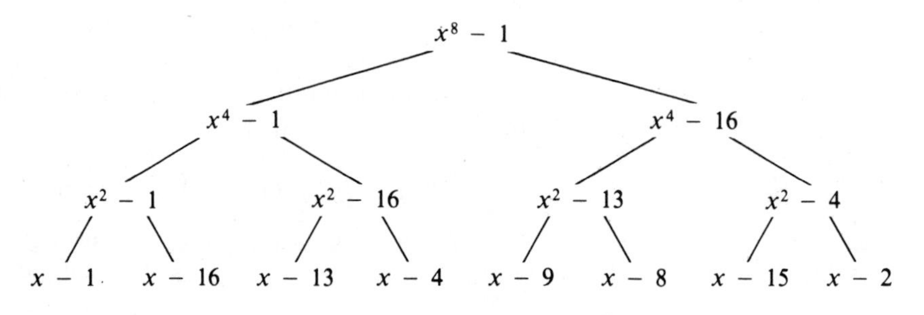

Figure 9.11 Factoring x^8-1 in $\mathbb{Z}_{17}[x]$

$5x^7 + x^6 + 7x^5 + 0x^4 + 4x^3 + 10x^2 + 16x + 5$

$9x^3 + 11x^2 + 6x + 5$ $16x^3 + 9x^2 + 9x + 5$

$15x + 16$ $14x + 11$ $13x + 3$ $5x + 7$

14 1 6 16 1 5 14 0

Figure 9.12 Remainders using Figure 9.11

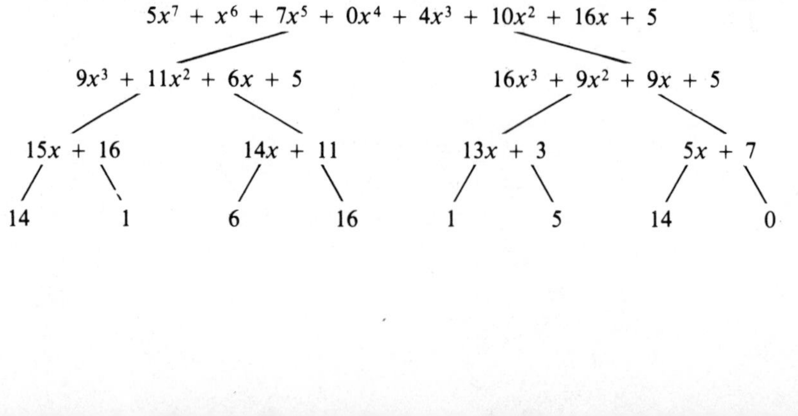

Since $F^{-1}F(\mathbf{f}*\mathbf{g}) = \mathbf{f}*\mathbf{g}$ and $\mathbf{f}*\mathbf{g}$ corresponds to polynomial multiplication,

$$p(x)q(x) = 0x^7 + 2x^6 + 7x^5 + 15x^4 + 6x^3 + 5x^2 + 15x + 6$$

Since $p(x)$ and $q(x)$ both have the low degree of 3, it is easy to check this answer for $p(x)q(x)$ directly. △

Example 9.43

Here is a way to multiply ordinary decimal numbers using polynomial multiplication. We compute $235 \cdot 462$. Let

$$p(x) = 2x^2 + 3x + 5$$

$$q(x) = 4x^2 + 6x + 2$$

Of course, $p(10) = 235$ and $q(10) = 462$. Then $235 \cdot 462$ equals $p(x)q(x)$ evaluated at $x = 10$. An easy calculation yields

$$p(x)q(x) = 8x^4 + 24x^3 + 42x^2 + 36x + 10$$

$p(10)q(10)$ is easily evaluated, lower order terms first, via

$$\begin{array}{r} 10 \\ 360 \\ 4200 \\ 24000 \\ 80000 \\ \hline 108570 \end{array}$$

Indeed, $235 \cdot 462 = 108{,}570$. △

The Schönhage-Strassen algorithm for multiplication follows the steps in Example 9.43. Its speed comes from using convolution and the fast Fourier transform, as in Example 9.42, to compute the polynomial multiplication. However, using the polynomial ring $\mathbb{C}[x]$ and ω as in (9.47) is not efficient since excessive precision is required for ω. Following the Schönhage-Strassen algorithm, we shall perform polynomial multiplication in the ring $\mathbb{Z}_M[x]$, with M and n as in Theorem 9.18. This will yield a fast algorithm for multiplication in the ring $\mathbb{Z}_{M'}$, $M' = 2^{2^{2n-1}}$. In turn, using $\mathbb{Z}_{M'}[x]$ yields a fast algorithm for multiplication in the ring $\mathbb{Z}_{M''}$, $M'' = 2^{2^{4n-3}}$. Any two integers in $\mathbb{Z}$ may be multiplied by multiplying them in $\mathbb{Z}_M$ with M sufficiently large. So we do obtain an algorithm for multiplying ordinary integers.

Example 9.44

We begin our description of the multiplication algorithm by computing $190 \cdot 111$ in $\mathbb{Z}_{257}$. An easy direct computation gives $190 \cdot 111 = 16$ in $\mathbb{Z}_{257}$, so we may check our final answer.

We write 190 and 111 in base 4 as follows:

$$190 = 2 \cdot 4^3 + 3 \cdot 4^2 + 3 \cdot 4 + 2$$
$$111 = 1 \cdot 4^3 + 2 \cdot 4^2 + 3 \cdot 4 + 3$$

We let $p(x)$ and $q(x)$ be the corresponding polynomials in $\mathbb{Z}[x]$.

$$p(x) = 2x^3 + 3x^2 + 3x + 2$$
$$q(x) = x^3 + 2x^2 + 3x + 3$$

so that $p(4) = 190$ and $q(4) = 111$. We wish to multiply $p(x)$ by $q(x)$ in $\mathbb{Z}[x]$; we denote $p(x)q(x)$ by

$$h(x) = h_6 x^6 + h_5 x^5 + \cdots + h_1 x + h_0$$

We claim that each h_m is determined by its remainders after division by 17 and by 4. Namely, $17 \cdot 4 = 68$. By the Chinese Remainder Theorem (Theorem 6.9), elements of $\mathbb{Z}_{68}$ are determined by their remainders in $\mathbb{Z}_{17}$ and in $\mathbb{Z}_4$. So it suffices to see that each h_i is less than 68. Since the coefficients of $p(x)$ and $q(x)$ are less than 4, each product $f_{m-i}g_i$ in (9.56) is less than 16, which is less than 17. Since $p(x)$ and $q(x)$ have degree 3, we are adding at most 4 terms in (9.56). So indeed, $h_m < 17 \cdot 4 = 68$.

The remainders for the h_m after division by 17 may be found by considering $p(x)$ and $q(x)$ as elements of $\mathbb{Z}_{17}[x]$ and multiplying in $\mathbb{Z}_{17}[x]$. This multiplication was done in Example 9.42. Since we have specified that $h(x)$ is an element of $\mathbb{Z}[x]$, rather than an element of $\mathbb{Z}_{17}[x]$, a convenient notation is

$$h(x) \equiv 2x^6 + 7x^5 + 15x^4 + 6x^3 + 5x^2 + 15x + 6 \pmod{17} \tag{9.59}$$

A direct calculation, without a fast Fourier transform, in $\mathbb{Z}_4[x]$ is easy because 4 is a small number.

$$h(x) \equiv 2x^6 + 3x^5 + 3x^4 + 3x^3 + 2x^2 + 3x + 2 \pmod{4} \tag{9.60}$$

Then for instance, $0 \le h_3 < 68$ and

$$h_3 \equiv 6 \pmod{17}$$
$$h_3 \equiv 3 \pmod{4}$$

As in Example 9.12 and Example 6.32, or more efficiently as in the exercises of this section, $h_3 = 23$. In all, (9.59) and (9.60) yield

$$h(x) = 2x^6 + 7x^5 + 15x^4 + 23x^3 + 22x^2 + 15x + 6$$

Recall that our desired answer is $h(4) \pmod{257}$. $257 = 4^4 + 1$. So, in evaluating $h(4) \pmod{257}$, we may use the relations

$$4^4 \equiv -1 \pmod{257}$$

$$4^5 \equiv -4 \pmod{257}$$

$$4^6 \equiv -16 \pmod{257}$$

Multiplying by powers of 4 is, of course, especially easy in binary notation. In all,

$$h(4) \equiv 16 \pmod{257}$$

in agreement with our initial answer. △

The computation of Example 9.44 is much slower than an ordinary calculation because $M = 17 = 2^4 + 1 = 2^{2^2} + 1$ corresponds to the low n of 2 in Theorem 9.18. Moreover, we used the decimal representation for integers, and the multiplication algorithm takes great advantage of the binary representation.

We now review Example 9.44 so as to describe the multiplication algorithm for large n. We assume that we already can multiply efficiently in $\mathbb{Z}_M$ with $M = 2^{2^n} + 1$. In Example 9.44, $n = 2$ and $M = 17$. The algorithm is given next for multiplication in $\mathbb{Z}_{M'}$ with $M' = 2^{2^{n'}} + 1$ and $n' = 2n - 1$. $n' = 3$ and $M' = 257$ in Example 9.44.

The given elements a and b of $\mathbb{Z}_{M'}$ are to be multiplied in $\mathbb{Z}_{M'}$. We regard a and b as ordinary integers and write them in base $2^{2^{n-1}} = \sqrt{M-1}$, which is 4 in Example 9.44. If either $a = M' - 1$ or $b = M' - 1$, then we treat the multiplication as a special case; see the exercises at the end of this section. Otherwise, since $a, b < M' - 1 = 2^{2^{2n-1}} = 2^{2^{n-1} \cdot 2^n} = (2^{2^{n-1}})^{2^n}$, a and b need at most 2^n places in the base $2^{2^{n-1}}$ representation. Let a and b correspond to respective polynomials $p(x)$ and $q(x)$ in $\mathbb{Z}[x]$, where $p(2^{2^{n-1}}) = a$, $q(2^{2^{n-1}}) = b$, and $p(x)$ and $q(x)$ have coefficients less than $2^{2^{n-1}} = \sqrt{M-1}$ and degree less than 2^n.

Let $h(x) = p(x)q(x)$ in $\mathbb{Z}[x]$. Then the coefficients of $h(x)$ are non-negative integers that are less than $2^n \cdot \sqrt{M-1} \cdot \sqrt{M-1}$, which in turn is less than $2^n \cdot M$. Since M is odd, the Chinese Remainder Theorem implies that we may compute $h(x)$ by computing $h(x) \pmod{M}$ and $h(x) \pmod{2^n}$. In $\mathbb{Z}_{M'}$, $a \cdot b$ is then given by $a \cdot b \equiv h(2^{2^{n-1}}) \pmod{M'}$. Thus we have the following theorem.

Theorem 9.19 Let M, n, M', n', a, b be as just given. Then $a \cdot b$ in $\mathbb{Z}_{M'}$ may be given by the following calculation. Let $N = 2^{n+1}$. By adding additional 0 coefficients, regard $p(x)$ and $q(x)$ from above as polynomials of degree $\leq N-1$. Let $\mathbf{f}$ and $\mathbf{g}$ be the column N-tuples given by the coefficients of $p(x)$ and $q(x)$ respectively.

1. Compute $F(\mathbf{f})$ and $F(\mathbf{g})$ via the fast Fourier transform algorithm for $\mathbb{Z}_M$, with $\omega = 2$.
2. For $m = 0, 1, \ldots, N-1$, compute $F(\mathbf{f} * \mathbf{g})_m = F(\mathbf{f})_m \cdot F(\mathbf{g})_m$ via multiplication in $\mathbb{Z}_M$.
3. $h(x) \pmod{M}$ has coefficients given by $\mathbf{f} * \mathbf{g}$. Compute $\mathbf{f} * \mathbf{g}$ from Step 2 and Theorem 9.18, using the fast Fourier transform algorithm.
4. Compute $h(x) \pmod{2^n}$.
5. Use the Chinese Remainder Theorem to compute $h(x)$ in $\mathbb{Z}[x]$.
6. $a \cdot b \equiv h(2^{2^{n-1}}) \pmod{M'}$. ◇

We conclude this section with a comparison between the number of bit operations needed for multiplication via Theorem 9.19 and via the usual algorithm. We shall see in the analysis how Theorem 9.19 exploits the binary representation. As in Chapter 6, we shall concentrate on asymptotic estimates, that is, estimates for large n.

The bit operations in Theorem 9.19 can be arranged to occur almost entirely in Steps 1, 2, and 3. So we shall analyze only these steps. Steps 1 and 3 require three fast Fourier transforms in $\mathbb{Z}_M$: for $\mathbf{f}$ and for $\mathbf{g}$ using $\omega = 2$ and for $\mathbf{f} * \mathbf{g}$ using $\omega^{-1} = 2^{N-1}$. As shown at the end of the last section, the fast Fourier transform requires $N \log_2 N$ multiplications and additions in $\mathbb{Z}_M$. But the multiplications are given from Proposition 9.16 with c a power of $\omega = 2$. In binary, c is represented by a 1 in a suitable place and 0's elsewhere. As explained in the exercises at the end of this section, for calculations in $\mathbb{Z}_M$, since $2^{2^n} = -1$ in $\mathbb{Z}_M$, it is convenient to represent some powers of 2 by the negatives of binary numbers with just one 1. This converts the additions in Proposition 9.16 into subtractions. As explained in the exercises, multiplication in $\mathbb{Z}_M$ by a c in $\mathbb{Z}_M$ with just one 1 in its binary representation is virtually equivalent to a subtraction. So the three fast Fourier transforms in Steps 1 and 3 each require approximately $2N \log_2 N$ additions or subtractions in $\mathbb{Z}_M$. Since $N = 2^{n+1}$, there are approximately

$$3 \cdot 2 \cdot 2^{n+1}(n+1) = 3 \cdot 2 \cdot 2 \cdot 2^n(n+1) \sim 12 \cdot 2^n \cdot n \qquad \textbf{(9.61)}$$

additions or subtractions needed to execute the fast Fourier transforms. Step 3 also requires N multiplications by N^{-1}. Since, in $\mathbb{Z}_M$, $2^N = 1$ and $N = 2^{n+1}$, $N^{-1} = 2^{N-n-1}$. So N^{-1} is a power of 2. Hence multiplication by N^{-1} is easy, and this part of Step 3 is negligible compared to (9.61). Since elements of $\mathbb{Z}_M$ are represented by approximately 2^n bits, the number of bit operations required for an addition or a subtraction is at most $A \cdot 2^n$, for some constant A that does not depend on N. In all then, for a suitable constant B, Steps 1 and 3 of Theorem 9.19 require at most

$$12 \cdot 2^n \cdot n \cdot B \cdot 2^n = 12 \cdot B \cdot 2^{2n} \cdot n \tag{9.62}$$

operations on bits.

Step 2 of Theorem 9.19 requires N multiplications in $\mathbb{Z}_M$. Our efficient multiplication in $\mathbb{Z}_M$ is via a recursive application of the algorithm of Theorem 9.19. Let $b(n)$ denote the number of bit operations required by this algorithm to multiply in $\mathbb{Z}_M$, $M = 2^{2^n} + 1$. The estimate of (9.62) is for $M' = 2^{2^{n'}} + 1$ with $n' = 2n - 1$. Then, adding to (9.62) the time needed for the N multiplications of Step 2,

$$b(2n-1) \leq 12 \cdot B \cdot 2^{2n} \cdot n + 2^{n+1} \cdot b(n) \tag{9.63}$$

It can be shown that (9.63) implies that, for some constant C independent of n,

$$b(n) \leq C \cdot 2^n \cdot n^2 \cdot \log_2 n \tag{9.64}$$

The Schönhage-Strassen algorithm achieves the better estimate

$$s(n) \leq D \cdot 2^n \cdot n \cdot \log_2 n$$

with D a suitable constant, for the number $s(n)$ of bit operations required for multiplication in $\mathbb{Z}_M$.

Example 9.45

Let us write out the multiplication, in $\mathbb{Z}$, $23 \cdot 19 = 437$ using binary notation and the usual algorithm.

$23 = 10111 \qquad 19 = 10011$

```
      10111
    × 10011
    -------
      10111
     10111
    00000
   00000
  10111
  ---------
  110110101
```

△

Observe that the 5-bit numbers 23 and 19 of Example 9.45 required a 5×5 array of bits in their multiplication. In general, the usual algorithm for multiplying two m-bit numbers requires the use of an $m \times m$ array of bits. So, for some constant E that is independent of m, the usual algorithm for multiplication requires approximately

$$E \cdot m^2 \tag{9.65}$$

bit operations.

Let us compare (9.64) and (9.65). With $M = 2^{2^n} + 1$, elements of $\mathbb{Z}_M$ require approximately $2^n = m$ bits in their binary representation. With $m = 2^n$, (9.65) yields $E \cdot 2^n \cdot 2^n$ required bit operations. Even though C is much larger than E, for large values of n, (9.64) is much smaller than (9.65).

Exercises 9.4

1. In $\mathbb{Z}$, compute $\mathbf{f}*\mathbf{g}$.
   a. $\mathbf{f} = (2, -1, 3, 0, 0, 0)$, $\mathbf{g} = (1, 0, -2, 0, 0, 0)$
   b. $\mathbf{f} = (1, 1, -2, 4, 0, 0, 0)$, $\mathbf{g} = (0, 0, 3, -5, 0, 0, 0)$
2. Consider the ring $\mathbb{Z}_5$ with primitive 4th root of unity $\omega = 2$. Let $\mathbf{f} = (4, 2, 0, 0)$ and $\mathbf{g} = (1, 1, 0, 0)$.
   a. Compute $F(\mathbf{f})$ and $F(\mathbf{g})$.
   b. Compute $\mathbf{f}*\mathbf{g}$ and $F(\mathbf{f}*\mathbf{g})$.
   c. Verify Theorem 9.17 for this $\mathbf{f}$ and $\mathbf{g}$.
3. Consider the ring $\mathbb{Z}_5$ with primitive 4th root of unity $\omega = 2$. Using Theorem 9.18, compute
   a. $F^{-1}(1, 0, 3, 4)$ b. $F^{-1}(3, 0, 0, 2)$
4. In $\mathbb{Z}_{17}$, let $\omega = 2$ be a primitive 8th root of unity. In $\mathbb{Z}_{17}[x]$, multiply $p(x) = 2x^3 + 3x^2 + 3x + 1$, $q(x) = x^3 + 3x^2 + 3x$ as follows. Let $\mathbf{f}$ and $\mathbf{g}$ be the 8-tuples given by regarding $p(x)$ and $q(x)$, respectively, as polynomials with 8 coefficients.
   a. Compute $F(\mathbf{f})$ and $F(\mathbf{g})$ via the fast Fourier transform algorithm.
   b. Compute $F(\mathbf{f}*\mathbf{g})$ via part (a) and Theorem 9.17.
   c. Compute $F^{-1}(F(\mathbf{f}*\mathbf{g}))$ via Theorem 9.18 and the fast Fourier transform algorithm.
   d. Compare your answer from part (c) with the answer from a usual calculation of $p(x)q(x)$.
5. Using $p(x)$ and $g(x)$ of Exercise 4, compute $189 \cdot 124$ in $\mathbb{Z}_{257}$ via the algorithm of Theorem 9.19.
6. Using the algorithm of Theorem 9.19, compute $102 \cdot 232$ in $\mathbb{Z}_{257}$.
7. Let ω be an Nth root of unity in the ring R.
   a. Explain why $\omega^{-1} = \omega^{N-1}$.
   b. Show that for any integer m, $(\omega^m)^{-1} = \omega^{N-m}$.

8. In Theorem 9.18,
   a. Show that $\omega^{N/2} = -1$.
   b. Show that ω is an Nth root of unity.
   c. Show that N is invertible in $\mathbb{Z}_M$.
9. In Theorem 9.18,
   a. Show that $\omega^0, \omega^1, \ldots, \omega^{(N/2)-1}$ are represented in $\mathbb{Z}_M$ as integers that are powers of 2.
   b. Show that $\omega^{N/2} = -\omega^0, \omega^{(N/2)+1} = -\omega^1, \ldots, \omega^{N-1} = -\omega^{(N/2)-1}$.
   c. Show that ω is a primitive Nth root of unity.
10. a. Let $N = 2^{n+1}$. Show that for any ring element α,

$$\sum_{j=0}^{N-1} \alpha^j = (1+\alpha)(1+\alpha^2)(1+\alpha^4)\cdots(1+\alpha^{N/2})$$

   Hint: Use the binary representation of j.

   b. In Theorem 9.18, consider ω^s, $0 < s < N$. Writing $s = t \cdot 2^u$, with t odd, show that $(\omega^s)^{2^{n-u}} = -1$ in $\mathbb{Z}_M$.
   c. Conclude that $\sum_{j=0}^{N-1} (\omega^s)^j = 0$.
11. Using Exercise 10(c), show that Ω^{-1} is as stated in Theorem 9.18.
12. Let $M = 2^{2^n} + 1$. With $a = 2^{2^n}$ and b arbitrary in $\mathbb{Z}_M$, show that $a \cdot b = -b$ in $\mathbb{Z}_M$.
13. a. Let n be a positive integer that can be written in decimal notation as the two-place number $n_1 n_0$. Show that $n \equiv n_0 - n_1 \pmod{11}$.
   b. Let $M = 2^{2^n} + 1$. Represent elements of $\mathbb{Z}_M$ in binary notation. Let $a = 2^m$ be an element of $\mathbb{Z}_M$ and let b be an arbitrary element of $\mathbb{Z}_M$. Using bit manipulations and the analog of part (a), show how to compute $a \cdot b$ in $\mathbb{Z}_M$.
14. Let $M = 2^{2^n} + 1$ and $N' = 2^n$. In the Chinese Remainder map $f: \mathbb{Z}_{MN'} \to \mathbb{Z}_M \times \mathbb{Z}_{N'}$, show that $f(M) = (0, 1)$ and $f(2^{N'}) = (-1, 0)$.

9.5 Fields; Finite Fields

In the previous sections, we made extensive use of rings and polynomial rings. Recall from Theorem 9.11 that, in a polynomial ring, division by a polynomial $p(x)$ is possible if the leading coefficient a_n of $p(x)$ is invertible. The leading coefficient a_n is automatically invertible in case $p(x) \neq 0$, and all nonzero elements of the coefficient ring are invertible; that is, in case the coefficient ring is a **field**. In this section, we see that a polynomial ring with field coefficients behaves very much like the ring $\mathbb{Z}$ of ordinary integers. In particular, we use such polynomial rings to construct additional fields.

Definition 9.6

A **field** K is a ring, as in Definition 9.1, such that every element $a \neq 0$ in K is invertible, as in Definition 9.3. ○

Examples 9.46

Let $\mathbb{Q}$ denote the set of all rational numbers, that is, the set of all fractions. Then $\mathbb{Q}$ is a field under the usual operations of addition and multiplication. Multiplicative inverses are given in the usual way: $a/b \neq 0$ requires that $a \neq 0$. Then $(a/b)^{-1} = b/a$. △

Let $\mathbb{R}$ denote the set of all real numbers. Then $\mathbb{R}$ is a field under the usual operations of addition and multiplication. △

Let $\mathbb{C}$ denote the set of all complex numbers, with the usual addition and multiplication. Then Example 9.21 shows that for $c \neq 0$ in $\mathbb{C}$, c^{-1} exists. So $\mathbb{C}$ is a field. △

The ring $\mathbb{Z}$ of integers is not a field since only 1 and -1 are invertible. △

Theorem 9.20

The modular number system $\mathbb{Z}_n$ is a field if and only if n is a prime number. ◇

Theorem 9.20 is an easy consequence of Theorem 9.4; details are left to the exercises.

Examples 9.47

$\mathbb{Z}_7$ is a field by Theorem 9.20. Indeed, multiplicative inverses are as follows in $\mathbb{Z}_7$:

$$1^{-1}=1 \qquad 2^{-1}=4 \qquad 3^{-1}=5 \qquad 4^{-1}=2 \qquad 5^{-1}=3 \qquad 6^{-1}=6$$

△

Let us find a noninvertible element of $\mathbb{Z}_9$. By Theorem 9.4, we look for an element a of $\mathbb{Z}_9$ such that $\gcd(a,9) \neq 1$. Since $3|9$, we may take $a=3$. Since $3 \cdot 3 = 0$ in $\mathbb{Z}_9$, 3 cannot be invertible, by Proposition 9.9. △

We now begin the construction of additional fields besides those in Example 9.46 and in Theorem 9.20. The idea is to mimic the construction of $\mathbb{Z}_p$, with p prime, using the polynomial ring $K[x]$ in place of the ring $\mathbb{Z}$. In order to get a field by this construction, rather than just a ring, it is important to take K to be a field, rather than just a ring.

Definition 9.7

Let K be a field. Let $p(x)$ and $d(x)$ be elements of $K[x]$. The polynomial $p(x)$ **divides** the polynomial $d(x)$, denoted by $p(x)|d(x)$, if there is a polynomial $q(x)$ such that $d(x) = q(x)p(x)$. ○

Examples 9.48

We consider the polynomial $p(x)=x^2+1$ in the ring $\mathbb{Z}_2[x]$. Then $(x^2+1)|(x^5+x^4+x^3+1)$ since $x^5+x^4+x^3+1=(x^3+x^2+1)(x^2+1)$. △

Continue with the ring $\mathbb{Z}_2[x]$. Then $(x^2+1)\nmid(x^4+x+1)$; that is, x^2+1 does *not* divide x^4+x+1. We see this by applying the division algorithm to obtain $x^4+x+1=(x^2+1)(x^2+1)+x$. The remainder, x, is not 0. The uniqueness part of Theorem 9.11 ensures that no other method of division may leave a different, 0, remainder, and show that x^2+1 divides x^4+x+1. △

Example 9.49

Let us consider the polynomials in $\mathbb{Z}_3[x]$ given by

$$p(x)=2x^2+x+1 \quad \text{and} \quad q(x)=x^2+2x+2$$

Then $q(x)=2p(x)$ and $p(x)=2q(x)$. That is, $p(x)|q(x)$ and $q(x)|p(x)$. △

Recall that for *positive* integers a and b, if $a|b$ and $b|a$, then $a=b$. In Example 9.49, $p(x)|q(x)$ and $q(x)|p(x)$ but $p(x)\neq q(x)$. However, for *monic* polynomials $a(x)$ and $b(x)$ in a ring $K[x]$, if $a(x)|b(x)$ and $b(x)|a(x)$, then $a(x)=b(x)$; see the exercises for a proof. Moreover, any polynomial

$$p(x)=a_nx^n+a_{n-1}x^{n-1}+\cdots+a_1x+a_0, \qquad a_n\neq 0$$

in $K[x]$ can be written uniquely as $p(x)=a_nq(x)$ with $q(x)$ a monic polynomial such that $p(x)|q(x)$ and $q(x)|p(x)$. So for questions related to divisibility, it is often convenient to consider only monic polynomials. Most of our examples will be from the ring $\mathbb{Z}_2[x]$. Since $\mathbb{Z}_2=\{0,1\}$, any polynomial $p(x)\neq 0$ in $\mathbb{Z}_2[x]$ is automatically monic. So we shall usually not have to worry about the subtleties of Example 9.49.

Let $a(x)$ and $b(x)$ be nonzero polynomials in $K[x]$, with K a field. Then the Euclidean algorithm, Theorem 9.1, may be applied to $a(x)$ and $b(x)$ to yield a last nonzero remainder $g(x)$. The proof of Theorem 9.1 may be easilv modified to show that $g(x)$ is *a* greatest common divisor for $a(x)$ and $b(x)$ in the sense that every common divisor for $a(x)$ and $b(x)$ is also a divisor of $g(x)$. In particular, $g(x)$ must be at least tied for having the greatest degree among all common divisors. As suggested by the previous paragraph, $a(x)$ and $b(x)$ have a unique greatest common divisor that is a *monic* polynomial.

Example 9.50

In the ring $\mathbb{R}[x]$, let us find a greatest common divisor for $a(x)=x^2+2x-3$ and $b(x)=x^2-1$ using the Euclidean algorithm.

$$x^2+2x-3=1(x^2-1)+(2x-2) \qquad r_1(x)=2x-2$$

$$x^2-1=\left(\frac{1}{2}x+\frac{1}{2}\right)(2x-2)+0 \qquad r_2(x)=0$$

$2x-2$ is a greatest common divisor. $2x-2=2(x-1)$. So $x-1$ is the monic greatest common divisor. △

Example 9.51

In the ring $\mathbb{Z}_2[x]$, let us find

$$\gcd(x^3+1, x^4+x^2+x+1)$$

that is, the greatest common divisor.

$$x^4+x^2+x+1=x\cdot(x^3+1)+(x^2+1) \qquad r_1(x)=x^2+1$$

$$x^3+1=x\cdot(x^2+1)+(x+1) \qquad r_2(x)=x+1$$

$$x^2+1=(x+1)\cdot(x+1)+0 \qquad r_3(x)=0$$

Then $x+1$ is the greatest common divisor. △

Example 9.52

From Example 9.51, in $\mathbb{Z}_2[x]$,

$$x+1=\gcd(x^3+1, x^4+x^2+x+1)$$

We apply the proof of Theorem 9.2 to find polynomials $\lambda(x)$ and $\mu(x)$ in $\mathbb{Z}_2[x]$ such that

$$\lambda(x)(x^4+x^2+x+1)+\mu(x)(x^3+1)=x+1$$

Following the divisions in Example 9.51 in reverse order and observing that $-a(x)=a(x)$ for any $a(x)$ in $\mathbb{Z}_2[x]$, we have

$$\begin{aligned} x+1 &= (x^3+1)+x(x^2+1) \\ &= (x^3+1)+x[(x^4+x^2+x+1)+x(x^3+1)] \\ &= x(x^4+x^2+x+1)+(x^2+1)(x^3+1) \end{aligned}$$

$\lambda(x)=x$ and $\mu(x)=x^2+1$. △

We need the notion of when a polynomial $p(x)$ is **prime**, or **irreducible** in the usual terminology. Let K be a field. Let $k\neq 0$ be an element of K. Then k may also be thought of as a polynomial in $K[x]$ of degree 0. Consider

$$p(x) = a_n x^n + a_{n-1} x^{n-1} + \cdots + a_1 x + a_0$$

in $K[x]$. Then $k|p(x)$. Namely, since k^{-1} exists,

$$p(x) = k(k^{-1} a_n x^n + k^{-1} a_{n-1} x^{n-1} + \cdots + k^{-1} a_1 x + k^{-1} a_0)$$

So in defining irreducibility, we must ignore such divisors, or else no polynomial will be irreducible.

Definition 9.8

Let K be a field. Let $p(x)$ be a polynomial in $K[x]$ of positive degree. The polynomial $p(x)$ is **reducible** if $p(x) = a(x)b(x)$ with $a(x)$, $b(x)$ in $K[x]$ and of positive degrees. If $p(x)$ is not reducible, then $p(x)$ is **irreducible**, or **prime**. ○

Suppose that a reducible $p(x)$ satisfies $p(x) = a(x)b(x)$, as in Definition 9.8. By Proposition 9.10,

$$\deg(a(x)) + \deg(b(x)) = \deg(p(x)) \tag{9.66}$$

Since $\deg(a(x)) > 0$, $\deg(b(x)) < \deg(p(x))$. Similarly, $\deg(a(x)) < \deg(p(x))$. If $a(x)$ and/or $b(x)$ is reducible, factor it further. Continue such factorizations for as long as possible. Since the degrees of the factors are decreasing, the factorization must terminate with only irreducible factors. So every nonzero polynomial in $K[x]$ may be written as a product of irreducible polynomials. This product is, in fact, essentially unique. Just as every positive integer may be written uniquely (up to the order of multiplication) as a product of primes, so may every monic polynomial in $K[x]$ be written uniquely as a product of monic irreducible polynomials. See the exercises for a proof.

To check if an integer N is prime, it suffices to verify that N has no prime divisors up through $N^{1/2}$. Consider a polynomial $p(x)$ in $K[x]$. If $a(x)$ is divisor of $p(x)$, then so is $b(x) = p(x)/a(x)$. By (9.66), either

$$\deg(a(x)) \leq \frac{1}{2}\deg(p(x)) \quad \text{or} \quad \deg(b(x)) \leq \frac{1}{2}\deg(p(x))$$

Since every divisor of $a(x)$ or of $b(x)$ is also a divisor of $p(x)$, to check that $p(x)$ is irreducible, it suffices to verify that $p(x)$ has no irreducible monic divisors of degree at most $\frac{1}{2}\deg(p(x))$. By Definition 9.8, every polynomial of degree 1 is prime. By Theorem 9.12, $x - a$ is a divisor of $p(x)$ if and only if $p(a) = 0$.

Example 9.53

Using the above ideas, we find the irreducible polynomials in $\mathbb{Z}_2[x]$ of degree at most 4. The polynomials of degree 1, which are necessarily irreducible, are

$$x, \quad x+1 \tag{9.67}$$

The polynomials of degree 2 are

$$q_1(x)=x^2, \quad q_2(x)=x^2+1, \quad q_3(x)=x^2+x, \quad q_4(x)=x^2+x+1$$

We check for divisibility by a polynomial from (9.67) via evaluation at 0 and 1, respectively. $q_1(0)=q_3(0)=0$, and indeed $x|q_1(x)$ and $x|q_3(x)$. $q_2(0)=q_4(0)=1\neq 0$, and indeed $x\nmid q_2(x)$ and $x\nmid q_4(x)$. $q_2(1)=q_3(1)=0$, so $(x+1)|q_2(x)$ and $(x+1)|q_3(x)$. $q_1(1)=q_4(1)=1\neq 0$, so $(x+1)\nmid q_1(x)$ and $(x+1)\nmid q_4(x)$. In all, the only irreducible polynomial of degree 2 is $q_4(x)$, namely,

$$x^2+x+1 \tag{9.68}$$

Since $2>3/2$, to check a polynomial of degree 3 for irreducibility, it suffices to consider only possible divisors from (9.67). An easy calculation shows that the irreducible polynomials of degree 3 are

$$x^3+x^2+1 \quad \text{and} \quad x^3+x+1$$

The polynomials of degree 4 that have no polynomial from (9.67) as a divisor are easily seen to be

$$x^4+x^3+1, \quad x^4+x^2+1, \quad x^4+x+1, \quad x^4+x^3+x^2+x+1$$

Of these polynomials, only $x^4+x^2+1=(x^2+x+1)^2$ has the irreducible polynomial from (9.68) as a divisor. Hence the other polynomials are all irreducible. △

Definition 9.9

Let K be a field. Let $p(x)$ be a polynomial in $K[x]$ such that $p(x)\neq 0$. Let $a(x)$ and $b(x)$ be arbitrary elements of $K[x]$. Then

$$a(x)\equiv b(x) \pmod{p(x)}$$

if $p(x)|(a(x)-b(x))$ ○

$\equiv \bmod p(x)$ of Definition 9.9 behaves very much like $\equiv \bmod N$ for integers. Details are left to the exercises. Let $n=\deg(p(x))$. By Theorem 9.11, each polynomial $d(x)$ in $K[x]$ satisfies

$$d(x)\equiv r(x) \pmod{p(x)}$$

for a unique polynomial $r(x)$ with $\deg(r(x)) < n$. Then, just as we formed $\mathbb{Z}_N = \{0,1,2,\ldots,N-1\}$ from all possible remainders after division by N, we may form a ring from all possible remainders after division by $p(x)$.

Definition 9.10

Let K be a field. Let $p(x) \neq 0$ be a polynomial in the ring $(K[x], +, \cdot)$. Then $(K[x]/(p(x)), +_p, \cdot_p)$, the **quotient ring** of $K[x]$ (mod $p(x)$), is given as follows.

$K[x]/(p(x))$ consists of all polynomials $a(x)$ in $K[x]$ such that $\deg(a(x)) < \deg(p(x))$.

For any $a(x)$ and $b(x)$ in $K[x]/(p(x))$,

$$a(x) +_p b(x) \equiv a(x) + b(x) \pmod{p(x)}$$

$$a(x) \cdot_p b(x) \equiv a(x) \cdot b(x) \pmod{p(x)}$$

○

Since $a(x)$ and $b(x)$ in Definition 9.10 have degree less than $\deg(p(x))$, $a(x) + b(x)$ must also have degree less than $\deg(p(x))$. So, in fact, in Definition 9.10,

$$a(x) +_p b(x) = a(x) + b(x)$$

and no division by $p(x)$ is necessary.

Example 9.54

We compute the addition and multiplication tables for $\mathbb{Z}_2[x]/(x^2+1)$. The elements of $\mathbb{Z}_2[x]/(x^2+1)$ consist of all polynomials of degree less than 2. Since there are only two choices, 0 and 1, for each coefficient, $\mathbb{Z}_2[x]/(x^2+1)$ consists of the following four polynomials:

$$0 \quad 1 \quad x \quad x+1$$

Here is a typical addition.

$$(x+1) +_p x \equiv (x+1) + x \equiv 1 \pmod{x^2+1}$$

Table 9.1 gives the complete addition table for $\mathbb{Z}_2[x]/(x^2+1)$.

Table 9.1 Addition table for $\mathbb{Z}_2[x]/(x^2+1)$

$+_p$	0	1	x	$x+1$
0	0	1	x	$x+1$
1	1	0	$x+1$	x
x	x	$x+1$	0	1
$x+1$	$x+1$	x	1	0

We compute $x \cdot_p (x+1)$. In $\mathbb{Z}_2[x]$,

$$x \cdot (x+1) = x^2 + x$$
$$\equiv x + 1 \pmod{x^2+1}$$

So $x \cdot_p (x+1) = x+1$. Table 9.2 gives the complete multiplication table for $\mathbb{Z}_2[x]/(x^2+1)$

Table 9.2 Multiplication table for $\mathbb{Z}_2[x]/(x^2+1)$

$\cdot_p$	0	1	x	$x+1$
0	0	0	0	0
1	0	1	x	$x+1$
x	0	x	1	$x+1$
$x+1$	0	$x+1$	$x+1$	0

Tables 9.1 and 9.2 may be condensed to Table 9.3, where each polynomial is denoted by the bits that are its coefficients. Thus the polynomial 1 equals $\underline{0} \cdot x + \underline{1} \cdot 1$ and is denoted by 01. △

Table 9.3 Addition and multiplication for $\mathbb{Z}_2[x]/(x^2+1)$

$+_p$	00	01	10	11
00	00	01	10	11
01	01	00	11	10
10	10	11	00	01
11	11	10	01	00

$\cdot_p$	00	01	10	11
00	00	00	00	00
01	00	01	10	11
10	00	10	01	11
11	00	11	11	00

Theorem 9.21

Let K be a field. Let $p(x)$ be a polynomial in $K[x]$. Then $K[x]/(p(x))$ is a field if and only if $p(x)$ is irreducible. ◇

The proof of Theorem 9.21 is entirely similar to the proof of Theorem 9.20, using the Euclidean algorithm for the polynomial ring $K[x]$. Details are left to the exercises. Let H denote $K[x]/(p(x))$ from Theorem 9.21, with $p(x)$ irreducible. Formally, H is called a **finite algebraic extension field** of K, but we shall simply call H an **extension field** of K.

Example 9.55

Let $K = \mathbb{R}$ and $p(x) = x^2 + 1$. No polynomial $x - c$ of degree 1 in $\mathbb{R}[x]$ can be a divisor of $p(x)$, since $p(c) = c^2 + 1 \neq 0$. So $p(x)$ is irreducible and $H = \mathbb{R}[x]/(x^2+1)$ is a field. H consists of all polynomials in $\mathbb{R}[x]$ of degree at most 1; that is, every element in H may be written as

$$a+bx$$

with a and b real numbers. Let $c+dx$ be another element of H. Then

$$(a+bx)+_p(c+dx)=(a+c)+(b+d)x$$

Since $x^2 \equiv -1 \pmod{x^2+1}$,

$$\begin{aligned}(a+bx)(c+dx) &= ac+(ad+bc)x+bdx^2 \\ &\equiv (ac-bd)+(ad+bc)x \pmod{x^2+1}\end{aligned}$$

So, with $a+bx$ corresponding to the complex number $a+bi$, H and $\mathbb{C}$ have the same laws of addition and multiplication. That is, H is isomorphic to $\mathbb{C}$. △

Example 9.56

Consider the polynomial $p(x)=x^3+x^2+1$ in the ring $\mathbb{Z}_2[x]$. The polynomial $p(x)$ is known to be irreducible from Example 9.53. $H=\mathbb{Z}_2[x]/(p(x))$ consists of all polynomials in $\mathbb{Z}_2[x]$ of degree less than $3=\deg(p(x))$ and is known to be a field by Theorem 9.21. As in Example 9.54, we may represent elements of H by their coefficients, yielding binary 3-tuples. For example, $x^2+1=1\cdot x^2+0\cdot x+1\cdot 1$ has the binary representation 101. Table 9.4 then gives the addition and multiplication tables for H. Observe that indeed every nonzero element of H has a multiplicative inverse. △

A **finite field** is a field with a finite number of elements. It turns out that every finite field H may be obtained via the construction of Theorem 9.21, using $K=\mathbb{Z}_p$ with p a prime integer. Let $n=\deg(p(x))$. Then, since H may be thought of as all polynomials of degree less than n with coefficients from $\mathbb{Z}_p$, and since $\mathbb{Z}_p$ has p elements, H has p^n elements. In particular, for any finite field H, $|H|=p^n$ for some prime number p. Moreover, it is true that if two finite fields H and H' satisfy $|H|=|H'|$, then H and H' are isomorphic. Given any prime power p^n, there is, in fact, a finite field H such that $|H|=p^n$. This field H is often called the **Galois field** with p^n elements and is denoted by $GF(p^n)$.

Example 9.57

We let $H=\mathbb{Z}_2[x]/(x^3+x^2+1)$ and $K=\mathbb{Z}_2[y]/(y^3+y+1)$. $|H|=|K|=8$. So, from the previous paragraph, H and K should be isomorphic. In fact, $f:H\rightarrow K$ given by

$$f(ax^2+bx+c)=(a+b)y^2+ay+c$$

Table 9.4 Addition and multiplication for $\mathbb{Z}_2[x]/(x^3+x^2+1)$

+	000	001	010	011	100	101	110	111
000	000	001	010	011	100	101	110	111
001	001	000	011	010	101	100	111	110
010	010	011	000	001	110	111	100	101
011	011	010	001	000	111	110	101	100
100	100	101	110	111	000	001	010	011
101	101	100	111	110	001	000	011	010
110	110	111	100	101	010	011	000	001
111	111	110	101	100	011	010	001	000

·	000	001	010	011	100	101	110	111
000	000	000	000	000	000	000	000	000
001	000	001	010	011	100	101	110	111
010	000	010	100	110	101	111	001	011
011	000	011	110	101	001	010	111	100
100	000	100	101	001	111	011	010	110
101	000	111	010	011	110	110	100	001
110	000	110	001	111	010	100	011	101
111	000	111	011	110	011	001	101	010

is the required isomorphism. We shall just check that

$$f(x \cdot_H x) = f(x) \cdot_K f(x)$$

$x \cdot_H x = x^2$, $f(x^2) = y^2 + y$, and $f(x) = y^2$. Then

$$f(x \cdot_H x) = y^2 + y \equiv y^4 \equiv y^2 \cdot y^2 = f(x) \cdot_K f(x) \pmod{y^3 + y + 1} \qquad \triangle$$

Let $(K, +, \cdot)$ be a finite field. Let K^* denote the set of nonzero elements of K. It is easily seen from the definitions that $(K^*, \cdot)$ is a finite commutative group, with 1 as the identity. The following theorem, which we shall not prove, says that $(K^*, \cdot)$ is as simple as possible.

Theorem 9.22 Let $(K, +, \cdot)$ be a finite field. Then $(K^*, \cdot)$ is a finite cyclic group. $\diamond$

Let ω be a generator for the group $(K^*, \cdot)$ of Theorem 9.22. Let $N = |K^*|$. Then ω has order N in the group K^*. That is,

$$\omega^N = 1 \quad \text{and} \quad \omega^i \neq 1 \quad \text{for } 1 \leq i < N$$

In the terminology of Section 9.3, ω is a primitive Nth root of unity.

Example 9.58

Consider the field $\mathbb{Z}_7$. Let us see that 3 generates $(\mathbb{Z}_7{}^*, \cdot)$. Compute in $\mathbb{Z}_7$:

$$3^1=3 \qquad 3^2=2 \qquad 3^3=6 \qquad 3^4=4 \qquad 3^5=5 \qquad 3^6=1 \qquad \triangle$$

Example 9.59

Consider the field $K=\mathbb{Z}_2[x]/(x^3+x^2+1)$ of Example 9.56. Its multiplication table is given in Table 9.4. Since $|K^*|=7$, a prime number, every element of K^* except for 1 serves as a generator. For example, using the notation of Table 9.4,

$$(011)^1=011 \qquad (011)^2=101 \qquad (011)^3=010$$
$$(011)^4=110 \qquad (011)^5=111 \qquad (011)^6=100 \qquad (011)^7=001 \qquad \triangle$$

Example 9.60

As shown in Example 9.53, x^4+x^3+1 is irreducible in $\mathbb{Z}_2[x]$. So $K=\mathbb{Z}_2[x]/(x^4+x^3+1)$ is a field. $|K^*|=15$. We verify that the element x in K^* has order 15. All congruences below are modulo x^4+x^3+1.

$$\begin{aligned}
x^1 &\equiv x\\
x^2 &\equiv x^2\\
x^3 &\equiv x^3\\
x^4 &\equiv x^3+1\\
x^5 &\equiv x^4+x \equiv x^3+x+1\\
x^6 &\equiv x^4+x^2+x \equiv x^3+x^2+x+1\\
x^7 &\equiv x^4+x^3+x^2+x \equiv x^2+x+1\\
x^8 &\equiv x^3+x^2+x\\
x^9 &\equiv x^4+x^3+x^2 \equiv x^2+1\\
x^{10} &\equiv x^3+x\\
x^{11} &\equiv x^4+x^2 \equiv x^3+x^2+1\\
x^{12} &\equiv x^4+x^3+x \equiv x+1\\
x^{13} &\equiv x^2+x\\
x^{14} &\equiv x^3+x^2\\
x^{15} &\equiv x^4+x^3 \equiv 1
\end{aligned} \qquad \triangle$$

Exercises 9.5

1. In $\mathbb{Z}_5$, find 1^{-1}, 2^{-1}, 3^{-1}, 4^{-1}.
2. In the ring $\mathbb{Z}_2[x]$, decide whether or not $p(x)|d(x)$.
   a. $p(x)=x^2+x+1$, $d(x)=x^4+x^3+x+1$
   b. $p(x)=x^2+1$, $d(x)=x^4+x+1$
   c. $p(x)=x^3+x+1$, $d(x)=x^5+x^4+x$

3. In $\mathbb{R}[x]$, find a greatest common divisor for $a(x)$ and $b(x)$.
   a. $a(x)=x^2+x+3$, $b(x)=x^3+x+1$
   b. $a(x)=x^3+3x^2+9x+7$, $b(x)=x^4+2x^3+8x^2+2x+7$
4. In $\mathbb{Z}_2[x]$, find the greatest common divisor for $a(x)$ and $b(x)$.
   a. $a(x)=x^3+x^2+1$, $b(x)=x^4+x^3+x^2+x$
   b. $a(x)=x^3+1$, $b(x)=x^4+x^2+1$
5. In Exercise 4, find polynomials $\lambda(x)$ and $\mu(x)$ in $\mathbb{Z}_2[x]$ such that $\lambda(x)a(x)+\mu(x)b(x)=\gcd(a(x),b(x))$.
6. State whether each of the following polynomials in $\mathbb{Z}_2[x]$ is reducible or irreducible.
   a. x^5+x^4+x+1 b. x^5+x^4+1
   c. $x^5+x^4+x^3+x+1$ d. $x^5+x^4+x^3+x^2+1$
7. a. Write out the addition and multiplication tables for $\mathbb{Z}_2[x]/(x^2+x+1)$.
   b. Verify that each nonzero element of $\mathbb{Z}_2[x]/(x^2+x+1)$ has a multiplicative inverse.
8. Find $(x+1)^{-1}$ in $\mathbb{Z}_2[x]/(x^3+x+1)$.
9. Let $K=\mathbb{Z}_2[x]/(x^2+x+1)$ from Exercise 7. Give and verify an explicit isomorphism between $(K^*,\cdot)$ and $(\mathbb{Z}_3,+)$.
10. Prove Theorem 9.20.
11. Let K be a field. Show that if $p(x)|d(x)$ in $K[x]$, then $\deg(p(x))\leq\deg(d(x))$.
12. Let K be a field. Let $a(x)$ and $b(x)$ be elements of $K[x]$ such that $a(x)|b(x)$ and $b(x)|a(x)$.
    a. Show that $\deg(a(x))=\deg(b(x))$.
    b. If $a(x)$ and $b(x)$ are monic, show that $a(x)=b(x)$.
13. State and prove the analog of Proposition 9.3 with n replaced by $p(x)\neq 0$ in $K[x]$.
14. Prove Theorem 9.21.
15. Let K be a field. State and prove the analogs of Section 9.1, Exercises 10–13 for the ring $K[x]$, using irreducible monic polynomials in place of prime integers.

9.6 Polynomial Codes; BCH Codes

In Chapter 1, we studied group codes, especially in terms of error detection and error correction. In this section, we study the special kind of group code given by polynomial multiplication in $\mathbb{Z}_2[y]$. Bose-Chaudhuri-Hocquenghem (BCH) codes are examples of such polynomial codes. BCH codes may easily be constructed to have large error-detection and/or error-correction capability. They are widely used where such capability is needed.

Consider the ring $\mathbb{Z}_2[y]$. It will be convenient later to have the variable be y in order to use x in the notation for field elements, as in the previous section. Consider G_n, the set of all polynomials in $\mathbb{Z}_2[y]$ of degree less than n. Then, as in Examples 9.54 and 9.56, elements of G_n may be represented by the n bits that correspond to their coefficients. Since addition in $\mathbb{Z}_2[y]$ is given by the addition in $\mathbb{Z}_2$ of the coefficients, $(G_n, +)$ is isomorphic to the group $(\mathbb{Z}_2{}^n, +)$. This can easily be seen in the addition tables of Tables 9.3 and 9.4. $(\mathbb{Z}_2{}^n, +)$ is the group used for group codes with code words that are binary n-tuples.

Following the usual convention for codes, we shall represent polynomials in $\mathbb{Z}_2[y]$ by their coefficients, *lowest order term first*. As in the previous sections of this chapter, entries in a binary m-tuple will be numbered $0,1,\ldots,m-1$. Thus the binary m-tuple $\mathbf{f}=(f_0,f_1,\ldots,f_{m-1})$ corresponds to the polynomial

$$f(y)=f_0+f_1y+\cdots+f_{m-1}y^{m-1} \qquad \textbf{(9.69)}$$

Recall Definition 1.1 for codes; the polynomial codes of Definition 9.11, which follows, are codes in the sense of Definition 1.1. In this text, we shall not discuss error correction for polynomial codes. But efficient error-correction schemes do exist.

Definition 9.11 An (m,n) **polynomial code** with **encoding polynomial** $g(y)$ in $\mathbb{Z}_2[y]$, $\deg(g(y))=n-m$, is given by the following:

(o) A message $\mathbf{f}$ is a binary m-tuple $\mathbf{f}=(f_0,f_1,\ldots,f_{m-1})$. The binary m-tuple $\mathbf{f}$ corresponds to the polynomial $f(y)$ of (9.69); $f(y)$ is called a **message polynomial**.

(i) $f(y)$ is encoded into the **code polynomial** $f(y)g(y)$ of degree $n-1$. With

$$f(y)g(y)=c_0+c_1y+\cdots+c_{n-1}y^{n-1}$$

the code word $\mathbf{c}$ corresponding to $\mathbf{f}$ is given by

$$\mathbf{c}=(c_0,c_1,\ldots,c_{n-1})$$

(ii) Let $\mathbf{r}=(r_0,r_1,\ldots,r_{n-1})$ be a received n-tuple. Let $r(y)=r_0+r_1y+\cdots+r_{n-1}y^{n-1}$. If $g(y)\mid r(y)$, then $r(y)$ is a code polynomial and $r(y)/g(y)$ is taken to be the original message polynomial. If $g(y)\nmid r(y)$, then a transmission error occurred. ○

Example 9.61 Let us consider the (3,6) polynomial code with encoding polynomial $g(y)=1+y+y^3$. Then the message (1 1 0) corresponds to the polynomial $f(y)=1+1\cdot y+0\cdot y^2=1+y$. The code polynomial for (1 1 0) is

$$f(y)g(y) = (1+y)(1+y+y^3) = 1+y^2+y^3+y^4$$
$$= 1+0\cdot y+1\cdot y^2+1\cdot y^3+1\cdot y^4+0\cdot y^5$$

So the code word for the message (1 1 0) is (1 0 1 1 1 0). Here is the complete list of messages and code words for this code.

Message	Code word
(0 0 0)	(0 0 0 0 0 0)
(0 0 1)	(0 0 1 1 0 1)
(0 1 0)	(0 1 1 0 1 0)
(0 1 1)	(0 1 0 1 1 1)
(1 0 0)	(1 1 0 1 0 0)
(1 0 1)	(1 1 1 0 0 1)
(1 1 0)	(1 0 1 1 1 0)
(1 1 1)	(1 0 0 0 1 1)

△

Implicit in Definition 9.11(i) was the presumption that distinct messages are encoded into distinct code words. This was true in Example 9.61. It is true in general for the following reason. Suppose that $\mathbf{f}_1$ and $\mathbf{f}_2$ are messages such that $f_1(y)g(y) = f_2(y)g(y)$. Then $0 = f_1(y)g(y) - f_2(y)g(y) = [f_1(y) - f_2(y)]g(y)$. Since $g(y) \neq 0$, $f_1(y) - f_2(y) = 0$; that is, $f_1(y) = f_2(y)$.

In contrast with the examples of codes in Chapter 1, the encoding scheme of Example 9.61 does not consist of the appending of suitable check bits. Messages are found via Definition 9.11(ii). As will be explained in the exercises, it is possible to alter the encoding scheme of Definition 9.11(i) without affecting error-detection capability, so that code words do come from messages via the appending of suitable check bits.

Example 9.62

We consider the (4,8) polynomial code with encoding polynomial $g(y) = 1+y+y^4$. We decode the following received 8-tuples.

$\mathbf{c}_1 = (1\ \ 1\ \ 1\ \ 0\ \ 0\ \ 0\ \ 1\ \ 1)$

$\mathbf{c}_2 = (0\ \ 0\ \ 1\ \ 1\ \ 0\ \ 0\ \ 1\ \ 1)$

$\mathbf{c}_3 = (0\ \ 0\ \ 1\ \ 0\ \ 1\ \ 0\ \ 1\ \ 1)$

$\mathbf{c}_1$ corresponds to the polynomial

$$c_1(y) = 1+y+y^2+y^6+y^7$$

Then, as may be easily verified,

$$c_1(y)=(1+y^2+y^3)g(y)$$

So the message polynomial for $\mathbf{c}_1$ is $1+y^2+y^3$ and the message is $(1 \quad 0 \quad 1 \quad 1)$.

$\mathbf{c}_2$ corresponds to the polynomial

$$c_2(y)=y^2+y^3+y^6+y^7$$

A straightforward division yields

$$c_2(y)=(y^3+y^2+1)g(y)+(y^3+y+1)$$

Since the remainder, y^3+y+1, is not 0, $g(y)\nmid c_2(y)$, and there was a transmission error.

$\mathbf{c}_3$ corresponds to the message $(0 \quad 0 \quad 1 \quad 1)$, since

$$y^2+y^4+y^6+y^7=(y^2+y^3)g(y)$$ △

Example 9.63

Let us consider the $(n-1,n)$ polynomial code with encoding polynomial $g(y)=1+y$. We let $f(y)$ be a message polynomial and $c(y)=f(y)g(y)$ be the corresponding code polynomial. We evaluate $g(y)$ at 1 in $\mathbb{Z}_2$ as follows:

$$g(1)=1+1=0$$

Then also

$$c(1)=f(1)g(1)=f(1)\cdot 0=0$$

Conversely, we let $h(y)$ be a received polynomial such that $h(1)=0$. Then, by Theorem 9.12, $(y+1)|h(y)$ and so $h(y)$ is a message polynomial.

The message polynomials of this code thus consist of all polynomials $h(y)$ such that $h(1)=0$. We let

$$h(y)=h_0+h_1y+\cdots+h_{n-1}y^{n-1}$$

Then $h(1)=h_0+h_1+\cdots+h_{n-1}$, with the sum calculated in $\mathbb{Z}_2$. As we saw in Example 1.32, $h(1)=0$ precisely when the binary n-tuple $(h_0,h_1,\ldots,h_{n-1})$ satisfies an even parity check. △

Proposition 9.23

Every polynomial code is a group code.

Proof of Proposition 9.23

We must show that the sum of code words is again a code word. Let $\mathbf{f}_1$ and $\mathbf{f}_2$ be messages; $\mathbf{f}_1$ and $\mathbf{f}_2$ yield the code polynomials $f_1(y)g(y)$ and $f_2(y)g(y)$ respectively. Then

$$f_1(y)g(y)+f_2(y)g(y)=[f_1(y)+f_2(y)]g(y)$$

is the code polynomial for the message $\mathbf{f}_1+\mathbf{f}_2$. □

We can verify directly that in Example 9.61, the sum of two code words is again a code word. Also, in Example 9.63, we know from Chapter 1 that the sum of two code words is again a code word.

Recall from Chapter 1 that d, the minimum Hamming distance between distinct code words, measures the error-detecting or error-correcting capabilities of a code. Moreover, by Proposition 9.23 and Theorem 1.8, d may be computed for a polynomial code by taking the minimum of the weights of the nonzero code words. For example, $d=3$ for the polynomial code of Example 9.61.

Example 9.63 correctly suggests that we may examine the code polynomials of a polynomial code by considering the zeros of the encoding polynomial $g(y)$. However, an encoding polynomial, such as $g(y)=1+y+y^3$ of Example 9.61, may have no zeros in $\mathbb{Z}_2$. Consider an extension field $K=\mathbb{Z}_2[x]/(p(x))$ of $\mathbb{Z}_2$. Then the elements of $\mathbb{Z}_2$ may also be thought of as elements of K. A polynomial $h(y)$ in $\mathbb{Z}_2[y]$ can thus also be thought of as a polynomial in $K[y]$ and can be evaluated at elements of K.

Example 9.64

Let $K=\mathbb{Z}_2[x]/(1+x^2+x^3)$. Let $g(y)=1+y+y^3$ be an element of $K[y]$. We evaluate $g(y)$ for various values of y in K. The calculations are done in $\mathbb{Z}_2[x]$, modulo $1+x^2+x^3$.

$$\begin{aligned} g(1+x) &= 1+(1+x)+(1+x)^3 \\ &= 1+1+x+1+x+x^2+x^3 \\ &= 1+x^2+x^3 \\ &\equiv 0 \pmod{1+x^2+x^3} \end{aligned}$$

$$\begin{aligned} g(x) &= 1+x+x^3 \\ &\equiv x+x^2 \pmod{1+x^2+x^3} \end{aligned}$$

$$\begin{aligned} g(x^2) &= 1+x^2+(x^2)^3 \\ &= 1+x^2+x^6 \\ &\equiv 1+x \pmod{1+x^2+x^3} \end{aligned}$$

$$\begin{aligned} g(1+x^2) &= 1+(1+x^2)+(1+x^2)^3 \\ &= 1+1+x^2+1+x^2+x^4+x^6 \\ &= 1+x^4+x^6 \\ &\equiv 0 \pmod{1+x^2+x^3} \end{aligned}$$

△

Theorem 9.24

Let $K = \mathbb{Z}_2[x]/(p(x))$, with $p(x)$ an irreducible polynomial in $\mathbb{Z}_2[x]$ of degree k. Let ω generate $(K^*, \cdot)$, as in Theorem 9.22. Suppose that $g(y)$ is a polynomial in $\mathbb{Z}_2[y]$ of degree r such that

$$g(\omega) = g(\omega^2) = \cdots = g(\omega^t) = 0$$

for some integer t. Let $n = 2^k - 1 = |K^*|$. Then the $(n-r,n)$ polynomial code with encoding polynomial $g(y)$ has minimum distance d at least equal to $t+1$.

Example 9.65

Before proving Theorem 9.24, we shall illustrate its statement. We let $p(x) = 1 + x^2 + x^3$, as in Example 9.64. $|K^*| = 7$, a prime number. So we may take ω to be any element in K^* other than 1. Choose ω to be $1 + x$. Let $g(y) = 1 + y + y^3$, also as in Example 9.64. From Example 9.64, since $\omega^2 = (1+x)^2 = 1 + x^2$,

$$g(\omega) = g(\omega^2) = 0$$

So $t = 2$ in Theorem 9.24. $\deg(p(x)) = 3$, $n = 2^3 - 1 = 7$, and $r = \deg(g(y)) = 3$. Then the $(4,7)$ polynomial code with encoding polynomial $g(y)$ has minimum distance $d \geq 3$.

Recall that $g(y)$ was the encoding polynomial for the $(3,6)$ polynomial code of Example 9.61. For the code of Example 9.61, $d = 3$. The $(3,6)$ polynomial code of Example 9.61 differs from the $(4,7)$ polynomial code of the previous paragraph only in requiring one less bit in the messages. △

Proof of Theorem 9.24

Let

$$c(y) = c_0 + c_1 y + c_2 y^2 + \cdots + c_{n-1} y^{n-1}$$

be a code polynomial. By Theorem 1.8, it suffices to show that if at most t of the c_i equal 1, then all of the c_i equal 0. Let $c_{i_1}, c_{i_2}, \ldots, c_{i_t}$ be the t coefficients that may possibly equal 1. Then

$$c(y) = c_{i_1} y^{i_1} + c_{i_2} y^{i_2} + \cdots + c_{i_t} y^{i_t}$$

Since $g(\omega) = g(\omega^2) = \cdots = g(\omega^t) = 0$ and $g(y) | c(y)$, also $c(\omega) = c(\omega^2) = \cdots = c(\omega^t) = 0$. That is, since $(\omega^j)^{i_k} = (\omega^{i_k})^j$,

$$\begin{aligned} c_{i_1}(\omega^{i_1}) + c_{i_2}(\omega^{i_2}) + \cdots + c_{i_t}(\omega^{i_t}) &= 0 \\ c_{i_1}(\omega^{i_1})^2 + c_{i_2}(\omega^{i_2})^2 + \cdots + c_{i_t}(\omega^{i_t})^2 &= 0 \\ &\cdots \\ c_{i_1}(\omega^{i_1})^t + c_{i_2}(\omega^{i_2})^t + \cdots + c_{i_t}(\omega^{i_t})^t &= 0 \end{aligned} \tag{9.70}$$

Regard (9.70) as showing that $(c_{i_1},c_{i_2},\ldots,c_{i_t})$ is a solution to the following set of simultaneous linear equations with $(z_1,z_2,\ldots,z_t)$ as the unknowns:

$$\begin{aligned}(\omega^{i_1})z_1+(\omega^{i_2})z_2+\cdots+(\omega^{i_t})z_t&=0\\(\omega^{i_1})^2z_1+(\omega^{i_2})^2z_2+\cdots+(\omega^{i_t})^2z_t&=0\\&\cdots\\(\omega^{i_1})^tz_1+(\omega^{i_2})^tz_2+\cdots+(\omega^{i_t})^tz_t&=0\end{aligned}\qquad\textbf{(9.71)}$$

$\omega^{i_1},\omega^{i_2},\ldots,\omega^{i_t}$ are all distinct since $i_1<i_2<\cdots<i_t$, and i_t is less than the order of ω in K^*. The determinant of the coefficients in (9.71) is known as a **Vandermonde determinant**. It can be shown that this determinant is nonzero in K and hence that the only solution to (9.71) is $(z_1,z_2,\ldots,z_t)=(0,0,\ldots,0)$. Hence $(c_{i_1},c_{i_2},\ldots,c_{i_t})=(0,0,\ldots,0)$, as desired. ◇

The usual application of Theorem 9.24 is for the construction, in Definition 9.12, of BCH codes with a desired minimum distance d. As in Theorem 9.24, let $K=\mathbb{Z}_2[x]/(p(x))$ with $\deg(p(x))=k$. Let α be any element of K. It can be shown that there is an irreducible polynomial $m_\alpha(y)$ in $\mathbb{Z}_2[y]$ such that $m_\alpha(\alpha)=0$. Moreover, $\deg(m_\alpha(y))\leq k$. This $m_\alpha(y)$ is called the **minimal polynomial** for α since if $g(\alpha)=0$ for $g(y)$ in $\mathbb{Z}_2[y]$, then $m_\alpha(y)|g(y)$.

Definition 9.12 Let $K=\mathbb{Z}_2[x]/(p(x))$, with $p(x)$ irreducible and of degree k. Let ω generate $(K^*,\cdot)$. Let $m_i(y)$ be the minimal polynomial for ω^i. Let $g(y)$ be the product in $\mathbb{Z}_2[y]$, without duplications, of the $m_i(y)$, $1\leq i\leq t$. Let $r=\deg(g(y))$ and $n=2^k-1$. The $(n-r,n)$ polynomial code with encoding polynomial $g(y)$ is a **BCH code**. ○

By Theorem 9.24, a BCH code as in Definition 9.12 has minimum distance d at least equal to $t+1$. By increasing t, that is, by increasing the number of $m_i(y)$ in the product for $g(y)$, we may increase d. Of course, this will usually decrease $n-r$, the number of bits in a message. The reason for using the minimal polynomial for ω^i in the construction of BCH codes is to yield an encoding polynomial $g(y)$ of as low degree as possible.

As shown in the exercises, for any α in K and any $f(y)$ in $\mathbb{Z}_2[y]$, $(f(\alpha))^2=f(\alpha^2)$. So ω^i and $(\omega^i)^2=\omega^{2i}$ have the same minimal polynomial.

Example 9.66 Let $K=\mathbb{Z}_2[x]/(1+x^3+x^4)$, as in Example 9.60. Then $\omega=x$ generates $(K^*,\cdot)$. Let us construct a BCH code with $d\geq 5$. We need to find the minimal polynomials $m_1(y)$, $m_2(y)$, $m_3(y)$, $m_4(y)$ for $x=x^1,x^2,x^3,x^4$ respectively.

From Example 9.53, $p(x)=1+x^3+x^4$ is irreducible in $\mathbb{Z}_2[x]$. Also,

$p(x) \equiv 0 \pmod{p(x)}$, that is, $p(x)=0$ in K. So $p(y)$ is the minimal polynomial for x; $m_1(y)=p(y)$.

As observed above, or as may be checked directly, $p(x^2)=0$. Thus $m_2(y)=p(y)$. Similarly, since $x^4=(x^2)^2$, $p(x^4)=0$ and $m_4(y)=p(y)$.

Let us check that $g_3(y)=1+y+y^2+y^3+y^4$ is in fact $m_3(y)$. From Example 9.53, $g_3(y)$ is irreducible in $\mathbb{Z}_2[y]$. Using the computations in Example 9.60, we see that

$$\begin{aligned} g_3(x^3) &= 1+x^3+x^6+x^9+x^{12} \\ &\equiv 1+x^3+x^3+x^2+x+1+x^2+1+x+1 \\ &\equiv 0 \pmod{1+x^3+x^4} \end{aligned}$$

So $g_3(x^3)=0$ in K and $g_3(y)$ is indeed the minimal polynomial for x^3.

Since $m_1(y)=m_2(y)=m_4(y)$, eliminating duplications in the product gives

$$\begin{aligned} g(y) &= m_1(y)m_3(y) = (1+y^3+y^4)(1+y+y^2+y^3+y^4) \\ &= 1+y+y^2+y^4+y^8 \end{aligned}$$

as the encoding polynomial. $r=\deg(g(y))=8$. $n=2^k-1=2^4-1=15$. So this BCH code is a (7,15) polynomial code. By construction, $d \geq 5$. Since $g(y)$ has 5 nonzero coefficients and since $1 \cdot g(y)=g(y)$ is a code polynomial, $d=5$. △

Example 9.67

As in Example 9.66, let $K=\mathbb{Z}_2[x]/(1+x^3+x^4)$ and $\omega=x$. Let us construct a BCH code with $d \geq 7$. We know $m_1(y), m_2(y), m_3(y), m_4(y)$ from Example 9.66. We need to find $m_5(y)$ and $m_6(y)$.

From Example 9.60, computing mod $1+x^3+x^4$,

$$\begin{aligned} 1+x^5+(x^5)^2 &= 1+x^5+x^{10} \\ &\equiv 1+x^3+x+1+x^3+x \\ &\equiv 0 \pmod{1+x^3+x^4} \end{aligned} \tag{9.72}$$

Let $g_5(y)=1+y+y^2$. (9.72) implies that $g_5(x^5)=0$ in K. By Example 9.53, $g_5(y)$ is irreducible. So $m_5(y)=g_5(y)=1+y+y^2$.

$$m_6(y)=m_3(y)$$

$$g(y)=m_1(y)m_3(y)m_5(y)=1+y^2+y^5+y^6+y^8+y^9+y^{10}$$

$\deg(g(y))=10$. So this BCH code is a (5,15) polynomial code. By construction, $d \geq 7$. Since $1 \cdot g(y)=g(y)$ is a code polynomial, in fact, $d=7$. △

Exercises 9.6

1. a. List all messages and their corresponding code words for the (2,4) polynomial code with encoding polynomial $g(y)=1+y+y^2$.
   b. What is the minimum Hamming distance d for this code?
2. Consider the (4,8) polynomial code with encoding polynomial $g(y)=1+y+y^4$. For each of the following received 8-tuples, give the original message or else indicate a transmission error.
   a. (1 1 0 1 0 0 0 1) b. (1 1 0 0 1 1 1 1)
   c. (0 1 0 0 1 1 1 1) d. (1 1 1 1 1 0 1 1)
3. Let $K=\mathbb{Z}_2[x]/(1+x+x^2)$. Evaluate each of the following polynomials in $\mathbb{Z}_2[y]$ at all elements of K.
   a. $1+y$ b. $1+y+y^2$ c. $1+y^3$
4. Let $K=\mathbb{Z}_2[x]/(1+x+x^2)$, as in Exercise 3.
   a. Verify that x generates $(K*,\cdot)$.
   b. Use Theorem 9.24 to show that the (1,3) polynomial code with encoding polynomial $g(y)=1+y+y^2$ has $d\geq 3$.
   c. Write out the messages and corresponding code words for the code of part (b).
5. Let $K=\mathbb{Z}_2[x]/(1+x^3+x^4)$, as in Examples 9.66 and 9.67.
   a. Verify that the minimal polynomial $m_7(y)$ for x^7 is given by $m_7(y)=1+y+y^4$.
   b. Construct the encoding polynomial $g(y)$ for the BCH code for this K, $\omega=x$, and $t=8$. What is $\deg(g(y))$?
   c. Show that $d=15$ for the BCH code of part (b).
6. Let $K=\mathbb{Z}_2[x]/(1+x+x^4)$.
   a. Verify that x generates $(K^*,\cdot)$.
   b. Verify that x^3 has the minimal polynomial $1+y+y^2+y^3+y^4$.
   c. Construct the encoding polynomial $g(y)$ for the BCH code for this K, $\omega=x$, and $t=4$. What is $\deg(g(y))$? What is $(n-r,n)$ in Definition 9.12?
7. We give an encoding scheme for "polynomial" codes that appends check bits. Consider a polynomial code as in Definition 9.11. Let **f** be a binary m-tuple as in Definition 9.11(o). Divide $x^{n-m}f(y)$ by $g(y)$:

$$x^{n-m}f(y)=q(y)g(y)+r(y), \qquad \deg(r(y))<n-m$$

   Let the new code polynomial $c'(y)$ for $f(y)$ be given as

$$c'(y)=x^{n-m}f(y)-r(y)$$

   a. Show that the m high-order coefficients of $c'(y)$ are the same as the coefficients of $f(y)$.
   b. Explain why $c'(y)$ is a multiple of $g(y)$.

c. Show that the encoding scheme from parts (a) and (b) yields the same *set* of code words as the encoding scheme from Definition 9.11(i).

8. Let $K = \mathbb{Z}_2[x]/(p(x))$ with $p(x)$ irreducible in $\mathbb{Z}_2[x]$ and of degree k. Let $\alpha = \alpha_0 + \alpha_1 x + \alpha_2 x^2 + \cdots + \alpha_{k-1} x^{k-1}$ be an element of K. We wish to find a polynomial $g(y)$ in $\mathbb{Z}_2[y]$ such that $g(\alpha) = 0$ in K and $\deg(g(y)) \leq k$.

$$g(y) = g_0 + g_1 y + g_2 y^2 + \cdots + g_k y^k$$

Regard the g_i as unknown elements of $\mathbb{Z}_2$.

a. Explain why the condition $g(\alpha) = 0$ may be regarded as k simultaneous linear equations in $\mathbb{Z}_2$.

b. How many unknowns are there in the equations of part (a)? Why should $g(y)$ exist?

9. Let K and α be as in Exercise 8. Let $m_\alpha(y)$ be a nonzero polynomial in $\mathbb{Z}_2[y]$ of minimal degree such that $m_\alpha(\alpha) = 0$ in K.

a. Show that $m_\alpha(y)$ is irreducible.

b. Suppose that $g(y)$ is a polynomial in $\mathbb{Z}_2[y]$ such that $g(\alpha) = 0$. Show that $m_\alpha(y) | g(y)$.

10. Let $K = \mathbb{Z}_2[x]/(p(x))$ with $p(x)$ irreducible. Let $g(y)$ be a polynomial in $\mathbb{Z}_2[y]$ and let α be an element of K. Show that $(g(\alpha))^2 = g(\alpha^2)$.
Hint: For a,b in K, $(a+b)^2 = a^2 + ab + ab + b^2 = a^2 + b^2$

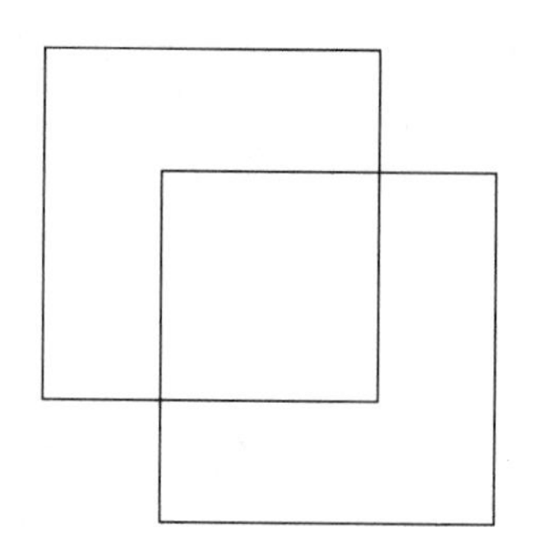

Appendix: Mathematical Induction

The **Principle of Mathematical Induction**, or more simply mathematical induction, is a powerful axiom of mathematics. It is particularly suited to problems about the integers and about finite sets. Occasionally in this text, there were explicit uses of mathematical induction in those proofs for which it substantially clarified the exposition. However, there were also many implicit uses of mathematical induction, especially where phrases such as "and so on" or "repeating the argument" were employed.

In the first section of this appendix, the Principle of Mathematical Induction is explained and used in a general context. This section may be read independently of the rest of this text. The second section discusses examples taken from this text and shows how they involve mathematical induction.

A.1 Statement and Examples

In this section the Principle of Mathematical Induction is stated and illustrated. We also briefly cover inductive definitions and their relation to recursive definitions.

Example A.1

We have a formula, (A.1), for the sum of the first n integers. How might we find and prove this formula?

$$1+2+\cdots+(n-1)+n=\frac{n(n+1)}{2} \tag{A.1}$$

We let

$$1+2+\cdots+(n-1)+n=S \tag{A.2}$$

We rewrite the sum in (A.2) as in (A.3) as follows:

$$n+(n-1)+\cdots+2+1=S \tag{A.3}$$

Then we add (A.2) and (A.3) and collect the terms as in (A.4).

$$\begin{array}{ccccccccccc} 1 & + & 2 & + \cdots + & (n-1) & + & n & = & S \\ n & + & (n-1) & + \cdots + & 2 & + & 1 & = & S \\ \hline (n+1) & + & (n+1) & + \cdots + & (n+1) & + & (n+1) & = & 2S \end{array} \qquad \textbf{(A.4)}$$

There are n summands on the left side of (A.4). So (A.4) yields (A.1). △

Example A.2 (A.5) gives a formula for the sum of the squares of the first n integers.

$$1^2 + 2^2 + \cdots + (n-1)^2 + n^2 = \frac{n(n+1)(2n+1)}{6} \qquad \textbf{(A.5)}$$

Let us check (A.5) for the first few values of n:

$$1^2 = 1 = \frac{1 \cdot 2 \cdot 3}{6}$$

$$1^2 + 2^2 = 5 = \frac{2 \cdot 3 \cdot 5}{6}$$

$$1^2 + 2^2 + 3^2 = 14 = \frac{3 \cdot 4 \cdot 7}{6}$$

So (A.5) *seems* correct, but these preceding examples are not a proof. There is no simple manipulation, as in (A.4) for Example A.1, to verify (A.5). The most convenient proof, as given in Example A.4 below, is via mathematical induction. Unfortunately, and this is typical, the Principle of Mathematical Induction is of little use in *finding* (A.5). △

Principle of Mathematical Induction Let $P(n)$ be a statement about the arbitrary positive integer n. Suppose that

(i) $P(1)$ is true.
(ii) Whenever $P(n)$ is true, then also $P(n+1)$ is true.

Then $P(n)$ is true for all positive integers. ○

(A.1) and (A.5) are typical formulas that may serve as $P(n)$ in the Principle of Mathematical Induction. Here are some other possibilities for $P(n)$:

$$2^n > n \qquad \textbf{(A.6)}$$

$$1+2+\cdots+n=n^2 \tag{A.7}$$

(Fermat's Last "Theorem") for $n \geq 3$, the equation

$$x^n+y^n=z^n \tag{A.8}$$

has no positive integral solutions.

(A.6) is true for all n (and easy to prove). (A.7) is true only for $n=1$. (A.8) is known to be true for many values of n, has no known counter-examples, but has not been proved for all n.

Strictly speaking, the Principle of Mathematical Induction must be assumed as an axiom of mathematics, just as postulates are assumed in Euclidean geometry. However, just as our intuition about points and lines provides a basis for accepting the Euclidean postulates, so may we appeal, as follows, to our intuition about integers in order to justify mathematical induction. It must be emphasized that the following justification is not a *proof*.

Justification for the Principle of Mathematical Induction $P(1)$ is given to be true. Let $n=1$ in (ii). Then also $P(2)$ is true. Now let $n=2$ in (ii). Then also $P(3)$ is true. Now let $n=3$ in (ii). "And so on." □

Here is how mathematical induction is used in practice.

Example A.3

We give another proof of (A.1), this time by mathematical induction. We follow the format of the statement above of the Principle of Mathematical Induction. Let $P(n)$ be (A.1).

(i) $P(1)$ is

$$1=\frac{1\cdot 2}{2}$$

which is true.

(ii) We assume that (A.1) is true for some particular value of n. We must deduce (A.1) for $n+1$: Add $(n+1)$ to both sides of (A.1) as follows:

$$1+2+\cdots+(n-1)+n+(n+1)=\frac{n(n+1)}{2}+(n+1) \tag{A.9}$$

We must show that the right side of (A.9) may be rewritten into the right side of $P(n+1)$, that is, into

$$\frac{(n+1)[(n+1)+1]}{2} = \frac{(n+1)(n+2)}{2}$$

$$\begin{aligned} \frac{n(n+1)}{2} + (n+1) &= \frac{n(n+1)+2(n+1)}{2} \\ &= \frac{(n+1)(n+2)}{2} \end{aligned}$$

The Principle of Mathematical Induction now implies that $P(n)$; that is, (A.1), is true for all n. △

Example A.4

We use mathematical induction to prove (A.5). Again we follow the format of the statement of the Principle of Mathematical Induction. Let $P(n)$ be (A.5).

(i) $P(1)$ was already verified in Example A.2.
(ii) We assume (A.5). We must deduce (A.5) for $(n+1)$.

Add $(n+1)^2$ to both sides of (A.5):

$$1^2 + 2^2 + \cdots + n^2 + (n+1)^2 = \frac{n(n+1)(2n+1)}{6} + (n+1)^2 \qquad \textbf{(A.10)}$$

We must rewrite the right side of (A.10) into the right side of $P(n+1)$, namely

$$\frac{(n+1)[(n+1)+1][2(n+1)+1]}{6} = \frac{(n+1)(n+2)(2n+3)}{6}$$

$$\begin{aligned} \frac{n(n+1)(2n+1)}{6} + (n+1)^2 &= \frac{n(n+1)(2n+1)+6(n+1)^2}{6} \\ &= \frac{(n+1)[n(2n+1)+6(n+1)]}{6} \\ &= \frac{(n+1)(2n^2+n+6n+6)}{6} \\ &= \frac{(n+1)(2n^2+7n+6)}{6} \\ &= \frac{(n+1)(n+2)(2n+3)}{6} \end{aligned}$$

The Principle of Mathematical Induction now implies that (A.5) is true for all n. △

Example A.5

Let us prove (A.6) for all positive integral n via mathematical induction. As usual, let $P(n)$ be the desired statement, (A.6) in this case.

(i) $P(1)$ is: $2^1 > 1$, which is true.
(ii) We assume (A.6). We must deduce

$$2^{n+1} > n+1 \tag{A.11}$$

We are only considering positive integers, so $n \geq 1$. So via (A.6),

$$2^n > 1 \tag{A.12}$$

We add (A.12) to (A.6):

$$2^n + 2^n > n+1$$

Since $2^{n+1} = 2 \cdot 2^n = 2^n + 2^n$, this proves (A.11). △

Example A.6

(A.7) is false for some values of n. Let us attempt to "prove" (A.7) using mathematical induction and see what goes wrong. As usual, let $P(n)$ be (A.7), the statement that we want to "prove."

(i) $P(1)$ is: $1 = 1^2$, which is true.
(ii) We assume (A.7) and wish to deduce

$$1 + 2 + \cdots + n + (n+1) = (n+1)^2 \tag{A.13}$$

Add $(n+1)$ to both sides of (A.7):

$$\begin{aligned} 1 + 2 + \cdots + n + (n+1) &= n^2 + (n+1) \\ &= n^2 + n + 1 \end{aligned}$$

But this does not equal $(n+1)^2$, the right side of (A.13). So the "proof" fails. △

Example A.7

Consider

$$P(n): 1 + 2 + \cdots + n = \frac{(n-1)(n+2)}{2} \tag{A.14}$$

Let us attempt to prove (A.14) using mathematical induction. Step (i) of the Principle of Mathematical Induction requires that $P(1)$, namely $1 = \frac{0 \cdot 3}{2}$, be true. But $P(1)$ is false. So we know immediately that (A.14) is not true for all values of n.

Nonetheless, we can verify Step (ii) in a "proof" of (A.14) by mathematical induction; from $P(n)$ we deduce $P(n+1)$. We add $(n+1)$ to both sides of (A.14) as follows:

$$\begin{aligned} 1+2+\cdots+n+(n+1) &= \frac{(n-1)(n+2)}{2}+(n+1) \\ &= \frac{(n-1)(n+2)+2(n+1)}{2} \\ &= \frac{n^2+n-2+2n+2}{2} \\ &= \frac{n^2+3n}{2} \\ &= \frac{n(n+3)}{2} \end{aligned}$$

And this is just the right side of $P(n+1)$. △

Examples A.6 and A.7, preceding, emphasize that any valid proof via mathematical induction must verify both (i) and (ii) in the hypotheses of the Principle of Mathematical Induction.

We stated the above Principle of Mathematical Induction starting at $P(1)$ in (i). But we could just as well start at $P(0)$, or at $P(14)$, or at any $P(m)$ in (ii). We then conclude that $P(n)$ is true for all integers n at least equal to m.

Example A.8

We show that

$$2^n < n! \qquad \textbf{(A.15)}$$

for all integers $n \geq 4$. Observe that for $n=3$, (A.15) is expressed as

$$2^3 < 3!$$

which is not true. Let $P(n)$ be (A.15).

(i) We check $P(4)$.

$$2^4 < 4!$$

means that $16 < 24$, which is true.

(ii) Assuming $P(n)$, we deduce $P(n+1)$. Since $n \geq 4$,

$$2 < n+1 \qquad \textbf{(A.16)}$$

Multiplying (A.15) by (A.16) gives $P(n+1)$. △

Often functions (or other mathematical objects) are defined **inductively**; that is,

(i) $f(1)$ is given
(ii) $f(n+1)$ is given in terms of $f(n)$, or even in terms of all $f(m)$, for $m = 1,2,\ldots,n$.

Then the Principle of Mathematical Induction implies that $f(n)$ is in fact defined for all positive integers.

Examples A.9 Here are some typical examples of inductive definitions.

$f(n) = n!$ is given by

(i) $1! = 1$
(ii) $(n+1)! = (n+1) \cdot n!$ △

$f(n) = 2^n$ is given by, for $n \geq 0$,

(i) $2^0 = 1$
(ii) $2^{n+1} = 2 \cdot 2^n$ △

With n denoting a positive integer, a function $f(n)$ is defined **recursively** if each value of $f(n)$ is either

(i) Given explicitly or
(ii) Given in terms of previously defined values of f

Recursive definitions are more general than are inductive definitions in that the value of $f(n)$ may be defined using previous values of $f(m)$ *with m greater than n.* Inductive definitions have the important advantage that it is easy to verify that they really are definitions. Recursive definitions often require special arguments to verify that $f(n)$ is indeed defined for all integers n.

Example A.10 Here is a recursive definition that is not an inductive definition.

$$f(n) = \begin{cases} 1, & \text{if } n \text{ is a multiple of 3} \\ 1 + f(n+1), & \text{if } n \text{ is not a multiple of 3} \end{cases}$$

From the first part of the definition,

$$f(3)=f(6)=f(9)=\cdots=1 \tag{A.17}$$

We compute $f(1)$ as follows: From the second part of the definition,

$$f(1)=1+f(2)$$

So we need to know $f(2)$. Again from the second part of the definition,

$$f(2)=1+f(3)$$

From (A.17), $f(3)=1$. So $f(2)=1+1=2$ and $f(1)=1+2=3$.

Here is a more compact computation of $f(n)$ for some other values of n:

$$f(4)=1+f(5)=1+1+f(6)=1+1+1=3$$
$$f(7)=1+f(8)=1+1+f(9)=1+1+1=3$$
$$f(8)=1+f(9)=1+1=2$$

△

It is not hard to show that a computation of $f(n)$ for Example A.10 always terminates after using at most two other values of n. So the function in Example A.10 is in fact defined for all n. Indeed, as shown in the exercises, $f(n)$ of Example A.10 may also be defined, nonrecursively, as

$$f(n)=\begin{cases} 1 & \text{for } n\equiv 0 \pmod 3 \\ 3 & \text{for } n\equiv 1 \pmod 3 \\ 2 & \text{for } n\equiv 2 \pmod 3 \end{cases}$$

Example A.11 Here is an attempt at a recursive definition that does not work for all n.

$$f(n)=\begin{cases} 1, & \text{if } n \text{ is } 1 \\ 1+f\left(\dfrac{n}{2}\right), & \text{if } n \text{ is even} \\ 1+f(3n-1), & \text{if } n \text{ is odd and greater than } 1 \end{cases}$$

Then

$$f(1)=1$$
$$f(2)=1+f(1)=1+1=2$$
$$f(3)=1+f(8)=2+f(4)=3+f(2)=5$$

$$f(4) = 1 + f(2) = 3$$
$$f(5) = 1 + f(14) = 2 + f(7) = 3 + f(20) = 4 + f(10)$$
$$= 5 + f(5) \ldots$$

But the computation for $f(5)$ now starts repeating and does not terminate. △

Example A.12

It is *not known* whether or not the following recursive "definition" is in fact a definition for all n.

$$f(n) = \begin{cases} 1, & \text{if } n \text{ is } 1 \\ 1 + f\left(\dfrac{n}{2}\right), & \text{if } n \text{ is even} \\ 1 + f(3n+1), & \text{if } n \text{ is odd and greater than } 1 \end{cases}$$

We compute $f(n)$ for some small values of n:

$$f(1) = 1$$
$$f(2) = 1 + f(1) = 2$$
$$f(3) = 1 + f(10) = 2 + f(5) = 3 + f(16) = 4 + f(8)$$
$$= 5 + f(4) = 6 + f(2) = 8$$
$$f(4) = 1 + f(2) = 3$$
$$f(5) = 1 + f(16) = 2 + f(8) = 3 + f(4) = 6$$
$$f(6) = 1 + f(3) = 9$$
$$f(7) = 1 + f(22) = 2 + f(11) = 3 + f(34) = 4 + f(17)$$
$$= 5 + f(52) = 6 + f(26) = 7 + f(13) = 8 + f(40)$$
$$= 9 + f(20) = 10 + f(10) = 11 + f(5) = 17$$

△

Exercises A.1

Prove the statements in Exercises 1–4 using the Principle of Mathematical Induction.

1. $1 + 3 + 5 + \cdots + (2n-1) = n^2, \quad n \geq 1$
2. $1^3 + 2^3 + 3^3 + \cdots + n^3 = \left[\dfrac{n(n+1)}{2}\right]^2, \quad n \geq 1$
3. $1 + r + r^2 + \cdots + r^n = \dfrac{1 - r^{n+1}}{1 - r}, \quad n \geq 1, r \neq 1$
4. $2^n \geq n^2, \quad n \geq 4.$

5. Show that $f(n)$ of Example A.10 may also be defined nonrecursively as

$$f(n)=\begin{cases}1 & \text{for } n\equiv 0 \pmod 3\\ 3 & \text{for } n\equiv 1 \pmod 3\\ 2 & \text{for } n\equiv 2 \pmod 3\end{cases}$$

In Exercises 6 and 7 give noninductive definitions for the indicated functions.

6. $f(n)=\begin{cases}1 & \text{if } n=1\\ 1+f(n-1) & \text{if } n>1\end{cases}$

7. $f(n)=\begin{cases}1 & \text{if } n=1\\ n+f(n-1) & \text{if } n>1\end{cases}$

8. Why is the following not a recursive definition?

$$f(n)=\begin{cases}1 & \text{if } n=1\\ 1+f(2n) & \text{if } n>1\end{cases}$$

9. Let $P(n)$ be a statement about integers. Suppose that

   (i) $P(m)$ is true.
   (ii) Whenever $P(n)$ is true, then also $P(n+1)$ is true.

   Use the Principle of Mathematical Induction to show that $P(n)$ is true for all integers $n\geq m$.
   Hint: Let $Q(n)$ be $P(n+m-1)$.

10. The Principle of **Complete** Mathematical Induction says: Let $P(n)$ be a statement about integers. Suppose that

   (i) $P(1)$ is true.
   (ii) Whenever $P(m)$ is true for all integers m such that $1\leq m\leq n$, then also $P(n+1)$ is true.

   Then $P(n)$ is true for all positive integers. Use the ordinary Principle of Mathematical Induction to prove the Principle of Complete Mathematical Induction.
   Hint: Let $Q(n)$ be: $P(m)$ is true for all integers m such that $1\leq m\leq n$.

11. Here is a heuristic argument that $f(n)$ of Example A.12 is defined for all positive, integral n. Give "reasons" for each of the following statements.

   a. It suffices to show that $f(n)$ is defined for all even integers n.

b. For n even, write $n=2^k m, k \geq 1$ and m odd. It suffices to show that, on the average, $3m/n \approx 3/4$.

c. "On the average," 2^{-k} is the fraction of even integers with a given value of k from part (b).

d. The "average" value of k in part (b) is

$$\frac{1}{2}+\frac{2}{4}+\frac{3}{8}+\cdots+\frac{k}{2^k}+\cdots=$$

$$\frac{1}{2}+\frac{1}{4}+\frac{1}{8}+\cdots+\frac{1}{2^k}+\cdots+$$

$$+\frac{1}{4}+\frac{1}{8}+\cdots+\frac{1}{2^k}+\cdots+$$

$$+\frac{1}{8}+\cdots+\frac{1}{2^k}+\cdots+$$

$$\cdots \qquad =$$

$$1+\frac{1}{2}+\frac{1}{4}+\cdots=2$$

12. How does the argument of Exercise 11 fail for Example A.11?

A.2 Applications to the Text

The Principle of Mathematical Induction was introduced in the previous section. In the text, mathematical induction is used formally only in two proofs about graphs in Chapter 4. However, mathematical induction is used implicitly fairly often. In most such cases, a formal use of mathematical induction would increase the rigor of the exposition, but not the clarity. In this section, some cases where mathematical induction allows a more compact presentation are discussed.

Example A.13

Definition 5.4 is really a recursive definition of a Boolean polynomial. Namely, Definition 5.4(ii) can be rewritten as

(ii) h is a **Boolean polynomial** if

$$h=f \vee g \quad \text{or} \quad h=f \wedge g \quad \text{or} \quad h=f'$$

where f and g are previously defined Boolean polynomials.

To see that this recursive definition works, consider it as an *inductive* definition on the number of times the symbols $\vee$, $\wedge$, and $'$ appear in the Boolean polynomial. △

Example A.14

Consider a merge sort, as in Example 6.6. We are given a list of 2^n elements that are to be sorted, say alphabetically. The technique of a merge sort may be defined recursively (or inductively) as follows. We assume that we already know how to merge two sorted lists. Except for starting at $n=0$, we follow the format of the Principle of Mathematical Induction, as stated in the previous section.

(i) For $n=0$, a list of $2^0=1$ element is already sorted.
(ii) For $n+1 \geq 1$, to sort a list L of 2^{n+1} elements
  a. Divide L into two lists L_1 and L_2, each having 2^n elements.
  b. Sort L_1 and L_2.
  c. Merge the sorted lists L_1 and L_2.

A recursive definition, as just given, is often very easy to implement in programming languages such as Pascal and ALGOL, which allow a procedure (or subroutine) to refer to itself.

Knowing that two sorted lists, each of length m, can be merged via at most $2m$ comparisons, let us prove via the Principle of Mathematical Induction that a merge sort requires at most $n \cdot 2^n$ comparisons to sort a list with 2^n elements.

(i) If $n=0$, no comparisons are needed. $0 \cdot 2^0 = 0$.
(ii) We assume the estimate for any list with 2^n elements.

Consider a list L with 2^{n+1} elements and follow the procedure of (ii) above. At most $n \cdot 2^n$ comparisons are needed to sort each of L_1 and L_2. Merging L_1 and L_2 requires at most $2 \cdot 2^n$ comparisons. In all, the number of comparisons required to sort L is at most

$$\begin{aligned} n \cdot 2^n + n \cdot 2^n + 2 \cdot 2^n &= (2n+2)2^n \\ &= (n+1)2 \cdot 2^n \\ &= (n+1)2^{n+1} \end{aligned}$$

△

Example A.15

The proof of Theorem 6.5 contains a very typical proof by mathematical induction. We retain the notation of the proof of Theorem 6.5. Then we wish to show that $[n \cdot (x-y)]_i$ is the same for all positive n. Here is a formal proof by mathematical induction.

(i) For $n=1$, $[x-y]_i$ cannot differ from itself.
(ii) We assume that all of the $[m \cdot (x-y)]_i$ are the same for $1 \leq m \leq n$. Let $z = n \cdot (x-y)$ in (6.21). Then

$$[(x-y)+n \cdot (x-y)]_i = [(n+1) \cdot (x-y)]_i = [n \cdot (x-y)]_i$$

So also $[(n+1)\cdot(x-y)]_i$ agrees with the common value for $[m\cdot(x-y)]$. △

Example A.16

The definition of S_i in Proposition 7.11 is an inductive definition. We observe that S_i is well defined for all $i \geq 0$ even if S is a set of transformations on an infinite set X. The finiteness of X is used only to ensure that S_i equals $\varnothing$ for all sufficiently large i.

Part of the proof of Proposition 7.11 is really a mathematical induction on k of (7.25). A formalization of the argument is left to the exercises. △

Example A.17

Proofs about formal languages are often by mathematical induction. Consider the grammar G of Example 8.13. We give a formal proof that $L(G)$ is as claimed.

The induction statement, $P(n)$, is: All derived strings $\mathbf{w}$ with n terminals are given by

Case (a) $\mathbf{w}$ is a string of 0's and 1's with an even number of 1's.
Case (b) $\mathbf{w}$ is a string $\mathbf{v}$ of 0's and 1's, with an even number of 1's, followed by s.
Case (c) $\mathbf{w}$ is a string $\mathbf{v}$ of 0's and 1's, with an odd number of 1's, followed by t.

Observe that each production in G increases the number of terminals by one. So the induction is also on the number of productions in the derivation of $\mathbf{w}$.

(i) $P(1)$? One production yields 0, $0s$, and $1t$ as derived strings. This is $P(1)$.
(ii) We assume $P(n)$ and deduce $P(n+1)$. We let $\mathbf{w}$ be a derived string with $(n+1)$ terminals. Then $\mathbf{w}$ is derived via a production from some string $\mathbf{w}'$ with n terminals. The preceding cases (a), (b), and (c) for $\mathbf{w}'$ are treated separately.

Case (a) No derivations may be applied to $\mathbf{w}'$. So this case does not occur for $\mathbf{w}$.
Case (b) The productions

$$s \to 0 \qquad s \to 0s \qquad s \to 1t$$

yield cases (a), (b), and (c) respectively for $\mathbf{w}$. Note that the last terminal for $\mathbf{w}$ is 0, 0, and 1, respectively.
Case (c) The productions

$$t \to 1 \qquad t \to 1s \qquad t \to 0t$$

yield cases (a), (b), and (c) respectively for **w**. Note that the last terminal for **w** is 1, 1, and 0, respectively.

Observe that cases (b) and (c) for **w**′ show that the last terminal in **w** is arbitrary. So we get *all* of the claimed strings as derived strings. △

The formal analysis in Example A.17 is rather longer than an informal argument. But it does provide a framework that is useful for more complicated grammars.

Example A.18

Here is a recursive statement of Theorem 9.1, the Euclidean algorithm.

We let a and b be positive integers and take $a \geq b$. If $b|a$, then $\gcd(a,b)=b$. Otherwise, we let r be the remainder for a divided by b. Then $\gcd(a,b)=\gcd(b,r)$.

The proof of this statement of the Euclidean algorithm is by mathematical induction on b as follows:

(i) If $b=1$, then $1|a$ and also $\gcd(a,1)=1$.
(ii) Consider arbitrary b. We assume the Theorem for all positive integers $r<b$ and deduce it for b. If $b|a$, then indeed $\gcd(a,b)=b$. Otherwise,

$$a=q\cdot b+r, \qquad 1 \leq r < b \tag{A.18}$$

(A.18) expresses a as an integral combination of b and r. So any common divisor of b and r is also a common divisor of a. Also by (A.18), r is an integral combination of a and b. So any common divisor of a and b is also a common divisor of r. That is, the pairs b,r and a,b have the same common divisors. Hence $\gcd(a,b)=\gcd(b,r)$. △

Exercises A.2

In Exercises 1–7 reprove each of the indicated results using the Principle of Mathematical Induction.

1. Theorem 4.5.
2. Proposition 5.7.
3. Proposition 7.7.
4. Proposition 7.11.
5. Example 8.11.
6. Example 8.14.
7. Theorem 9.2.

8. Give a recursive definition for *postorder* of Definition 4.13.
9. Give a recursive definition for *preorder* of Definition 4.14.

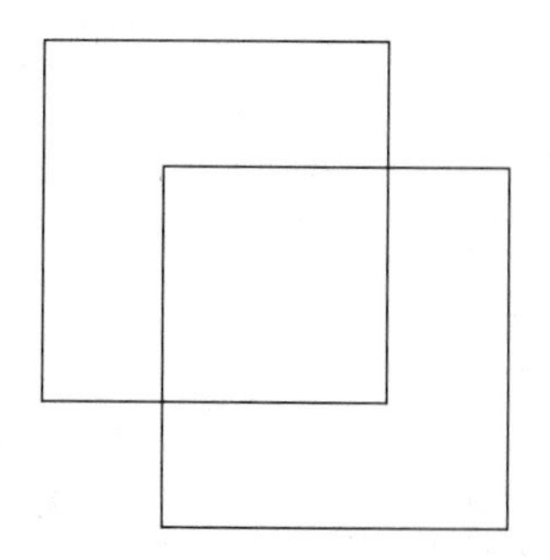

Answers to Selected Exercises

Exercises 1.1 (Page 10)

1. **a.** Even **c.** Odd

2. **a.** 00101 0 **c.** 011101 0

3. **a.** 110 011 **c.** Parity Error

4. **a.** 000 **c.** 000

7. 0 and 8 have the same code word. 1 and 9 have the same code word.

9. **a.** The row and column of the bit in error have an odd parity.
b. The check bit for that row or column is in error.

10. **d.** $1-(1-p)^n-np(1-p)^{n-1}$

Exercises 1.2 (Page 16)

1. **a.** 3. **c.** 4

2. **a.**

	101	100	000
101	–	1	2
100	1	–	1
000	2	1	–

$d=1$

c.

	010	100	111
010	–	2	2
100	2	–	2
111	2	2	–

$d=2$

3.

Code Word	a. 10000	c. 00111
00110	3	1
01011	4	2
10001	1	3
11100	2	4
Most likely:	10001	00110

4. **a.** 100011 **c.** 011011 **e.** 011011

6. For the subset, d is computed by taking a minimum over a smaller set of distinct code words. So there are fewer candidates for the minimum value d.

9. **a.** Let $\mathbf{r}$ be a received n-tuple. If there is a code word $\mathbf{c}$ such that $H(\mathbf{r},\mathbf{c})$ is 0 or 1, decode $\mathbf{r}$ as the message for $\mathbf{c}$. Otherwise, indicate a transmission error.
b. Let $\mathbf{c}$ and $\mathbf{c}'$ be code words with $H(\mathbf{c},\mathbf{c}')=4$. Let $\mathbf{r}$ be an n-tuple such that $H(\mathbf{r},\mathbf{c})=H(\mathbf{r},\mathbf{c}')=2$. There is no unique way to correct the reception of r.

10. No. By Theorem 1.2, for such a code, $d\geq 3$. Let $\mathbf{c}_1$ and $\mathbf{c}_2$ be distinct 3-tuples that are code words. Then $H(\mathbf{c}_1,\mathbf{c}_2)=3$, so $\mathbf{c}_1$ and $\mathbf{c}_2$ differ in all three bits. Let $\mathbf{c}_3$ be another code word. Then $\mathbf{c}_3$ cannot differ from both $\mathbf{c}_1$ and $\mathbf{c}_2$ in all bits.

Exercises 1.3 (Page 25)

1. b. (0 1 0 1 0 0)

3. The fourth and the fifth places.

4. b.

+	(0 0 0)	(1 0 0)	(0 1 1)	(1 1 1)
(0 0 0)	(0 0 0)	(1 0 0)	(0 1 1)	(1 1 1)
(1 0 0)	(1 0 0)	(0 0 0)	(1 1 1)	(0 1 1)
(0 1 1)	(0 1 1)	(1 1 1)	(0 0 0)	(1 0 0)
(1 1 1)	(1 1 1)	(0 1 1)	(1 0 0)	(0 0 0)

Yes

6. a. 2 **c.** 3

8. a. 4

9. $\mathbf{r}+\mathbf{e}=\mathbf{c}+\mathbf{e}+\mathbf{e}=\mathbf{c}+\mathbf{0}=\mathbf{c}$

13. Let m be the number of code words. Forming an addition table requires m^2 additions. Computing d involves computing $m(m-1)$ Hamming distances. For large m, m^2 and $m(m-1)$ differ by only a small percentage.
(*Note.* Since $\mathbf{a}+\mathbf{b}=\mathbf{b}+\mathbf{a}$ and $H(\mathbf{a},\mathbf{b})=H(\mathbf{b},\mathbf{a})$, both computations could be roughly halved in complexity.)

Exercises 1.4 (Page 41)

1. b. $(1+0)\cdot 1=1\cdot 1=1;\ 1\cdot 1+0\cdot 1=1+0=1$

2. a. 18

3. a. 1 **c.** 0

4. a. (1) **c.** $\begin{pmatrix}0\\0\end{pmatrix}$

5. $A\cdot(B+C)=(1\ \ 1\ \ 0)\cdot\begin{pmatrix}0 & 1\\ 1 & 1\\ 1 & 1\end{pmatrix}=(1\ \ 0)$

$A\cdot B+A\cdot C=(1\ \ 1)+(0\ \ 1)=(1\ \ 0)$

7.

$\mathbf{c}$	$H\cdot\mathbf{c}^t$	Code word?
(0 0)	$\begin{pmatrix}0\\0\end{pmatrix}$	Yes
(0 1)	$\begin{pmatrix}0\\1\end{pmatrix}$	No
(1 0)	$\begin{pmatrix}0\\1\end{pmatrix}$	No
(1 1)	$\begin{pmatrix}0\\0\end{pmatrix}$	Yes

8. **a.** No **c.** Yes **e.** Yes

10. **a.** $\begin{pmatrix}0\\0\\0\end{pmatrix}, \begin{pmatrix}1\\0\\1\end{pmatrix}$; $d=2$

d. $\begin{pmatrix}0\\0\\0\\0\\0\\0\\0\end{pmatrix}, \begin{pmatrix}0\\0\\1\\0\\1\\1\\1\end{pmatrix}, \begin{pmatrix}0\\1\\0\\0\\0\\0\\0\end{pmatrix}, \begin{pmatrix}0\\1\\1\\0\\1\\1\\1\end{pmatrix},$

$\begin{pmatrix}1\\0\\0\\1\\0\\1\\0\end{pmatrix}, \begin{pmatrix}1\\0\\1\\1\\1\\0\\1\end{pmatrix}, \begin{pmatrix}1\\1\\0\\1\\0\\1\\0\end{pmatrix}, \begin{pmatrix}1\\1\\1\\1\\1\\0\\1\end{pmatrix}$; $d=1$

11. 2^{n-r}

13. **a**

15. None

Exercises 1.5 (Page 50)

1. (1 0 0 0), (0 1 0 0), (0 0 1 0), (0 0 0 1)

2. **a.** $\begin{pmatrix}1\\0\end{pmatrix}$ **c.** $\begin{pmatrix}0\\1\end{pmatrix}$

3. **a.** $\begin{pmatrix}1\\1\\0\end{pmatrix}$ **c.** $\begin{pmatrix}0\\0\\1\\0\end{pmatrix}$

4. (0 0 0 0 0) and (0 1 0 0 0). Other answers are possible.

6. **a.** Neither **c.** Single-error-correction
e. Single-error-detection only

7. (1 1 1 1)

9. The minimum number of check positions is 3. Many sets of code words are possible.

10. 5, 6

14. Appending a parity check bit may be achieved by appending a row of 1s and the column $(0\ldots0\quad 1)^t$ to the initial H. By Exercise 13, conditions (i) and (iii) of Exercise 12 are satisfied. Since the columns of H are distinct and non-**0**, condition (ii) is also satisfied by the new matrix.

Exercises 1.6 (Page 59)

1. a. $\begin{pmatrix} 1 \\ 1 \\ 0 \end{pmatrix}$ **c.** $\begin{pmatrix} 0 \\ 0 \\ 0 \end{pmatrix}$

2. a. $\begin{pmatrix} 1 \\ 0 \\ 0 \end{pmatrix}$ **c.** $\begin{pmatrix} 0 \\ 0 \\ 1 \end{pmatrix}$

3. a. First **c.** Second

4. a. Code word: (1 0 1 1 0); message: (1 0)
c. Code words: (1 1 1 0 1); message: (1 1)
e. Code word: (1 0 1 1 0); message: (1 0)

5. The first four bits; the last four bits
a. Code word: (0 1 1 0 0 1 0 1); message: (0 1 1 0)
c. Code word: (0 0 0 1 1 0 0 1); message: (0 0 0 1)

6. a. $\begin{pmatrix} 0 & 0 & 0 & 0 & 0 & 0 & 0 & 1 & 1 & 1 \\ 0 & 0 & 0 & 1 & 1 & 1 & 1 & 0 & 0 & 0 \\ 0 & 1 & 1 & 0 & 0 & 1 & 1 & 0 & 0 & 1 \\ 1 & 0 & 1 & 0 & 1 & 0 & 1 & 0 & 1 & 0 \end{pmatrix}$
b. 1, 2, 4, 8; 3, 5, 6, 7, 9, 10
c. (i) (0 0 1 0 0 1 1 1 0 1)
d. (i) Code word: (1 0 1 0 0 0 0 1 0 1);
message: (1 0 0 0 0 1)

7. Since there are $2^r - 1$ different non-**0** columns, each with r entries, every non-**0** syndrome is a column.

8. $2^r - 1 - n$

10. a. Code word: (0 1 1 1 0 1 0)
c. Code word: (1 1 1 0 0 0 1)

Exercises 2.1 (Page 69)

1. a.

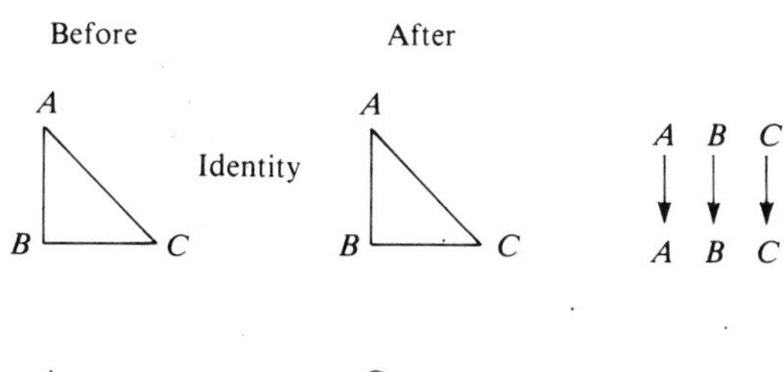

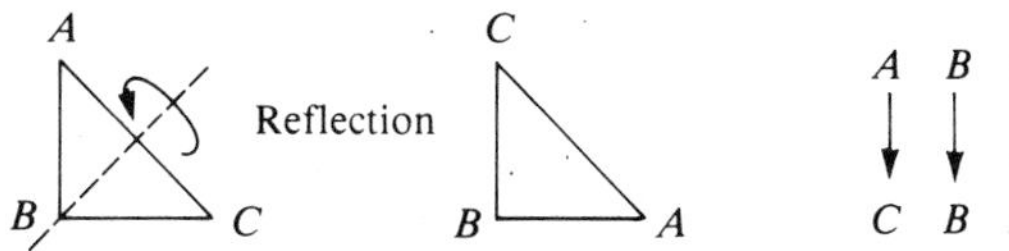

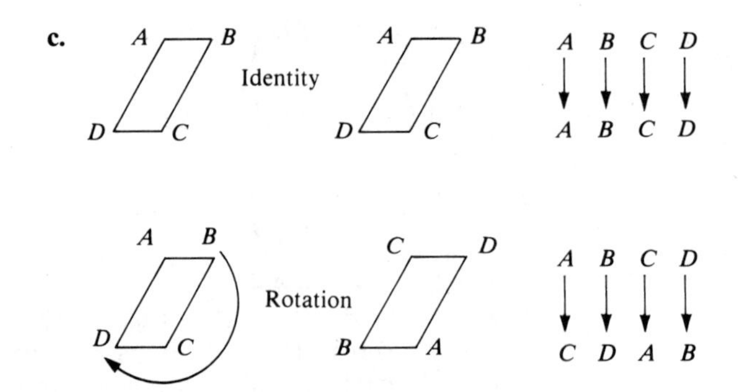

e. Rigid Motion Permutation of the Vertices

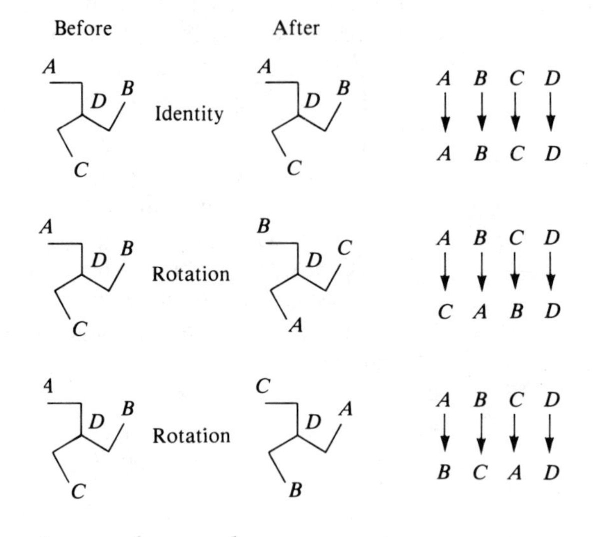

2. **a.** h_4 **c.** h_8 **e.** h_3

3. Table 2.26

6. One, the identity. All of the angles are different so each vertex is fixed by a symmetry.

10. The circle may be rotated about its center through *any* angle.

12. Any vertex may be mapped to any vertex via a symmetry.

14. **a.** No **b.** A rotation about the point of intersection of the axes of reflection

Exercises 2.2 (Page 79)

2. **a.** $(b \circ a) \circ a = c \circ a = a$; $b \circ (a \circ a) = b \circ b = b$. Other answers are possible.

3. **a.** b is the identity. **c.** d is the identity.

4. a^{-1}: d; b^{-1}: c; c^{-1}: b,g; d^{-1}: a; e^{-1}: e; f^{-1}: none; g^{-1}: c

5. **a.** Commutative

7. **a.** $(2.6 \times 1.3) \times 3.7 = 3.4 \times 3.7 = 12.6$; $2.6 \times (1.3 \times 3.7) = 2.6 \times 4.8 = 12.5$

10. **a.** 1 **b.** $\frac{1}{r}$

12. No. For example, $2 \div 3 \neq 3 \div 2$.

Exercises 2.3 (Page 88)

1. 18

2. **a.** 2 **c.** 1

4.

+	0	1	2
0	0	1	2
1	1	2	0
2	2	0	1

6. **a.**

·	0	1	2	3
0	0	0	0	0
1	0	1	2	3
2	0	2	0	2
3	0	3	2	1

b. 0 and 2 lack inverses.

8. $2 \cdot 3$, $3 \cdot 2$, $3 \cdot 4$, and $4 \cdot 3$ are not in S. (Any one product suffices for an answer.)

9. **a.** $(0,3)$ **c.** $(2,1)$

11. **a.** $(0,0,1)$

13. $(g_1,h_1)*(g_2,h_2)=(g_1 \circ g_2,\ h_1 \cdot h_2)$
$(g_2,h_2)*(g_1,h_1)=(g_2 \circ g_1,\ h_2 \cdot h_1)$

But $g_1 \circ g_2 = g_2 \circ g_1$ since $(G,\circ)$ is commutative and $h_1 \cdot h_2 = h_2 \cdot h_1$ since $(H,\cdot)$ is commutative.

15. Table 2.1 comes from a noncommutative group. $(\mathbb{Z}_8,+)$ is commutative.

18. **a.**

·	1	2	3	4
1	1	2	3	4
2	2	4	1	3
3	3	1	4	2
4	4	3	2	1

c. There are two possible answers:
$1 \to 0$ $2 \to 1$ $3 \to 3$ $4 \to 2$ and
$1 \to 0$ $2 \to 3$ $3 \to 1$ $4 \to 2$

Exercises 2.4 (Page 96)

1. **a.** h_3 **c.** h_2

2. **a.** h_7, h_7, h_3, h_8, h_7 **c.** 5, 1, 4, 3, 1

3. **a.** $b \circ a^{-1}$ **c.** $a^{-1} \circ c^{-1} \circ b^{-1} \circ a^{-1}$

5. Given; by composition with a^{-1}; by associativity; by the definition of a^{-1}; by the definition of e.

7. Associativity fails. Each row and column *is* a permutation of the outside row and column.

9.

$x \circ a = y \circ a,$	equation given
$(x \circ a) \circ a^{-1} = (y \circ a) \circ a^{-1},$	by composition with a^{-1}.
$x \circ (a \circ a^{-1}) = y \circ (a \circ a^{-1}),$	by associativity
$x \circ e = y \circ e,$	by definition of a^{-1}
$x = y,$	by definition of e

14.

$\circ$	a	b	c	d
a	b	a	d	c
b	a	b	c	d
c	d	c	b	a
d	c	d	a	b

Exercises 2.5 (Page 106)

1. **a.** No **c.** No

2. **a.** No **c.** Yes

3. **a.** 6, $\{0,1,2,3,4,5\}$ **c.** 2, $\{0,3\}$ **e.** 1, $\{0\}$ **g.** 2, $\{h_1, h_5\}$

4. Closure and associativity. No. $\mathbb{Z}$ is not finite.

6. $m \cdot g + n \cdot g = (m+n) \cdot g$ (other letters are possible).

8. $\langle g \rangle$ is contained in every subgroup of G that contains g.

10. The law of composition on K is the same as the law of composition on H, which is the same as the law of composition on G. Since K is given to be a subgroup of H, this law of composition makes K into a group. Hence K is also a subgroup of G.

12. **a.** 2 and 3 are elements of $\langle 2 \rangle \cup \langle 3 \rangle$, but $2+3=5$ is not.
b. No

15. (2.27) should hold. Let $i=0$ in (2.27): $g^0 \circ g^j = g^j$. This is true for $g^0 = e$. Similarly, (2.27) holds for $j=0$. Now consider (2.27) with $i=n$ and $j=-n$: $g^n \circ g^{-n} = g^0$. From before, $g^0 = e$. Since $g \circ g^{-1} = e$, indeed $g^n \circ g^{-n} = e$. The other possibilities for i and j in (2.27) are also true.

Exercises 2.6 (Page 118)

1. **a.** Yes **c.** Yes

2. **a.** $\begin{pmatrix} A & B & C & D \\ C & D & B & A \end{pmatrix}$ **c.** $\begin{pmatrix} A & B & C & D & E \\ A & E & D & C & B \end{pmatrix}$

3. **a.** $\begin{pmatrix} A & B & C & D & E \\ D & A & B & E & C \end{pmatrix}$ **c.** $\begin{pmatrix} A & B & C & D & E & F \\ C & D & E & F & B & A \end{pmatrix}$

4. **a.** No **c.** Yes

5. **a.** $(ACD)(B)$ or (ACD) **c.** $(A)(BDG)(CFE)$

6. **a.** $\begin{pmatrix} A & B & C & D \\ C & A & D & B \end{pmatrix}$ **c.** $\begin{pmatrix} A & B & C & D & E \\ D & E & C & A & B \end{pmatrix}$

7. **a.** $(ADEC)(B)$

8. $f_1 = e, f_2 = (ABC), f_3 = (ACB), f_4 = (BC), f_5 = (AC), f_6 = (AB)$

11. Definition 2.1 with f replaced by $f \circ g$ and with g replaced by h; Definition 2.1 with x replaced by $h(x)$; Definition 2.1 with g replaced by $g \circ h$; Definition 2.1 with f replaced by g and with g replaced by h.

14. b. (132) and (321) are different notations for the same permutation.

15. a. Let $(x_1 x_2 \ldots x_n) = f$ be a cycle.
$f(x_1) = x_2 \neq x_1$, $f^2(x_1) = x_3 \neq x_1, \ldots, f^{n-1}(x_1) = x_n \neq x_1$. So the order of f is more than $n-1$. But $f^n(x_i) = x_i$, $1 \leq i \leq n$. So f has order n.

b. The cycles in a cycle decomposition are disjoint and so compose independently. So $f^n = e$ for a permutation f if and only if $g^n = e$ for each cycle g in the cycle decomposition of f. $g^n = e$ precisely for n a multiple of the order of g.

Exercises 3.1 (Page 129)

1. a. (i) No; (ii) No; (iii) No **c.** (i) Yes; (ii) Yes; (iii) No

2. b. $\{1\} \cup \{2,3,4\} \cup \{5\}$

4. No. All vertices are G-equivalent under the group G of symmetries of the rectangle.

6. If xRy, then yRx by symmetry. So $x = y$ by antisymmetry. If $x = y$, then xRy by reflexivity.

8. Let A and B be elements of X. Then A is $\langle g \rangle$-equivalent to B if and only if $g^i(A) = B$ for some positive integer i. But $g^i(A) = B$ is the condition that B be in the cycle containing A.

9. c. $S_3 = \{e\} \cup \{(12), (13), (23)\} \cup \{(123), (132)\}$

10. b. $x \equiv y \pmod 1$ if and only if x and y have equal fractional parts.

Exercises 3.2 (Page 136)

1. a. True **c.** False

3. $\mathbb{Z}_2 \times \mathbb{Z}_4 = \{(0,0), (1,2)\} \cup \{(1,0), (0,2)\} \cup \{(0,1), (1,3)\} \cup \{(1,1), (0,3)\}$

5. $0 \sim 1$ since $0 + 1 = 1$. $1 \sim 2$ since $1 + 1 = 2$.
But 0 is not equivalent to 2. (Other answers are possible.)

7. a. True **c.** False

9. a. Let $(H, \circ)$ be a subgroup of the group $(G, \circ)$. Let g be an element of G. The **right coset**, Hg, of g with respect to H consists of all elements in G of the form $h \circ g$.

c. $S_3 = \{e, (12)\} \cup \{(13), (132)\} \cup \{(23), (123)\}$

11. a. $\mathbb{Z}_2{}^3 = \{(0\ 0\ 0), (1\ 1\ 1)\} \cup \{(0\ 0\ 1), (1\ 1\ 0)\} \cup \{(0\ 1\ 0), (1\ 0\ 1)\} \cup \{(1\ 0\ 0), (0\ 1\ 1)\}$

b. In the order from part (a): no error, third bit, second bit, first bit

13. By Lagrange's Theorem, 5 divides $|G|$ and also 7 divides $|G|$. Then also $5 \cdot 7 = 35$ divides $|G|$. So $|G| \geq 35$.

Exercises 3.3 (Page 150)

1. a. $X_e = X$, $X_{(12)} = \{3\}$, $X_{(23)} = \{1\}$, $X_{(13)} = \{2\}$, $X_{(123)} = \varnothing$, $X_{(132)} = \varnothing$
$G_1 = \{e, (23)\}$, $G_2 = \{e, (13)\}$, $G_3 = \{e, (12)\}$

2. a. i. $X = \{1,2,3\}$ ii. $6 = 3 \cdot 2$

4. a. $\frac{1}{6}(3 + 3 \cdot 1 + 2 \cdot 0) = 1$

5. 10

7. 8

9. a. Permuting the vertices preserves the number of vertices with any given color.

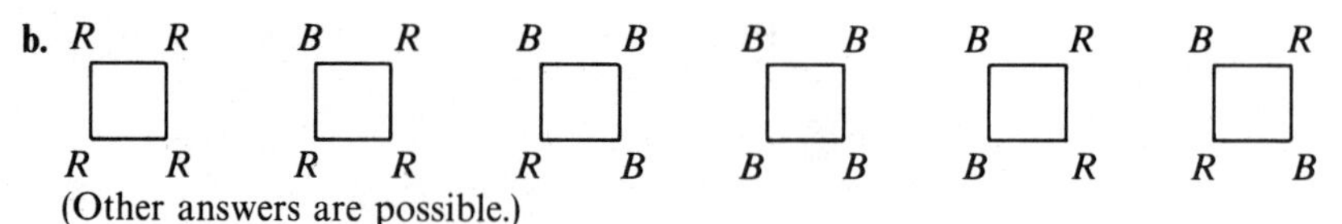

(Other answers are possible.)

12. b. 36

13. a. $G_y = \{e, (xz)\}$; $G = \{e, (xz)\} \cup \{(xy), (xzy)\} \cup \{(yz), (xyz)\}$

b. $e[y] = y = (xz)[y]$; $(xy)[y] = x = (xzy)[y]$; $(yz)[y] = z = (xyz)[y]$

14. c. $\frac{1}{48}[2^8 + 7\cdot 2^4 + 3(2\cdot 2^6 + 4\cdot 2^2 + 2\cdot 2^4) + 2(4\cdot 2^2 + 4\cdot 2^4)] = 22$

Exercises 3.4 (Page 160)

1. a. No **c.** No **e.** Yes; not a total order

2.

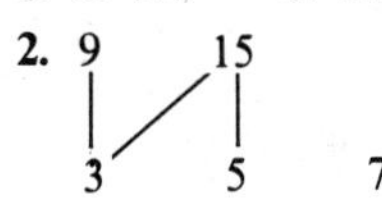

4. a. True. True. False. False.

5. Both conditions imply that $A \supsetneqq B$. If $A - B$ contains two distinct elements x and y, then $A \supsetneqq A - \{x\} \supsetneqq B$, so A does not cover B. If A does not cover B, then there is a set C such that $A \supsetneqq C \supsetneqq B$. Then $A - B$ must have at least two elements.

7. $x \geq y$ if and only if $y \leq x$.
Reflexivity. $x \geq x$ since $x \leq x$ by the reflexivity of $\leq$.
Antisymmetry. $x \geq y$ and $y \geq x$ is given. So $y \leq x$ and $x \leq y$. Hence $x = y$ by the antisymmetry of $\leq$.
Transitivity. $x \geq y$ and $y \geq z$ is given. Then $y \leq x$ and $z \leq y$. By the transitivity of $\leq$, $z \leq x$. Hence $x \geq z$.

9. $x < y$ if and only if $x \leq y$ and $x \neq y$. $x < y$ and $y < z$ are given. By transitivity for $\leq$, $x \leq z$. Also, $x = z$ contradicts Exercise 8 because $x = z$ implies $z \leqq x$, by reflexivity.

13. a. $\begin{pmatrix} 0 & 0 & 0 & 0 & 0 \\ 0 & 0 & 0 & 0 & 0 \\ 1 & 0 & 0 & 0 & 0 \\ 1 & 1 & 0 & 0 & 0 \\ 0 & 0 & 1 & 0 & 0 \end{pmatrix}$

b. $C(|)^2 = \begin{pmatrix} 0 & 0 & 0 & 0 & 0 \\ 0 & 0 & 0 & 0 & 0 \\ 0 & 0 & 0 & 0 & 0 \\ 0 & 0 & 0 & 0 & 0 \\ 1 & 0 & 0 & 0 & 0 \end{pmatrix}$ $C(|)^3 = \begin{pmatrix} 0 & 0 & 0 & 0 & 0 \\ 0 & 0 & 0 & 0 & 0 \\ 0 & 0 & 0 & 0 & 0 \\ 0 & 0 & 0 & 0 & 0 \\ 0 & 0 & 0 & 0 & 0 \end{pmatrix}$

c. $\begin{pmatrix} 1 & 0 & 0 & 0 & 0 \\ 0 & 1 & 0 & 0 & 0 \\ 1 & 0 & 1 & 0 & 0 \\ 1 & 1 & 0 & 1 & 0 \\ 1 & 0 & 1 & 0 & 1 \end{pmatrix}$

Exercises 4.1 (Page 172)

1. a. $\begin{pmatrix} 0 & 0 & 0 & 1 \\ 0 & 0 & 1 & 0 \\ 0 & 1 & 0 & 1 \\ 1 & 0 & 1 & 0 \end{pmatrix}$ **c.** $\begin{pmatrix} 0 & 1 & 0 & 1 & 1 \\ 1 & 0 & 1 & 0 & 1 \\ 0 & 1 & 0 & 1 & 1 \\ 1 & 0 & 1 & 0 & 1 \\ 1 & 1 & 1 & 1 & 0 \end{pmatrix}$

2. a.

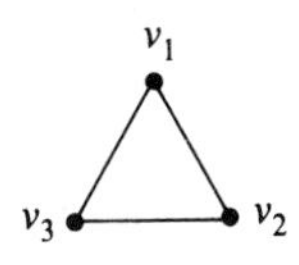

c.

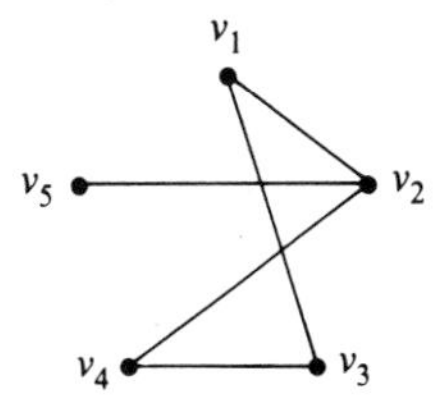

3. a. Nonconnected.

(i)

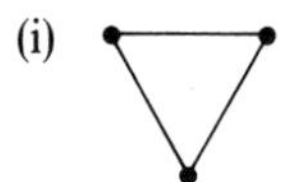

(ii) •

c. Nonconnected

(i)

(ii)

(iii) •

4. a. $\begin{pmatrix} 0 & 1 & 0 \\ 0 & 0 & 0 \\ 1 & 1 & 0 \end{pmatrix}$ **c.** $\begin{pmatrix} 0 & 0 & 0 & 0 & 0 \\ 1 & 0 & 0 & 1 & 1 \\ 1 & 1 & 0 & 1 & 0 \\ 0 & 0 & 1 & 0 & 0 \\ 1 & 0 & 0 & 0 & 0 \end{pmatrix}$

5. a.

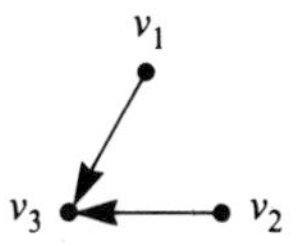

c.

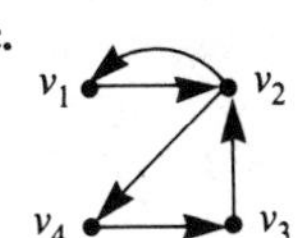

6.

	Initial vertex	Accessible vertices
a.	v_1	v_1, v_2
	v_2	v_2
	v_3	v_1, v_2, v_3
c.	v_1	v_1
	v_2	v_1, v_2, v_3, v_4, v_5
	v_3	v_1, v_2, v_3, v_4, v_5
	v_4	v_1, v_2, v_3, v_4, v_5
	v_5	v_1, v_5

8. An edge e that connects vertices v_i and v_j creates a 1 in the A_{ij} and A_{ji} entries, and so contributes a total of 2 towards the sum of all the entries.

10. **a.** *Reflexivity:* Use a path of length 0. *Symmetry:* Reverse the path. *Transitivity:* If v_1 is connected to v_2 via path P_1 and v_2 is connected to v_3 via path P_2, then the path P_1, P_2 (with the duplicate vertex v_2 omitted) connects v_1 to v_3.

e. $V' = V''$ and $E' \neq E''$ cannot happen, since E' consists of all edges that are incident at elements of V'. Suppose that v'' is in $V'' - V'$. Then, by the definition of V', v'' cannot be connected to any vertex of V' via paths in G, and hence certainly not via paths in G''.

12. For $(X, \leq)$ a poset, $C(\leq)$ is the adjacency matrix for the directed graph that is the Hasse diagram of $(X, \leq)$. The condition "...there exist elements $z_1, z_2, \ldots, z_m$ in X such that y covers z_m, z_m covers $z_{m-1}, \ldots$, z_2 covers z_1, z_1 covers x" is equivalent to requiring that y be connected to x via a directed path of length $m+1$. Since Boolean addition corresponds to taking maximums, $[C(\leq)]^{m+1}$ may be found from A^{m+1} by replacing each positive $A_{ij}{}^{m+1}$ by 1.

Exercises 4.2 (Page 184)

1. **a.** No **c.** No

3. **a.** **c.**

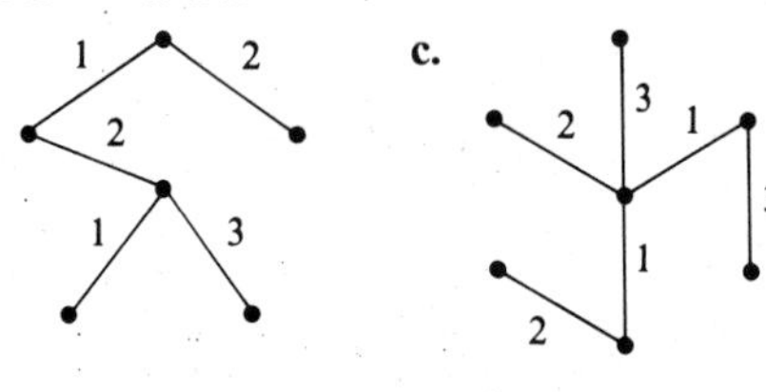

5. Add new edges for as long as possible without creating a cycle. Call this subgraph G'. It must be shown that G' is connected and hence a (spanning) tree. Suppose that vertices v and v' cannot be connected in G'. Connect v and v' by a simple path P in G. Let e be any edge in P that is not in G'. Then adding e to G' cannot create a cycle C, since deleting e from C preserves connectivity and v cannot be connected to v' in G'. This contradicts the maximality of G'.

Exercises 4.3 (Page 201)

1. **a.** No **c.** No

2. Draw

3. A

4. **a.** (i) (ii)

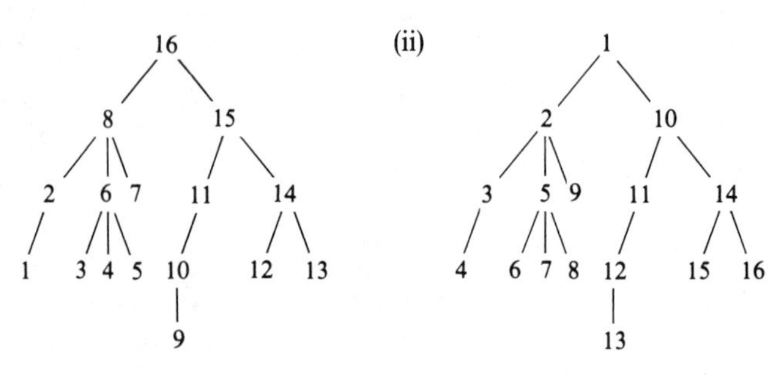

6. a.

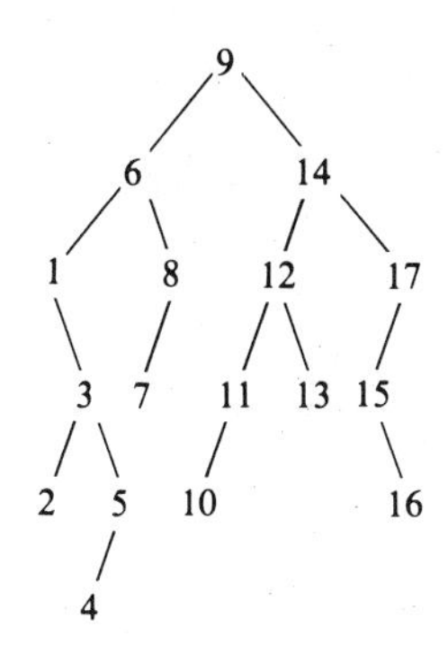

7. A.

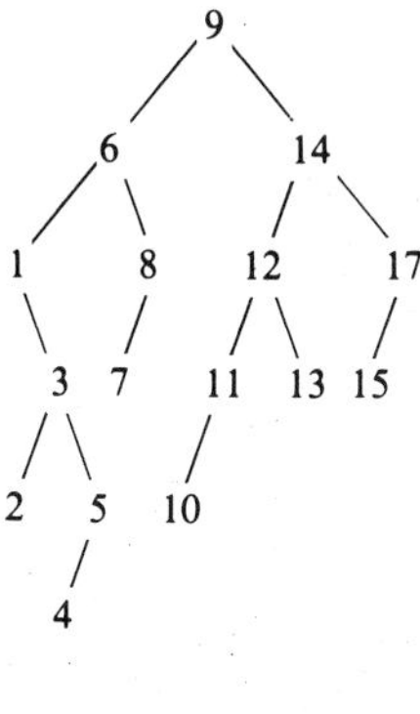

B.

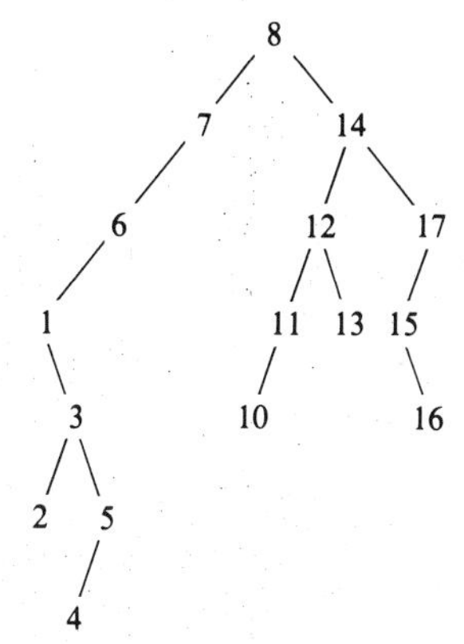

8. Theorem 4.3 implies that r_1 and r_2 may be joined by only one simple undirected path. The edges of T have a unique direction. Hence there can be no edges in the path. So $r_1 = r_2$.

10. Definition 4.13(i) applies if either P_1 or P_2 is a subpath of the other. Definition 4.13(ii) applies otherwise. So all vertices may be compared via postorder. Postorder is a partial order: *Reflexivity:* $P_1 = P_2$ for $v = v$. *Antisymmetry:* Suppose that $v \le w$ and $w \le v$. Then Definition 4.13(ii) cannot occur. So P_1 is a subpath of P_2, and P_2 is a subpath of P_1. $v = w$. *Transitivity:* Suppose that $v \le w$ and $w \le x$. There are four cases: Definition 4.13(i) and (ii) for $v \le w$ and Definition 4.13(i) and (ii) for $w \le x$. Let P_3 denote the simple path connecting r to x. In case (i)/(i), P_1 is a subpath of P_3. In case (i)/(ii), P_1 is either a subpath of P_3 or the first edge in which P_1 and P_3 differ equals the first edge in which P_2 and P_3 differ. In case (ii)/(i), the first edge in which P_1 and P_3 differ equals the first edge in which P_2 and P_3 differ. In case (ii)/(ii), the first edge in which P_1 and P_3 differ is either the first edge in which P_1 and P_2 differ or else is the first edge in which P_2 and P_3 differ.

12. Take $v \ne w$. If $v = w_i$ is a vertex of P_2, then $w < v$ or $v < w$ according to $w_{i+1} = l(v)$ or $w_{i+1} = r(v)$. Otherwise, let $v_{i-1} = w_{i-1}$ be the last common vertex in P_1 and P_2. Then $w < v$ or $v < w$ according to $w_i = l(v_{i-1})$ or $w_i = r(v_{i-1})$.

14. Suppose that s is in T. Then the simple path connecting r to s specifies a sequence of left and right successors as in Steps 4 and 6. If s is not in T, then the search of Proposition 4.7 cannot end at Step 2.

17. Let P be a directed path from v to v'. If P has length 1, then P is simple.

Otherwise, suppose that two differently numbered vertices in P coincide. Then a subpath of P would be a cycle, which is impossible. Hence P is simple and so unique by Theorem 4.3.

Exercises 5.1 (Page 216)

1. 4

a.

$\cup$	$\varnothing$	$\{1\}$	$\{2\}$	$\{1,2\}$
$\varnothing$	$\varnothing$	$\{1\}$	$\{2\}$	$\{1,2\}$
$\{1\}$	$\{1\}$	$\{1\}$	$\{1,2\}$	$\{1,2\}$
$\{2\}$	$\{2\}$	$\{1,2\}$	$\{2\}$	$\{1,2\}$
$\{1,2\}$	$\{1,2\}$	$\{1,2\}$	$\{1,2\}$	$\{1,2\}$

$\cap$	$\varnothing$	$\{1\}$	$\{2\}$	$\{1,2\}$
$\varnothing$	$\varnothing$	$\varnothing$	$\varnothing$	$\varnothing$
$\{1\}$	$\varnothing$	$\{1\}$	$\varnothing$	$\{1\}$
$\{2\}$	$\varnothing$	$\varnothing$	$\{2\}$	$\{2\}$
$\{1,2\}$	$\varnothing$	$\{1\}$	$\{2\}$	$\{1,2\}$

b.

$^-$	$\varnothing$	$\{1\}$	$\{2\}$	$\{1,2\}$
	$\{1,2\}$	$\{2\}$	$\{1\}$	$\varnothing$

3.

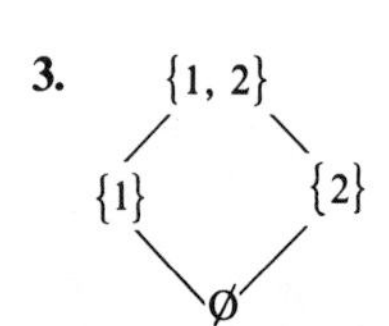

4. a. A and C; **c.** $\{D,E,F\}$

5. $y=x \vee x$ in the first absorption law; $y=x$ in the second absorption law. By Step 2, $x \wedge (x \vee x)$ of Step 1 may be replaced by x.

7. a. Universal bounds, complements, distributivity, commutativity and $x \wedge y = O$ is given, universal bounds; by Definition 5.2, $y \leq x'$ if $y = y \wedge x'$.

b.

$x = x \vee O$, by universal bounds
$= x \vee (y \wedge y')$, by complements
$= (x \vee y) \wedge (x \vee y')$, by distributivity
$= I \wedge (x \vee y')$, $x \vee y = I$ is given
$= x \vee y'$, by universal bounds
$x' = (x \vee y')'$, by taking complements
$= x' \wedge (y')'$, by de Morgan's Laws
$= x' \wedge y$, by involution

Hence $x' \leq y$ by Definition 5.2.

c. $y = x'$ by antisymmetry.

9. $\vee$ is sometimes called Boolean addition. $x \vee O = x$ by the universal bounds axiom. Also, $O \vee x = x$ by commutativity. So O is an identity for the law of composition $\vee$.

10. $(B, \vee)$ satisfies closure, associativity, and the existence of an identity.

12. Let y and z be least upper bounds for a set S. Then $y \leq z$ because z is an upper bound and y is a least upper bound. Similarly, $z \leq y$. Then $y = z$ by antisymmetry.

13. a. For any x in B, $O \leq x \leq I$ by the universal bounds axiom. By Chapter 3, Section 3.4, Exercise 8, since $O = I$, also $x = O = I$.

Exercises 5.2 (Page 231)

1. a. Idempotency, distributivity

2. a. $(x \vee x') \wedge (y \vee y) = (x \vee x') \wedge y,$ by idempotency
$= I \wedge y,$ by complements
$= y,$ by universal bounds

3. a.

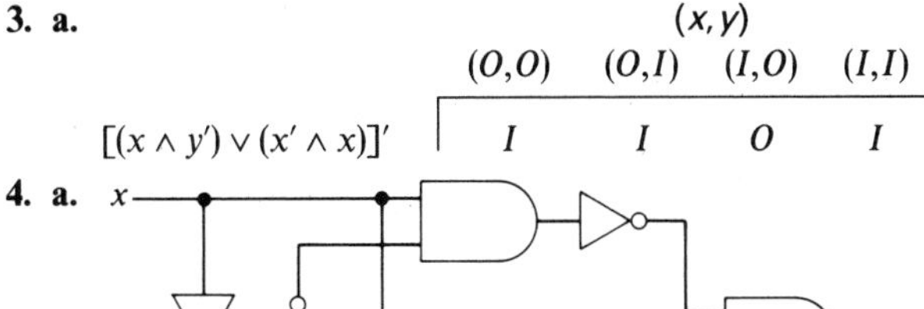

	(x, y)			
	(O,O)	(O,I)	(I,O)	(I,I)
$[(x \wedge y') \vee (x' \wedge x)]'$	I	I	O	I

4. a.

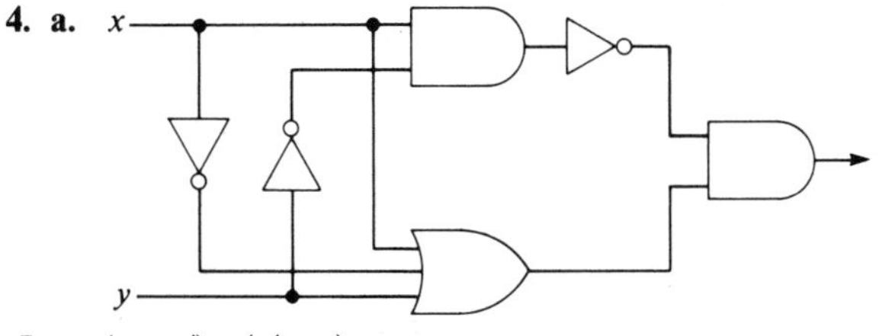

5. a. $(x \wedge y') \vee (x' \wedge y)$

6. a. $(x' \wedge y') \vee (x \wedge y')$

7. a. $0 \wedge [0' \wedge (1 \vee x)] \wedge y'$

8.

	(p, q)			
	(T,T)	(T,F)	(F,T)	(F,F)
$(p \vee q)' \vee (p' \wedge q')$	F	F	F	T

11. a. For instance, the idempotency law for the polynomial x requires that $x \vee x$ be written the same way as is x. This is not so. Therefore, the polynomials do not form a Boolean algebra.

b. Let $[f]$ denote the equivalence class of the Boolean polynomial f. We just verify the idempotency axiom. The verifications for the other axioms are entirely similar. We define $[f] \vee [g]$ as $[f \vee g]$. However, we must show that this definition is independent of the choice of, say, f in the equivalence class $[f]$. So suppose that $[h] = [f]$; that is, $h = f$. Then also $h \vee g = f \vee g$. So $[h \vee g] = [f \vee g]$. Now look at $[f] \vee [f]$. Since $f \vee f = f$ by the idempotency axiom, also $[f] \vee [f] = [f \vee f] = [f]$.

12. Substitute I for p in $p \wedge q = p$, yielding $I \wedge q = I$. By the universal bounds axiom, $I \wedge q = q$. Hence $q = I$.

Exercises 5.3 (Page 240)

1. a. $[(x \vee y') \wedge z] \wedge (x \wedge y')$

2. b. $(x \wedge y' \wedge x') \vee (y \wedge z \wedge x')$

3. b. $(x' \wedge y \wedge z) \vee (x' \wedge y \wedge z')$

4. a. $(x \wedge y) \vee (x \wedge y')$

c. $(x \wedge y \wedge z) \vee (x \wedge y' \wedge z) \vee (x \wedge y \wedge z') \vee (x \wedge y' \wedge z')$

5. b. The first half of the proof of Proposition 5.1 writes $x \vee (x \wedge y)$ into disjunctive normal form, which is also the disjunctive normal form for x. The second half of the proof writes the disjunctive normal form into x.

6. b. $1 + 2^n$

8. Using the usual laws of algebra, every polynomial $p(x)$ may be simplified either to 0 or to a unique polynomial in the indicated form. Also, two polynomials yield the same function of x if and only if they both simplify to the same indicated polynomial, or to 0.

Exercises 5.4 (Page 247)

1. Suppose that s is an atom. $O \leq s$ by the universal bounds axiom. $O \neq s$ by Definition 5.8(i). So $O < s$. Let $O \leq x \leq s$. Then, by Definition 5.8(ii), $O = x$ or $x = s$. Hence $O < x < s$ is impossible, and s covers O. Conversely, suppose that s covers O. Since $s > O$, $s \neq O$. Consider x such that $x \leq s$. Then also $O \leq x \leq s$. Since $O < x < s$ is impossible, necessarily $x = O$ or $x = s$. Then s is an atom.
3. Since m_1 and m_2 are distinct, for some i, x_i and x_i' occur in m_1 and m_2. We know that $x_i \wedge x_i' = O$. By commutativity and the universal bounds axiom, $m_1 \wedge m_2 = O$.
5. Let x be any element of B_1. Then $x \wedge x' = O_1$.

$$f(x \wedge x') = f(O_1) = f(x) \wedge f(x') = f(x) \wedge [f(x)]' = O_2$$

Similarly, using $x \vee x' = I_1, f(I_1) = I_2$.
7. Let X be the set of atoms of B. Then B is isomorphic to $\mathscr{P}(X)$ and so has the same number of elements. Let $n = |X|$. Then $|\mathscr{P}(X)| = 2^n$.
9. **a.** The proof for infinite X is exactly the same as the proof for finite X.
   b. Since X is infinite, X is not the finite union of finite sets.

Exercises 6.1 (Page 257)

1. **a.** 10
   b. 1, 2, 3, 4, 5 (Other lists, in ascending order, are possible.)
3. **a.** 321
   b. For a bubble sort, $M(64) = 2016$, which is much larger than the estimate of part (a).
4. **b.** 1, 16, 2, 3, 4, 7, 5, 6, 8, 15, 9, 10, 11, 14, 12, 13 (Other answers are possible.)
6. If R is much larger than $N \log_2 N$, then a merge sort is faster. If R is much smaller than $N \log_2 N$, then a bucket sort is faster.
8. **a.** $\binom{2m}{m} = \dfrac{(2m)!}{m!\, m!}$

   b. $\dfrac{(2m)!}{m!\, m!} \sim \dfrac{\sqrt{2\pi}e^{-2m}(2m)^{2m+(1/2)}}{(\sqrt{2\pi}e^{-m}m^{m+(1/2)})^2} = \dfrac{2^{2m+(1/2)}}{\sqrt{2\pi}\sqrt{m}}$

   Let N denote the needed number of comparisons.

$$2^N > \frac{2^{2m+(1/2)}}{\sqrt{2\pi}\sqrt{m}}$$

$$N > (2m + \tfrac{1}{2}) - \log_2(\sqrt{2\pi}) - \tfrac{1}{2}\log_2 m \sim 2m$$

Exercises 6.2 (Page 268)

5. c_8, 9

7.

	2^m	Number of modules
$m=6$	64	1758
$m=7$	128	5339

9. b. $S_{m+1} = S_m + \dfrac{2^m}{3^{m+1}} + \dfrac{1}{3^{m+1}}$

c. Except for the initial term, the infinite series is the sum of two geometric series. Its sum is $\frac{5}{2}$.

10. a.

	Input (x, y)			
	(0,0)	(0.1)	(1,0)	(1,1)
Output	00	01	01	10

b. $b(x,y) = (x' \wedge y) \vee (x \wedge y')$

$c(x,y) = x \wedge y$

c.

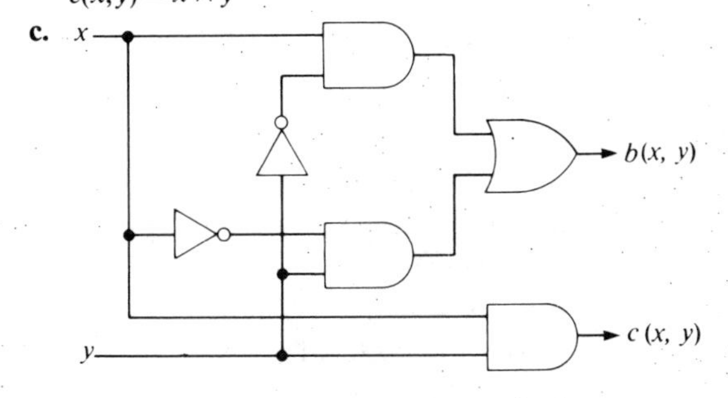

Exercises 6.3 (Page 275)

1. 27

2. b depends on x: $b(0,0,0) = 0$, $b(1,0,0) = 1$

4. a. 4, 2 **c.** 12, 3 **e.** 33, 4

6. 2^{2^r}

7. a. There are $2^{2^4} = 2^{16}$ different 4-input, 1 output modules. There are $(2^{2^2})^3 = (2^4)^3 = 2^{12}$ essentially different configurations in Figure 6.12. $2^{12} < 2^{16}$.

b. At least two time units.

c. The i/o relationships that may be computed in two time units all come from computations via Figure 6.12. Part (a) shows that some i/o relationships cannot be computed via Figure 6.12.

9. a. Start with two equal 2^m-bit numbers as input. Changing any one input changes the output.

c. We use two different kinds of 2-input, 1-output modules. Module A yields 0 or 1 according to whether the inputs are unequal or equal. Module B yields the maximum of the inputs. (See figure overleaf.)

Exercises 6.4 (Page 285)

1. a.

	00	01	10
00	00	01	10
01	01	10	00
10	10	00	01

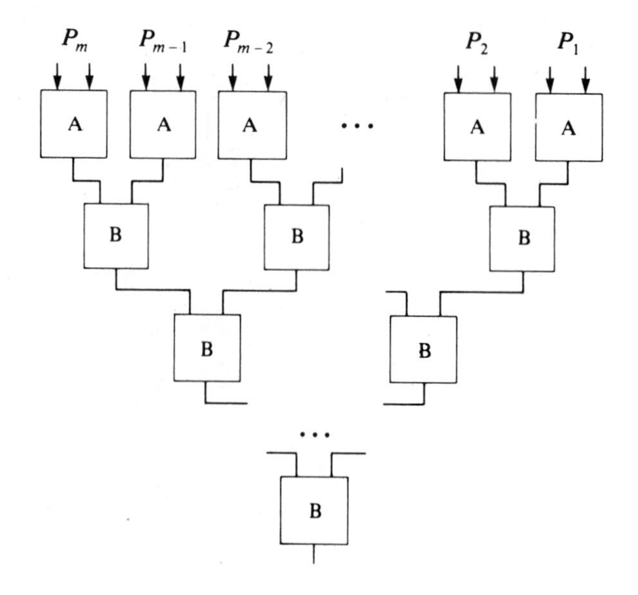

2. a. $0\underline{0}+01=\underline{0}1$ $\quad$ $0\underline{1}+01=\underline{1}0$
$\underline{0}0+00=\underline{0}0$ $\quad$ $\underline{1}0+00=\underline{1}0$

4. a. $\{0,1,2,3,4\}$ **c.** $\{0,1,2,3,4\}$

5. $\langle x-y\rangle=\{000,001\}$

7. a. Not possible **c.** 5^3 **e.** 3^6

9. a. 7, 3 **c.** 5, 2

11. $\langle 2\rangle=\{0,2,4,6,8\}$, $\langle 5\rangle=\{0,5\}$, $\langle 2\rangle\cap\langle 5\rangle=\{0\}$

13. Let $N=a\cdot b$, with $a,b\geq 2$ and with a and b having no common prime factor. Then N is the last common multiple of a and b. So $\langle a\rangle\cap\langle b\rangle=\{0\}$.

15. Suppose that u is ubiquitous and $H\neq\{e\}$. Let $g\neq e$ be an element of H. Then $u\in\langle g\rangle$. Hence $u\in H$. Now suppose that $u\in H$ for all $H\neq\{e\}$. Let $g\in G$, $g\neq e$. Take $H=\langle g\rangle$. Then $u\in\langle g\rangle$.
By Theorem 6.4, in Exercises 17–19, it suffices to show that the output depends on at least $\log_2 N$ bits of each of the inputs.

17. Suppose that the output depends on less than $\log_2 N$ bits of the first element. Since $\mathbb{Z}_N$ has N elements, there exist $a\neq b$ in $\mathbb{Z}_N$ that agree in these bits. The input (a,b) should produce the output 0 while the input (b,b) should produce the output 1. But (a,b) and (b,b) agree in all bits that are actually accepted by the circuit.

19. The output for (a,c) should be 0, while the output for (b,c) should be 1.

Exercises 6.5 (Page 297)

1. a. $3\cdot 3\cdot 3=3^3$ **c.** $2\cdot 73=2^1\cdot 73^1$

2. a. $(\mathbb{Z}_8\times\mathbb{Z}_3,+)$ **c.** $(\mathbb{Z}_3\times\mathbb{Z}_{25},+)$

3. $f(0)=(0,0)$, $f(1)=(1,1)$, $f(2)=(0,2)$, $f(3)=(1,3)$, $f(4)=(0,4)$, $f(5)=(1,0)$, $f(6)=(0,1)$, $f(7)=(1,2)$, $f(8)=(0,3)$, $f(9)=(1,4)$

4. a. (2,4) **c.** (4,0)

5. a. (3,31) **c.** (1,40)

6. a. (3,2,5) **c.** (1,0,6)

7. a. 37 **c.** 26

8. b. 92

9. Addition in $\mathbb{Z}_4$

	0	2	1	3
0	0	2	1	3
2	2	0	3	1
1	1	3	2	0
3	3	1	0	2

Renaming

	(0,0)	(0,0)	(1,1)	(1,1)
(0,0)	(0,0)	(0,0)	(1,1)	(1,1)
(0,0)	(0,0)	(0,0)	(1,1)	(1,1)
(1,1)	(1,1)	(1,1)	(0,0)	(0,0)
(1,1)	(1,1)	(1,1)	(0,0)	(0,0)

The condensed renaming table *is* that of a subgroup of $(\mathbb{Z}_2 \times \mathbb{Z}_2, +)$.

11. (Other answers are possible.)
a. $f(1+1) \neq f(1)+f(1)$ **c.** $f(2+2) \neq f(2)+f(2)$ **e.** $f(1+1) \neq f(1)+f(1)$

12. By Theorem 6.9, $(\mathbb{Z}_5 \times \mathbb{Z}_6, +)$ is isomorphic to $(\mathbb{Z}_5 \times \mathbb{Z}_2 \times \mathbb{Z}_3, +)$ and $(\mathbb{Z}_2 \times \mathbb{Z}_{15}, +)$ is isomorphic to $(\mathbb{Z}_2 \times \mathbb{Z}_3 \times \mathbb{Z}_3, +)$.

13. n is given to divide $a-b$ and $c-d$. Then n also divides $a+c-(b+d)=(a-b)+(c-d)$ and $a \cdot c - b \cdot d = a \cdot c - a \cdot d + a \cdot d - b \cdot d = a \cdot (c-d) + (s-b) \cdot d$.

14. Let m_i denote the remainder for m after division by Q_i. Let $f_i(m)$ denote the "component" of $f(m)$ in $\mathbb{Z}_{Q_i}$.

$$f_i(a) = a_i \qquad f_i(b) = b_i \qquad f_i(a \cdot b) = (a \cdot b)_i$$

By Exercise 13, $a_i \cdot b_i \equiv (a \cdot b)_i \pmod{Q_i}$. So $f_i(a \cdot b) = f_i(a) \cdot f_i(b)$.

16. By the definition of e_G; by the definition of homomorphism; by composing with $[f(e_G)]^{-1}$; by the definition of $[f(e_G)]^{-1}$; by the definition of e_H.

18. Use Theorem 2.10. Suppose that h_1 and h_2 are in S; $f(g_1) = h_1$ and $f(g_2) = h_2$. Then $f(g_1 \circ g_2) = h_1 * h_2$. So $h_1 * h_2$ is in S. If h is in S with $f(g) = h$, by Exercise 17, $h^{-1} = f(g^{-1})$ is also in S.

20. Suppose that $f(a) = f(b)$. $f(a \circ b^{-1}) = f(a) * f(b^{-1}) = f(a) * [f(b)]^{-1} = f(a) * [f(a)]^{-1} = e_H$. Then $a \circ b^{-1} = e_G$ and $a = b$.

Exercises 7.1 (Page 310)

1.

Input:	0	1	2	3	4	5	6	7	8	9
Output:	9	8	7	6	5	4	3	2	1	0

4. a.

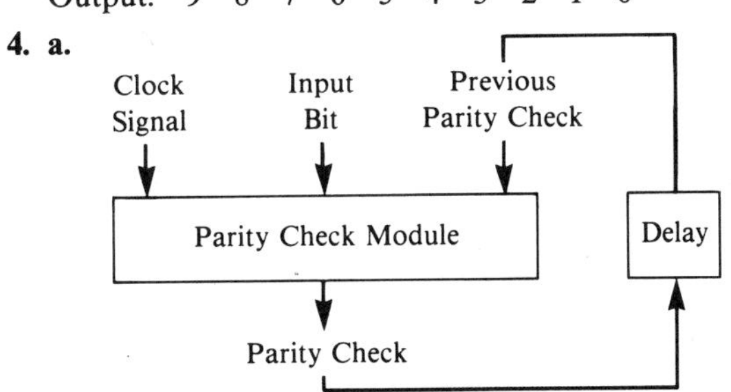

b.

Current state	Input 0	1
0	0	1
1	1	0

5.

Current state	Input 0	1	2
EVEN	ODD	EVEN	EVEN
ODD	EVEN	ODD	ODD

Starting State: EVEN

7.

Current state	e	0	1
A	A	A	B
B	B	A	B

9. a.

	Next-state function		Output function	
Current state	Input 0	1	Input 0	1
A	A	A	0	1

b. 1 **c.** Yes

Exercises 7.2 (Page 316)

1. a.

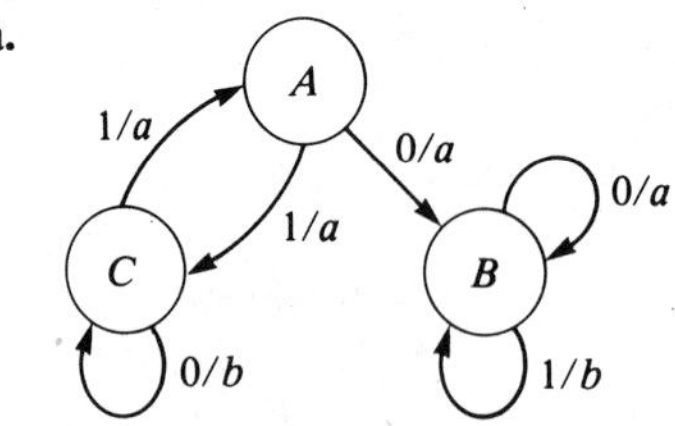

2. a.

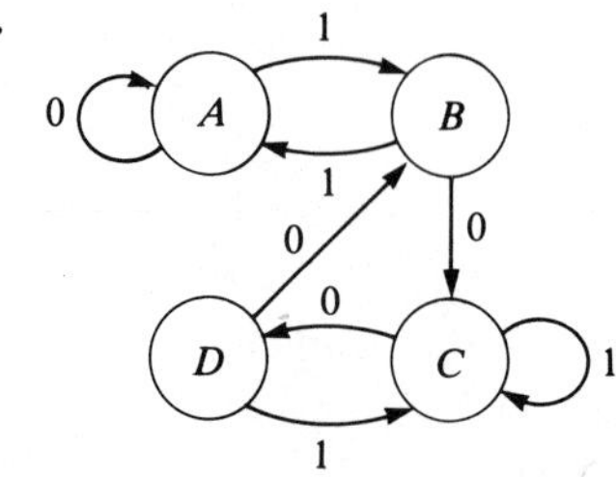

c.

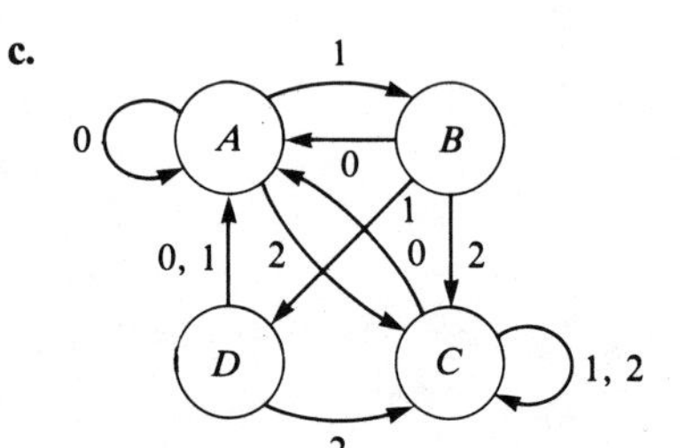

3. a.

	Next-state function		Output function	
Current state	Input 0	1	Input 0	1
A	A	C	a	b
B	B	A	b	b
C	A	A	a	a

4. a.

Current state	Input 0	Input 1
A	B	D
B	A	C
C	A	D
D	B	C

5. a.

Current state	Next-state function Input 0	Next-state function Input 1	Output function Input 0	Output function Input 1
A	A	B	0	1
B	B	C	1	2
C	C	D	2	3
D	D	A	3	0

c. A

6.

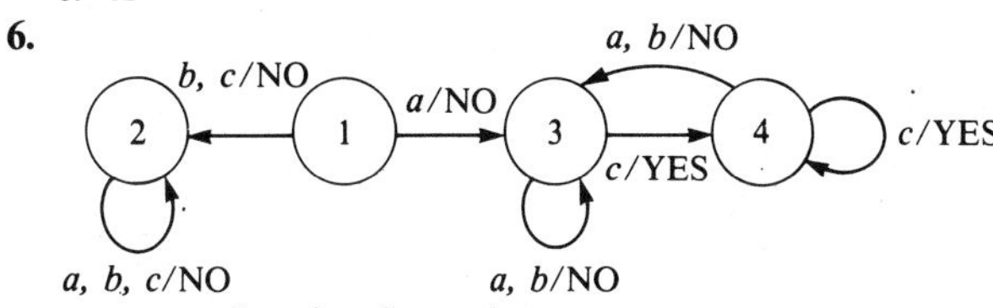

Starting State: 1

8. Let x be the input. In starting state (1,0), the machine computes $3x+1$; in starting state (1,1) it computes $3x+2$.

Exercises 7.3 (Page 323)

1. a. b, c, a, a, b, a

2. β_2 recognizes strings that begin with a and/or end with aba.

4. a. $2^{2^{21}}$

5. a.

Current state	Next-state function Input 0	Next-state function Input 1	Output function Input 0	Output function Input 1
00	00	10	0	0
01	00	10	1	1
10	01	11	0	0
11	01	11	1	1

Starting State: 00

b. Output the next-to-the-last input.

8. Suppose that a finite-state machine has n states. Consider the palindrome consisting of $n+1$ a's, $n+1$ b's, $n+1$ a's. By Theorem 7.1, the state before accepting the last a coincides with a state before accepting one of the first n of the latter group of a's. The output from this state, upon accepting an input of a, cannot be both NO and YES.

10. Suppose that the machine has n states. Consider the input numbers $2^{n+1}-1$ and 1, that is, $n+1$ 1's and n 0's followed by a 1. Since the output bits all depend on the last pair of input bits, at least $n+1$ blanks must be appended to the input numbers. The last blank must result in an output of 1, while the other blanks produce an output of 0. By Theorem 7.1, this is impossible.

13.

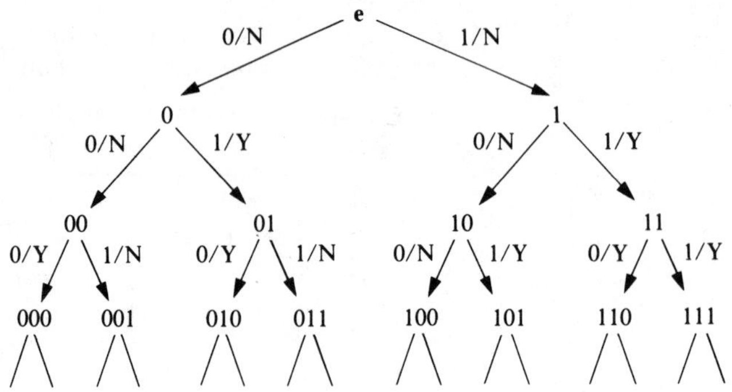

e
0/N 1/N
0 1
0/N 1/Y 0/N 1/Y
00 01 10 11
0/Y 1/N 0/Y 1/N 0/N 1/Y 0/Y 1/Y
000 001 010 011 100 101 110 111

Exercises 7.4 (Page 339)

1. a. $[A]=\{A\}$ $[B]=\{B\}$ $[C]=\{C\}$

Current state	Next-state function Input 0	Next-state function Input 1	Output function Input 0	Output function Input 1
$[A]$	$[C]$	$[B]$	x	x
$[B]$	$[A]$	$[B]$	y	x
$[C]$	$[A]$	$[C]$	x	x

c. $[A]=\{A,C\}$ $[B]=\{B,D\}$ $[E]=\{E\}$ $[F]=\{F\}$

Current state	Next-state function Input 0	Next-state function Input 1	Output function Input 0	Output function Input 1
$[A]$	$[E]$	$[B]$	x	x
$[B]$	$[B]$	$[F]$	x	x
$[E]$	$[B]$	$[A]$	x	y
$[F]$	$[E]$	$[B]$	x	y

2. a. i. $xxxyx$ ii. $[C]$ **c.** i. $xxxxyxx$ ii. $[A]$

6. a.

	Current state	Next-state function Input 0	1	Output function Input 0	1
$[A]_2$	A	F	A	x	x
	C	G	C	x	x
	D	G	E	x	x
$[B]_2$	B	C	D	x	y
$[E]_2$	E	F	B	x	x
$[F]_2$	F	F	B	y	x
	G	G	B	y	x

b. Replacing each state by its 2-equivalence class does not give a consistent table.

8. Equivalent inputs may be replaced by just one input, with the same columns.

Exercises 7.5 (Page 353)

1. a. Yes **c.** No

Current state	Input 0	1
A	B	A
B	A	B

3. Output string for M': *yyxxxx*
Output string for M: *bbcaaa*

4. b.

M' Current state	Input i'	Next state	M Current state	$h_i(i')$	Next state s	$h(s)$
X	5	Z	B	2	F	Z
Z	3	Y	F	1	D	Y
Y	3	Y	D	1	D	Y
Y	4	Y	D	1	D	Y
Y	5	X	D	2	B	X

5. a.

M_1 Current state	Input 1	2	Renaming Current state	Input 6	5
H	A	D	W	X	Z
A	D	B	X	Z	X
B	D	F	X	Z	X
F	D	A	X	Z	X
C	G	H	Y	Y	W
G	C	H	Y	Y	W
D	A	G	Z	X	Y

6. a. Starting at state 0, M is in state i precisely when the number n of 1's in the input string satisfies $n \equiv i \pmod 4$.

8. Let s' be a state of M that is accessible from s via the input string $i_1 i_2 \ldots i_k$. Let $j_1 j_2 \ldots j_l$ be another input string that moves M from s' to s''. Then s'' is accessible from s via the input string $i_1 i_2 \ldots i_k j_1 j_2 \ldots j_l$.

9. a. Let **i** move M' from X to Y. Then $h_i(\mathbf{i})$ moves M from A to some state B. Then starting M in state B simulates starting M' in state Y.

12. a. The i-column for M_1 is a subset of the i-column for M. Hence it has no duplications and hence is a permutation.

b. Since all states of M_1 appear in the i-column for M_1, all states of M' appear in the i'-column for M'. Hence the i'-column is a permutation of the states of M'.

Exercises 7.6 (Page 369)

1. a. $(c \circ b) \circ b = a \neq c = c \circ (b \circ b)$; No

2. $(\mathbb{Z}_6, \cdot)$

$\cdot$	0	2	4	1	3	5
0	0	0	0	0	0	0
2	0	4	2	2	0	4
4	0	2	4	4	0	2
1	0	2	4	1	3	5
3	0	0	0	3	3	3
5	0	4	2	5	3	1

Renaming via f

	0	0	0	1	1	1
0	0	0	0	0	0	0
0	0	0	0	0	0	0
0	0	0	0	0	0	0
1	0	0	0	1	1	1
1	0	0	0	1	1	1
1	0	0	0	1	1	1

4. b. $\begin{pmatrix} A & B & C \\ A & B & C \end{pmatrix}, \begin{pmatrix} A & B & C \\ B & A & C \end{pmatrix}, \begin{pmatrix} A & B & C \\ B & B & B \end{pmatrix}, \begin{pmatrix} A & B & C \\ A & A & A \end{pmatrix}$

5. b. $\begin{pmatrix} w & z \\ x & z \\ y & z \\ z & z \end{pmatrix}$

6. a. f_e, f_0, f_{00}

c. f_e, f_1, f_2

8. a. In the composition table for $(\mathbb{Z}_2, +)$, both elements appear twice. This is not true for the composition table for $(\mathbb{Z}_2, \cdot)$.

b. Let e denote the identity in $(G, \circ)$. The composition for $(G, \circ)$ must begin as follows:

$\circ$	e	a
e	e	a
a	a	–

$(G, \circ)$ is isomorphic to $(\mathbb{Z}_2, +)$ or to $(\mathbb{Z}_2, \cdot)$ according to whether $a \circ a = e$ or $a \circ a = a$.

11. Use the proof of Theorem 2.4.

18. Uniqueness: $f^*(\mathbf{e}) = e_G$ by Definition 7.13(ii).
$f^*(i_1 i_2 \ldots i_k) = f(i_1) \circ f(i_2) \circ \cdots \circ f(i_k)$ by Definition 7.13(i).

f^* is a homomorphism:

$$f^*(i_1 i_2 \ldots i_k j_1 j_2 \ldots j_l) = f(i_1) \circ f(i_2) \circ \cdots \circ f(i_k) \circ f(j_1) \circ f(j_2) \circ \cdots \circ f(j_l)$$
$$= f^*(i_1 i_2 \ldots i_k) \circ f^*(j_1 j_2 \ldots j_l)$$

by associativity in $(G, \circ)$.

Exercises 8.1 (Page 379)

1. a.

Rule	**Derived string**
	S
S → NP VP	NP VP
NP → N	N VP
N → *John*	*John* VP
VP → V NP	*John* V NP
V → *saw*	*John saw* NP
NP → N	*John saw* N
N → *Mary*	*John saw Mary*

3. a.

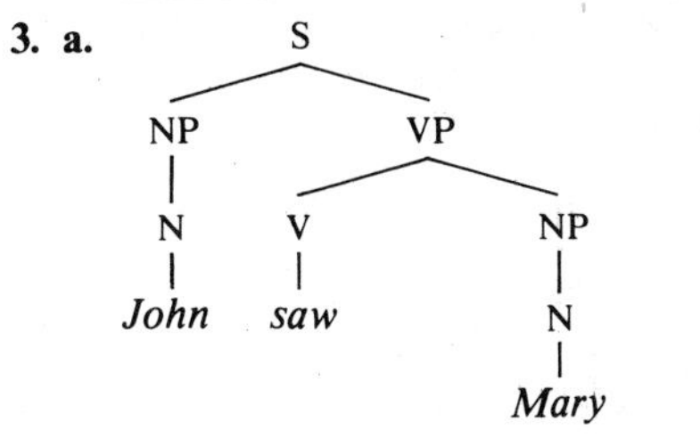

4. a.

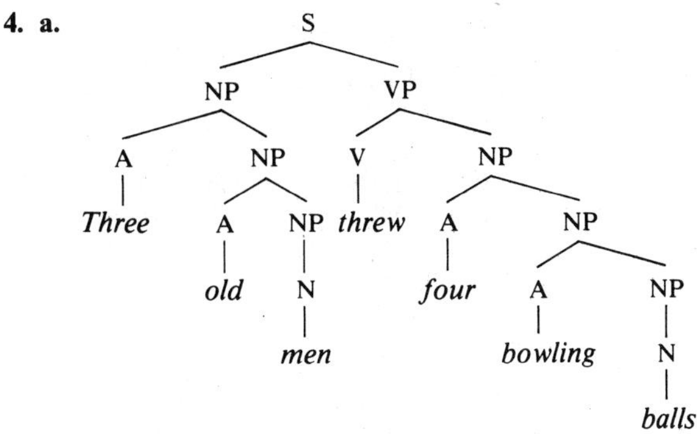

5. a. **c.**

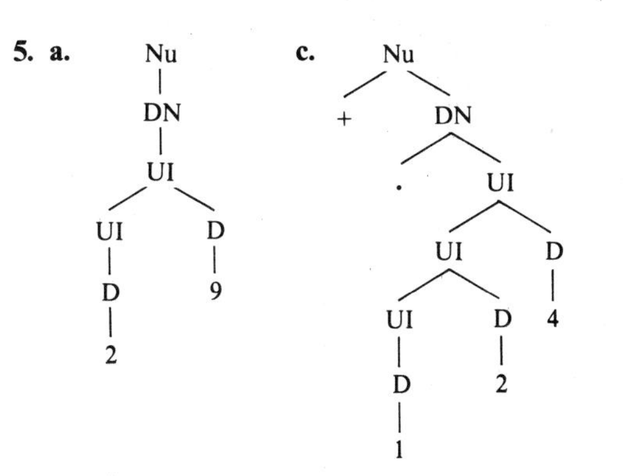

6. a.

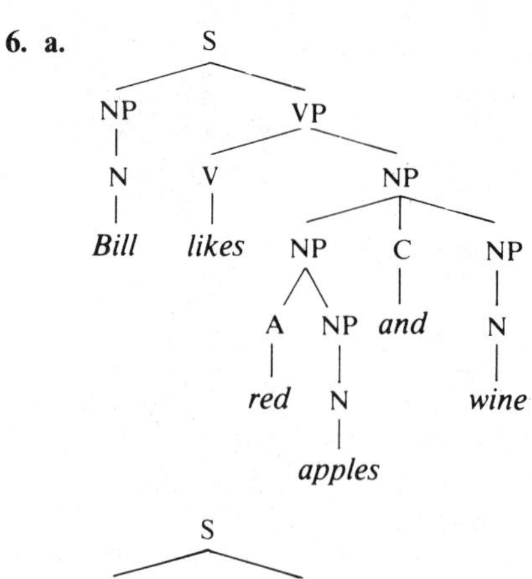

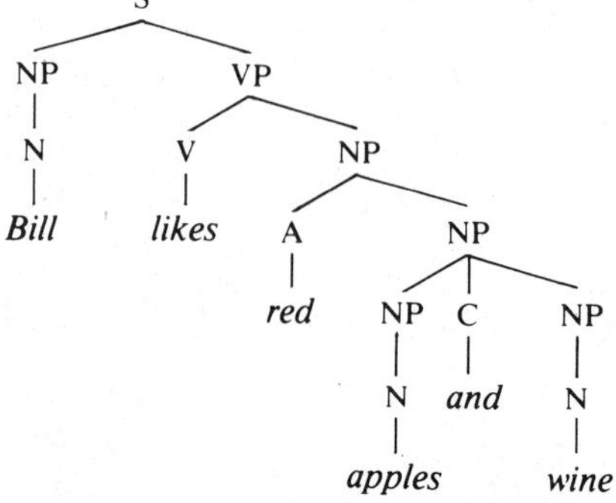

7. a. Add the rules

$$\text{NP} \rightarrow \{\text{Ar}\quad \text{NP}', \text{NP}'\}$$
$$\text{NP}' \rightarrow \{\text{A}\quad \text{NP}', \text{N}\}$$
$$\text{Ar} \rightarrow \{\textit{the}, \textit{a}, \textit{an}\}$$

8. a. (Other answers are possible.)
i → {l, la}
a → {xa, x}
x → {l, d}
l → {A, B, C, ..., X, Y, Z}
d → {0, 1, 2, ..., 8, 9}

10. b. Here is a derivation tree for .37 as an ALGOL number:

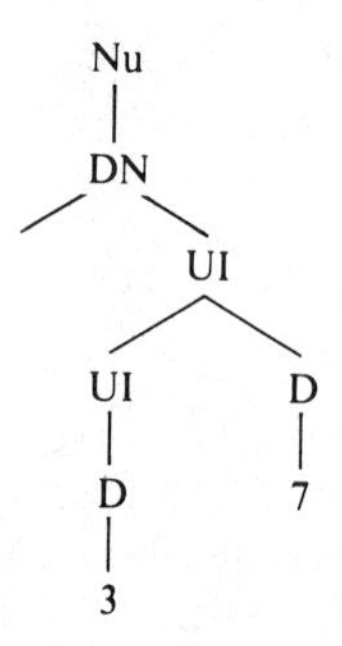

Pascal decimal constants must have at least one digit to the left of the decimal point.

Exercises 8.2 (Page 388)

1. $N = \{\text{D, UI, DN, Nu}\}$, $s = \text{Nu}$, $T = \{0,1,2,3,4,5,6,7,8,9,.,+,-\}$

P consists of:

$$\text{D} \to 0 \quad \text{D} \to 1 \quad \ldots \quad \text{D} \to 9$$

$$\text{UI} \to \text{D} \quad \text{UI} \to \text{UI D}$$

$$\text{DN} \to \text{UI} \quad \text{DN} \to .\text{UI} \quad \text{DN} \to \text{UI}.\text{UI}$$

$$\text{Nu} \to \text{DN} \quad \text{Nu} \to +\text{DN} \quad \text{Nu} \to -\text{DN}$$

2. **a.** Context-free **c.** Not context-free **e.** Context-free

4.

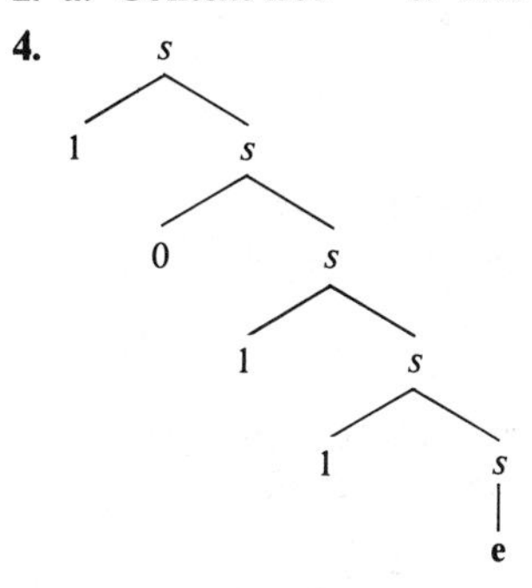

5. **b.** $s \to 1$ $s \to 1s$ $s \to 0t$ $t \to 1$ $t \to 1s$
d. $s \to 0a$ $s \to 1a$ $a \to 0$ $a \to 1$ $a \to 0a$ $a \to 1a$

6. **b.** $\{\mathbf{v} \in \{0,1\}^* | \mathbf{v} = 0^m 1 0^n \text{ with } m,n \leq 1\}$

10. L is generated by the context-free grammar with productions as follows:

$$s \to x \quad s \to y \quad s \to z \quad s \to O \quad s \to I$$

$$s \to (s)' \quad s \to (s) \vee (s) \quad s \to (s) \wedge (s)$$

Exercises 8.3 (Page 401)

1. **a.** Regular **c.** Regular

2. **a.** (ii) s, $1s$, $11s$, $110t$, $1101s$, 1101
b. Start with the initial derived string s; 0 occurs in a derived string precisely via the production $s \to 0t$. The productions $t \to 1s$ and $t \to \mathbf{e}$ prevent the 0 from being followed by a 1, yet allow all other possibilities.

3. **b.** $s \to 0s$ $s \to 1s$ $s \to 0t$ $t \to 1u$ $u \to 0u$ $u \to 1u$ $u \to \mathbf{e}$

4. Every state, that is, s_0, is a YES state.

6. If the machine reaches s_3, then it remains in s_3. From starting state s_0, an input of 1 moves the machine to s_3. So strings with an initial 1 are not recognized. An initial 0 moves the machine to s_1, a YES state. Then a 0 moves the machine to s_3, while a 1 moves it to the YES state s_2. From s_2 the machine must go to s_3.

8. b. $s_0 \to 0s_2$ $s_0 \to 1s_1$ $s_1 \to 0s_0$ $s_1 \to 1s_2$
$s_2 \to 0s_0$ $s_2 \to 1s_2$ $s_0 \to \mathbf{e}$ $s_1 \to \mathbf{e}$

9. b.

Current state	Input 0	Input 1	State type
$\varnothing$	$\varnothing$	$\varnothing$	NO
$\{s\}$	$\varnothing$	$\{t\}$	YES
$\{t\}$	$\{s,t\}$	$\{t\}$	NO
$\{s,t\}$	$\{s,t\}$	$\{t\}$	YES

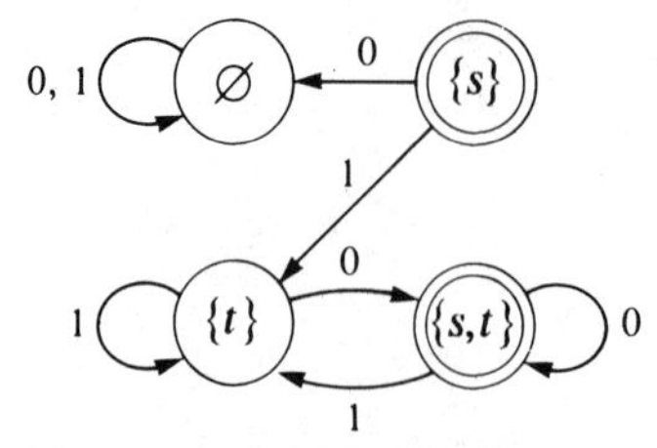

No states may be deleted.

13. a. L is generated by the regular grammar G having the following productions:

$$s \to 0t \quad t \to 0t \quad t \to 1u \quad u \to 1u \quad u \to \mathbf{e}$$

b. L is context free since it is generated by the context-free grammar having the following productions:

$$s \to 01 \quad s \to 0s1$$

L is not regular since a machine with n states cannot correctly recognize both $0^{n+1}1^n$ and $0^{n+1}1^{n+1}$, by Theorem 7.1 and Theorem 8.3.

15. a.

1/NO
0/YES s_0 s_1 0/NO
1/YES

16. Let L be recognized by the machine M, as in Theorem 8.3. Form the machine M' by changing all YES states of M to NO states and all NO states of M to YES states. Then M' recognizes $T^* - L$. Then $T^* - L$ is regular by Theorem 8.2.

Exercises 8.4 (Page 412)

1. a. i, a, b, c, d **c.** i, c, d

2. a.

Current State	Input a	Input b
i	a	b
a	a	c
b	a	d
c	a	a
d	a	b

Composition Table for $(\bar{G}, \diamond)$

$\diamond$	f_e	f_a	f_b	f_{ab}	f_{bb}
f_e	f_e	f_a	f_b	f_{ab}	f_{bb}
f_a	f_a	f_a	f_{ab}	f_{ab}	f_a
f_b	f_b	f_a	f_{bb}	f_{ab}	f_b
f_{ab}	f_{ab}	f_a	f_a	f_{ab}	f_{ab}
f_{bb}	f_{bb}	f_a	f_b	f_{ab}	f_{bb}

4. a.

0 A B 1 0, 1

b.

$\diamond$	f_e	f_0	f_1	f_{01}
f_e	f_e	f_0	f_1	f_{01}
f_0	f_0	f_0	f_{01}	f_{01}
f_1	f_1	f_0	f_e	f_{01}
f_{01}	f_{01}	f_0	f_0	f_{01}

c. Consider $F(\mathbf{v})$. If $\mathbf{v}$ has a 0, by part (b), $F(\mathbf{v})$ equals f_0 or f_{01}. If $\mathbf{v}$ has no 0's, then $F(\mathbf{v})$ equals f_e or f_1 according to whether the number of 1's is even or odd.

d. Let A be a YES state in part (a). Start M in state A. With the notation of Theorem 8.5, consider $L = F^{-1}(\{f_e, f_0\})$. L may also be thought of as all input strings that move M from A to A.

$$F^{-1}(f_0) = L - F^{-1}(f_e)$$

By parts (a) and (c), $F^{-1}(f_0)$ is as claimed.

5. c. i is the starting symbol. The productions are as follows:

$$i \to 0a \qquad i \to 1b \qquad a \to 0a \qquad a \to 1c$$

$$b \to 0a \qquad b \to 1d \qquad c \to 0a \qquad c \to 1a$$

$$d \to 0a \qquad d \to 1b \qquad c \to \mathbf{e}$$

6. $\langle I \rangle$ has fewer elements than has G. Also, $\langle I \rangle$ and $\bar{G}$ have the same number of elements.

Exercises 9.1 (Page 425)

1. a. For 30: 1, 2, 3, 5, 6, 10, 15, 30
b. 1, 2, 3, 6; $\gcd(30, 42) = 6$

2. b. 3

3. b. $7 \cdot 39 - 3 \cdot 90$

4. a. 2

5. a. 11

6. 100

7. **a.** 45 **c.** 36

9. a is a multiple of g, so ka is a multiple of $kg=n$. If $a\cdot x=1$, then $a\cdot x\cdot k=k\neq 0$. But $a\cdot k=0$, so also $a\cdot x\cdot k=0$.

13. Let $n=p_1 p_2 \ldots p_j = q_1 q_2 \ldots q_k$ be two factorizations of n into primes. Since p_1 divides $q_1 q_2 \ldots q_k$, by Exercise 12, p_1 divides some q, call it q_1. Since q_1 is prime, $p_1=q_1$. Hence $p_2 p_3 \ldots p_j = q_2 q_3 \ldots q_k$. Continue in this fashion until all of the p's have been eliminated. There can be no more q's either, since their product must be 1.

Exercises 9.2 (Page 437)

1. **a.** $3x^2+5$ **c.** $2x^2+4x$

2. **a.** $q(x)=2x-5$, $r(x)=15x-9$

3. **a.** $q(x)=x$, $r(x)=x+1$

4. **a.** $q(x)=3x+3$, $r(x)=3$

5. **a.** $p(0)=1$, $p(1)=0$

6. **a.** $p(1)=0$, $p(2)=1$, $p(4)=3$

10. Let $p(x)=a_n x^n + a_{n-1}x^{n-1} + \cdots + a_0$, $a_n \neq 0$

$q(x)=b_m x^m + b_{m-1}x^{m-1} + \cdots + b_0$, $b_m \neq 0$

Then $p(x)q(x)=a_n \cdot b_m x^{n+m}$ + (terms of degree at most $n+m-1$). Also, $a_n b_m \neq 0$ by Proposition 9.9.

12. Divide $x-a$ into $p(x)$: $p(x)=q(x)\cdot(x-a)+r$

By Theorem 9.12, $r=0$ if and only if $p(a)=0$. But $r=0$ if and only if $(x-a)\,|\,p(x)$.

Exercises 9.3 (Page 452)

1. **a.** $\theta=\dfrac{3\pi}{2}$ **c.** $\theta=\dfrac{7\pi}{6}$

3. **a.** $(5,1,-3,1)$

4. **a.** $(1,3,1,4)$

5. **b.** $-2x+1$

6. **a.**

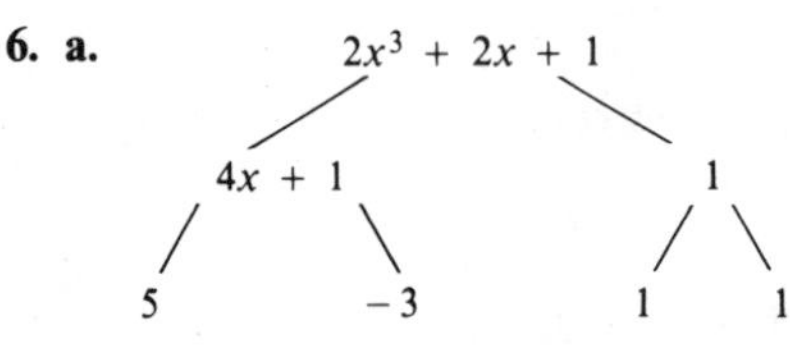

7.

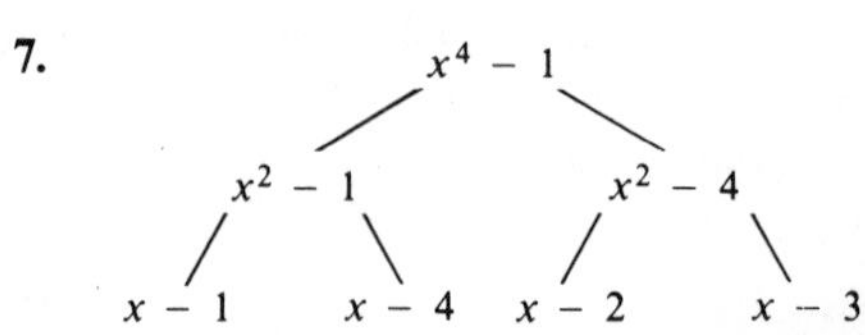

8. a.

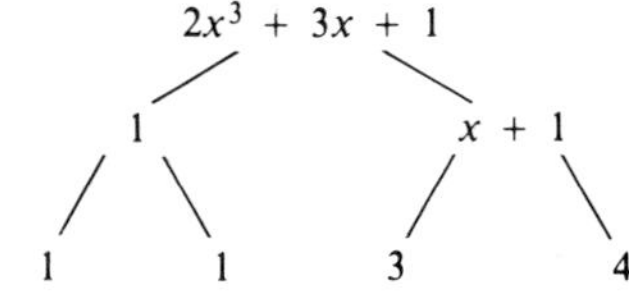

13. $(\alpha^m)^N = \alpha^{mN} = (\alpha^N)^m = 1^m = 1$

Exercises 9.4 (Page 464)

1. a. $(2, -1, -1, 2, -6, 0)$

2. a. $(1,3,2,0)$; $(2,3,0,4)$

b. $(4,1,2,0)$; $(2,4,0,0)$

3. a. $(2,4,0,0)$

4. a. $(9,1,2,0,16,8,11,12)$; $(7,9,5,14,16,15,6,13)$

b. $(12,9,10,0,1,1,15,3)$

c. $(0,3,12,2,1,9,2,0)$

5. 49

7. a. $\omega^{N-1} \cdot \omega = \omega^N = 1$

8. a. Since $M = 2^{2^n} + 1$, $2^{2^n} = \omega^{N/2} \equiv -1 \pmod{M}$

b. Since $\omega^{N/2} = -1$, $\omega^N = (-1)^2 = 1$

c. Exercise 7b

13. a. $10 \equiv -1 \pmod{11}$, so $n = 10n_1 + n_0 \equiv -n_1 + n_0 \pmod{11}$.

Exercises 9.5 (Page 475)

1. 1, 3, 2, 4

2. a. Yes **c.** No

3. a. 1

4. a. 1

5. a. $\lambda(x) = x^2 + x + 1$, $\mu(x) = x + 1$

6. a. Reducible **c.** Irreducible

8. $x^2 + x$

Exercises 9.6 (Page 484)

1. a.

Message	Code word
(0 0)	(0 0 0 0)
(0 1)	(0 1 1 1)
(1 0)	(1 1 1 0)
(1 1)	(1 0 0 1)

b. 2

2. a. (1 0 0 1) **c.** (0 1 1 1)

3. b. $p(0) = 1$, $p(1) = 1$, $p(x) = 0$, $p(1 + x) = 0$

4. a. In $(K^*, \cdot)$; $x^1 = x$, $x^2 = x + 1$, $x^3 = 1$

c.

Message	Code word
(0)	(0 0 0)
(1)	(1 1 1)

5. a. $m_7(y)$ is irreducible by Example 9.53.
$m_7(x^7)=1+x^7+x^{28}\equiv 1+x^7+x^{13}\equiv 1+x^2+x+1+x^2+x\equiv 0$

b. $1+y+y^2+y^3+y^4+y^5+y^6+y^7+y^8+y^9+y^{10}+y^{11}+y^{12}+y^{13}+y^{14}$; degree $=14$

c. This is a (1,15) code, with just one non-**0** code word.

9. a. Suppose that $m_\alpha(y)=a(y)b(y)$. Then $0=m_\alpha(\alpha)=a(\alpha)b(\alpha)$. So either $a(\alpha)=0$ or $b(\alpha)=0$. But the degree of $m_\alpha(y)$ is minimal. So either $m_\alpha(y)=a(y)$ or $m_\alpha(y)=b(y)$, and $m_\alpha(y)$ is irreducible.

b. Divide $m_\alpha(y)$ into $g(y)$: $g(y)=q(y)m_\alpha(y)+r(y)$ with $\deg(r(y))<\deg(m_\alpha(y))$. Since $g(\alpha)=m_\alpha(\alpha)=0$, also $r(\alpha)=0$. Since $m_\alpha(y)$ has minimal degree, $r(y)=0$. Hence $m_\alpha(y)|g(y)$.

Exercises A.1 (Page 494)

1. $P(1): 1=1^2$

Assume $P(n): 1+3+5+\cdots+(2n-1)+(2n+1)=n^2+2n+1=(n+1)^2$, which is $P(n+1)$.

3. $P(1): 1+r=\dfrac{1-r^2}{1-r}=\dfrac{(1-r)(1+r)}{1-r}$

Assume $P(n)$:

$$1+r+r^2+\cdots+r^n+r^{n+1}=\frac{1-r^{n+1}}{1-r}+r^{n+1}=\frac{1-r^{n+1}+r^{n+1}-r^{n+2}}{1-r}$$
$$=\frac{1-r^{n+2}}{1-r}, \text{ which is } P(n+1).$$

6. $f(n)=n$

8. The computation $f(2)=1+f(4)=2+f(8)=3+f(16)=\cdots$ never terminates since 2, 4, 8, ... is an increasing sequence.

Exercises A.2 (Page 499)

1. Let $P(n)$ be: The construction is valid for all connected graphs with at most n edges. $P(1)$ is true since the construction gives the unique edge as the edge of the minimum-cost spanning tree. Now assume $P(n)$. Consider a given graph G with $n+1$ edges. Let e_{n+1} be any edge in G with a maximum cost. Temporarily delete e_{n+1} from G, forming G_1. There are two cases: (i) G_1 is connected. Since G_1 has n edges, $P(n)$ applies to show that the construction is valid for G_1. Since e_{n+1} has maximum cost, a minimum-cost spanning tree for G_1 is also a minimum-cost spanning tree for G. (ii) G_1 is not connected. Then $G_1=G'\cup G''$, with G' and G'' nonempty connected graphs, each with less than n edges. e_{n+1} must appear in any spanning tree. Hence a minimum-cost spanning tree for G is found by adding e_{n+1} to minimum-cost spanning trees for G' and G''. But the construction is valid for G' and G''.

3. The proof is just a formalization of the proof in the text. Let $P(q)$ be: $m+q-1$-equivalence classes coincide with $m+q$-equivalence classes. $P(1)$ is given. $P(q+1)$ is derived from $P(q)$ as in the text. By the Principle of Mathematical Induction, $P(q)$ is true for all $q\geq 1$. That is, m-equivalence is the same as state-equivalence.

8. (i) For an ordered directed tree T with one vertex, that vertex is first in postorder.